MILLER'S Collectables PRICE ◆ GUIDE

Compiled and Edited by
Judith and Martin Miller

General Editor: Robert Murfin

MILLERS PUBLICATIONS

A soldier's bear, 3in
(7.5cm).
£250-300 *C*

MILLER'S COLLECTABLES PRICE GUIDE

Compiled, edited and designed by
M.J.M. Publishing Projects for
Millers Publications Limited
Mitchell Beazley International Limited
The Cellars, High Street
Tenterden, Kent TN30 6BN
Telephone: (058 06) 6411

Compiled and edited by
Judith & Martin Miller

General Editor: Robert Murfin
Editorial co-ordinator: Sue Boyd
Editor: June Bryant
Artwork: Nigel O'Gorman, Chris Howson, Tim Arundel
Photographic co-ordinator and advertising executive: Elizabeth Smith
Production assistant: Trudi Hinkley
Index compiled by DD Editorial Services, Beccles
Additional photography by Ian Booth and Robin Saker

Reissued 1992

A CIP catalogue record for this book is
available from the British Library

ISBN 1 851 522 573

Typeset by Mainline Typesetters, St Leonards-on-Sea
Printed and bound in England by William Clowes Ltd
Beccles and London

Introduction

It is hard to believe that a year has passed since the first edition of *Miller's Collectables Price Guide* was published, and what a year it has been for collectors. Probably the most newsworthy event was the sale at auction of a German made Steiff teddy bear for an amazing £55,000, a good return on the £2 it originally cost in Gamages seventy years ago.

The collection from the Meccano Museum was sold by Christie's South Kensington last September, representing a terrific selection of Meccano products from 1901 until the firm's closure in 1982. Lots included their famous constructor kits and toys, Hornby clockwork and Dublo electric trains from the 1920s and 1930s, Dinky toys from 1934 onwards and Matchbox toys from 1947, including the 'Models of Yesteryear' from 1956. Good results were achieved as can be seen from the relevant sections of this book.

The Coluzzi collection, also sold by Christie's South Kensington, was arguably the world's largest and finest collection of tinplate and model railways, accessories and model ships, many in their original boxes and wrappers, again a good selection from the sale is featured in this new volume. Toys, like almost all other collectables, are so dependent upon condition for their value, original finish and original box furnish the collector with the premium items for any collection.

Ceramics still provide a rich and varied field for the collector. Art Deco potters, Clarice Cliff, Susie Cooper and Shelley go from strength to strength and collectors are moving to other makers: watch out for Buckley, Grays and particularly Shorter Ware. Glass is a similar story, pressed glass is still affordable and undervalued; carnival glass is now sought after by collectors from both sides of the Atlantic.

As with all our price guides, it is always our intention to reflect both prices and trends in the market. Some areas which have increased in popularity are shown more than others, this year for example, radios, telephones, juke boxes and slot machines are featured. In sport we have highlighted football, and in smoking, pipes. Collections too have been selected, like the "Boer War", to illustrate the wonderful range of items that can be collected around a central theme, from ephemera to militaria, from ceramics to postage stamps.

Martin and I are very touched by the number of letters we have received since last year. Your comments, ideas and suggestions are both constructive and fascinating and some of your collections, Volkswagens and cigarette lighters among others are featured in this new volume, so please keep writing.

Finally, as I said last year, I hope this new book will continue to provide you with solid information, interesting facts, photographs and prices, not only helping to make collecting more fun but perhaps starting you off on a new direction or even a whole new area but, above all, good luck and good hunting.

Acknowledgements

The publishers would like to acknowledge the great assistance given by our consultants.

AERONAUTICA, AUTOMOBILIA, RAILWAYS & SHIPPING:	**Patrick Bogue, John Jenkins,** *Onslow's, Metro Store, Townmead Road, London, SW6.*
CAMERAS:	**David Lawrence,** *Jessops, 67 Great Russell Street, London, WC1.*
ART DECO:	**Beverley,** *30 Church Street, London, NW8.*
	Eric Knowles, *Bonhams, Knightsbridge, London, SW7.*
POTTERY:	**Islwyn Watkins,** *1 High Street, Knighton, Powys.*
ROYAL DOULTON:	**Tom Power,** *The Collector, Alfies Antique Market, 13-25 Church Street, London, NW8.*
GOSS & CRESTED WARE:	**Nicholas Pine,** *Goss & Crested China Ltd., 62 Murray Road, Horndean, Hants.*
EPHEMERA:	**Trevor Vennett-Smith,** *11 Nottingham Road, Gotham, Nottingham.*
FISHING:	**Jamie Maxtone Graham,** *Lyne Haugh, Lyne Station, Peebles, Scotland.*
MONART GLASS:	**Frank Andrews,** *10 Vincent Road, Wood Green, London, N22.*
MILITARIA:	**Roy Butler,** *Wallis & Wallis, West Street Auction Galleries, Lewes, East Sussex.*
MEDALS, BUTTONS & BADGES:	**Jim Bullock,** *Romsey Medal Centre, 101 The Hundred, Romsey, Hants.*
PLAYING CARDS:	**Yasha Beresiner,** *Intercol, 1a Camden Walk, Islington Green, London, N1.*
POLICE ITEMS:	**Mervyn Mitton,** *161 The Albany, Manor Road, Bournemouth, Dorset.*
SMOKING:	**John Bullion,** *Karen House, Higher Cheddar Road, Taunton, Devon.*
	Phillips, *1 Old King Street, Bath*
TOYS, SPORTING ITEMS:	**Duncan Chilcott,** *Bonhams, 65-69 Lots Road, London, SW10.*

Key to Illustrations

Each illustration and descriptive caption is accompanied by a letter-code. By reference to the following list of Auctioneers (denoted by *) and Dealers (•), the source of any item may be immediately determined. In no way does this constitute or imply a contract or binding offer on the part of any of our contributors to supply or sell the goods illustrated, or similar articles, at the prices stated. Advertisers in this year's directory are denoted by †.

AA	•	Acorn Antiques, Sheep Street, Stow-on-the-Wold, Gloucestershire. Tel: (0451) 31519
AB	•	A & B Antiques, Alfies Antique Market, 13-25 Church Street, London NW8. Tel: 01-724 5650
AC	•	Angela Charlesworth, 99 Dodsworth Road, Barnsley, S. Yorks. Tel: (0226) 282097
ACC	•†	Albert's, 113 London Road, Twickenham, Middx. Tel: 01-891 3067
AD	•	Anne & Dolores, Victorian lace, linen & costume, Bartlett Street Antique Market, Bath. Tel: (0225) 330267
AG	*	Anderson & Garland, Marlborough House, Marlborough Crescent, Newcastle-upon-Tyne. Tel: 091-232 6278
AH	*	Andrew Hartley Fine Arts, Victoria Hall, Little Lane, Ilkley, W. Yorks. Tel: (0943) 816363
AI	•†	Antiques & Interiors, 22 Ashford Road, Tenterden, Kent. Tel: (05806) 5462
AL	•†	Ann Lingard, Ropewalk Antiques, Ropewalk, Rye, Sussex. Tel: (0797) 223486
ALL	*	Allen & Harris (with Osmond Tricks), Regent Street Auction Rooms, Clifton, Bristol, Avon. Tel: (0272) 737201
AOS	•	Antiques on the Square, 2 Sandford Court, Church Stretton, Shropshire. Tel: (0694) 724111
AP	•	Angela Page, Tunbridge Wells, Kent. Tel: (0892) 22217
ARB	•	Arbour Antiques Ltd., Poet's Arbour, Sheep

Street, Stratford-on-Avon, Warks. Tel: (0789) 293453

ASA • AS Antiques & Decorative Arts, 26 Broad Street, Pendleton, Salford 6, Manchester. Tel: 061-737 5938

ASc • Ascott Antiques, Narborough, Leicestershire. Tel: (0533) 863190

AW • A. Waine, Tweedale, Rye Mill Lane, Feering, Colchester, Essex. Tel: (0376) 71078

BA • Burman Antiques, 5A Chapel Street, Stratford-on-Avon, Warks. Tel: (0789) 293917/295164

BAD • Colin Baddiel, B24, Grays Mews, 1-7 Davies Mews, London W1. Tel: 01-629 2813

BAL • Sharon Ball, Stratford-on-Avon Antique Centre, Ely Street, Stratford-on-Avon, Warks. Tel: (0789) 204180

BCA • Bow Cottage Antiques, Antique Arcade, 4 Sheep Street, Stratford-on-Avon, Warks (R. Harvey-Morgan). Tel: (0789) 297249

BC • British Collectables, 1st Floor, Georgian Village, Camden Passage, Islington, London N1. Tel: 01-359 4560

Bea * Bearnes, Rainbow, Avenue Road, Torquay, Devon. Tel: (0803) 26277

BEB • Judy Bebber, Antique Dolls, L14 Grays Antique Market, 1-7 Davies Mews, London W1. Tel: 01-499 6600

BEE •† Beehive Antiques, Janice Paull, Warwick Antique Centre, 16-18 High Street, Warwick. Tel: (0926) 492482/55253

BEN • R. S. Benjamin, Alfies Antique Market, 13-25 Church Street, London NW8. Tel: 01-723 6066

BEV •† Beverley, 30 Church Street, London NW8. Tel: 01-262 1576

BH • Bob Hoare, Pine Antiques, Unit Q, Phoenix Place, North Street, Lewes, Sussex. Tel: (0273) 480557

BIA • Biarritz, The Antique Arcade, Sheep Street, Stratford-on-Avon. Tel: (0789) 297249/204011 Evening

Bon * Bonhams, Montpelier Galleries, Montpelier Street, Knightsbridge, London SW7. Tel: 01-584 9161

BRE • Brenin Porcelain & Pottery, Cowbridge, South Glamorgan

BT • Bampton Telephone & General Museum of Communication and Domestic History, 4 Brook Street, Bampton, Devon.

C * Christie, Manson & Woods Ltd, 8 King Street, St James's, London SW1. Tel: 01-839 9060

CA • Crafers Antiques, The Hill, Wickham Market, Suffolk. Tel: (0728) 747347

CAC • Cranbrook Antique Centre, Stone Street, Cranbrook, Kent. Tel: (0580) 712173

CAm * Christie's Amsterdam, Cornelis Schuystraat 57 1071 JG, Amsterdam, Hollan·Avon. Tel: 020 64 20 11

Cas • Simon Castle, 38B Kensington Church Street, London W8. Tel: 01-892 2840

CAS • P. & S. Cashman, Great Western Antique Centre, Bath. Tel: (0225) 20686/469497

CB • Christine Bridge Antiques, 78 Castelnau, London SW13. Tel: 01-741 5501

CBA • Chateaubriand Antiques Centre, High Street, Burwash, E. Sussex. Tel: (0435) 882535

CCA • Combe Cottage Antiques, Castle Combe, Chippenham, Wilts. Tel: (0249) 782250

CDC * Capes Dunn & Co, Auction Galleries, 38 Charles Street, off Princess Street, Manchester. Tel: 061-273 1911

CEd * Christie's & Edmiston's Ltd, 164-166 Bath Street, Glasgow. Tel: 041-332 8134

CIR • Cirdeco, 24 North Street, St. Leonards-on-Sea, E. Sussex. Tel: (0424) 421187/436996

CLI • Cliffe Antiques, Warwick Antique Centre, 20 High Street, Warwick. Tel: (0926) 495704

CNY * Christie, Manson & Woods International Inc, 502 Park Avenue, New York, NY 10022, USA. Tel: 212 546 1000 (including Christie's East)

COB •† Cobwebs, 78 Northam Road, Southampton. Tel: (0703) 227458

CSK * Christie's (South Kensington) Ltd, 85 Old Brompton Road, London SW7. Tel: 01-581 7611

CT • Children's Treasures, 17 George Street, Hastings, E. Sussex. Tel: (0424) 444117/422758

DAN • Danby Antiques, 61 Heworth Road, York. Tel: (0904) 415280

DBP • Donat B. Perbohner, Grays Antique Market, L22-23, 1-7 Davies Mews, London W1. Tel: 01-629 1184

DBu • David Burns, 116 Chestnut Grove, New Malden, Surrey. Tel: 01-949 7356

DEC • Decodence, 59 Brighton Road, Surbiton, Surrey. Tel: 01-390 1778

DEN * Denham Associates, Horsham Auction Galleries, Warnham, Nr Horsham, W. Sussex. Tel: (0403) 55699/53837

DF • Diana Foley, Richard Digby, Stand L18-21, Grays Antique Market, 1-7 Davies Mews, London W1. Tel: 01-408 1089

DH •† The Dog House, 309 Bloxwich Road, Walsall, W. Midlands. Tel: (0922) 30829

DIM • Dimech, 248 Camden High Street, London NW1. Tel: 01-485 8072

DL • Dunsdale Lodge Antiques, Westerham, Kent. Tel: (0959) 62160

DN * Drewett Neate, Donnington Priory, Donnington, Newbury, Berks. Tel: (0635) 31234

DOW • Mrs M. Downworth, Great Western Antiques, Wednesday Market, Bartlett Street, Bath,

DP • David Payne, Bartlett Street Antiques Market, 9 Bartlett Street, Bath, Avon. Tel: (0225) 330267

DSH * Dacre, Son & Hartley, 1-5 The Grove, Ilkley, W. Yorks. Tel: (0943) 600655

EA • Eleanor Antiques, Smith Street Antique Centre, Warwick. Tel: (0926) 497864

EAS •† Eastgate Antiques, Alfies Antique Market, 13-25 Church Street, London NW8. Tel: 01-724 5650 (see LAT)

EUR • Eureka Antiques, 18 Northenden Road, Sale, Cheshire. Tel: 061-962 5629 and 105 Portobello Road, W11 (Saturdays)

FA • Frank Andrews, 10 Vincent Road, London N22. Tel: 01-881 0658 (Home)/ 01/889 3445 (Business)

FAN • Fan-Attic, Stratford-on-Avon Antiques Centre, Ely Street, Stratford, Warks. Tel: (0789) 297496

FAL • Falstaff Antiques, 63-67 High Street, Rolvenden (Motor Musuem), Kent. Tel: (0580) 241234

FEN * R. A. Fenner & Co, The Stannary Gallery, Drake Road, Tavistock, Devon. Tel: (0822) 617799

FF • Fan-Fayre Antiques, High Street, Rhosneigr, Gwynedd, Anglesey.

FT • Fred Topping, Warwick Antique Centre, 20 High Street, Warwick. Tel: (0926) 499078

FW • Final Whistle, Alfies Antique Market, 2nd Floor, 61-63, 13-25 Church Street, NW8. Tel: 01-262 3423

G&CC •† Goss & Crested China Ltd, Nicholas J. Pine, 62 Murray Road, Horndean, Hants. Tel: (0705) 597440

GCo • Gosh Comics, 39 Great Russell Street, WC1. Tel: 01-636 1011

GEN • Lionel Geneen Ltd, 781 Christchurch Road, Boscombe, Bournemouth. Tel: (0202) 422961

GIL * Gildings, Roman Way, Market Harborough, Leicestershire. Tel: (0858) 410414

GKR •† GKR Bonds Ltd, PO Box 1, Kelvedon, Essex. Tel: (0376) 71711

GSP * Graves, Son & Pilcher, 71 Church Road, Hove, E. Sussex. Tel: (0273) 735266

GW • George Weiner, 2 Market Street, The Lanes, Brighton, E. Sussex. Tel: (0273) 729948

GWT • Great Western Toys, Great Western Antique Centre, Bartlett Street, Bath.

HAM * Hamptons Fine Arts, 93 High Street, Godalming, Surrey. Tel: (04868) 23567

HCC * H. C. Chapman & Son, The Auction Mart, North Street, Scarborough, N. Yorks. Tel: (0723) 372424

HCH * Hobbs & Chambers, Market Place, Cirencester, Glos. Tel: (0285) 4736

HOD * Hoddell, GA Property Services, Six Ways, Clevedon, Avon. Tel: (0272) 876699

HOW • Howards Antiques, 73 Wyle Cop, Shrewsbury, Shropshire. Tel: (0743) 60737

HP * Hobbs Parker, Romney House, Ashford Market, Elwick Road, Ashford, Kent. Tel: (0233) 22222

HSS * Henry Spencer & Sons, 20 The Square, Retford, Notts. Tel: (0777) 708633

IC • InterCol London, Yasha Beresiner, 1A Camden Walk, Islington Green, London N1. Tel: 01-354 2599

IMA • Images (Peter Stockham), 16 Cecil Court, Charing Cross Road, London WC2. Tel: 01-836 8661

IW •† Islwyn Watkins, 1 High Street, 29 Market Street, Knighton, Powys, Wales. Tel: (0547) 520145/528940

J •† Jessops, 67 Great Russell Street, London WC1. Tel: 01-831 3640

JAG • J.A.G. Applied Arts, 248 Camden High Street, London NW1. Tel: 01-485 8072

JAS • Jasmin Cameron, 259 Kings Road, London SW3. Tel: 01-352 0837

JAZ •† Jazz, Civic Hall, Rother Street, Stratford-on-Avon, Warwickshire. Tel: (0789) 298362/021-705 9858

JBB •† Jessie's Button Box, Great Western Antique Centre, Stand 17, Bartlett Street, Bath, Avon. Tel: (0272) 299065

JH • Janet Handcock, Warwick Antique Centre, 20 High Street, Warwick. Tel: (0926) 495704

JLB • John Bullion, Karen House, Higher Cheddar Road, Taunton, Somerset. Tel: (0823) 279362

JMG •† Jamie Maxtone Graham, Lyne Haugh, Lyne Station, Peebles, Scotland. Tel: (07214) 304

JO •† Jacqueline Oosthuizen, Shop 12 (1st Floor), Georgian Village, Camden Passage, London N1. Tel: 01-226 5393/01-352 5581

K •† Keith Gretton, 26 Honeywell Road, London SW11 and Unit 14, Northcote Road Antiques Market, Battersea, London SW11. Tel: 01-228 0741

KOL • Kollectomania, 4 Catherine Street, Rochester, Kent. Tel: (0634) 45099

LAM • Penny Lampard, 31-33 High Street, Headcorn, Kent. Tel: (0622) 890682

LAT •† C. Latford, Eastgate Antiques, Alfies Antique Market, 13-25 Church Street, London NW8. Tel: 01-724 5650 (See EAS)

LB •† The Lace Basket, 1a East Cross, Tenterden, Kent. Tel: (05806) 3923

MA • Manor Antiques, 2A High Street, Westerham, Kent. Tel: (0959) 64810

MAI * Moore, Allen & Innocent, 33 Castle Street, Cirencester, Glos. Tel: (0285) 61831/2862

MAG • MacGregor Nash & Co, Lodge House, 9-17 Lodge Lane, Finchley, London N12. Tel: 01-445 9000/01-445 5153

MAN • F. C. Manser & Son Ltd, 53-54 Wyle Cop, Shrewsbury. Tel: (0743) 51120

MB • Mostly Boxes, 92 & 52b High Street, Eton. Tel: (0753) 858470

MCA •† Millers of Chelsea Antiques Ltd, Netherbrook House, 86 Christchurch Road, Ringwood, Hampshire. Tel: (0425) 472062

McC * McCartneys, 25 Corve Street, Ludlow, Shropshire. Tel: (0584) 2636

MG • Michael G. German, 38B Kensington Church Street, London W8. Tel: 01-937 2771

MGC •† Midlands Goss & Commemoratives, Warwick Antiques Centre, 22 High Street, Warwick. Tel: (0926) 495704

MGM * Michael G. Matthews, Devon Fine Art Auction House, Dowell Street, Honiton, Devon. Tel: (0404) 41872/3137

MIC • Trevor Micklem, Frog Pool Farm, Moorwood, Oakhill, Bath. Tel: (0749) 840754

MIN •† Mint & Boxed, 110 High Street, Edgware, Middx. Tel: 01-952 2002

MIT Mervyn A. Mitton, 161 The Albany, Manor Road, Bournemouth

MN * Michael Newman, The Central Auction Rooms, Kinterbury House, St. Andrew's Cross, Plymouth, Devon. Tel: (0752) 669298

MR • Magic Radios. Tel: (0384) 872744/ (0562) 66354 Eves (after 5 pm)

MS • Mike Sturge, 39 Union Street, Maidstone, Kent. Tel: (0622) 54702

MW • Mary Wellard, Stand 165, Grays Antique Market, Davies Street, London W1

N * Neales of Nottingham, The Nottingham Salerooms, 192 Mansfield Road, Nottingham. Tel: (0602) 624141

NA •† Nostalgia Amusements, 73 Angus Close, Chessington, Surrey. Tel: 01-397 6867

NM • Nick Marchant, Bartlett Street Antique Market, Bath, Avon. Tel: (0225) 310457

OD • Offa's Dyke Antique Centre, 4 High Street, Knighton, Powys, Wales. Tel: (0547) 528635

OBJ • Objects, Stand T101, Alfies Antique Market, 13-25 Church Street, London NW8. Tel: 01-706 2969/01-801 6626

OBS •† The Old Button Shop (Mrs T. Johns), Lytchett Minster, Dorset. Tel: (0202) 622169

OMH • The Old Mint House, Pevensey, East Sussex. Tel: (0323) 762337/761251

ONS * Onslow's, Metro Store, Townmead Road, London SW6. Tel: 01-793 0240

OR • The Originals, Alfies Antique Market, Stand 37, 13-25 Church Street, London NW8. Tel: 01-724 3439/7

OSc • Old School Antiques (P. Rumble), Chittering, Cambridge. Tel: (0223) 861831

P * Phillips, Blenstock House, 101 New Bond Street, London W1. Tel: 01-629 6602 and 10 Salem Road, London W2. Tel: 01-229 9090

PAR • Park House Antiques, Park Street, Stow-on-the-Wold, Glos. Tel: (0451) 30159

PAT • Patrician, 1st Floor, Georgian Village, Camden Passage, Islington, London N1. Tel: 01-359 4560/01-435 3159

PBA • Pryce & Brise, 79 Moore Park Road, Fulham, London SW6. Tel: 01-736 1864

P(Ba) * Phillips, Bath, 1 Old King Street, Bath. Tel: (0225) 310609/310709

P(C) * Phillips, Cardiff, 9-10 Westgate Street, Cardiff. Tel: (0222) 396453

PC Private Collection

PCA • Paul Cater Antiques, High Street, Moreton-in-Marsh, Glos. Tel: (0608) 51888

PCh • Peter Cheney, Western Road Auction Rooms, Western Road, Littlehampton, W. Sussex. Tel: (0903) 722264/713418

PGA •† Paul Gibbs Antiques, 25 Castle Street, Conwy, N. Wales. Tel: (0492) 593429

PH • Pennard House Antiques, Piccadilly, Bath, Avon. Tel: (0225) 313791

P(M) * Phillips, Manchester, Trinity House, 114 Northenden Road, Sale, Manchester. Tel: 061-962 9237

PO • Pieter Oosthuizen. Tel: 01-352 1094/1493 (Business) Tel: 01-376 3069 (Home)

PP • Pauline Parkes, Stratford Arcade, 4 Sheep Street, Stratford-on-Avon. Tel: (0789) 297249

PPS • Pleasure of Pastimes, 11 Cecil Court, Charing Cross Road, London WC2. Tel: 01-836 1142

PVH • Peter & Valerie Howkins, 39, 40 & 135 King Street, Gt. Yarmouth, Norfolk. Tel: (0493) 844639

PW • Philip Wilson, Stratford Antiques Arcade, 4 Sheep Street, Stratford-on-Avon. Tel: (0789) 297249

PWA • Pat Walker, Georgian Village, Camden Passage, Islington, London N1. Tel: 01-226 1571/01-731 0999

RA • Richmond Antiques, Warwick Antique Centre, 20 High Street, Warwick. Tel: (0926) 495704

RBB * Russell Baldwin & Bright, Ryelands Road, Leominster, Hereford. Tel: (0568) 611166

RBE • Ron Beech, 150 Portland Road, Hove, E. Sussex. Tel: (0273) 724477

RC • Radio Crafts, 56 Main Street, Sedgeberrow, Nr Evesham, Worcs. Tel: (0386) 881988

REL • Relic Basement, Philip Bond, 248 Camden High Street, London NW1. Tel: 01-485 8072

RG • Rob Gee, The Fleamarket, Pierrepont Row, Camden Passage, London N1. Tel: 01-226 6627 (Wed & Sat)

RIP • Ripley Antiques, 67 High Street, Ripley, Surrey. Tel: (0483) 224981

RMC •† Romsey Medal Centre, 101 The Hundred, Romsey, Hants. Tel: (0794) 512885

RPM • Rosemary Antiques & Paper Moon Books, The Antiques Arcade, 4 Sheep Street, Stratford-on-Avon. Tel: (0789) 297249

RR • Jonathan Hill, 2-4 Brook Street, Bampton, Devon. Tel: (0398) 31310

RT • Rotation Antiques, Pierrepont Row Fleamarket, Camden Passage, Islington, London N1. Tel: 01-226 8211

RYA • Robert Young Antiques, 68 Battersea Bridge Road, London SW11. Tel: 01-228 7847

SA • Studio Antiques, Stratford Antique Arcade, Sheep Street, Stratford-on-Avon. Tel: (0789) 297249

SAA * Southgate Antique Auction Rooms, r/o Southgate Town Hall, Green Lanes, Palmers Green, London N13. Tel: 01-886 7888

SAD • Old Saddlers Antiques, Church Road, Goudhurst, Kent. Tel: (0580) 211458

SAI • Sailor Ceramics, Camden Lock Antique Centre, 248 Camden High Street, London NW1. Tel: 01-981 1180

SAR • Sarah Baddiel, The Book Gallery, B12 Grays Mews, Davies Mews, London W1. Tel: 01-408 1239/01-452 7243

SCO • Scott's, Stand 24, Great Western Antique Centre, Bartlett Street, Bath. Tel: (0225) 310388

SM •† Stephen Maitland, Now & Then Telephones, 7-9 West Crosscauseway, Edinburgh. Tel: (0592) 890235

SN • Sixty Nine Antiques (now retired).

Som • Somervale Antiques, 6 Radstock Road, Midsomer Norton, Bath. Tel: (0761) 412686

SR • Sebastian Hawkin & Ricky Ma, K17-18, Grays Antique Market, 1-7 Davies Mews, London W1. Tel: 01-629 1184

SSA • Smith St. Antique Centre (E. Brook), 7 Smith Street, Warwick. Tel: (0926) 497864/400554

STU • Studio Antiques, Alfies Antique Market, 13-25 Church Street, London NW8. Tel: 01-723 6066

SWa •† Stephen Watson, Alfies Antique Market, 13-25 Church Street, London NW8. Tel: 01-723 0678

SWO * Sworders, G. E. Sworder & Sons, 15 Northgate End, Bishops Stortford. Tel: (0279) 51388

TM * Thos. Mawer & Son, The Lincoln Salerooms, 63 Monks Road, Lincoln. Tel: (0522) 24984

TP • Tom Power, The Collector, Alfies Antique Market, 13-25 Church Street, London NW8. Tel: 01-883 0024

Tri • Trio, Stand L24, Grays Mews, 1-7 Davies Mews, London W1. Tel: 01-629 1184
TS •† Tim's Spot, Carnival Corner, Stratford-on-Avon Antique Centre, Ely Street, Stratford, Warks. Tel: (0789) 297496
UC • Up Country, The Old Corn Stores, 68 St. John's Road, Tunbridge Wells, Kent. Tel: (0892) 23341
UP • Utopia Antiques Ltd, Holme Mills, Burton-in-Kendal, Carnforth, Lancs. Tel: (0524) 781739
V • Peter Viola, Warwick Antique Centre, 16-18 High Street, Warwick. Tel: (0926) 495704
VAG •† V.A.G. & Co, Possingworth Craft Centre, Brownings Farm, Blackboys, Uckfield, E. Sussex. Tel: (0323) 507488
VB • Variety Box, 16 Chapel Place, Tunbridge Wells, Kent. Tel: (0892) 31868/21589
VF • Victorian Fireplaces, Simon Priestley, Ground Floor, Cardiff Antique Centre, 69-71 St. Mary Street, Cardiff. Tel: (0222) 230970/226049
VS *† T. Vennett Smith, 11 Nottingham Road, Gotham, Nottingham. Tel: (0602) 830541
WA • Windmill Antiques, Warwick Antique Centre, 20 High Street, Warwick. Tel: (0926) 495704
WAD • Jo Waddams, Stratford Antique Arcade, Stratford, Warwickshire. Tel: (0789) 297249
WAL *† Wallis & Wallis, West Street Auction Galleries, Lewes, E. Sussex. Tel: (0273) 480208
WD * Weller & Dufty, 141 Bromsgrove Street, Birmingham. Tel: 021-692 1414/5
WH *† Walton & Hipkiss, 194A Worcester Road, Hagley, Stourbridge, West Midlands. Tel: (0562) 885555/883426
WHA • Wych House Antiques, Wych Hill, Woking, Surrey. Tel: (04862) 64636
WHB * William H. Brown, Westgate Hall, Westgate, Grantham, Lincs. Tel: (0476) 68861
WHI • Whittington Galleries, 22 Woodend, Sutton, Surrey. Tel: 01-644 9327
WIL * Peter Wilson, Victoria Gallery, Market Street, Nantwich, Cheshire. Tel: (0270) 623878
WIN • Winstone Stamp Co, Gt. Western Antique Market, Bartlett Street, Bath, Avon. Tel: (0225) 310388
WM • Carol Warner and Gavin Morgan, Alfies Antique Market, 13-25 Church Street, London NW8. Tel: 01-723 6066
WO • Woodville Antiques, The Street, Ham Street, Ashford, Kent. Tel: (023373) 2981
WRe • Walcot Reclamations, 108 Walcot Street, Bath, Avon. Tel: (0225) 66291/63245
WW * Woolley & Wallis, The Castle Auction Mart, Castle Street, Salisbury. Tel: (0722) 21711
WWA • William Wain, Camden High Street, London NW1.
YC • Yonna Cohen, B19, Grays Antique Market, 1-7 Davies Mews, London W1. Tel: 01-629 3644
ZIG • Ziggurat, Stand J22, Grays Mews, 1-7 Davies Mews, London W1. Tel: 01-629 3788.

INDEX TO ADVERTISERS

CONTENTS

Aeronautica

Prices for aeronautical collectables have continued to rise steadily throughout the past twelve months. As in most fields of collecting, rare and desirable objects are proving to be the best investment. New areas to watch are not only general space travel memorabilia and souvenirs but just about anything to do with the space shuttle.

Air magazines, 1931.
£5-6 each *COB*

Books & Programmes

Aircraft identification books, 1939-1944.
£5-8 each *COB*

A passage folder with ticket inside, 1943.
£10-12 *COB*

A Bassett-Lowke catalogue of models, May 1910.
£100-150 *ONS*

Early space flight ephemera, 1962.
£5-6 *COB*

An illustrated book on ballooning, 1895.
£25-30 *COB*

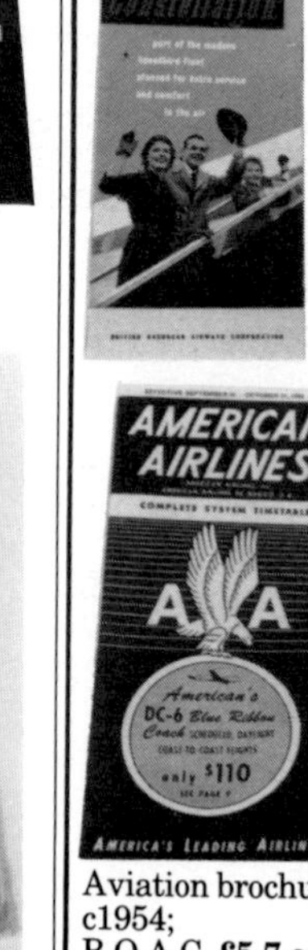

Aviation brochures, c1954;
B.O.A.C. **£5-7 each**
American Airlines.
£10-12 each *COB*

Flying magazine, 1925.
£9-12 *COB*

A souvenir of the Aero Exhibition at Olympia, 1920.
£60-70 *CSK*

General

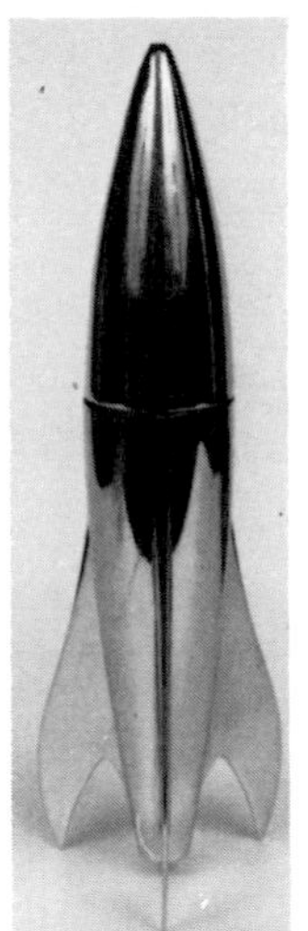

A chrome lighter in the form of a rocket, c1935, 8in (20cm).
£40-50 *COB*

Flying helmets and goggles.
From **£150-440 each**
ONS

A silver and enamelled Royal Air Force lapel brooch, 2in (5cm) long.
£100-150 *ONS*

A silver model of a 1914 Vickers Fighting Biplane FB5, nicknamed Gunbus, London 1916, wingspan 15½in (39.5cm) wide.
£2,000-2,500 *CSK*

A spelter cigarette lighter, 10½in (26cm) high.
£200-250 *CSK*

An R.F.C. propeller boss clock, with French movement, inscribed Made by 1st AM W.J. Nobbs, 16in (41cm) high.
£120-150 *ONS*

A toffee tin, 1955.
£10-15 *COB*

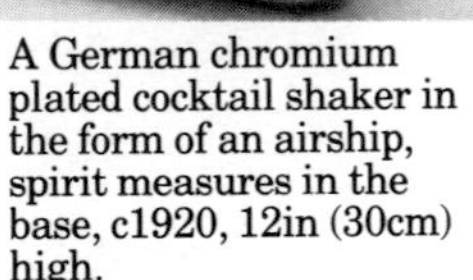

A German chromium plated cocktail shaker in the form of an airship, spirit measures in the base, c1920, 12in (30cm) high.
£600-650 *CSK*

A laminated wood two-blade propeller, 78in (198cm) long.
£400-500 *CSK*

A glass tray with 1931 Schneider Trophy design.
£80-90 *COB*

DID YOU KNOW?
Britain's Jim and Amy Mollison were so exhausted after their transatlantic flight on the 24th July 1933 that they forgot to mail the 4 souvenir letters they were carrying until 14th August!

Toys & Models

An aluminium model of a Sopwith Camel, inscribed 'A Tribute to Sir Thomas 1888-1989', wingspan 9in (24cm) wide.
£300-400 *CSK*

A Lines Bros. interceptor model fighter.
£40-45 *HCH*

A bronze model of a Sunderland flying boat, 1943.
£75-80 *COB*

A French miniature with ballooning scene, set in a green bois durci box, with a view of the Tuileries Chateau, 3in (7cm).
£450-550 *CSK*

A Dinky pre-war Aeroplane set No. 60, 2nd issue.
£500-600 *CSK*

A Dinky pre-war set No. 62k, The King's Aeroplane.
£100-150 *CSK*

Meccano No. 1 Aeroplane Constructor Outfits, c1930.
£200-300 each *CSK*

A Merit Rocket game, c1950.
£15-18 *COB*

Dinky pre-war aircraft, on original card.
£250-300 *CSK*

Cross Reference
Toys
Diecast
Aircraft

Posters & Prints

An Air France poster, c1954, 36 by 26in (91 by 65cm).
£20-25 *COB*

Sunderland in Flight, oil on canvas, by Roy Nockolds, signed and dated '46, 13 by 18in (34 by 45cm).
£250-300 *CSK*

General Aircraft Freighter over Sydney Harbour, watercolour by Margaret Olley, dated '47, 12 by 15in (30 by 38cm).
£100-150 *CSK*

A German identification poster, 1941, 48 by 30in (120 by 75cm).
£25-30 *COB*

'In our Darkest Hour came the Spitfire', oil on canvas by Alan King, 20 by 30in (50 by 75cm).
£350-400 *CSK*

F/Lt R. D. Trevor-Roper, D.F.C., D.F.M., of 617 Squadron, a portrait in charcoal by Cuthbert Orde, signed, 1943, 11 by 8in (29 by 20cm).
£250-300 *CSK*

A German Junkers poster, 1937.
£15-18 *COB*

'The Last Encounter', 1917, watercolour by Phil May, 14½ by 20in (37 by 50cm).
£150-200 *CSK*

Spitfire MkVIII of No. 87 Squadron, watercolour by John Howell, signed and dated 1982.
£100-150 *CSK*

Vision d'Avenir, Office d'Aviation, a coloured lithograph by Gamy, 14 by 31½in (35 by 80cm).
£450-500 *CSK*

Automobilia

In a year which has seen substantial price increases in most types of classic cars, particularly 'supercars' and post-war British sports cars, it is not surprising to note a good increase in collectable automobilia values. Be wary though as some areas, notably car mascots, are now receiving the faker's attention.

Accessories

A pair of Lucas King of the Road acetylene headlamps, 7in (18cm) diam, in canvas cases.
£2,200-2,500 *C*

A pair of Marchal headlamps, 10in (25cm) diam.
£900-1,000 *C*

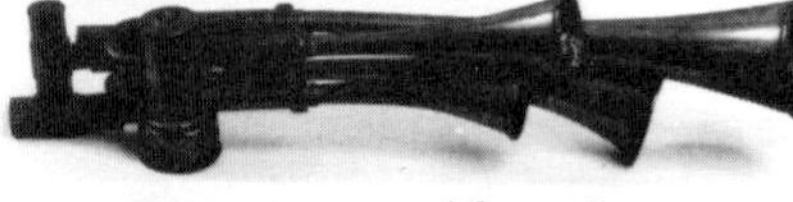

A brass four-note testophone horn, 21in (52cm) long.
£300-400 *ONS*

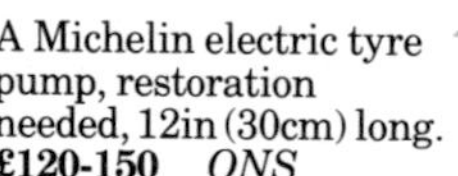

A Michelin electric tyre pump, restoration needed, 12in (30cm) long.
£120-150 *ONS*

Badges

A brass and enamelled United Commercial Travellers of America badge, 4in (11cm) high.
£50-60 *ONS*

A chrome and enamel Brooklands BARC badge, No. 1031, 4in (10cm) high.
£600-650 *ONS*

A chrome and enamel Brooklands 120 mph badge, stamped Jack Dunfee 1–4–29, driving the 2 litre Sunbeam, 4in (10cm) high.
£4,000-5,000 *ONS*

Brooklands Automobilia Racing Club, 4in (10cm) high.
£400-500 *ONS*

Frazer Nash Car Club, 4in (10cm) diam.
£150-200 *ONS*

Hermes, a gilt and enamelled badge, 4in (10cm) high.
£50-80 *CSK*

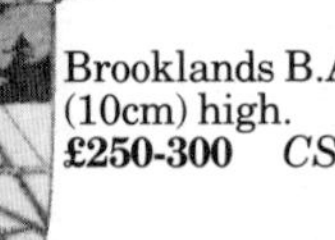

Brooklands B.A.R.C., 4in (10cm) high.
£250-300 *CSK*

Minerva, a gilt and enamelled badge, 2½in (6cm) high.
£100-150 *CSK*

J.R.D.C. enamelled badge, 3½in (9cm) high.
£500-550 *CSK*

Three automobile badges, South Africa, Poland and Finland, 4in (10cm).
£50-200 each *ONS*

Five motor car club badges.
£40-50 *WH*

European enamelled motor club badges.
£50-70 each *WH*

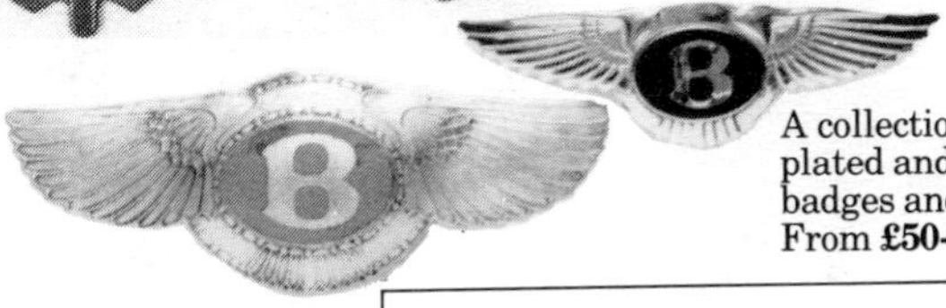

A collection of chromium plated and enamelled badges and brooches.
From **£50-300** *ONS*

This assortment of car badges demonstrates the range of prices that you can currently expect to pay, averaging between £100-200 each, with the Napier Motors radiator badge at £10, the Rally badges being the most sought after. *ONS*

A collection of chromium plated and enamelled badges.
Motor Cycling Club badge **£10-15**
24 heures du Mans **£700-750**
Others **£100-200 each** *ONS*

Two 10ct gold and blue enamelled Indianapolis drivers lapel brooches dated 1953 and 1954.
£150-175 each *ONS*

Mascots

A red Ashay goddess head, 4½in (11cm) high.
£300-350 *ONS*

A bronze mascot from a design by Jean Martel, 4½in (12cm).
£900-1,000 *ONS*

A nickel-plated highlander, inscribed Phineas, Mascot of U.C.L. and U.C.H., 6½in (16cm) high.
£200-250 *CSK*

A brass pierrot holding a lantern, base signed M. Guiraud-Riviere, 4½in (11cm) high.
£150-200 *CSK*

A Hassell aviator car mascot, in brass with ceramic head, 1920s.
£700-900 *WH*

A silver-plated cat, 4½in (11cm) high.
£500-600 *C*

A nickel-plated dancing couple, the base stamped A.E.L., 5in (13cm) high.
£100-150 *CSK*

Two nickel-plated figures, the base of the figure of the policeman stamped Asprey, 5in (12.5cm) high.
£150-300 each *CSK*

A figure entitled Speedy, 5½in (14cm) high.
£300-350 *Bon*

A nickel-plated goat's head, base inscribed Banquet de Massais, Stelline, 5½in (14cm) high.
£700-800 *CSK*

A nickel-plated bulldog, on marble plinth, 4in (10cm) high.
£300-350 *C*

Chromium-plated animal heads, 4½in (11cm) high.
£100-150 each *CSK*

A nickel-plated Wills Sainte Claire flying goose, c1923, 5in (12cm) high.
£400-500 *C*

Books, Prints & Posters

Grand Prix de L'ACF, July 1958, by Pierre Jacotin, 25 by 19in (64 by 47cm).
£150-200 *ONS*

Automobiles à Vapeur, V. Lorant Heilbronn, a poster 23 by 31in (58 by 79cm).
£400-600 *ONS*

An oil on board, Hughie Hughes on his winning Mercer, by Guy Lipscombe, Aurora Trophy, Elgin, Illinois, 1912, signed, 18in (45cm) square.
£6,500-7,500 *ONS*

Stirling Moss in the Maserati, oil on board, by Roy Nockolds, signed, 20 by 30in (50 by 75cm).
£2,000-2,500 *ONS*

A poster, You can be sure of Shell, by Paul Nash, No. 438, unmounted, 30 by 46in (76 by 115cm).
£800-1,000 *ONS*

Poster, C. Foulon, published by Kossuth, 36in (90cm) wide.
£800-900 *ONS*

A photograph of Boillot, Winner of the Grand Prix de France, 1912, fitted with Continental Tyres, 39½ by 28in (99 by 69cm).
£2,000-2,500 *ONS*

Andre Bermond, Grand Prix Automobile, Pau, April 1950, colour lithograph, 15½ by 12in (39 by 30cm).
£1,000-1,200 *ONS*

E. Montaut, The Rail Vanquished by Michelin Tyres, colour lithograph, 29 by 21in (73 by 53cm).
£700-800 *ONS*

Michael Turner, Longbeach 1982, gouache, signed and dated, 13 by 20in (33 by 50cm).
£1,400-1,600 *C*

A poster, Bayard, by F. Hugo d'Alesi, 46in (115cm) wide.
£1,000-1,500 *ONS*

A poster, Monet Goyon, by Roger Perot, 47 by 31in (118 by 77cm).
£500-600 *ONS*

Beligond, Rouen, Les Grands Prix de France, 10 Juillet 1966, original poster, 23½ by 16in (59 by 40cm).
£100-150 *CSK*

Ferrari sales pamphlets, c1968.
£50-100 each *CSK*

Gamy, Indianapolis, Boillot sur Peugeot, hand coloured lithograph, 1913, 17 by 33½in (43 by 85cm).
£500-600 *C*

Two watercolour posters by Michael Wright, Mike Hawthorn 1952 and 1953, French Grand Prix, 8 by 9in (20 by 23cm).
£500-600 *ONS*

Phil May, Segrave sets the record at 231.44 mph, Daytona 1929, watercolour, 7½ by 7in (19 by 18cm).
£220-250 *CSK*

Peter Robertson Rodger, Le Mans 1942, charcoal heightened with white, 10 by 12in (25 by 31cm).
£100-150 *CSK*

Peter Robertson Rodger, The Southport '100', watercolour, 11 by 15in (29 by 38cm).
£30-35 *CSK*

Peter Robertson Rodger, Brooklands, J. Houldsworth in his Bugatti, Empire Trophy Race, 1934, 13 by 17in (33 by 43cm).
£30-50 *CSK*

S. W. de Fenay, Raleigh, The Gold Medal Motorcycle, poster on linen, 76 by 57in (192 by 143cm).
£750-1,000 *ONS*

Dum, Motos Peugeot, colour poster, 31 by 20in (78 by 51cm).
£150-250 *CSK*

Beligond, Reims, Trophee France Amerique, 3 & 4 Juillet 1965, original poster, 23½ by 16in (60 by 40cm).
£150-200 *CSK*

E. Montaut, En Visite, hand coloured lithograph poster, damaged, 16 by 31½in (40 by 79cm).
£700-800 *C*

Tony Smith, 1969 Dutch Grand Prix, oil on canvas, signed and dated 1983, 30 by 20in (75 by 50cm), framed.
£600-700 *Bon*

Original black and white publicity photograph, Jaguar C-type, Le Mans 1953, 26 by 20in (65 by 50cm), framed and glazed.
£150-200 *Bon*

Grand Prix de L'ACF, 1906, a collection of 32 original photographs, taken by M. Branger, each 5 by 7in (12 by 17cm).
£4,000-5,000 *ONS*

Carlo Demand, Vanderbilt Cup 1937, Nuvolari and Ferrari, signed, charcoal and pencil, 19½ by 32in (49 by 81cm).
£2,000-2,500 *ONS*

F. Hugo d'Alesi, Automobiles Bayard, Paris, linen poster, 47 by 63in (117 by 158cm).
£2,000-2,500 *ONS*

Darrell Warner, Ferrari, a design as a collage, watercolour, signed, 30 by 21½in (76 by 52cm).
£500-600 *C*

Nicholas Watts, Mille Miglia 1957, Piero Taruffi in the Ferrari, gouache, signed, 26 by 37in (66 by 94cm).
£3,000-3,500 *C*

Berne Grand Prix 1948, Jean-Pierre Wimille in the Alfa Romeo, limited edition colour print by Roy Nockolds, 10 by 13in (26 by 32cm).
£150-200 *ONS*

A poster for Peugeot, by Rene Vincent, published by Draeger, 63 by 47in (158 by 117cm).
£6,000-7,000 *ONS*

Liége-Rome-Liége, August 1933, poster on linen, 29 by 21in (73 by 53cm).
£450-500 *ONS*

German Grand Prix 1938, Seaman leading in the Mercedes, von Brauchitsch's car on fire in the pits, signed, 12 by 17in (31 by 43cm).
£2,000-2,300 *ONS*

DID YOU KNOW?
Miller's Collectables Price Guide is designed to build up, year by year, into the most comprehensive reference system available.

After E. Montaut, L'Allumage Moderne Magneto Lavalette Eisemann.
£250-300 *ONS*

A Triumph Motorcycle poster, 1950s.
£45-50 *COB*

A watercolour by James Dugdale, Monaco Grand Prix 1928, Bugatti and Mercedes at the station hairpin, 17 by 20in (43 by 52cm).
£150-200 *ONS*

Edouard Montaut, un très honorable 'gentleman' après avoir tripoté sa 100 chevaux, charcoal and crayon, signed, 8 by 12in (20 by 30cm).
£1,300-1,500 *C*

A photograph of an Alfa Romeo 8C Monza, 30 by 40in (76 by 100cm).
£300-400 *ONS*

Gardiner, Coupe des Alpes, gouache, signed and dated '79, 12 by 14in (30 by 35cm).
£300-350 *C*

Clement Cycles & Automobiles, by Bombled, 36in (90cm) high.
£300-400 *ONS*

Minerva, original three-dimensional advertisement in original frame, 20 by 22in (50 by 56cm).
£300-400 *ONS*

After Gamy, Renault 1911, 15 by 26in (37 by 65cm).
£250-300 *ONS*

A Castrol poster by Jean Pillod, Sir Malcolm Campbell's Bluebird and the locomotive La 'Mountain' de l'Etat, 31½ by 23in (79 by 58cm).
£600-700 *ONS*

A poster, Automobiles Brasier, by S. Houtte, 62 by 46in (156 by 115cm).
£800-1,000 *ONS*

General

Two china plates with humorous motoring scenes, Les Automobiles, 8in (20cm) diam.
£100-200 *ONS*

A stained glass panel, illustrating the finish of a motor race, c1935, 16½ by 28in (41.5 by 71cm).
£300-500 *C*

A sterling silver vesta case, engraved with racing scene, 2½in (6cm) high.
£500-600 *ONS*

A double sided enamel advertising sign, 12 by 17in (30 by 42cm).
£100-150 *Bon*

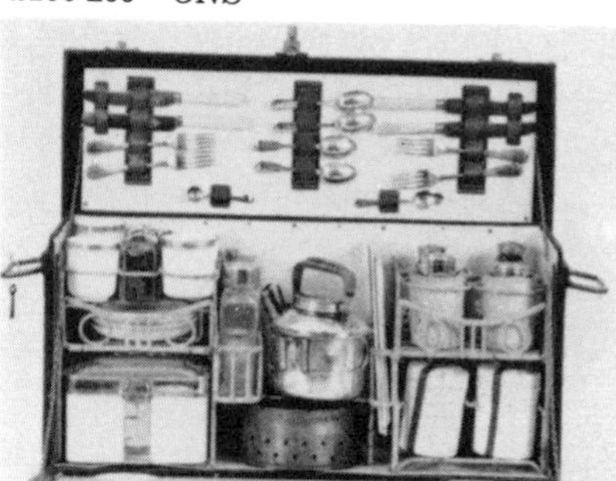

A black leatherette picnic hamper, 24in (61cm) wide.
£700-800 *C*

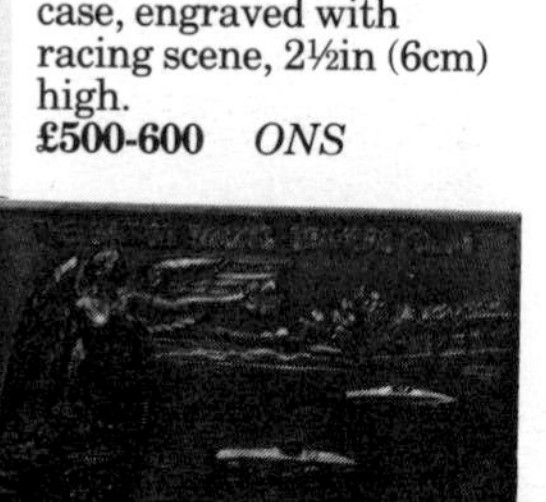

A British Racing Drivers Club bronze plaque, 500 miles race, 1931, 1st Bentley No. 46 driven by Jack Dunfee.
£2,000-2,500 *ONS*

A drinks decanter in the shape of a Bentley radiator, chrome with enamel badge, 7½in (19cm) high.
£100-120 *WH*

A brown leather picnic hamper, stamped Asprey London, 15in (38cm) wide.
£250-300 *CSK*

An 18ct gold pocket watch engraved with motoring scene, reverse inscribed MB.
£2,000-2,500 *ONS*

An AA hotel illuminated sign, pre-war, 24in (61cm) high.
£200-250 *WH*

A selection of Automobilia items.
£50-100 each *ONS*

A Bugatti Grand Prix d'Europe armband, 1924, in red and white cotton.
£500-600 *ONS*

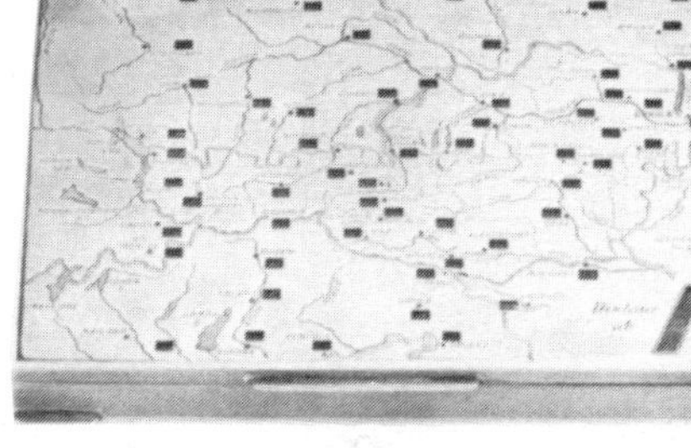
A silver cigarette case, inscribed Hotchkiss, Paris, 5in (12cm) wide.
£1,500-1,700 *C*

Silver medallion, Saltburn Speed Trials 1922, Open Event Racing Cars Unlimited Capacity Flying Start, 1st award, M. Campbell, 127.10 mph, 3in (8cm) diam, in presentation box.
£800-1,000 *ONS*

A hallmarked silver model of Austin House, the plaque with various signatures, London 1962, 8in (20cm) long.
£450-500 *CSK*

A portrait sketch of Sir Malcolm Campbell, by L. Ollier, signed by the subject, and letter dated 1st May 1934.
£300-400 *ONS*

Bicycles

A grocer's delivery tricycle, late 1930s, replacement box.
£600-700 *Bon*

A Raleigh 'X' frame bicycle, c1900.
£150-200 *Bon*

Signs & Branded Products

A Standard Triumph glass garage sign, 1960s.
£50-60 *COB*

Bosch, by Bernhard Rosen, printed tin, 18½ by 26in (46 by 65cm).
£200-250 *ONS*

A Lucas Batteries enamel sign, 24½in (61cm) diam.
£5-10 *ONS*

Give Me Mobiloil, printed tin, 29½ by 20in (74 by 50cm).
£300-400 *ONS*

Shell Huiles Pour Moteurs, double sided enamel sign, 27½in (69cm) high.
£400-500 *ONS*

Vauxhall Cars, a double sided enamel sign, 30½in (76cm) wide.
£150-200 *ONS*

Petrol Pump Globes

A Shell glass petrol pump globe.
£90-100 *Bon*

A Shell penny-in-the-slot petrol lighter dispenser, 20in (50cm) high.
£250-300 *ONS*

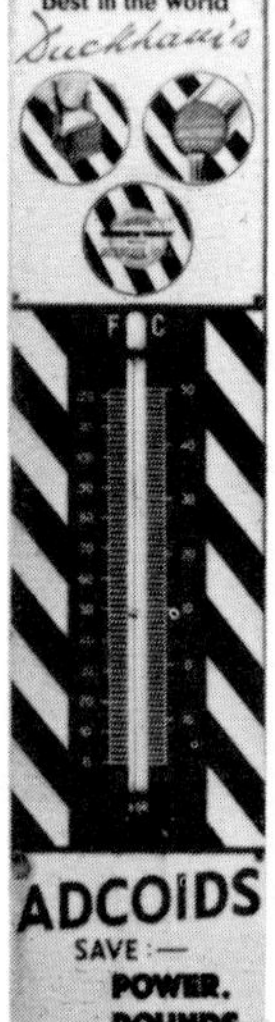

Duckham's enamel sign with thermometer, 46in (115cm) high.
£100-150 *ONS*

l. Esso Ethyl Pump, illuminated sign, 20in (50cm) diam.
£300-350 *ONS*

r. A painted cast iron figure of the Michelin man, 16in (40cm) high.
£100-200 *ONS*

Bottles & Flasks

Bottle collecting has still not recovered its former popularity, although printed advertisements, particularly for 'quack' medicines, are sought after.

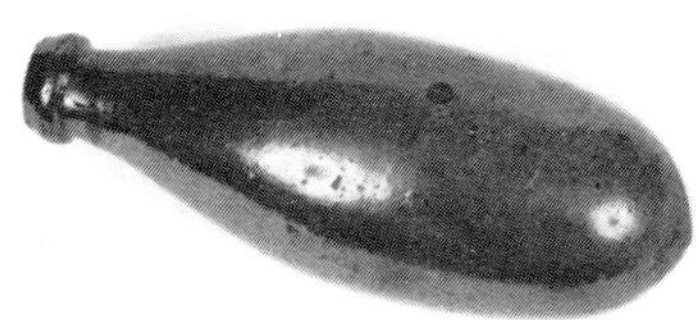

A Hamilton bottle, for aerated waters, 8in (20.5cm).
£100-120 *RG*

Stoneware

An earthenware jar, c1910.
£10-15 *COB*

A stoneware bottle, c1840, 8in (20.5cm).
£150-200 *RG*

Early stoneware bottles, 6 to 7in (15 to 18cm).
£2-5 each *RG*

A Doulton 'leather bottle', with Nottingham coat-of-arms, 8½in (22cm).
£65-75 *RG*

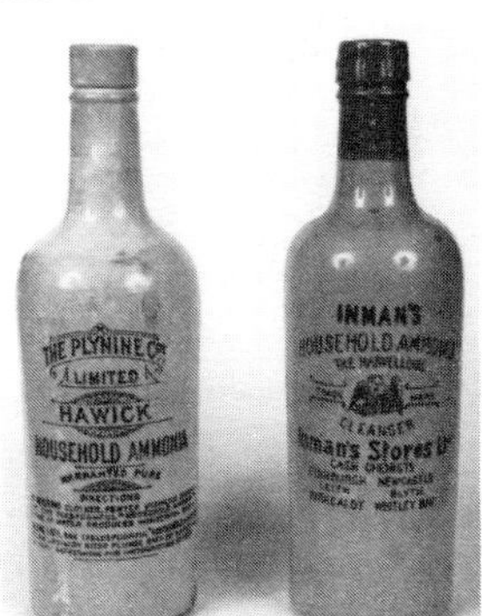

Household ammonia bottles, 11in (28cm) high.
£8-15 each *RG*

Transfer printed stoneware bottles, 7in (18cm).
£3-12 each *RG*

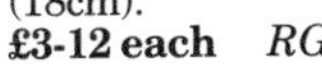

Glass

A baby's feeding bottle, c1890, 5in (12.5cm).
£12-15 *RG*

This type of bottle was known as a murder bottle, as it was fitted with a rubber tube which if not washed properly led to gastro-enteritis and consequently death.

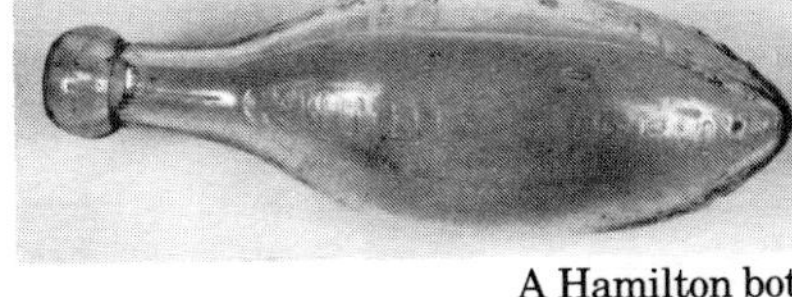

A Hamilton bottle, Carter & Co., Established 1831, 9½in (24cm).
£2-5 *RG*

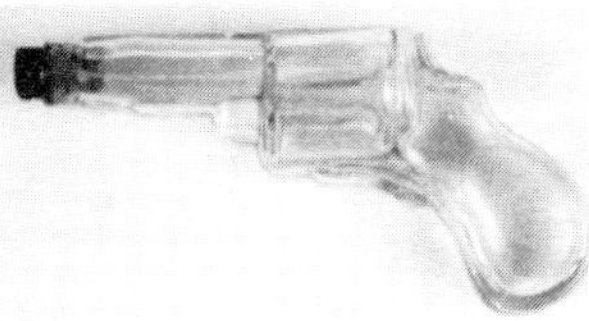

A glass sweet container for children, c1940.
£12-15 *RG*

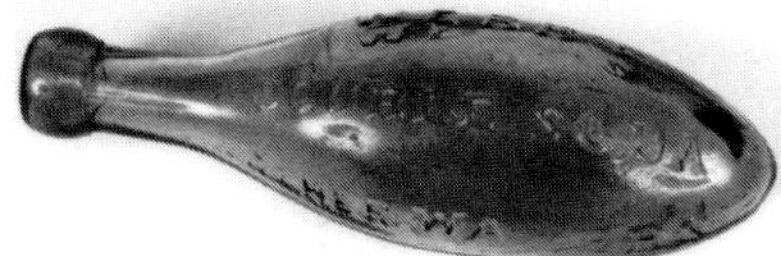

A Hamilton green glass bottle, Webbs Double Soda.
£40-50 *RG*

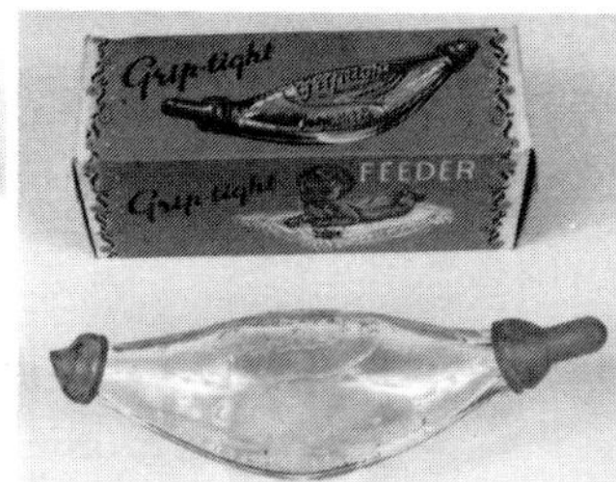

A baby's feeding bottle, c1925, in original box.
£8-10 *RG*

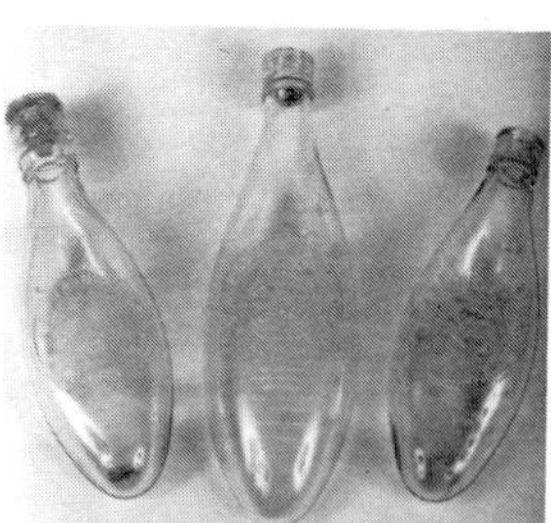

Babies feeding bottles, with measures, The Modern Feeder, c1910.
£15-18 each *RG*

Two 'quack' cure bottles, produced by Warner, 7 and 9in (18 and 23cm).
£12-15 *RG*

Warner was an American safe manufacturer who then started a business producing 'quack' cures, which were worthless as they only contained acid and wine. A picture of a safe is depicted on each bottle along with the city name.

l. & r. Codd bottles, c1900, 8½in (21cm).
£2-5 each *RG*
c. 7½in (19cm), c1875.
£30-40 *RG*

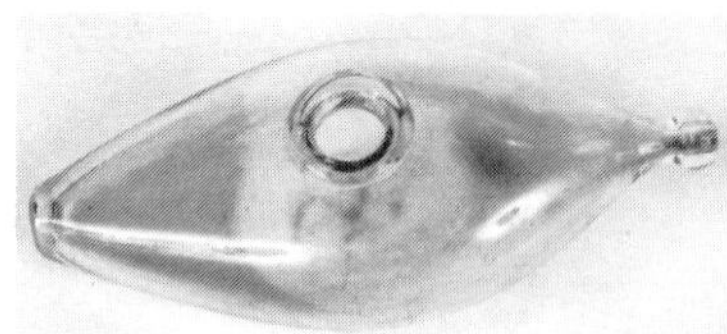

A baby's feeding bottle, c1810, 7½in (19cm).
£45-55 *RG*

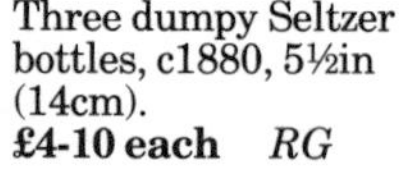

Three dumpy Seltzer bottles, c1880, 5½in (14cm).
£4-10 each *RG*

Chemists

A storage bottle, c1820, 14in (35.5cm) high.
£20-30 *RG*

A storage bottle, c1870, 17in (43cm).
£60-80 *RG*

A Bristol blue poison bottle with stopper, 9½in (24cm) high.
£60-80 *RG*

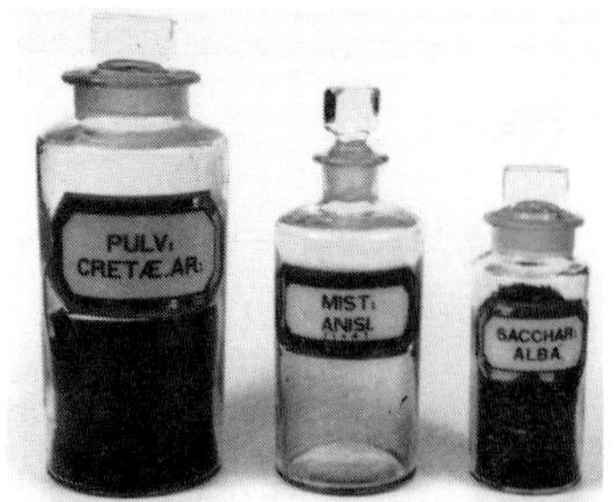

Three labelled storage bottles, c1900, 7 to 10in (18 to 25.5cm).
£12-18 each *RG*

Poison

Blue glass poison bottles, c1890, 2½ to 5in (6.5 to 14cm) high.
£3-12 each *RG*

DID YOU KNOW?
Miller's Collectables Price Guide is designed to build up, year by year, into the most comprehensive reference system available.

Three blue glass poison bottles, with star design, 6 to 8½in (15 to 22cm).
£12-18 each *RG*

Three blue glass bottles, Poisonous Not to be Taken, 3 to 6in (7.5 to 15cm).
£3-9 each *RG*

Three dark blue poison bottles, c1880, 7 to 10½in (18 to 27cm).
£40-60 each *RG*

Inhalers

Maw's Portable Inhaler, c1890, 5in (12.5cm).
£25-30 *RG*

Maw's earthenware inhaler, with blue transfer print, c1890, 9in (23cm).
£60-70 *RG*

A Boots inhaler, c1920, 5½in (14cm).
£25-35 *RG*

An inhaler bottle, with multi-coloured transfer print, c1860, 5in (12.5cm).
£65-75 *RG*

Flasks

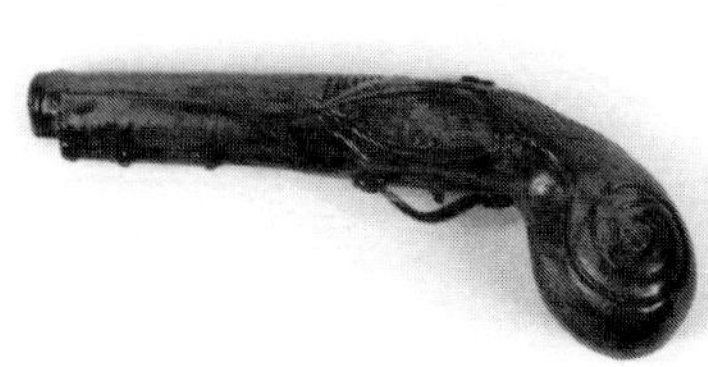

A stoneware pistol flask, 9in (23cm).
£65-75 *RG*

A Rockingham treacle glaze flask, 7in (18cm).
£20-30 *RG*

Three stoneware fish flasks, c1840, 6 to 9in (15 to 23cm).
£85-120 each *RG*

Boxes

Two Tunbridgeware boxes.
£80-100 each *VB*

A Spanish steel bound walnut hutch, with hinged flap and panelled sides, on turned feet, 22in (56cm) wide.
£300-400 *C*

A Continental painted salt box, 15in (38cm) high.
£90-100 *MCA*

A rosewood writing slope, 19thC, 23in (58cm) open.
£100-150 *PCA*

A coromandel work box, early 19thC, 12in (30.5cm) wide.
£225-250 *MB*

An ebony nécessaire, the lid applied with mother-of-pearl, the velvet interior fitted with silver needlework implements, with mirrored lid, 19thC, 8½in (21cm) wide.
£1,100-1,300 *P*

A walnut veneered box, inlaid with holly, ebony and mother-of-pearl.
£75-100 *OBS*

An old offertory box, 16in (40cm) wide.
£90-100 *MCA*

A French provincial salt box in walnut, 17in (43cm) high.
£350-400 *MCA*

A rustic candle box, 18in (45cm) high.
£40-45 *MCA*

Cross Reference
Metalware
Silver

A brown leather studded box, 14in (35cm) long.
£150-200 *PH*

Buckles

A pair of cut steel shoe buckles.
£10-15 *OBS*

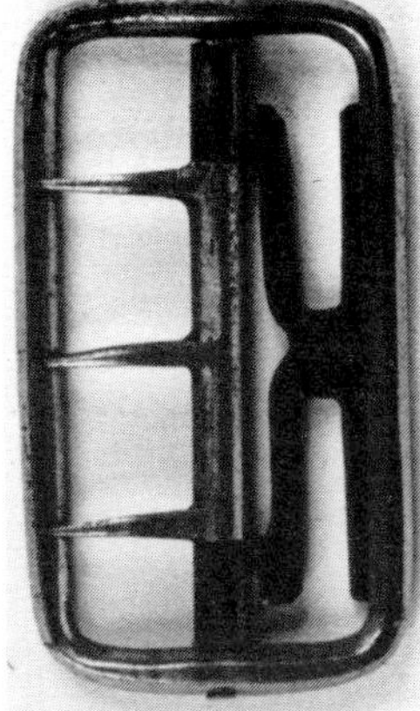

A small steel buckle, 1¼in (3cm) long.
£15-20 *DF*

A pair of cut steel buckles, 2 by 1½in (5 by 4cm).
£60-70 *DF*

A Danish silver buckle by Möller, signed.
£50-70 *ASA*

A pair of cut steel buckles, 1 by 1½in (2.5 by 4cm).
£80-90 *DF*

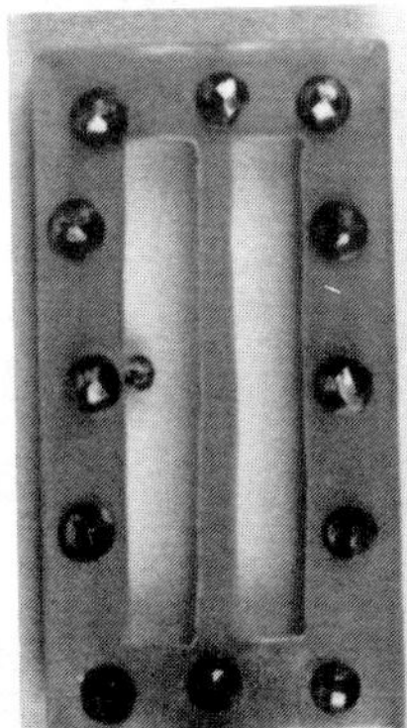

An aluminium buckle, 19thC, 2½in (6cm) square.
£100-150 *DF*

A mother-of-pearl buckle, c1840, 1¼in (3cm) long.
£15-20 *DF*

A paste buckle on velvet, 19thC, 3½ by 2½in (9 by 6cm).
£200-250 *DF*

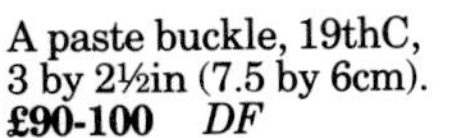

A paste buckle, 19thC, 3 by 2½in (7.5 by 6cm).
£90-100 *DF*

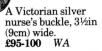

Nurses Buckles

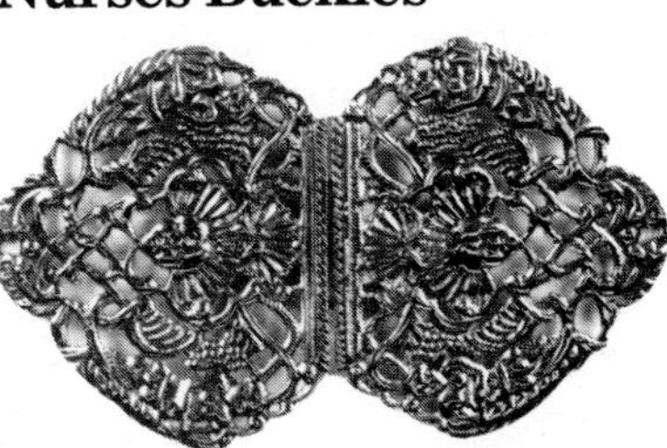

A Victorian silver nurse's buckle, 5½in (15cm) wide.
£150-160 *WA*

A Victorian silver nurse's buckle, 3½in (9cm) wide.
£95-100 *WA*

Button Hooks

An extensive selection of button hooks is featured in Miller's Collectables Price Guide 1989-90, pages 48-49.

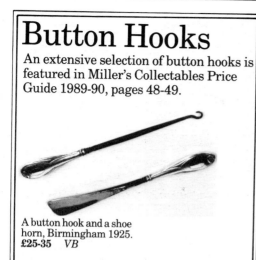

A button hook and a shoe horn, Birmingham 1925.
£25-35 *VB*

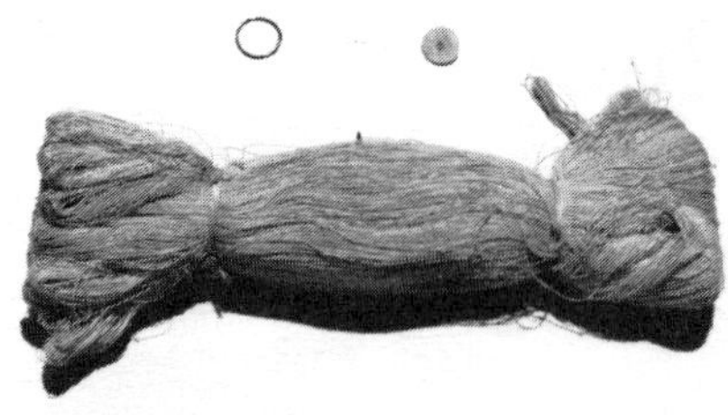

A shank of linen thread, metal ring, and a disc of sheep's horn, raw materials for Dorset buttons, c1700.
£12-15 *OBS*

Buttons

Buttons evolved to replace simple 'toggle' type fastenings on fine clothes during Tudor times. The requirement was fulfilled not only by jewellers and silversmiths but also by porcelain manufacturers, especially from the Orient.

In Dorset, a thriving industry was developed, founded by Abraham Case in the early 17th century. The earliest examples were known as 'high top', comprising a disc of sheep's horn covered in linen and then worked with a delicate threadwork pattern. An example of Case's work can be seen at Longleat House on the silk waistcoat worn by King Charles I at his execution in 1649.

These buttons are still manufactured today.

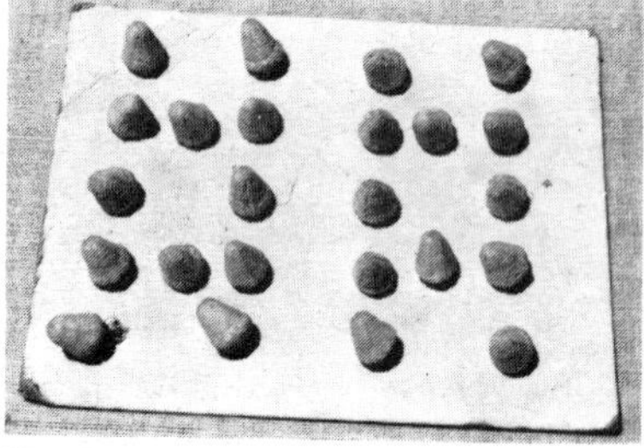

Hand-stitched 'high top' Dorset buttons, c1700.
£10-12 each *OBS*

A selection of buttons hand-stitched in linen, c1700.
From £1-20 each *OBS*

Dorset Buttons

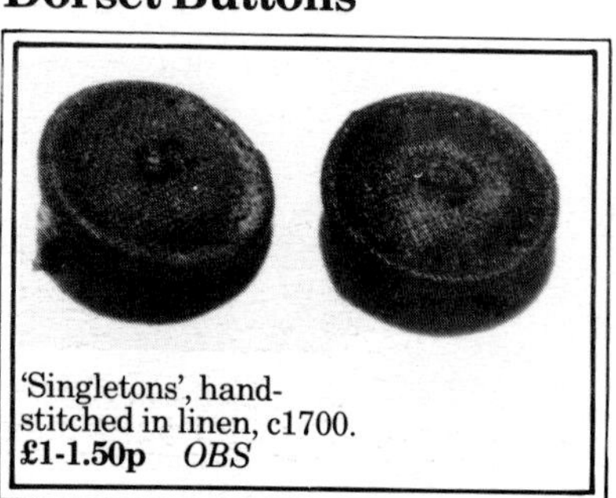

'Singletons', hand-stitched in linen, c1700.
£1-1.50p *OBS*

FURTHER READING
Peacock, Primrose, *Discovering Old Buttons*, Princes Risborough, U.K. 1978.
Bright, M., *Buttony, The Dorset Heritage*, Lytchett Minster, 1971.

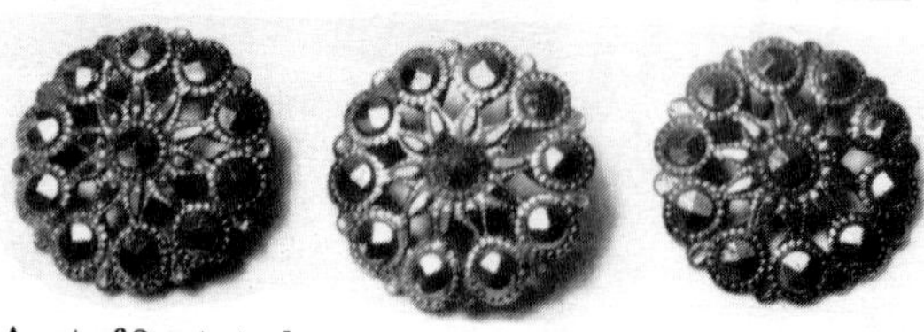

A set of 3 cut steel buttons.
£12-15 *OBS*

'Singleton' buttons, hand-stitched in linen, on original card, c1700.
£40-45 for 36 *OBS*

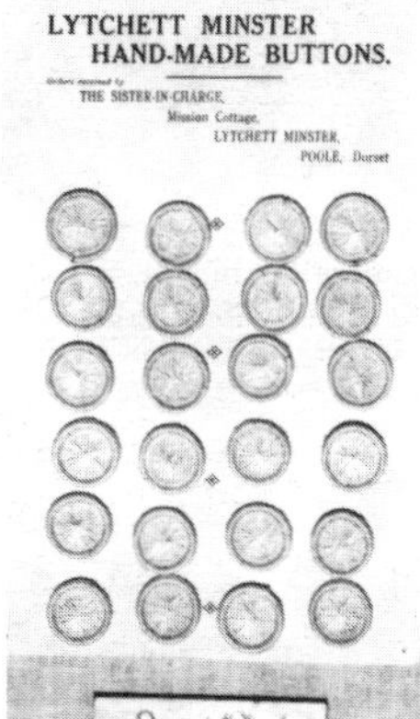

Hand-made buttons with the Dorset Wheel pattern, c1700.
£20-22 each *OBS*

Hand-stitched 'bird's eye' buttons, on original card, c1700.
£40-45 for 36 *OBS*

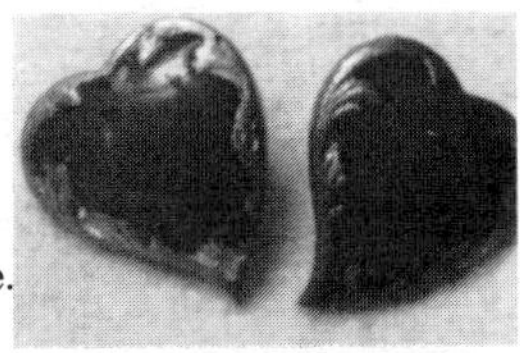

A set of 9 brass buttons, enamelled in bright blue.
£15-20 *OBS*

DID YOU KNOW?
'Singleton' Dorset buttons in black are extremely rare, having only been made between 1658 and 1682.

A set of Arts & Crafts silver buttons, Keswick School of Industrial Arts.
£100-150 *OBJ*

A set of 5 brass driving coat buttons, embossed with Hermes, the god of speed.
£20-25 *OBS*

A set of 3 French enamelled buttons, marked R &G Paris, c1880.
£30-35 *OBS*

A pair of Victorian enamelled buttons.
£10-15 *OBS*

A late Victorian mother-of-pearl hand-carved button, 2.5cm diam.
£2-3 *OBS*

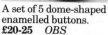

A set of 3 painted enamel buttons.
£10-15 *OBS*

A set of 5 dome-shaped enamelled buttons.
£20-25 *OBS*

A set of 3 painted brass buttons.
£10-15 *OBS*

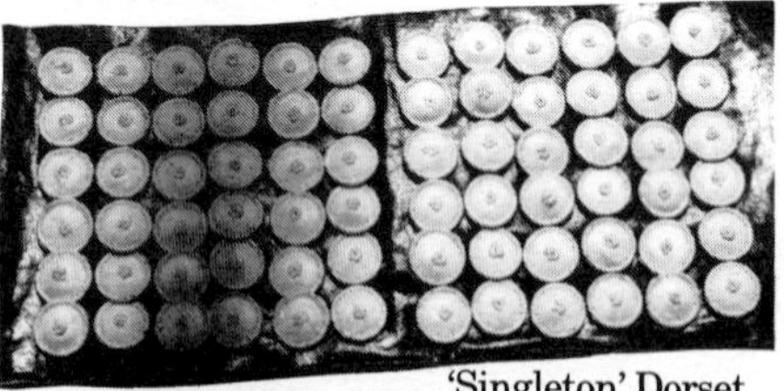

'Singleton' Dorset buttons.
£40-45 for 36 *OBS*

A set of 3 cut steel and enamel buttons.
£12-15 *OBS*

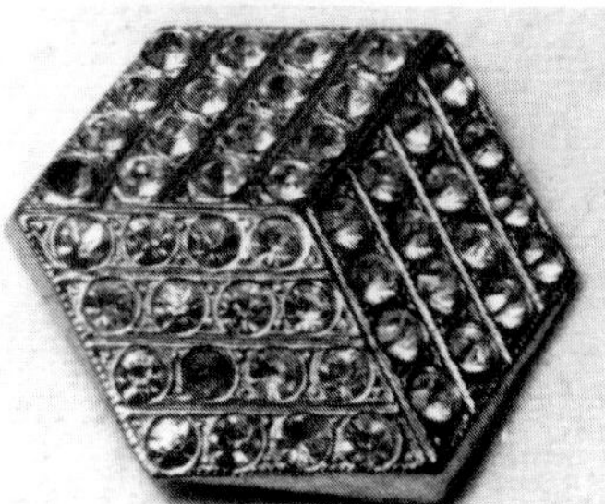

A pair of paste buttons, c1930.
£10-12 *OBS*

A pair of paste buttons. **£8-10** *OBS*

A set of 6 Edwardian mother-of-pearl and brass coat buttons.
£15-20 *OBS*

Victorian black glass and cut steel buttons, 2cm diam.
£3-5 each *OBS*

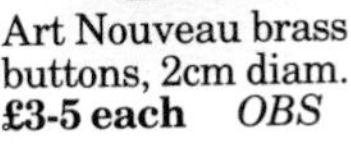

Art Nouveau brass buttons, 2cm diam.
£3-5 each *OBS*

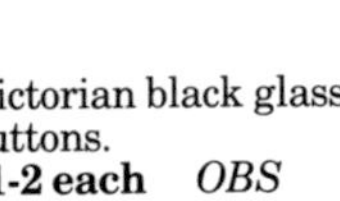

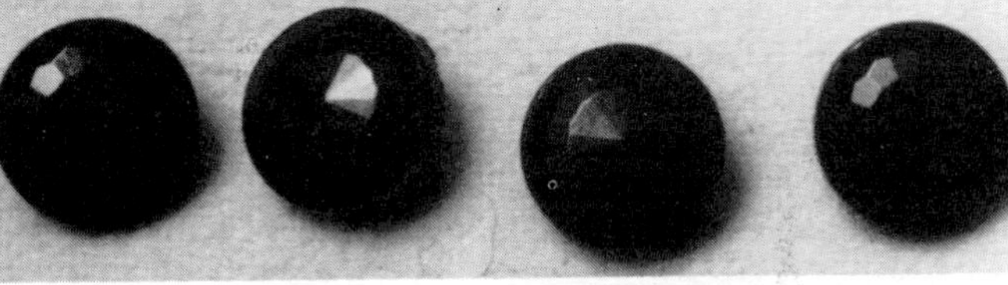

Victorian black glass buttons.
£1-2 each *OBS*

A pair of enamelled buttons.
£8-10 *OBS*

A pair of late Victorian enamel buttons.
£8-10 *OBS*

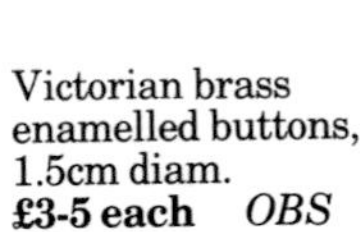

Victorian brass enamelled buttons, 1.5cm diam.
£3-5 each *OBS*

Cameras

An Agfa 120 roll film camera, Prontor II shutter, c1929.
£17-20 *LAT*

A Stereo Mikroma camera, with green leather covered body, with accessories.
£150-200 *CSK*

A Chinese twin lens reflex camera, Five Goats, 6in (15cm) high.
£75-100 *J*

A German Excelsior quarter-plate folding camera, with plate holders in leather case, c1905.
£40-50 *LAT*

A Houghton's half-plate mahogany and brass triple diamond camera, with tripod, c1905.
£300-350 *LAT*

A Roland camera No. S.1137, by Kleinbild-Plasmat, with fitted leather case.
£450-500 *CSK*

A whole plate brass and mahogany tailboard camera, by Henry Park, London.
£100-150 *CSK*

A rare 9.5mm cinematographic hand camera, by Arthur S. Newman, London, c1926.
£1,000-1,500 *CSK*

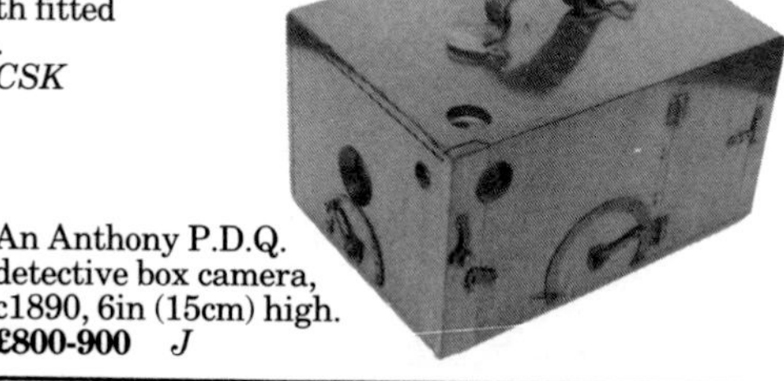

An Anthony P.D.Q. detective box camera, c1890, 6in (15cm) high.
£800-900 *J*

An Ensign roll film reflex camera No. E1053 by Houghton-Butcher Mfg. Co. Ltd. London, in leather case.
£300-350 *CSK*

A half-plate brass and mahogany studio camera, with Ross Zeiss patent Tessar f4.5 210mm lens and tripod.
£100-120 *CSK*

A Dento camera No. 3192, by Adams & Co, London, with adaptor and boxes of plates.
£70-100 *CSK*

A Newman and Guardia camera, New Special Sybil, c1914-30, 6in (15cm).
£100-200 *FT*

A Clarissa camera No. S.14 by E. Lorenz, Berlin, together with lens No. 291549, in leather case.
£1,200-1,500 *CSK*

A polished interior folding plate camera, c1905, 8in (20cm) long.
£80-100 *LAT*

A miniature Fotal camera, by Fabrik Fotografische Apparate, Germany.
£600-800 *CSK*

An Exakta camera No. 484797.
£500-600 *CSK*

A Univex vest pocket model, AF, 3½in (8cm) wide.
£25-50 *J*

A Minolta Crown II camera, 5½in (14cm) high.
£250-300 *J*

An Ihagee Exa-1 camera, 35mm, 6in (15cm) wide.
£40-50 *J*

A Coronet 020 box camera.
£30-50 *J*

A Mycro miniature camera, by Sanwa Co. Ltd, 2in (5cm) wide.
£80-100 *J*

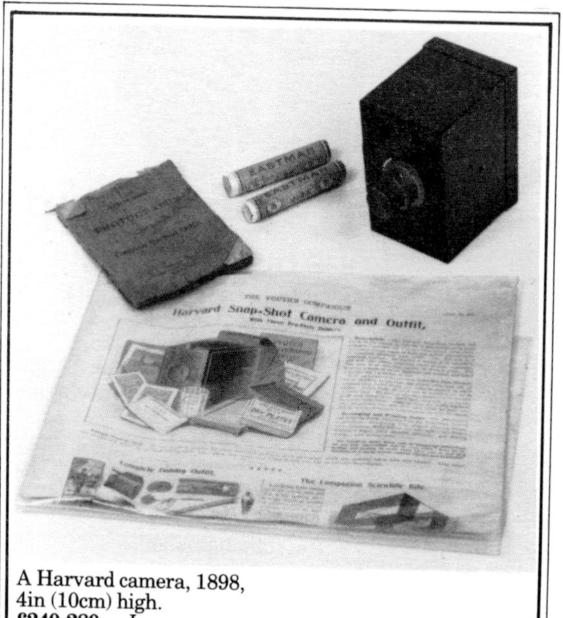

A Harvard camera, 1898, 4in (10cm) high.
£240-280 *J*

A French Sigriste camera, with a shutter speed of 10,000 per second, c1900, 7½in (18.5cm) high.
£5,500-6,000 *J*

A Newman & Guardia camera, 'Nydia', c1907.
£400-500 *LAT*

A J.B. Ensign box camera, by Houghton Butcher, 6in (15cm) square.
£5-10 *LAT*

A Klito No. 0 falling plate camera, c1905, 8in (20cm) long.
£40-60 *LAT*

A Stylophot miniature camera, c1955, 5in (12cm) long.
£60-80 *FT*

A Sanderson plate camera, regular model, 7in (17.5cm) high.
£350-400 *J*

An Asahi Pentax S1a camera, 6in (15cm) wide.
£70-90 *J*

A Canon S. camera No. 10594, with a Nippon Kogaku Nikkor lens No. 50114.
£1,400-1,800 *CSK*

The Canon S camera was produced between 1938 and 1945 with an estimated production run of 1,600 units. Most fall within the serial number range 10529 to 12500.

A Praktica F x 2, German, 6in (15cm) wide.
£45-55 *J*

Kodak

An Eastman Kodak Panoram-Kodak camera No. 3a, 1926-28.
£200-250 *CSK*

An Eastman Kodak stereo camera Model 1, 1920s.
£200-250 *CSK*

An Eastman Kodak No. 4 folding camera.
£220-250 *CSK*

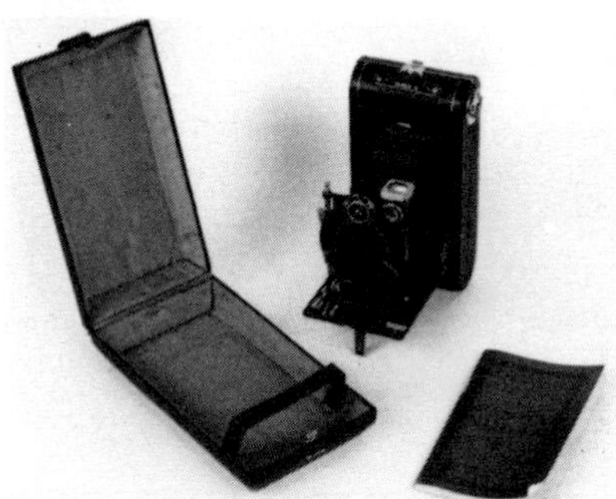

A red Kodak Pocket Vanity camera, with original purse, box and instructions, c1928, 5in (13cm) wide.
£160-180 *LAT*

A Kodak 'new type' Retina IIIC camera.
£300-350 *CSK*

A Kodak Suprema camera.
£200-250 *CSK*

A Super Kodak Six-20 camera.
£650-700 *CSK*

A brown Vanity Kodak camera, c1930.
£120-140 *CSK*

A red Vanity Kodak camera.
£140-160 *CSK*

Leica

A Leica M4-P camera, made by Leitz, Canada, 5½in (14cm) wide.
£800-900 *J*

Thornton Pickard

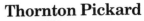

A Thornton Pickard Imperial Triple Extension camera, c1920.
£150-200 *FT*

A Thornton Pickard Special Ruby Reflex quarter-plate, 6 single metal slides, c1915.
£115-125 *LAT*

A Thornton Pickard stereo Puck, model 2, stereo or 16 single photos on 120 film, c1930.
£55-65 *LAT*

Voigtlander

A pre-war Prominant camera, in maker's leather case.
£400-450 *CSK*

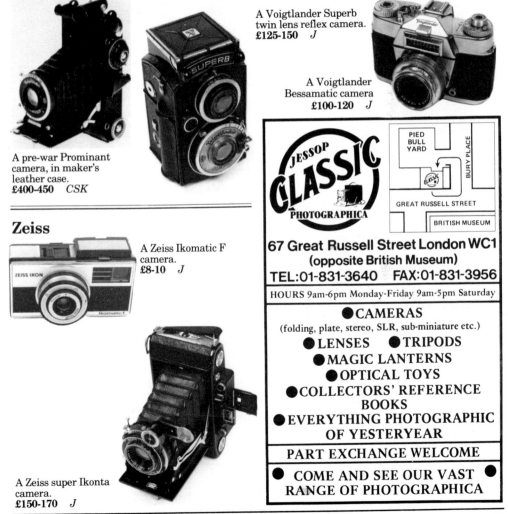

A Voigtlander Superb twin lens reflex camera.
£125-150 *J*

A Voigtlander Bessamatic camera
£100-120 *J*

Zeiss

A Zeiss Ikomatic F camera.
£8-10 *J*

A Zeiss super Ikonta camera.
£150-170 *J*

Card Cases

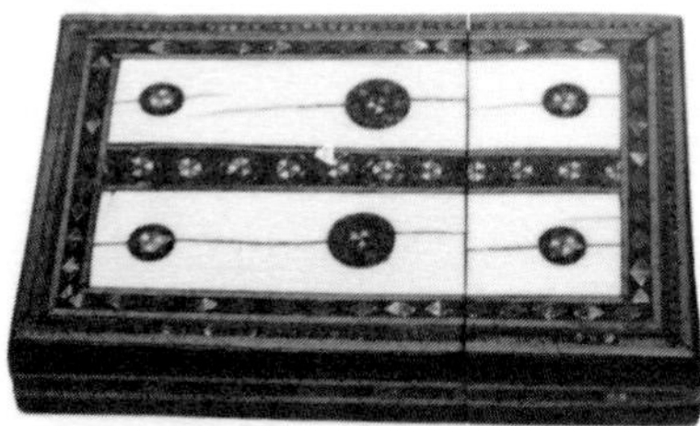

An Indian micro mosaic card case.
£20-30 *DP*

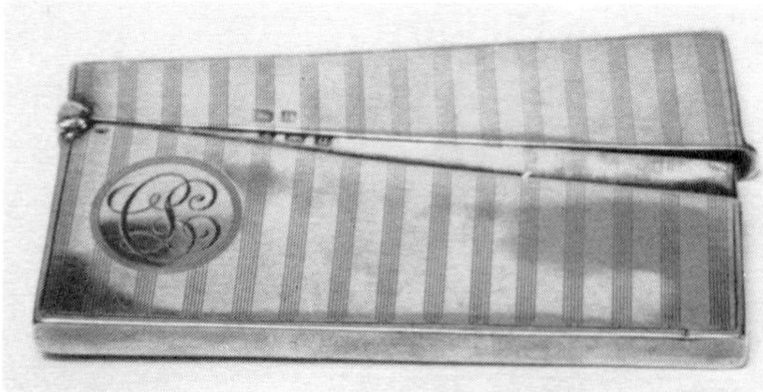

A silver card case, hallmarked 1919.
£50-60 *DP*

Leather and silver mounted card cases.
£20-30 *DP*

A leather and silver mounted card case.
£30-40 *DP*

A mother-of-pearl card case, 4in (10cm) long.
£75-95 *AB*

An Indian carved sandalwood card case.
£30-40 *DP*

A leather and silver mounted card case.
£40-50 *DP*

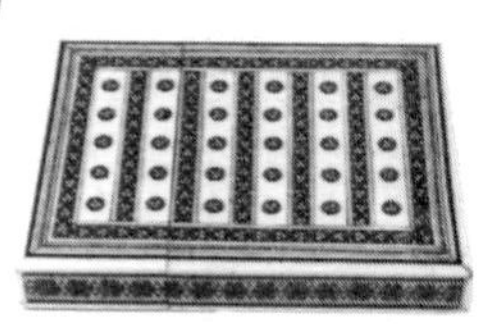

Indian micro mosaic card cases.
£40-60 *DP*

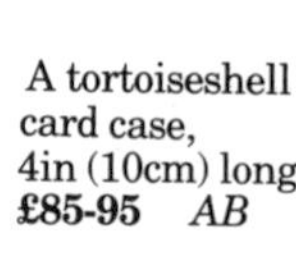

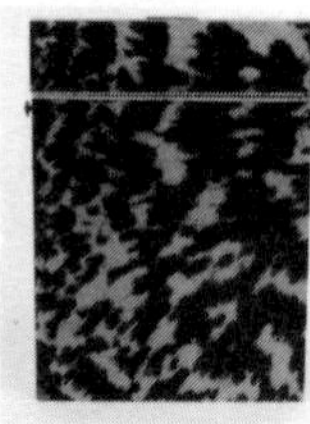

A tortoiseshell card case, 4in (10cm) long.
£85-95 *AB*

MAKE THE MOST OF MILLERS
Price ranges in this book reflect what one should expect to *pay* for a similar example. When selling, however, one should expect to receive a lower figure. This will fluctuate according to a dealer's stock, saleability at a particular time, etc. It is always advisable, when selling, to approach a reputable specialist dealer or an auction house which has specialist sales.

A silver plated card case.
£60-70 *DP*

Candlesticks

A Ratakaffe iron candlestick, German, 12in (30.5cm).
£75-85 *MCA*

A pair of cut glass, brass and blue glass candlesticks, 11½in (29cm).
£550-600 *C*

A pair of copper candlesticks, c1900.
£35-40 *OBS*

An iron candelabrum, 23in (58cm).
£110-120 *MCA*

Dutch design candlesticks, late 18thC, 9in (23cm).
l. Bell metal. **£170-200**
r. Brass. **£200-230** *WIL*

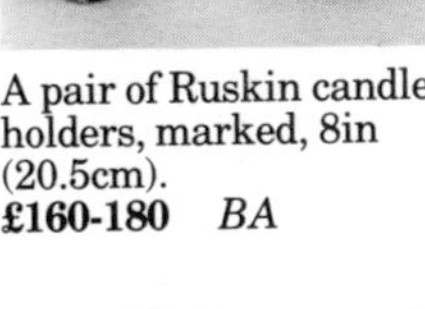

A pair of Ruskin candle holders, marked, 8in (20.5cm).
£160-180 *BA*

Cross Reference
Ceramics

A pair of silver classical Corinthian column candlesticks, hollow bases, damaged, 8in (20.5cm), 20oz.
£300-350 *WIL*

A German iron candlestick, 16½in (42cm).
£75-85 *MCA*

A pair of Wemyss pottery candlesticks, painted with roses, one damaged, impressed and painted mark, 7in (18cm).
£300-350 *HSS*

French metal candlesticks, formed as caricatures, 19thC, 13 and 14in (33 and 35.5cm).
£200-300 each pair
CSK

A pair of silver candlesticks with sconces, Sheffield 1881, 5½in (14cm) high.
£250-300 *PCh*

FURTHER READING
Michaelis, R. F., *Old Domestic Base Metal Candlesticks,* Antique Collectors' Club, Woodbridge, Suffolk, 1978.

Clocks

Whilst we feel that clocks generally are outside the scope of the Collectables Price Guide, they are featured in detail in Miller's Antiques Price Guides.

This very desirable selection of early 20thC clocks reflects the current demand for any items from this period.

A silver mounted Art Nouveau clock, with mahogany back and enamelled dial, c1900, 5in (12.5cm) square.
£80-140 *ASA*

A silver mounted clock with wooden back, c1900, modern movement.
£40-60 *ASA*

A Walker & Hall silver mounted clock, with polished oak back, c1910, 4in (10cm) square.
£40-80 *ASA*

A silver mantel clock, indistinct hallmarks, c1930.
£30-40 *ASA*

A green enamel dressing table clock, with copper and wood backing, c1920, 3in (7.5cm) square.
£15-20 *ASA*

A miniature silver clock, mounted on wooden back, Birmingham hallmarks, c1910.
£50-70 *ASA*

A silver dressing table clock, with 8-day movement, c1920.
£30-60 *ASA*

A Walker & Hall blue enamel on silver dressing table clock, hallmarked, 1928.
£50-80 *ASA*

A silver on wood Art Nouveau mantel clock, with enamel dial, c1900.
£60-100 *ASA*

A Walker & Hall silver mantel clock, with wooden back and easel stand, c1925.
£40-80 *ASA*

A silver engine turned watch stand containing silver pocket watch, c1910.
£70-100 *ASA*

CERAMICS

Ceramics continue to provide a plentiful hunting ground for the collector. There is a wealth of subjects, styles, types, potters and factories to explore; obviously some areas will become fashionable and expensive, e.g. Moorcroft. Some potters will have more fashionable and expensive patterns, e.g. Clarice Cliff — Bizarre, but many areas are just waiting to be discovered.

As last year we have sectioned the ceramics into collectable factories and potters, arranged alphabetically, then Victorian ceramics, including this year ironstone wares and particularly featuring transfer printed wares. Finally we have grouped ceramics into collectable items, e.g. egg cups and teapots.

Don't forget to use the Cross Reference boxes and also Volume I of Collectables. It is a valuable growing reference series.

Beswick

Pheasants, 1940 to 1971, 8½ to 12in (21.5 to 30.5cm).
£80-100 *STU*

A Loch Ness Monster containing Scotch Whisky, 5in (12.5cm) wide.
£10-15 *STU*

Cross Reference
Teapots

Teapots, c1950, 6½ and 7½in (16.5 and 19cm) high.
£40-50 each *STU*

A muffin dish, c1950, 6in (15.5cm) high.
£30-40 *STU*

Sairey Gamp.
£50-60 *STU*

A vase, with palm tree design, beige, 8½in (22cm) high.
£25-35 *STU*

A yellow biscuit barrel in Gardenia pattern, 7½in (19cm) high.
£60-70 *DEC*

Chickadee, 1941-1967, 6½in (16.5cm) high.
£35-45 *STU*

Ping Pong.
£30-35 *STU*

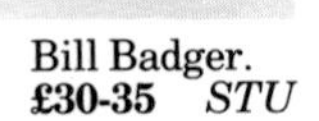

Bill Badger.
£30-35 *STU*

A Mr. Bumble jug, c1935, 5in (12.5cm).
£60-70 *STU*

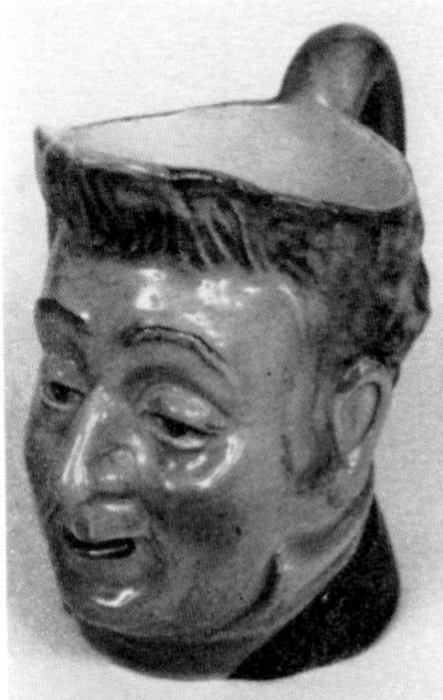

Pecksniff cream jug, c1935, 3½in (9cm).
£25-35 *STU*

A Lord Mayor water jug, 9in (23cm).
£60-70 *STU*

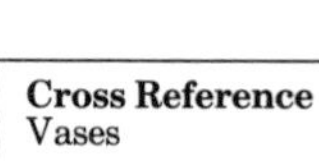

Cross Reference
Vases

Brannam

Brannam pottery is currently becoming extremely collectable; it was a small family business run from Barnstaple in Devon. For the history of the factory refer to *A Family Business, The Story of a Pottery,* by Peter Brannam, 1982.

A jug, made for Liberty, with mustard and brown decoration, c1920, 8in (20.5cm) high.
£150-200 *BIA*

A Brannam vase, c1899, 11in (28cm).
£100-150 *ASc*

DID YOU KNOW?
The Rupert Bear series was introduced in 1980 and withdrawn in 1986. The Rupert Bear figure is extremely hard to find @ **£50-70.**

A puffin jug, signed, dated 1901, 6½in (16.5cm).
£50-80 *ASc*

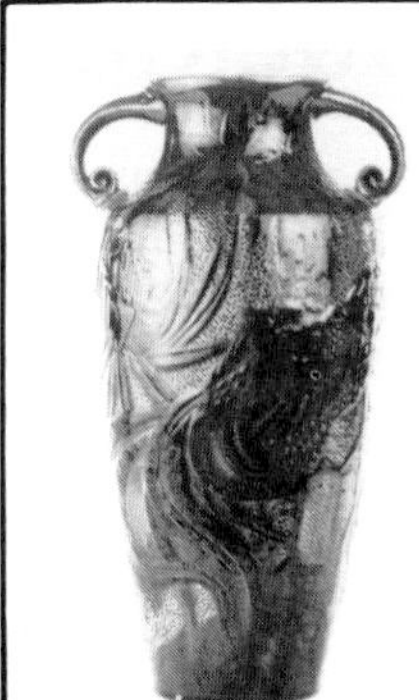

A vase with 2 scroll handles, the decoration in blue, green and orange, inscribed on base F.B.C.H. Brannam, Barum 1907, registered number 44561, 15in (38cm) high.
£300-350 *P(M)*

A wall vase, Autumn Breeze, signed, dated 1899, 10½in (26cm).
£100-150 *ASc*

A double bowl with stylised dolphin supports, slip trailed and sgraffito decoration of fish and seaweed in green and brown, dated 1895, 8½in (22cm) high.
£350-400 *BIA*

A jug, dated 1907, 2in (5cm).
£15-25 *ASc*

A slip-trailed Art Nouveau pot, dated 1907, 2½in (6cm) high.
£35-45 *BIA*

A dish, c1910, 5 by 4in (12.5 by 10cm).
£20-25 *ASc*

Bennett

A vase in shades of green, unsigned, 8in (20cm) high.
£65-70 *JAZ*

A two-handled vase, signed, 1930s, 6in (15cm) high.
£65-70 *JAZ*

A Burleigh vase, designed and signed by Bennett, the Art Director who followed Charlotte Rhead at the factory, 1930s, 7in (17.5cm) high.
£70-75 *JAZ*

Bretby

Bretby started a factory during the last quarter of the 19thC with his partner William Ault. Following a quarrel, Ault left to found his own factory.

A pair of Art Nouveau style twin-handled vases, with bronze glaze, c1900, 10in (25cm) high.
£150-200 *BIA*

A Bretby figure of a Dutch boy, c1915, 7½in (19cm).
£25-30 *AA*

An Ault vase, showing a monkey climbing a tree, c1880, 11in (28cm) high.
£50-60 *ASc*

A Bretby vase, c1880, 6in (15cm) high.
£30-50 *ASc*

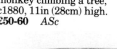

A Bretby glazed bowl, c1890, 7½in (19cm) wide.
£30-40 *ASc*

Buckley Pottery

Some forty kiln sites have been recorded at Buckley, a Welsh town near Chester, and a pottery centre from medieval times until the early '50s. Products were exported to the USA, Australia and even to Stoke-on-Trent. Wares available today date mostly from the early 19thC to the potteries' demise.

Characteristic wares have rich iron red bodies with yellow sliptrailing or glossy black or dark brown glazes. All kinds of utilitarian and decorative wares were made.

Lamb & Sons, Powells, and Buckley Art Pottery are marks occasionally found on pots. The robust and lively character of these wares has led to a growth of appreciation among collectors and decorators.

A Buckley milk pan, mid-19thC, 14in (35cm) high.
£30-50 *IW*

A brewing jar, possibly Buckley, c1900, 16in (40cm) high.
£40-60 *IW*

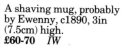

A shaving mug, probably by Ewenny, c1890, 3in (7.5cm) high.
£60-70 *IW*

Formerly believed to be Buckley and as such, exhibited in the Buckley Exhibition in 1985.

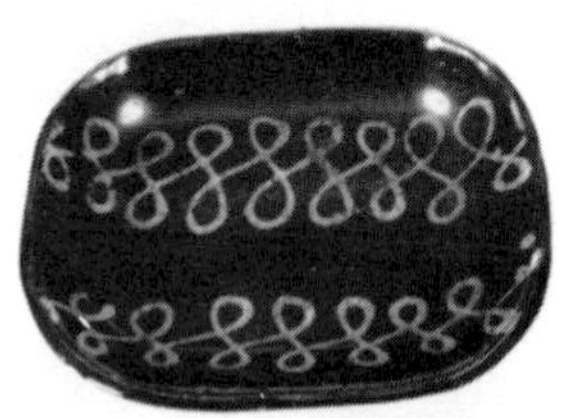

4 Buckley slipware dishes, c1890, 12 and 14in (30 and 35cm) wide.
£225-250 each *IW*

A Buckley banded storage jar, c1900, 8in (20cm) high.
£40-50 *IW*

Two Buckley steans, c1900, 8 and 9½in (20 and 24cm) high.
£25-40 each *IW*

DID YOU KNOW?
Miller's Collectables Price Guide is designed to build up, year by year, into the most comprehensive reference system available.

A Buckley banded stean, 8in (20cm) high.
£40-45 *IW*

A stean is a local name from the Welsh border area; it is also known as a pancheon.

A Buckley chip-ware butter pot, marked 1941, 8in (20cm) high.
£50-60 *IW*

The latest known dated example.

Burleigh

A blue Burleigh jug with a brown rabbit, c1930, 7in (18cm) high.
£50-60 *BEV*

A Burleigh basket, 9½in (24cm) high.
£35-40 *DEC*

A jug with rabbit, 6in (15cm) high.
£40-45 *CIR*

A jug with a golfing figure, 7½in (19cm) high.
£200-250 *BEV*

Cross Reference
Golfing

A Burleigh jug, c1930, 8in (20cm) high.
£50-60 *DEC*

A jug with a Pied Piper design, 8in (20cm) high.
£75-80 *BEV*

A jug with orange, grey and blue design, 9in (23cm).
£35-40 *BEV*

A jug with a kingfisher design, 7in (18cm) high.
£65-70 *BEV*

Burmantofts

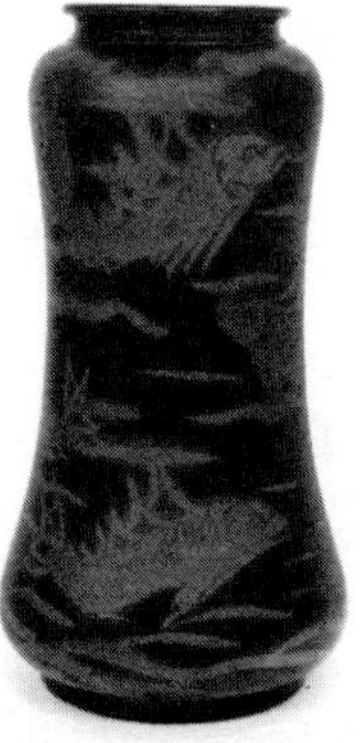

A lustre pottery vase, marked, c1890, 7in (18cm) high.
£200-250 *ASc*

An ochre coloured vase in Oriental style, c1880, 9½in (24cm) high.
£80-120 *ASc*

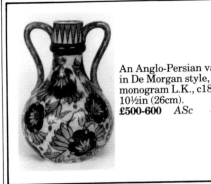

An Anglo-Persian vase, in De Morgan style, monogram L.K., c1880, 10½in (26cm).
£500-600 *ASc*

A pair of yellow vases, with sunburst decoration, c1880, 5½in (14cm) high.
£30-50 *ASc*

Cross Reference
Wall Vases

MAKE THE MOST OF MILLERS
Price ranges in this book reflect what one should expect to *pay* for a similar example. When selling, however, one should expect to receive a lower figure. This will fluctuate according to a dealer's stock, saleability at a particular time, etc. It is always advisable, when selling, to approach a reputable specialist dealer or an auction house which has specialist sales.

A turquoise jardinière, c1890, 11½in (29cm) high.
£120-150 *ASc*

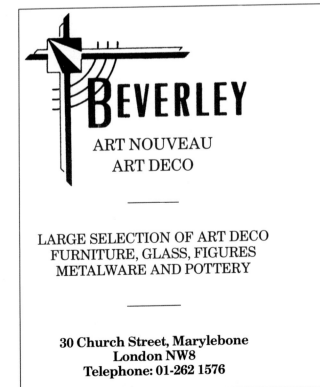

An Anglo-Persian vase, 5½in (14cm) high.
£80-120 *ASc*

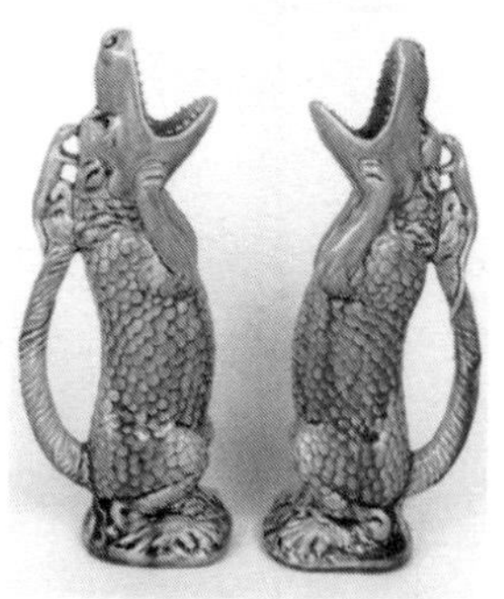

A pair of turquoise dragon jugs, c1885, 11½in (29cm).
£500-600 *ASc*

A three-footed yellow toad, c1885, 6½in (16cm) high.
£150-250 *ASc*

Based on an Oriental original — supposed to be lucky.

A framed tile, marked, c1880, 8 by 16in (20 by 40cm). **£150-200** *ASc*

An Anglo-Persian vase, in De Morgan style, with L.K. monogram, c1880.
£500-600 *ASc*

A brown glazed jardinière, with sunflower design, c1890.
£400-500 *ASc*

A pair of dragon vases, some restoration, c1885, 14in (35cm). **£500-600** *ASc*

A lustre vase, c1890, 5in (13cm) high.
£60-80 *ASc*

Carlton Ware

A biscuit barrel, c1930, 5½in (14cm) high.
£40-50 *STU*

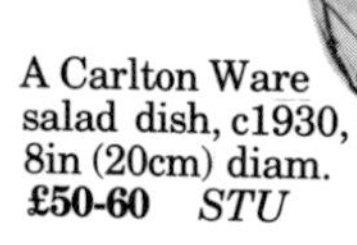

A Carlton Ware salad dish, c1930, 8in (20cm) diam.
£50-60 *STU*

A Carlton Ware jug, 8in (20cm) high.
£85-95 *DEC*

A Carlton teaset for two, in green and gold, with fin handles, c1930.
£300-350 *BEV*

A Carlton Ware charger, 13in (33cm) diam.
£100-110 *DEC*

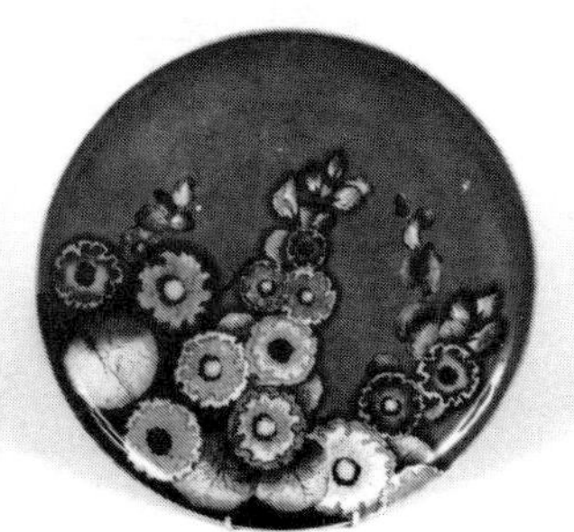
A charger with green background, 13in (33cm) diam.
£100-110 *DEC*

A Carlton Ware sugar sifter, 5½in (14cm).
£15-20 *TS*

Clarice Cliff

Bowls

A Bizarre cauldron bowl, decorated in the Luxor pattern, in orange, blue, purple and green on a cream coloured ground, restored, rubber stamp mark, 4½in (11cm) diam.
£450-500 *CSK*

A Fantasque Bizarre Hiawatha bowl, decorated with the Farmhouse pattern, in black, brown, green and yellow on a cream coloured ground, lithograph mark, 10in (25.5cm) diam.
£750-850 *CSK*

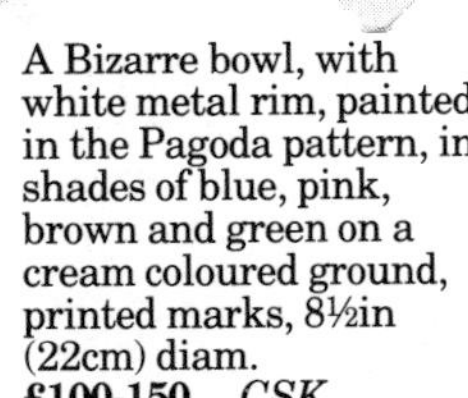
A Bizarre bowl, with white metal rim, painted in the Pagoda pattern, in shades of blue, pink, brown and green on a cream coloured ground, printed marks, 8½in (22cm) diam.
£100-150 *CSK*

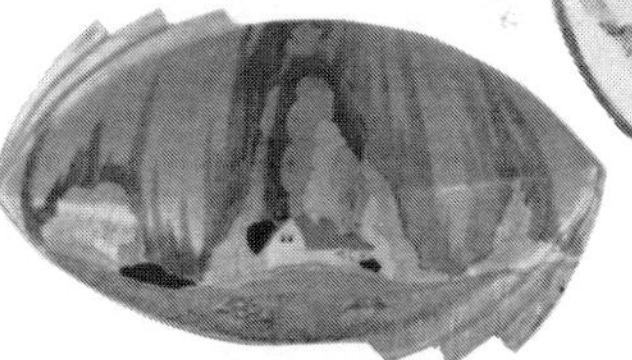
A Bizarre oval bowl with fanned handles, shape No. 475, decorated in the Newlyn pattern in orange and blue, rubber stamp mark, 12½in (31.5cm). **£550-650** *CSK*

A conical bowl, shape No. 383, the body glazed in black, the feet glazed yellow, orange, blue and red, printed Clarice Cliff mark, 8in (20cm) diam.
£1,400-1,600 *CSK*

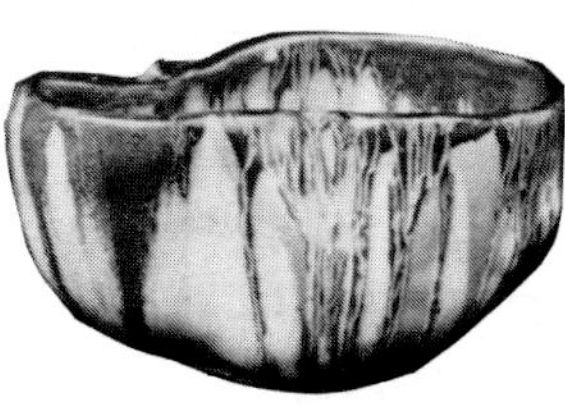
A painted bowl, in green, orange and amber with a trailed design, painted inscription and signature, 1932, 5½in (14cm) high.
£450-500 *C*

Jugs

Three jugs.
£50-80 *OBS*

A Bizarre single handled Lotus jug, decorated in the Rudyard pattern, in pastel shades on a cream coloured ground, some overpainting, lithograph mark, 11½in (29cm) high.
£2,000-2,500 *CSK*

A Bizarre double handled Lotus jug, decorated in the Brookfield pattern, naturalistically painted on a cream ground, with green, yellow and blue banding, rubber stamp mark, 11½in (29cm) high.
£800-1,000 *CSK*

Plates and Chargers

A Bizarre pottery plate, designed by Dame Laura Knight, printed and painted in colours with 3 clowns within a border of a circus audience, printed marks, 10in (25.5cm) diam.
£800-900 *CSK*

A Clarice Cliff Biarritz plate, painted with the Forest Glen design, 9in (23cm) wide.
£500-550 *Bea*

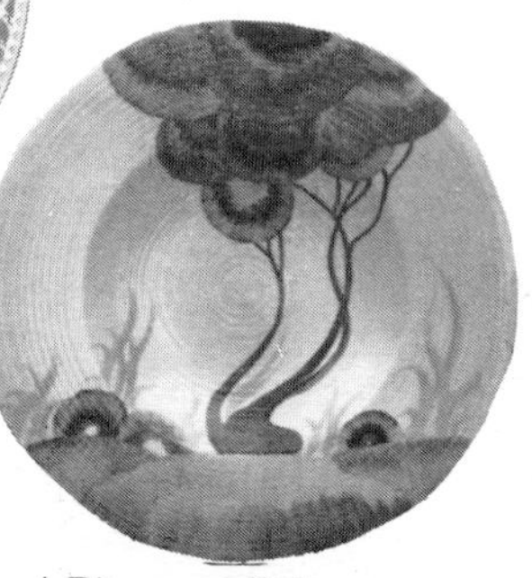

A Bizarre wall charger, decorated in the Rhodanthe pattern, painted in shades of orange, brown and yellow on a cream coloured ground, rubber stamp mark, 18in (45.5cm) diam.
£900-1,000 *CSK*

A set of 6 Bizarre Circus pattern plates, designed by Dame Laura Knight, each plate printed and enamelled in a different shade of blue and heightened with gilt, printed marks in blue, painted marks, impressed date code for 1936, 9in (23cm) diam.
£11,000-12,000 *CSK*

It is believed that these plates are experimental versions of the outline print of this pattern, which was originally pink.

Services

A Bizarre lemonade set, decorated in the Pastel Melon pattern, painted in pastel shades on a cream coloured ground, above blue, pink and green banding, some damage, lithograph mark, jug 8in (20cm) high.
£900-1,000 *CSK*

A Bizarre dinner service for 12, decorated with a stencil enamelled floral spray in colours on a cream coloured ground, some damage, rubber stamp mark, printed Made for Woman's Journal, impressed date code for 1931.
£1,300-1,500 *CSK*

A Fantasque tea service for 2, decorated with red, orange, yellow and black linear motifs on a cream coloured ground, printed marks, saucer and plate with chip to rim, teapot 3in (7.5cm) high.
£600-700 *CSK*

A Bizarre Daffodil teaset for 2, decorated in the Amber Rose pattern in pink and yellow on a cream coloured ground, cracks and restoration, lithograph mark, teapot 5in (13cm) high.
£1,500-1,600 *CSK*

Vases

A vase painted in black, orange, blue, yellow and green, printed factory marks and facsimile signature, 9in (22.5cm) high.
£800-900 *P*

A Fantasque vase, with painted polychrome decoration, stamped marks Fantasque, Hand-Painted Bizarre by Clarice Cliff, 8in (20cm) high.
£600-700 *C*

A Bizarre vase, decorated with Café-au-Lait pattern in shades of green, yellow, blue, orange, red, purple and brown, crack to rim, printed marks, 6½in (16cm) high.
£180-200 *CSK*

A Bizarre Isis vase, decorated in the Nasturtium pattern, lithograph mark, 11½in (29cm) high.
£400-500 *CSK*

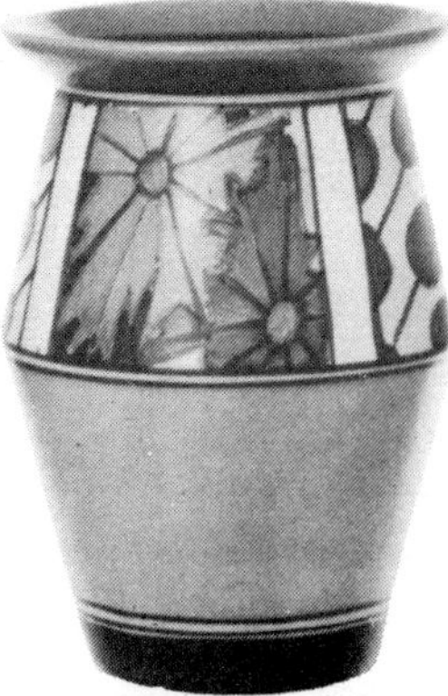

A Fantasque vase decorated in the Umbrellas and Rain pattern, in orange, green, yellow, blue and brown, the rim in orange with brown and green bands, printed marks, 7½in (19cm) high.
£600-800 *CSK*

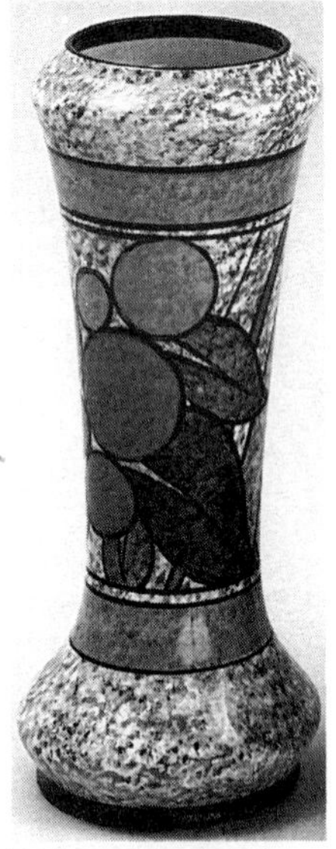

A Bizarre cylindrical vase, shape No. 187, decorated in the Café-au-Lait Berries pattern, with multi-coloured stylised fruit, rubber stamp mark, 9in (23.5cm) high.
£600-700 *CSK*

A Fantasque vase, shape No. 362, decorated in the Umbrellas and Rain pattern, painted in orange, green, blue and yellow, large rubber stamp mark, 8in (20cm) high.
£800-900 *CSK*

A Bizarre vase, painted in the Kandina pattern in blue, green, brown, purple, orange and yellow on a cream ground, painted and stamped marks, 7½in (19cm) high.
£900-1,000 *CSK*

A Goldstone Lotus vase, with an iron-speckled beige ground, printed marks Goldstone, Hand-Painted Bizarre by Clarice Cliff, Newport Pottery, England, 11½in (29cm) high.
£450-500 *C*

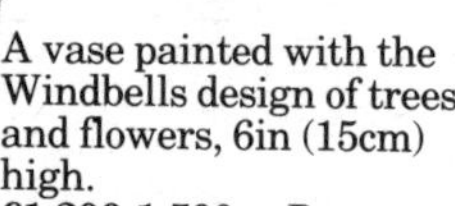

A vase painted with the Windbells design of trees and flowers, 6in (15cm) high.

£1,200-1,500 *Bea*

A vase with stepped fanlike handles, painted with a rural landscape in yellow, orange, brown, green and black, printed marks, 5in (13cm) high.
£350-400 *CSK*

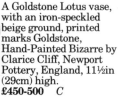

A Fantasque trumpet-form vase, shape No. 280, painted with a frieze of black trees against a multi-coloured background, interior firing crack, rubber stamp mark, 6in (15cm) high.
£350-450 *CSK*

A Fantasque Isis vase, painted in orange, black, blue and green, with yellow borders, rubber stamp mark, 10in (25.5cm) high.
£1,500-1,800 *CSK*

A Bizarre Isis vase, decorated in the Green Japan pattern with a pagoda in an Oriental garden, lithograph mark, 10in (25.5cm) high.
£1,800-2,000 *CSK*

A vase painted in blue, yellow, orange and green with stylised leaf and triangular panels, printed factory marks and facsimile signature, shape No. 362, 8in (20.5cm) high.
£700-800 *P*

General

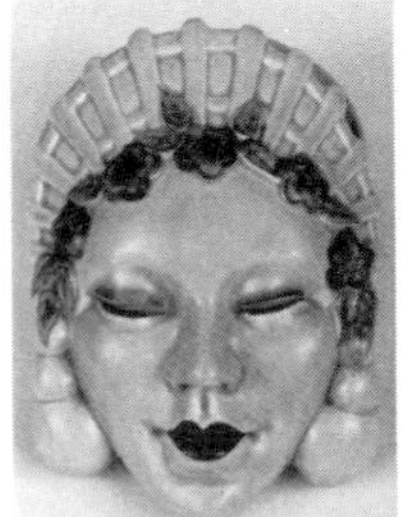

A Flora wall mask, 7in (17.5cm).
£100-120 *BIA*

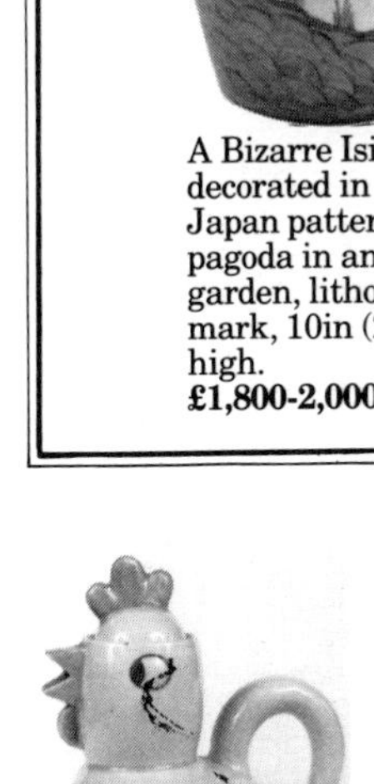

A chick cocoa pot, 6½in (16cm) high.
£400-450 *BIA*

A hand-painted blackbird pie funnel, designed by Clarice Cliff, marked Newport Pottery, 1933, 4½in (11cm) high.
£40-45 *BIA*

Being stamped with the registered number distinguishes it from the many fakes.

A Bizarre tureen and cover, painted with purple flowerhead garlands and highlighted in gilt, the cover with a clown, painted in various colours, printed marks, Designed by Laura Knight A.R.A., 6in (15cm) high.
£200-300 *CSK*

Susie Cooper

A breakfast set for 2, teapot 5½in (14cm) high.
£50-80 *BEV*

A vase painted with a pattern of wavy lines, leaves and cross-hatching, in green, beige, pink and grey on a cream ground, painted signature and M 76 K, 5in (12cm) high.
£100-150 *CSK*

A blue and white cruet, 3in (7.5cm) wide.
£18-20

A coffee pot, 5½in (14cm) high.
£35-40 *CIR*

Elton Ware

A tyg with floral design in shades of blue and green, c1900, 8½in (21.5cm).
£500-600 *OBJ*

A platinum glazed vase with squirrel design supports, signed Elton, 13in (33cm) high.
£500-1,000 *HOD*

A gold lustre plaque with lemon crackle glazed ground, signed Elton, 10in (25.5cm).
£350-450 *HOD*

Aller Vale

A three-handled mug, with slip trailed cockerel decoration, c1910, 2½in (6cm) high.
£35-40 *BIA*

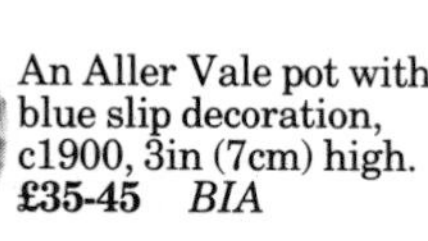

An Aller Vale pot with blue slip decoration, c1900, 3in (7cm) high.
£35-45 *BIA*

An Aller Vale slip trailed and sgraffito jug, with scrolling and incised motto, c1910, 7in (18cm) high.
£35-45 *BIA*

Foley

An Intarsio vase, printed and painted with a galleon pattern in green, brown, yellow and blue, cracks to rim, printed marks, 7½in (19cm) high.
£50-80 *CSK*

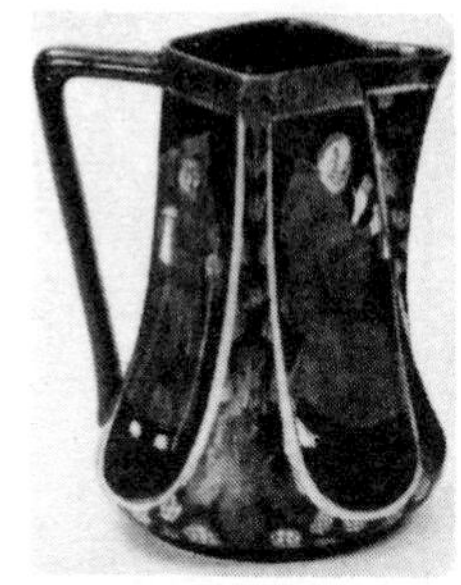

An Inarsio jug, printed and painted with panels of comic monks, with inscription, in shades of brown, green, yellow and blue, cracks to rim, printed marks, 7½in (19cm) high.
£160-200 *CSK*

Crown Devon

A selection of Crown Devon coffee cups, 1930s.
£25-30 each *JAZ*

A pair of Crown Devon vases, 1930s, 5in (12.5cm) high. **£45-50** *JAZ*

A high glaze vase, 5½in (14cm) high.
£50-55 *JAZ*

A Crown Devon lustre vase, 5in (12.5cm) high.
£50-55 *JAZ*

Three Crown Devon vases, marked:
c. **£30-35**
l. & r. **£30-35 pair** *JAZ*

A vase with enamel decoration, 10in (25cm) high. **£200-225** *JAZ*

Grays

A pottery jug, clipper mark, 8in (20.5cm) high.
£60-80 *DEC*

Two pottery plates, clipper marks, 10½in (26cm).
£75-100 each *DEC*

A pottery dish, clipper mark, signed, 9in (23cm).
£40-50 *DEC*

A pottery planter, with clipper mark, 4in (10cm) high.
£75-100 *DEC*

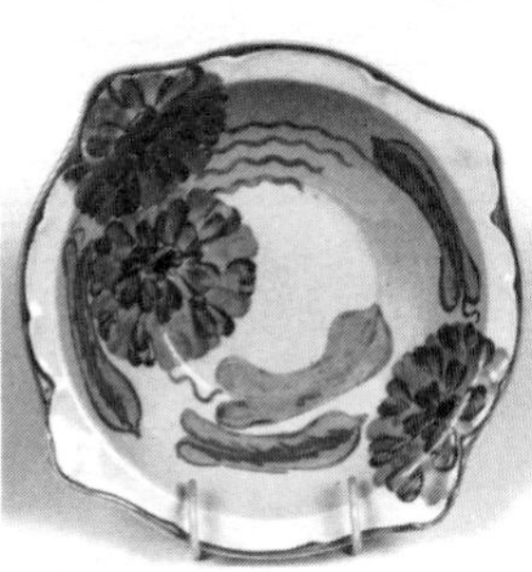

A Grays pottery bowl, clipper mark, 10in (25.5cm) diam.
£35-45 *DEC*

An hors d'oeuvres dish, in pink, clipper mark, 10½in (25.5cm) diam.
£50-60 *DEC*

A Grays pottery plate, clipper mark, 7in (18cm) diam.
£40-50 *DEC*

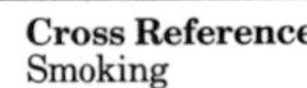

Cross Reference
Smoking

Grays pottery chargers, clipper marks, c1930, 13½in (34cm).
£140-200 each *DEC*

A silver lustre pin tray, with a boating scene, 4½in (11cm) square.
£20-30 *BEV*

A pottery bowl, 5in (12.5cm) diam.
£25-30 *DEC*

A pottery charger, clipper mark, 13½in (34cm) diam.
£170-200 *DEC*

A pottery jug, clipper mark, 5in (12.5cm). **£35-45** *DEC*

A Grays pottery ash tray, 4½in (11.5cm) diam.
£30-40 *DEC*

Two Grays plates, 1930s.
£140-160 each *JAZ*

A pottery lamp, clipper mark, A897D, 7in (18cm) high.
£55-65 *DEC*

A pottery dish, clipper mark, 16in (40.5cm) wide.
£140-180 *DEC*

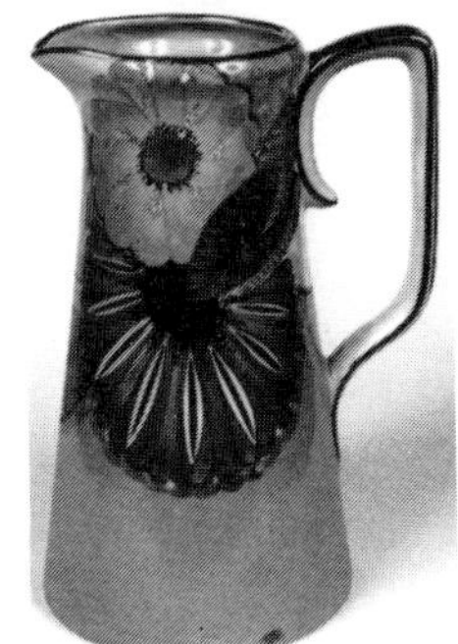

Two pottery jugs, clipper marks, 7½ and 8½in (19 and 22cm) high.
£55-65 each *DEC*

Goss China

The Goss market is very strong and the number of collectors is growing. The First period products 1858-1887 have increased in popularity, especially parian busts and figurines of notable politicians, musicians, etc., of the Victorian era. The Second period heraldic ware, for which Goss was most famous, has seen a 10% rise in value in one year, as has Third period coloured ware including ladies in crinoline dresses and cottage pottery. The tremendous interest in Art Deco porcelain, such as Clarice Cliff and Charlotte Rhead, has extended to the thirties products of the Goss factory, and the once unpopular 'Goss England' items, at one time considered 'not proper Goss', are now commanding interest from enthusiasts.

Prices quoted here are for perfect items, any cracks or chips halve the value. For the exact price of each shape see *The Concise Encyclopaedia and Price Guide to Goss China* by Nicholas Pine (Milestone Publications), and for the additional value of the decoration or crest refer to *Goss China, Arms Decorations and their values* by Nicholas Pine (Milestone Publications, 62 Murray Road, Horndean, Hants.

A cream jug, 2½in (6cm) high.
£25-30 *MGC*

A Stratford Toby jug and bowl, jug 3in (7.5cm) high.
£85-95 each *MGC*

A mug, c1880.
£75-85 *BRE*

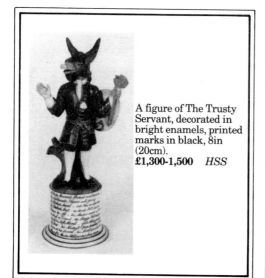

A figure of The Trusty Servant, decorated in bright enamels, printed marks in black, 8in (20cm).
£1,300-1,500 *HSS*

A sack bottle, 4in (10cm) high.
£15-18 *MGC*

Bournemouth Pilgrim bottle.
£12-15 *G&CC*

MAKE THE MOST OF MILLERS
Price ranges in this book reflect what one should expect to *pay* for a similar example. When selling, however, one should expect to receive a lower figure. This will fluctuate according to a dealer's stock, saleability at a particular time, etc. It is always advisable, when selling, to approach a reputable specialist dealer or an auction house which has specialist sales.

A selection of buildings, stones and monuments.
£45-550 each *G&CC*

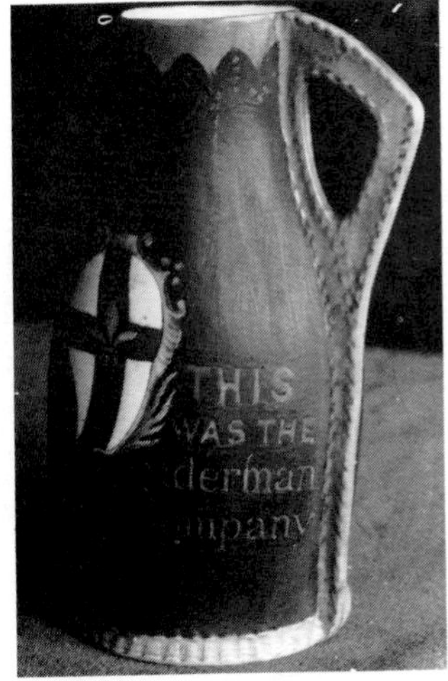

A rare black Lincoln jack.
£950-1,000 *G&CC*

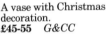

Circular pin trays.
£5-35 each *G&CC*

Cornish models and crests.
£7-125 each *G&CC*

A vase with Christmas decoration.
£45-55 *G&CC*

A three-handled loving cup, 5in (12.5cm) high.
£80-85 *MGC*

Bath jug with London related arms.
£35-40 *G&CC*

A three-handled giant loving cup, with profile of W. H. Goss in relief.
£125-150 *G&CC*

A parian bust of the Prince of Wales in naval uniform.
£185-195 *G&CC*

Rye cannon ball on plinth.
£75-100 *G&CC*

Shakespeare's house.
£100-130 *PCh*

A large Burns nightlight cottage.
£150-160 *G&CC*

Look-out House at Newquay.
£90-100 *G&CC*

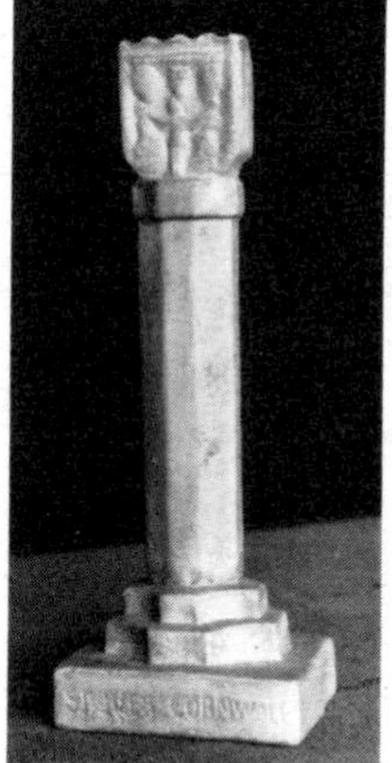

St. Ives cross, Cornwall, in brown parian.
£300-350 *G&CC*

Chester Roman altar, International League, model for 1931.
£800-900 *G&CC*

The lion of Lucerne, glazed.
£45-55 *G&CC*

Venus emerging from a shell, glazed.
£450-500 *G&CC*

A selection of shoes.
£10-100 each
MGC

Crested China

There were over 10,000 different shapes produced between 1880-1930 providing a massive field for collectors of crested china. Novelty shapes, buildings and animals are still enormously popular as is World War I military china.

A Podmore cock and hen, cock 4in (10cm) high.
£8-12 each *MGC*

A lady on a horse, unmarked, 4in (10cm) high.
£10-15 *MGC*

A Grafton snail, 3in (7.5cm) long.
£12-15 *MGC*

A Gemma standing cat.
£20-25 *G&CC*

A Grafton cow.
£65-75 *G&CC*

A Grafton dog, 4in (10cm) long.
£25-30 *MGC*

A Grafton cricketing dog match holder, 3in (7.5cm) high.
£45-50 *MGC*

A donkey, 3½in (9cm) long.
£12-15 *MGC*

Blackpool souvenirs.
£8-55 each *G&CC*

World War I busts and figures.
£45-100 each *G&CC*

Various buildings.
£8-125 each *G&CC*

A fleet of ships, various makers.
Lifebelt **£5-7**
Lusitania and paddleboat
£75-85 each *G&CC*

An Irish Mather, 6in (15cm) high.
£55-60 *MGC*

King Charles scent bottle and lid, by Grafton.
£45-50 *MGC*

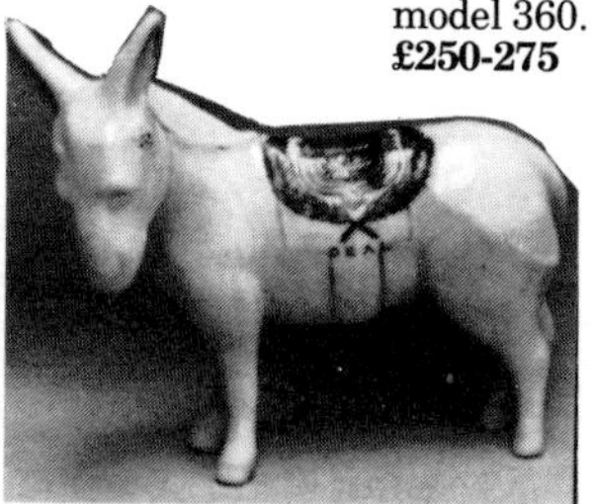

A Carlton donkey.
£30-35 *G&CC*

A Shelley crested coupé, model 360.
£250-275 *MGC*

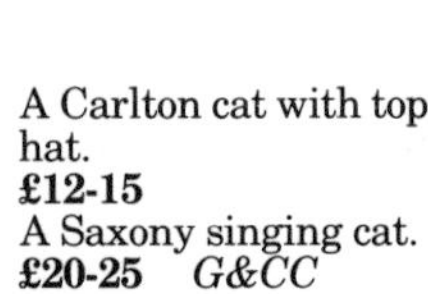

A Carlton cat with top hat.
£12-15
A Saxony singing cat.
£20-25 *G&CC*

Chesterfield Church.
£45-50 *MGC*

Seaside shapes by various potteries.
£4-40 each *G&CC*

Scottish related crests and shapes.
£3-55 each *G&CC*

Queen Mary by Swan.
£45-55 *MGC*

A pride of lions.
£7-15 each *G&CC*

Arcadian one-wheeled tank.
£350-400 *G&CC*

Swan china Tommy and his machine gun.
£35-45 *G&CC*

FURTHER READING
Pine Nicholas, *The 1989 Price Guide to Crested China,* Milestone Publications, 62 Murray Road, Horndean, Hants.

Linthorpe

Linthorpe Pottery was founded in 1879 by John Harrison with Henry Tooth as Manager, and C. Dresser as Art Director. Similar pieces were made, also to Dresser's designs, at Bretby Art Pottery, run by Tooth and Wm. Ault, 1882-87 and at Ault Pottery from 1887 to early 20thC.

Two small Linthorpe vases, in reds and yellows, c1880, 2½in (6cm) high.
£30-40 each *ASc*

Two Linthorpe flour- glazed vases. c1880, 3 and 4in (7.5 and 10cm).
£30-40 each *ASc*

This process was invented by Henry Tooth.

A pottery jardinière, in green and brown glazes, repaired, 10in (25cm) high. **£100-150** *SWO*

DID YOU KNOW?
Art Pottery was designed by the artist and made by the potters whereas Studio Pottery was made and designed by one man. Linthorpe was one of the earliest producers of Art Pottery.

Pilkington's

A Royal Lancastrian vase, the blue ground decorated with 3 leopards walking beneath trees, in typical lustre, the decoration by R. Joyce, base with impressed bee mark, c1910, 12in (30cm) high.
£600-700 *P(G)*

A Pilkington's Lancastrian vase, c1914-23, 9in (23cm) high.
£80-125 *ASc*

A Royal Lancastrian vase, by Gladys Rogers, marked, c1914-23, 5in (13cm) high.
£50-100 *ASc*

A Lancastrian lustre charger with a Celtic design, by William S. Mycock, dated 1919, 19in (48cm) diam.
£800-1,000 *ASc*

A Pilkington's Lancastrian pottery bowl with lid, by Charles Cundall, marked, c1907, 3in (7.5cm) diam.
£50-100 *ASc*

A Pilkington's Lancastrian pottery vase, impressed mark, c1906-13, 4in (10cm) high. **£30-60** *ASc*

Lancastrian pottery polar bears, 1908-36, 7in (17.5cm) wide.
£150-200 *ASc*

Morris Ware

A Morris vase by Hancocks, signed, designed by George Cartlidge, c1900, 7in (17.5cm) high.
£350-400 *BIA*

Cross Reference
Vases

A Morris bowl, designed by George Cartlidge, 12in (30cm) diam.
£250-300 *BIA*

Majolica

A majolica candlestick, 4in (11cm).
£150-180 *AA*

A game pie dish, with impressed registration lozenge, with liner, damaged, 12in (30cm) long.
£800-900 *OBS*

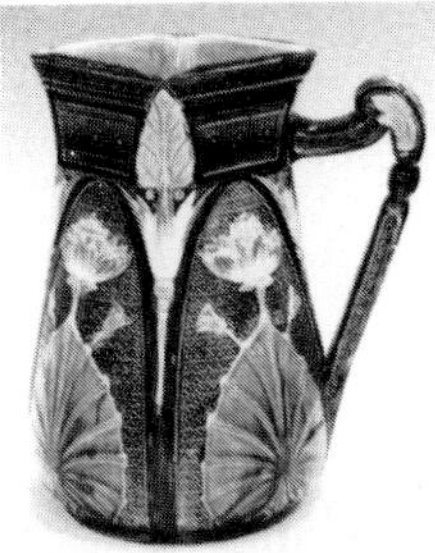

A Copeland majolica jug, with floral and leaf decoration on a grey and blue ground, late 19thC, 7in (7.5cm) high.
£150-200 *PCh*

Minton

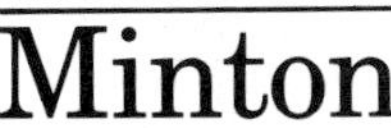

A Minton lion and lioness, c1930, 7½in (19cm) wide.
£80-120 each *ASc*

Moorcroft

A Moorcroft floral decorated blue ground vase, 4in (10cm) high.
£80-100 *ASc*

A Walter Moorcroft vase, painted with fruit and leaves in autumnal colours, on a dark blue ground, impressed facsimile signature and painted marks, c1945, 9in (23cm) high.
£400-500 *WIL*

Poole

A Poole pottery vase, c1930, 5½in (14cm) high.
£40-50 *ASc*

Red clay was used until 1931, then white clay was used although sometimes it was painted with pink slip to make it look like pre-1930 pottery.

A Poole pottery vase, c1930, 6½in (16cm) high. **£60-80** *ASc*

Bernard Moore

A pair of flambé candleholders, 2in (5cm) high.
£50-100 *ASc*

Three Bernard Moore flambé vases, c1905, 1½ to 2½in (4 to 6cm).
£50-100 each *ASc*

A flambé 'grotesque bird', marked, c1915, 4in (10cm) high.
£200-400 *ASc*

Only one other made in earthenware.

Two green vases with special lustre finish, c1905, 2 to 3in (5 to 7.5cm) high.
£50-100 each *ASc*

A flambé tortoise, c1915, 3in (7.5cm) wide.
£200-400 *ASc*

A Bernard Moore flambé glaze dog, c1915, 4in (10cm) wide.
£200-400 *ASc*

A flambé vase, 5½in (14cm) high.
£50-100 *ASc*

DID YOU KNOW?
Bernard Moore animals almost always have glass eyes.

Quimper

All Quimper pottery is marked, whether old or new.

A flambé Diakokan, c1915, 2in (5cm) high.
£200-400 *ASc*

Diakokan was supposed to carry all the troubles of the world on his shoulders.

An illustration of a Quimper mark, c1900.

An hors d'oeuvres dish, c1955, 9in (23.5cm) square.
£45-50 *MCA*

A Quimper cider jug and 4 cups in green with blue design, c1930, jug 7in (17.5cm) high.
£90-100 *MCA*

An Art Deco posy vase, c1930, 8in (20cm) wide.
£30-40 *MCA*

A Quimper vase, c1930, 5in (12.5cm) high.
£55-75 *MCA*

A Quimper bowl, signed P. Fouitten, 6in (15cm) wide.
£40-50 *MCA*

A pair of vases, c1920, 11½in (29cm) high.
£150-180 *MCA*

A Quimper pottery jug, c1900, 6in (15cm) high.
£65-85 *MCA*

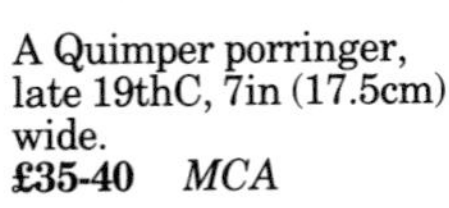

A Quimper porringer, late 19thC, 7in (17.5cm) wide.
£35-40 *MCA*

A Quimper bowl, c1930, 6in (15cm) square.
£30-40 *MCA*

A Quimper plate, damaged, c1900, 7in (17.5cm) diam.
£30-40 *MCA*

A Quimper liqueur set, signed, c1930, stand 11in (28cm) high.
£90-100 *MCA*

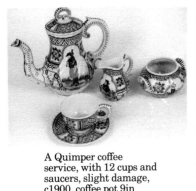

A Quimper coffee service, with 12 cups and saucers, slight damage, c1900, coffee pot 9in (23cm) high.
£350-400 *MCA*

Royal Doulton

Jarge, 1950s, 6in (15cm) high.
£150-200 *TP*

Sir Francis Drake, hatless, 1940, 6in (15cm).
£2,000-2,300 *TP*

Santa with reindeer handle, produced 1982 only, 7in (18cm) high.
£55-65 *TP*

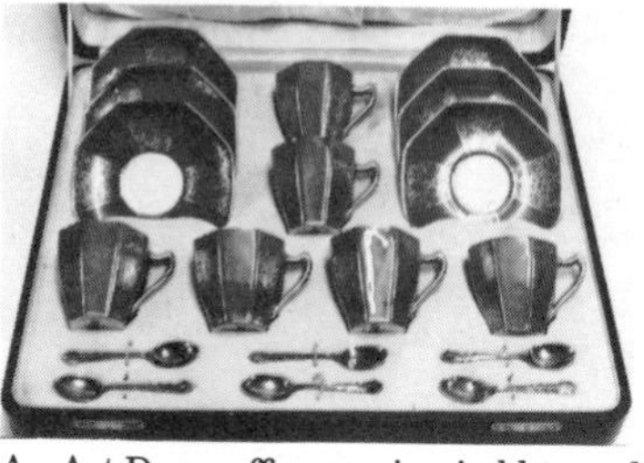

An Art Deco coffee service, in blue and gilt, with 6 Mappin & Webb silver gilt coffee spoons, Sheffield 1936, in presentation box.
£250-300 *PCh*

Clark Gable, prototype 1984, 6½in (17cm) high.
£1,800-2,200 *TP*

A pair of Doulton chamber pots in blue and white, with square bases.
£150-180 *PAR*

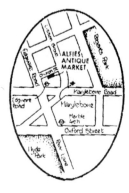

A Royal Doulton jug, with blue and black design, c1930, 5½in (14cm) high.
£25-30 *AA*

A miniature W.C., 4in (10cm) high.
£45-50 *STU*

A Doulton green conservatory heater, c1885, 19 by 12in (48 by 30.5cm).
£500-600 *ASc*

A pair of Burslem vases, with blue ground decorated with leaf pattern, 16in (40.5cm) high.
£100-120 *PCh*

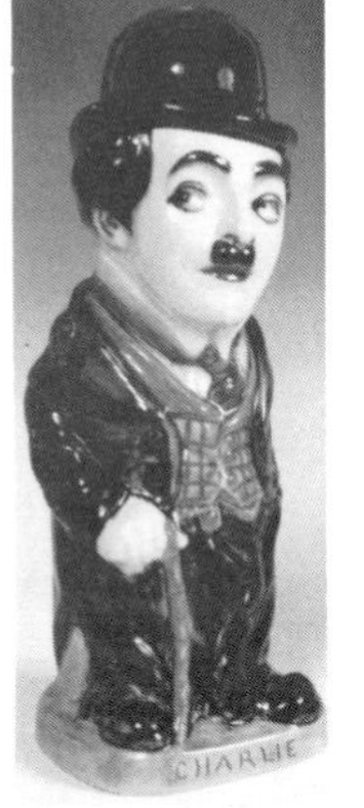

Charlie Chaplin, with removable hat, 1918, 11in (28cm) high.
£2,200-2,750 *TP*

'Ard of 'Earing, c1964-67, 6in (15cm) high.
£450-550 *TP*

Rockingham

A treacle glaze flask, 6in (15cm) high.
£20-30 *RG*

A treacle glaze flask, c1860, 10in (25cm) high.
£40-50 *RG*

Stoneware is more collectable.

Radford Ware

A Radford jug, 1930s, 6in (15cm) high.
£40-45 *JAZ*

A vase with green and gilt decoration, 7in (18cm) high.
£45-50 *JAZ*

A bowl, 1930s, 7in (18cm) diam. **£35-40** *JAZ*

Rye Pottery

A blue and gold lustre vase, c1910, 4cm high.
£20-30 *ASc*

A Rye Greek style blue ewer, c1900, 2½in (6cm) high. **£30-50** *ASc*

Miniatures were a speciality of Rye Pottery.

Shelley

A Shelley teacup, saucer and plate, with black leafy tree design, Queen Anne shape, c1927. **£50-60** *JAZ*

A Shelley Mabel Lucie Attwell teapot, modelled as a toadstool, transfer printed and enamelled, 5in (12.5cm) high, and a matching sugar bowl, printed factory marks. **£200-250** *CSK*

A Shelley trio, with yellow butterfly wing design, Mode shape, c1930. **£145-165** *JAZ*

A Shelley coffee set for 6, Regent shape, in blue polka dot design, c1933. **£200-225** *JAZ*

A Shelley powder bowl in black and orange. **£35-45** *PAR*

A pair of vases, designed and signed by Walter Slater, c1921, 5in (12cm) high. **£150-200** *JAZ*

Shorter Ware

The firm of Shorter & Son started as a majolica factory in the 1870s, reproducing designs which reflected the influence of Toft and Bodley. In the 1920s and 30s Shorter's went on to produce art pottery, including Art Deco shapes decorated with experimental glazes. Shorter's most prestigious ware was designed by Mabel Leigh in the 1930s.

Some of the examples illustrated are from the collection of Irene and Gordon Hopwood of Gloucestershire who have been researching and collecting Shorter pottery for some years.

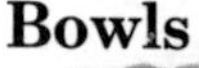

Bowls

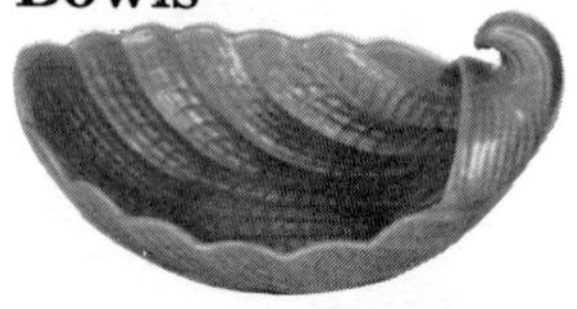

A Shell-shaped bowl, c1935, 12in (30.5cm) long. **£30-35** *PC*

Art Deco bulb bowls, with matt glaze, c1930, 8in (20.5cm) wide. **£20-25 each** *PC*

Flower Troughs

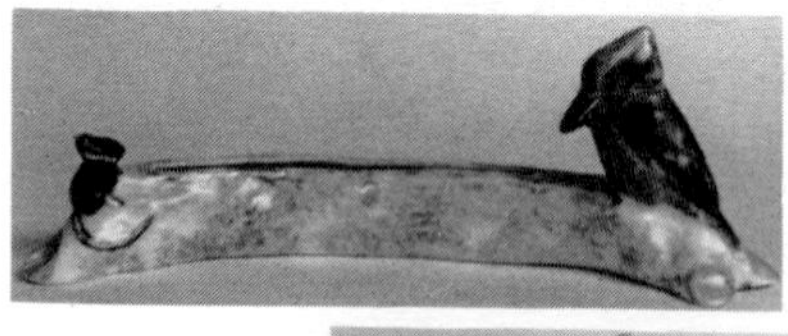

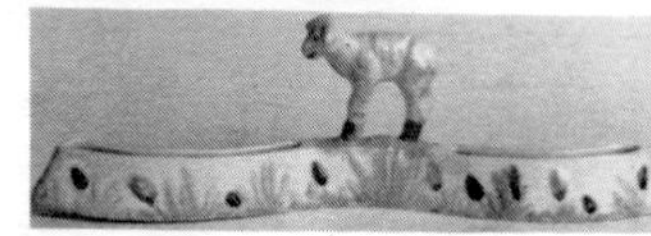

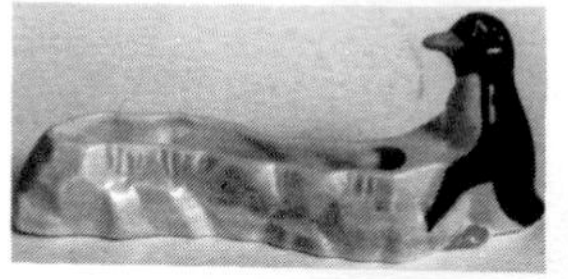

Hand painted flower troughs, c1935. **£20-25 each** *PC*

Dishes

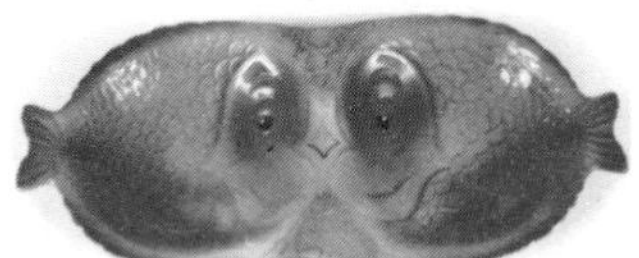

A Shorter ware dish, 13½in (34cm) wide.
£25-30 *RT*

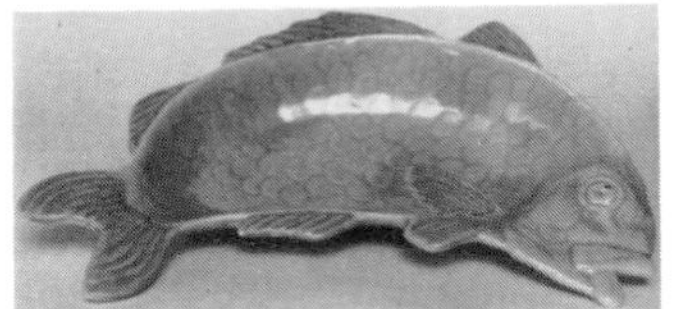
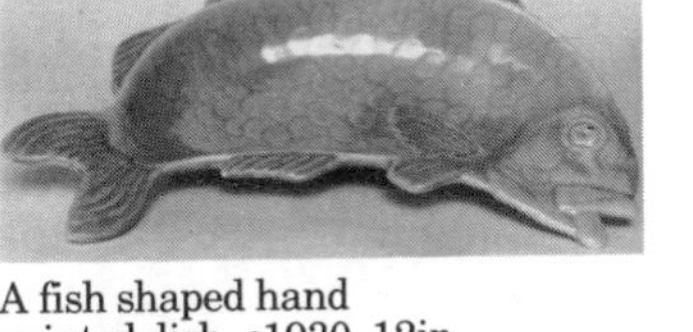

A fish shaped hand painted dish, c1930, 12in (30.5cm) long.
£25-30 *PC*

An Art Deco dish with yacht motif, hand painted, c1935, 13in (33cm).
£30-40 *PC*

'Anemone', a hand painted cheese dish, c1950, 7in (18cm) long.
£25-35 *PC*

'Harmony', a hand painted dish, mid-1950s, 10½in (27cm) long.
£20-25 *PC*

'Bouquet', a hand painted hors d'oeuvres dish, c1955, 15in (38cm) long.
£25-35 *PC*

General Tableware

'Aztec', a selection of sgraffito and hand painted jugs and vases, designed by Mabel Leigh, c1930, large jug 13in (33cm) high.
Large jug **£75-85**
Other pieces
£35-40 *PC*

'Medina', a sgraffito and hand painted jug, designed by Mabel Leigh, c1930, 8in (20.5cm).
£60-65 *PC*

DID YOU KNOW?
Miller's Collectables Price Guide is designed to build up, year by year, into the most comprehensive reference system available.

'Strauss', an embossed and hand painted jug, c1950, 9in (23cm).
£45-55 *PC*

Hand painted character jugs, 'Old King Cole', 5½in (14cm) high.
£25-30
Long John Silver, 10in (25.5cm) high.
£50-60 *PC*

'Mendoza' a sgraffito and hand painted jug, c1940, 10½in (27cm).
£55-65 *PC*

'Medina', a sgraffito and hand painted ewer, designed by Mabel Leigh, c1930, 4in (10cm) high.
£35-40 *PC*

'Medina', sgraffito and hand painted pitcher, designed by Mabel Leigh, c1930, 7½in (19cm) high.
£50-60 *PC*

'Aztec', a sgraffito and hand painted plaque, designed by Mabel Leigh, c1930, 12½in (32cm) diam.
£75-85 *PC*

'Wild Ducks', a hand painted biscuit barrel, c1950, 5in (12.5cm).
£30-35 *PC*

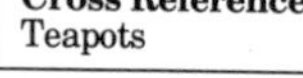

Cross Reference
Teapots

Hand painted 'Wild Rose' tableware items, c1950.
Jug **£20-25**
Jam pot and toast rack
£15-20 each *PC*

A hand painted child's plate, c1949, 9in (23.5cm) diam.
£30-35 *PC*

A hand painted sauceboat and stand, c1930, 7in (18cm) long.
£20-25 *PC*

A teapot, hand painted and embossed with fruit and leaves, c1930, 5½in (14cm) high.
£40-50 *PC*

An Art Deco morning tea set, with tray, c1930, teapot 3½in (9cm) high.
£40-50 *PC*

'Harmony', a hand painted teapot, c1955, 6in (15cm) high.
£25-30 *PC*

A hand painted 'Water Lily' tableware group, c1950.
£20-30 each piece *PC*

A 'Harmony' morning tea set, c1955, teapot 4in (10cm) high.
£25-30 *PC*

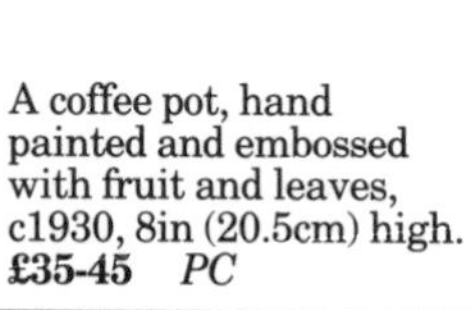

A coffee pot, hand painted and embossed with fruit and leaves, c1930, 8in (20.5cm) high.
£35-45 *PC*

A Toby teapot, cream jug and sugar basin, hand painted, c1940, teapot 6in (15cm) high.
£50-60 *PC*

An Art Deco teapot, milk jug and sugar basin, c1930, teapot 4½in (11cm) high.
£20-25 *PC*

A hand painted morning tea set, c1930, teapot 4½in (11cm) high.
£35-45 *PC*

Vases

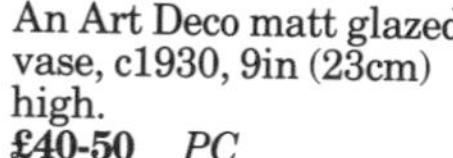

An Art Deco matt glazed vase, c1930, 9in (23cm) high.
£40-50 *PC*

A hand painted vase, late 1930s, 7½in (19cm) high.
£30-35 *PC*

A matt glazed vase, c1940, 9in (23cm).
£40-50 *PC*

'Khimara', a sgraffito and hand painted vase, designed by Mabel Leigh, c1930, 8in (20.5cm) high.
£50-60 *PC*

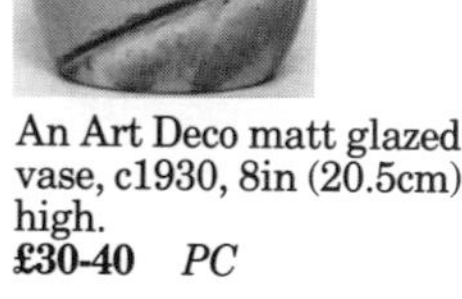

An Art Deco matt glazed vase, c1930, 8in (20.5cm) high.
£30-40 *PC*

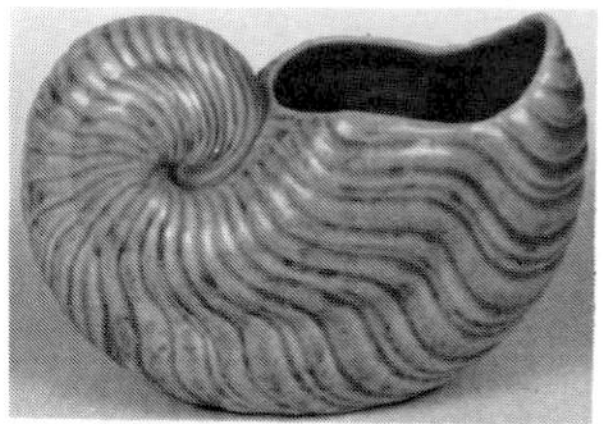

A conch shell vase, mid-1930s, 9in (23cm) long.
£25-35 *PC*

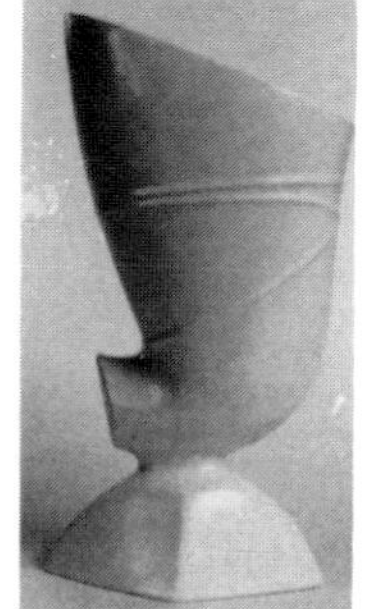

A white matt glazed vase, c1950, 11½in (29cm) high.
£30-35 *PC*

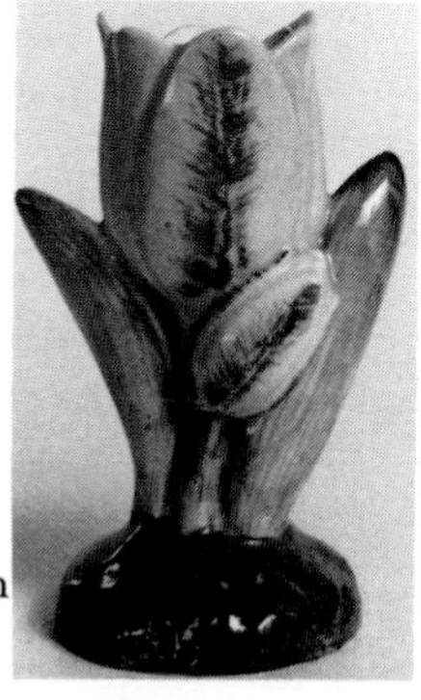

A hand painted tulip posy holder, c1950, 5½in (14cm) high.
£20-25 *PC*

Spongeware

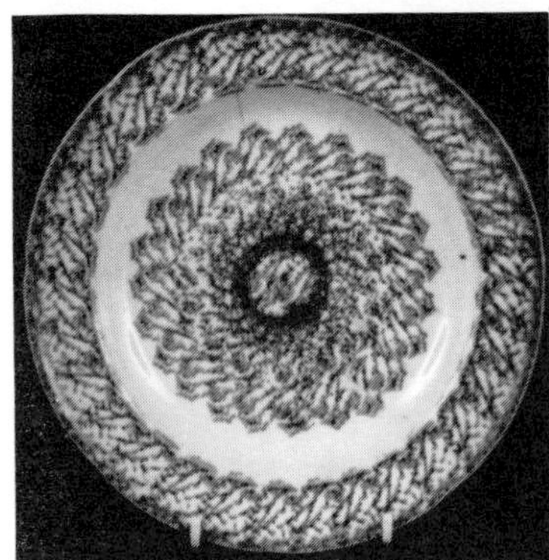

A spongeware plate.
£60-80 *AP*

A shell pattern plate.
£80-90 *AP*

A spongeware mug.
£60-80 *AP*

An extensive selection of spongeware is featured in Miller's Collectables Price Guide 1989-90, pages 107-111.

A small spongeware bowl.
£70-80 *AP*

Potato Printed Ware

A potato printed bowl with pink and green flowers and blue stylised leaves, mid-19thC.
£70-80 *AP*

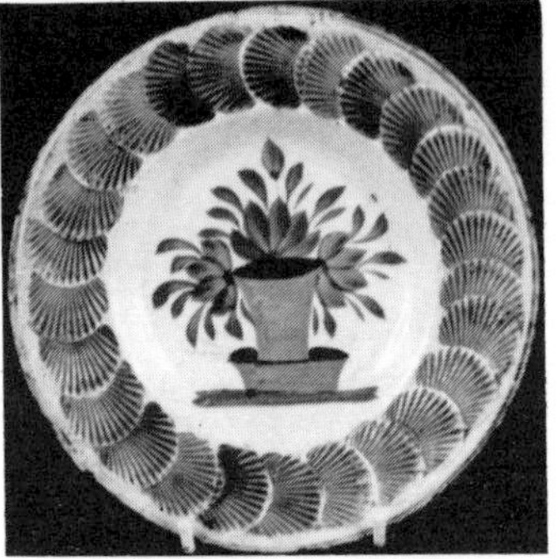

A bowl with potato print flower pattern.
£80-90 *AP*

A potato printed plate, the brown border with pink and blue flowers, mid-19thC.
£90-100 *AP*

A potato stamped plate, mid-19thC.
£110-120 *AP*

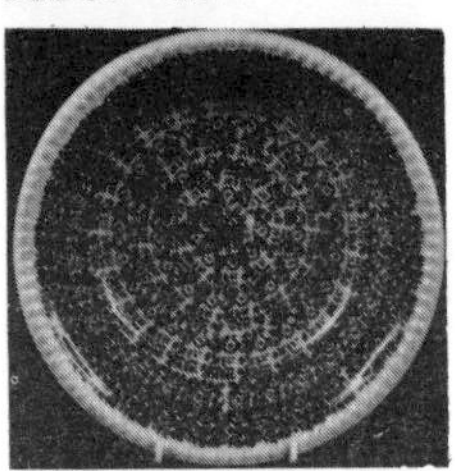

A potato printed dish, possibly Scottish, mid-19thC.
£120-130 *AP*

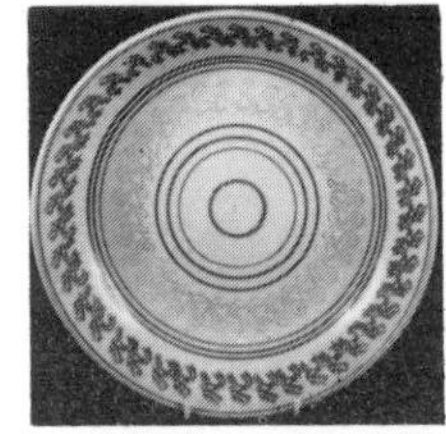

A potato printed dish with stylised border, mid-19thC.
£90-110 *AP*

Sylvac Ware

The Sylvac factory was responsible for producing a range of small animal figures known as 'Fancies', the green matt rabbit being the most popular.

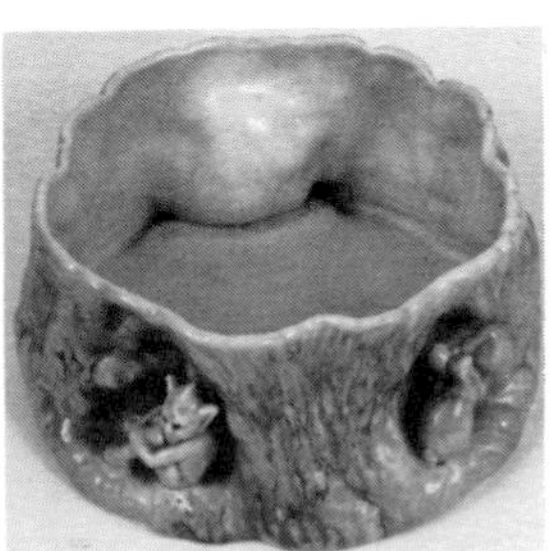

A vase with pixie and rabbits, 8in (20.5cm) diam.
£35-45 *CIR*

A beige dog, 5½in (14cm) high.
£15-20 *CIR*

A vase with poodle, printed mark, 9in (23cm) high.
£30-35 *OD*

A green squirrel, 5in (12.5cm) high.
£15-20 *CIR*

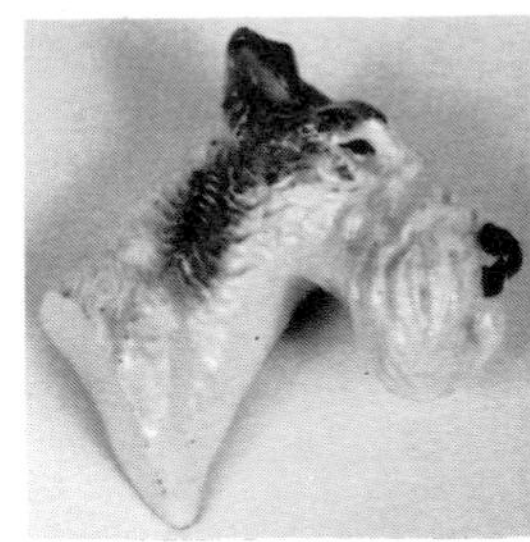

A dog plaque, impressed mark, 4in (10cm) high.
£15-20 *OD*

A green dog, 9½in (24cm) high.
£17-25 *CIR*

A green rabbit, 4in (10cm) high.
£15-20 *CIR*

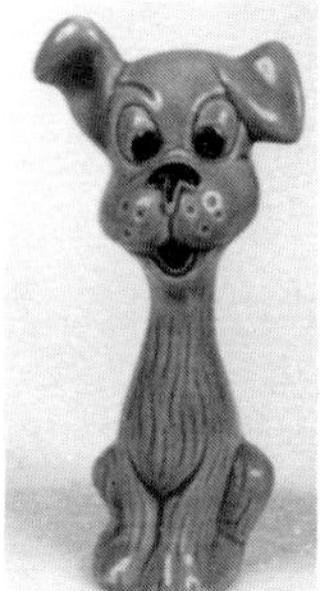

A beige dog, 5½in (14cm) high.
£10-15 *CIR*

A green glazed spill holder.
£12-18 *CIR*

FURTHER READING
Verbeek, Susan Jean, *The Sylvac Story, The History and Products of Shaw and Copestake Ltd.*, Pottery Publications 1989.
Collins, Mick and Derry, *An Introduction to Sylvac.*

Wemyss Ware

A large seated pig with black decoration, impressed mark.
£1,500-2,000 *HAM*

A tankard, 6in (15cm) high.
£220-250 *PCh*

Ironstone

A Chamberlain's Worcester Ironstone comport, c1835, 12in (30.5cm) wide.
£120-150 *CA*

A Hicks & Meigh plate, early 19thC.
£20-30 *PCA*

A Mason's Ironstone breakfast cup and saucer, in the Japan pattern, saucer 7in (18cm) diam.
£110-150 *BEE*

Two dishes, decorated in blue, red and gilt, late 19thC, 12½ and 13½in (32 and 34cm) wide.
£60-80 *PCh*

A Mason's Ironstone platter, with the Table and Flowerpot pattern, impressed mark, c1820, 18in (45.5cm) wide.
£320-400 *BEE*

Mason's Ironstone jugs, with chinoiserie panels, c1835, 4 to 6½in (10 to 16cm).
£80-160 each *BEE*

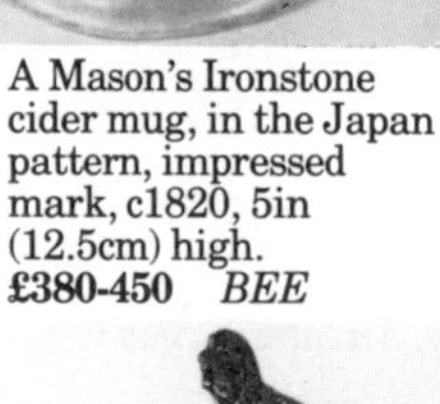

A Mason's Ironstone cider mug, in the Japan pattern, impressed mark, c1820, 5in (12.5cm) high.
£380-450 *BEE*

A Mason's Ironstone spittoon, in the Japan pattern, c1820, 5in (12.5cm) high.
£300-380 *BEE*

A Hicks & Meigh hot water plate, c1825, 10in (25.5cm) diam.
£180-200 *BEE*

Better quality than Mason's.

A Mason's Ironstone sauce tureen and stand, in the Japan pattern, c1820, 8in (20.5cm) high.
£280-320 *BEE*

Staffordshire

Animals

A pair of calves, 2in (5cm) high.
£175-225 *BRE*

A tiger, c1850, 7½in (19cm) high.
£300-350 *DL*

Figures

Gladstone and Beaconsfield, in porcelain, c1870, 11½in (29cm) high.
£300-350 *DL*

The Soldier's Return, in porcelain, c1850, 11in (28cm) high.
£300-350 *DL*

A Lloyd Shelton figure Victoria and child, marked, c1840, 7½in (17cm) high.
£400-450 *DL*

Napoleon and Albert, porcelain, brightly coloured, c1850, 11in (28cm).
£350-400 *DL*

Holy Water Font, c1860.
£85-95 *BRE*

Balaam And His Talking Ass, c1850, 11in (28cm) high.
£200-250 *BRE*

Marshal Arnaud and Lord Raglan, c1860, in mint condition, 10in (25.5cm) high.
£600-650 *DL*

A Staffordshire porcelain group, 8in (20.5cm) high.
£150-200 *DL*

General

Poseidon on marbled base, 14½in (37cm) high.
£350-400 *BRE*

Nelson, a portrait jug, 19thC, 12in (30.5cm) high.
£200-250 *HCC*

A set of 11 Wilkinson Royal Staffordshire Pottery character jugs, modelled by Sir F. Carruthers Gould, printed marks and retailer's mark for Soane & Smith, 10 to 12in (25 to 30cm) high.
£5,500-6,000 *HSS*

Printed Ware

A Ralph Hall plate, Fulham Church, c1820, 8½in (21.5cm) diam. **£100-120** *SCO*

A mug, with railway scene, c1830, 4½in (11.5cm). **£190-220** *SCO*

A chocolate mug with lid, maker unknown, c1840, 5½in (14cm) high. **£90-100** *SCO*

A footed comport, depicting a Bewick Stag, c1820, 11½in (29cm) wide. **£300-335** *SCO*

A two-handled cup with country scene, maker unknown, c1820, 3½in (9cm) high. **£70-80** *SCO*

A Swinnertons basin, Old Willow Pattern, 4½in (11cm) high. **£5-10** *AL*

A footbath with rural scene, unrecorded pattern and maker unknown, c1820, 18in (47cm). **£1,750-2,000** *SCO*

A dish, probably Spode, Boy on a Buffalo pattern, c1790, 12in (30.5cm) wide. **£150-170** *SCO*

A jug, maker unknown, c1825.
£300-325 *SCO*

A Davies Cookson & Wilson plate, c1820, 8½in (22cm).
£70-80 *SCO*

A Ridgway plate, Osterley Park, c1820, 10in (25.5cm).
£100-120 *SCO*

A Rogers dessert dish, Tivoli, c1825, 8½in (22cm) wide.
£70-80 *SCO*

A Bovey Tracey Mess plate, No. 22, c1860, 9½in (24cm).
£100-120 *SCO*

A lidded pot, Eastern Port scene, 4½in (12cm) high.
£100-120 *SCO*

MAKE THE MOST OF MILLERS
Condition is absolutely vital when assessing the value of any item. Damaged pieces appreciate much less than perfect examples. However, a rare, desirable piece may command a high price even when damaged.

A soup tureen, Hospitality pattern, maker unknown, c1825, 12in (30.5cm).
£475-525 *SCO*

A commemorative jug, Nelson, c1805, 4½in (11cm) high.
£200-225 *SCO*

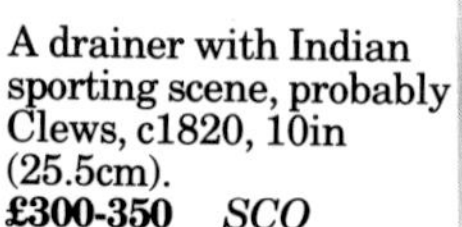

A drainer with Indian sporting scene, probably Clews, c1820, 10in (25.5cm).
£300-350 *SCO*

A blue and white pottery dish, Temple and Deer pattern, 19thC, 11in (28cm) wide, and a pair of Patent Ironstone blue and white transfer printed dishes, 9in (23cm) wide.
£130-150 *PCh*

A jar, 3in (7.5cm) high.
£140-160 *RG*

A selection of 11 stone china meat dishes and plates, 19thC.
£600-700 *PCh*

A Davenport blue and white plate, with perforated border, c1825, 8in (20.5cm).
£35-45 *BRE*

A blue and white pottery bourdalou, c1850.
£350-400 *BRE*

FURTHER READING
Bedford, J., *Old English Lustreware,* London 1965.

A silver resist jug with hunting scene, c1825, 5in (12.5cm) high.
£400-450 *SCO*

A Staffordshire pearlware cheese coaster, with Castle pattern, impressed mark, early 19thC, 17in (43cm) wide. **£350-400** *PCh*

Printed Pot Lids

Bloater Paste.
£45-55 *RG*

Alexandra Tooth Paste.
£60-80 each *RG*

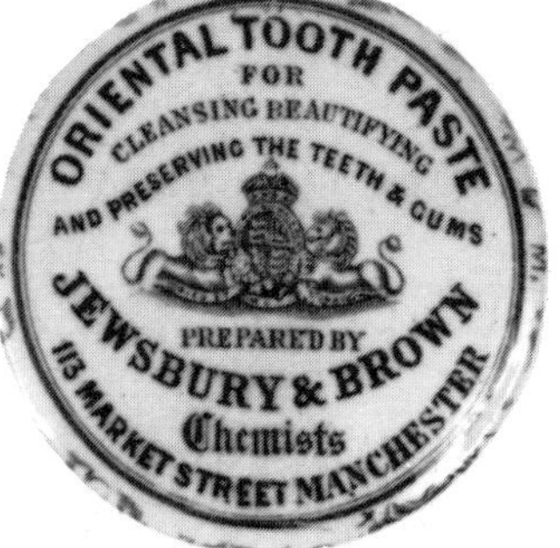

Oriental toothpaste.
£12-15 *RG*

Heal-All Ointment.
£25-30 *RG*

Cherry Tooth Paste.
£45-50 *RG*

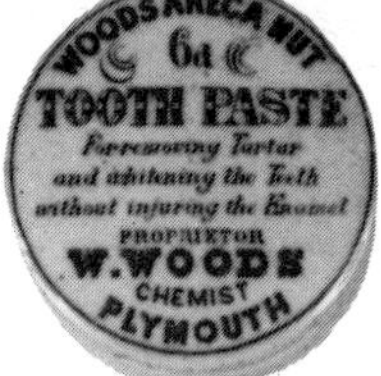

Woods Toothpaste.
£6-8 *RG*

Swiss Violet
in violet
and brown.
£85-95 *RG*

Boots Cold Cream.
£10-15 *RG*

Holloway's Ointment: Lid **£30-35** Pots **£10-12 each**

Magla, blue.
£40-50 *RG*

Roger & Gallet.
£25-30 *RG*

About 400 pot lid designs have been identified. These have been documented and numbered by A. Ball in his invaluable reference work *Price Guide to Pot Lids* which all collectors should possess. The listing which follows contains a representative selection of the pot lids most likely to be encountered by the general collector. The number refers to the listing system devised by Mr Ball in his book.

No. Description

1. Alas! Poor Bruin.
£80-100
2. Bear attacked by Dogs.
£500-700
3. Bear's Grease Manufacturer, lettering on marbled border.
£2,000-3,000
5. Bears Reading Newspapers.
£600-700
9. Bears at School.
£80-100
11. Bear with Valentines.
£1,800-2,400
15. The Ins.
£100-150
16. The Outs.
£100-150
17. Arctic Expedition.
£400-500
18. Polar Bears.
£100-140
20. All but Trapped.
£1,000-1,400
21. Pegwell Bay.
£600-800
24. Lobster Fishing, damaged.
£80-120
25. Pegwell Bay, Lobster Fishing.
£100-120
27. Belle Vue Tavern.
£200-230
29. Belle Vue Tavern.
£220-250
33. Shrimping.
£60-80
34. The Dutch Fisherman.
£1,000-1,200
35. Still Life – Game.
£100-120
37. Ramsgate, Farmyard Scene.
£60-80
38. Landing the Fare – Pegwell Bay.
£50-60
41. Royal Harbour.
£50-60
42. Royal Harbour, Ramsgate.
£40-50
43. Nelson Crescent, Ramsgate.
£80-100
45. Walmer Castle.
£50-60
48. Pretty Kettle of Fish.
£75-95
49. Lobster Sauce.
£40-50
52B. Shell.
£45-55
53. Examining the Nets.
£50-60

Belle Vue Tavern, Pegwell Bay.
£40-45 *RG*

Red Bull Inn.
£80-100 *RG*

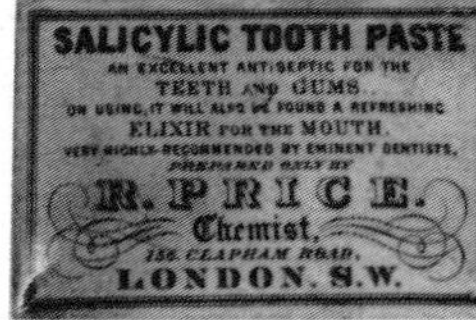

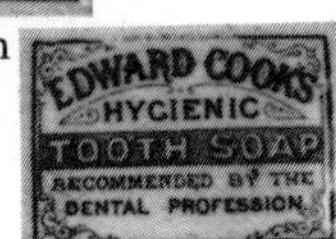

Tooth Paste and Tooth Soap.
£15-20 each *RG*

Sir Robert Peel.
£180-200 *RG*

Napoleon & Eugenie
£200-250 *RG*

Victoria and Albert.
£350-400 *RG*

Wellington.
£150-200 *RG*

Tria Juncta in Uno.
£350-400 *RG*

Belle Vue without bay window (30).
£70-100 *P*

MAKE THE MOST OF MILLERS
Price ranges in this book reflect what one should expect to *pay* for a similar example. When selling, however, one should expect to receive a lower figure. This will fluctuate according to a dealer's stock, saleability at a particular time, etc. It is always advisable, when selling, to approach a reputable specialist dealer or an auction house which has specialist sales.

No. Description
55. Landing the Catch.
£30-40
60. The Net-Maker.
£200-250
62. Foreign River Scene.
£50-60
63. The Shrimpers.
£40-60
64. Sea Nymph and Trident.
£200-250
76. Charge of the Scots Greys at Balaklava.
£120-140
78. Fall of Sebastopol.
£120-140
97. The Bride.
£120-150
98. An Eastern Repast.
£100-120
101. The Mirror.
£100-120
106. Lady with Hawk.
£90-100
107. Lady with Guitar.
£60-70
110. Lady Fastening Shoe.
£150-200
111. Lady Brushing Hair.
£160-200
114. The Matador.
£350-450
116. Jenny Lind.
£1,200-1,500
118. The Trysting Place.
£70-100
119. The Lovers.
£60-90
123. Musical Trio.
£80-100
143. Dublin Industrial Exhibition 1853.
£90-110
144. International Exhibition 1862.
£150-180
145. L'Exposition Universelle de 1867.
£75-100
149. England's Pride.
£125-155
153. The Late Prince Consort.
£75-85
156. Napoleon III and Empress Eugenie.
£100-120
157. Albert Edward, Alexandra, Prince of Wales and Princess on their marriage 1863.
£75-100
159. Wellington with Cocked Hat.
£1,500-2,500
160A. Wellington with clasped hands.
£100-140
166. Balaklava, Inkerman, Alma.
£250-300
168. The Allied Generals.
£90-100
170. Sir Robert Peel.
£200-230
171. Peabody.
£80-120
175. Dr. Johnson.
£30-50

The Blue Boy (174).
£80-100 *P*

Napirima Trinidad.
£180-200 *RG*

Wouvermann Pinx 'Peace'.
£60-70 *RG*

A military scene, 'L'Egypte en 1882'.
£40-50 *RBE*

Harbour of Hong Kong (221).
£50-60 *RBE*

Burgess's Anchovy Paste, George V.
£8-10 *RG*

Burgess's Anchovy Paste, Victoria.
£8-10 *RG*

Harriet Beecher Stowe (172).
£700-1,000 *P*

Swiss Riverside Scene (65).
£60-90 *P*

S. Banger, Shrimp Sauce Manufacturer (32).
£300-400 *P*

MAKE THE MOST OF MILLERS
Condition is absolutely vital when assessing the value of any item. Damaged pieces appreciate much less than perfect examples. However, a rare, desirable piece may command a high price even when damaged.

No. Description
176. Buckingham Palace.
£90-120
179. Drayton Manor.
£50-80
180. Windsor Park, Returning from Stag Hunting.
£120-150
181. Sandringham.
£60-80
183. New Houses of Parliament, Westminster.
£190-250
185. St. Paul's Cathedral and River Pageant.
£90-120
188. Strathfieldsaye.
£70-110
189. Westminster Abbey.
£200-250
192. St. Paul's Cathedral.
£150-200
193. Charing Cross.
£80-100
195. New Houses of Parliament.
£100-150
201. Trafalgar Square.
£40-60
202. Holborn Viaduct.
£60-80
205. The Thirsty Soldier.
£60-80
206. Embarking for the East.
£60-80
209. Sebastopol.
£60-75
210. The Battle of the Nile.
£55-75
211. Meeting of Garibaldi and Victor Emmanuel.
£50-60
214. The Volunteers.
£90-120
216. The Redoubt.
£500-600
219. War.
£35-45
220. Peace.
£40-50
222. Ning Po River.
£80-100
223. Rifle Contest, Wimbledon 1864.
£50-60
224. Wimbledon, July 1860.
£45-55
226. Shakespeare's Birthplace – Exterior.
£40-50
227. Shakespeare's Birthplace – Interior.
£30-60
228. Anne Hathaway's Cottage.
£50-60
229. Holy Trinity Church.
£80-100
233. May Day Dancers at the Swan Inn.
£30-50
236. The Parish Beadle.
£90-110
237. The Children of Flora.
£70-80
240. The Village Wedding.
£20-30

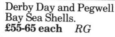

Derby Day and Pegwell Bay Sea Shells.
£55-65 each *RG*

Shrimpers, damaged (31).
£60-80 *P*

The Skater.
£85-95 *RG*

Little Red Riding Hood.
£65-75 *RG*

The First Appeal.
£55-65 *RG*

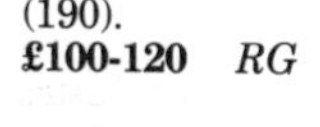

Albert Memorial (190).
£100-120 *RG*

Back view of Pegwell Bay Inn.
£65-75 *RG*

Pratt Fenton stone jetty.
£65-75 *RG*

Bear subjects.
£85-95 each *RG*

6 pomade pot lids.
£220-250 *PCh*

Crystal Palace, Interior (139).
£260-300 *P*

The Times (327).
£40-60 *RBE*

A trefoil shape pot lid.
£65-75 *RG*

No. Description

241. Our Home.
£100-150

245. The Enthusiast.
£40-50

248. Chiefs Return from Deer-stalking.
£90-100

249. Dangerous Skating.
£50-70

250. Fair Sportswoman.
£40-60

253. Snapdragon.
£70-90

257. A Race or Derby Day.
£30-50

258. The Skaters.
£70-90

259. The Game Bag.
£40-50

261. Pheasant Shooting.
£30-50

263. Children Sailing Boats in Tub.
£70-90

264C. Six Dogs.
£400-450

265. Good Dog.
£50-60

266. Contrast.
£60-70

267. Feeding the Chickens.
£50-60

269. Deerhound Guarding Cradle.
£130-160

270. The Begging Dog.
£70-90

272. Both Alike.
£45-65

273. Country Quarters.
£70-80

277. The Skewbald Horse.
£60-70

289. The Sea Eagle.
£80-100

309. The Faithful Shepherd.
£60-80

314. The Breakfast Party.
£90-100

315. Cattle and Ruins.
£50-70

318. The Old Water Mill.
£50-60

319. The Queen, God Bless Her.
£50-70

322. The Rivals.
£75-85

323. The Dentist.
£100-120

324. The Farriers.
£50-60

325. The Shepherdess.
£50-60

328. Uncle Toby.
£30-50

329C. The First Appeal.
£50-60

331. Strasbourg.
£40-50

334. The Trooper.
£50-70

337. The Flute Player.
£30-50

340. On Guard.
£40-60

341. The Fisher-boy.
£50-70

347. Tam O'Shanter.
£90-110

348. Peasant Boys.
£50-70

351. Preparing for the Ride.
£50-70

352. The Quarry.
£100-150

358. Little Red Riding Hood.
£60-80

359. The Red Bull Inn.
£50-70

361. The Wolf and the Lamb.
£40-60

365. The Waterfall.
£60-80

397. Tyrolean Village Scene.
£40-60

Stoneware

A lead glazed cider pot, cracked, 13½in (34cm) high.
£120-150 *MIC*

A pair of John Barnacle cider or ale flasks, 6 to 8in (15 to 20.5cm).
£130-150 each *RG*

A stoneware flask, damaged, 7in (18cm) high.
£90-100 *RG*

A death mask of Wellington, marked Thompson, 6in (15cm) high.
£55-65 *RG*

A French faience wine jar, 19thC, 11½in (29cm) high.
£110-120 *MIC*

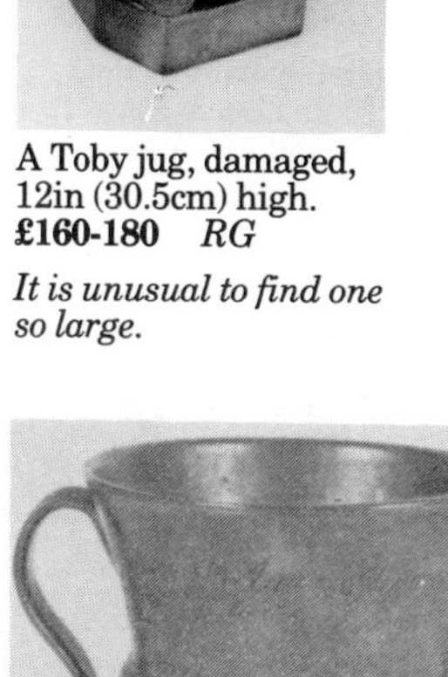

A Toby jug, damaged, 12in (30.5cm) high.
£160-180 *RG*

It is unusual to find one so large.

A brown saltglazed jug, decorated with hunting scenes, silver coloured metal rim, mid-18thC, 5½in (13.5cm) high.
£500-550 *HSS*

A Dorset Owl pottery cider jar, with slip glaze, c1800.
£80-100 *MIC*

A Derbyshire brown salt glazed stoneware loving cup, with inscription, dated May 4th, 1830, damaged, 10½in (26cm) high.
£360-400 *HSS*

A saltglazed jug of Wellington, Stephen Green, not Doulton, c1830, 6in (15cm) high.
£90-110 *SN*

Children's Ceramics

A pair of blue transfer ware plates, probably Spode, c1820, 3½in (9cm) diam.
£30-40 *BRE*

Paragon mugs with Louis Wain designs, 2½in (6in) high.
£50-70 each *BEV*

A Shelley cup, saucer and plate, by Mabel Lucie Attwell.
£85-95 *BEV*

A Shelley cup, saucer and plate, by Mabel Lucie Attwell.
£85-95 *BEV*

A Shelley baby's plate, by Mabel Lucie Attwell, 7½in (19cm) diam.
£45-55 *BEV*

A child's teaset, c1860, teapot 2½in (6cm) high.
£55-65 *PAR*

A child's plate, maker unknown, 5in (12.5cm) diam.
£15-20 *BRE*

Cruets

A Beswick Shakespeare's house cruet, c1950, 7in (18cm) long.
£45-55 *STU*

A pig cruet, 5in (12.5cm).
£15-20 *MCA*

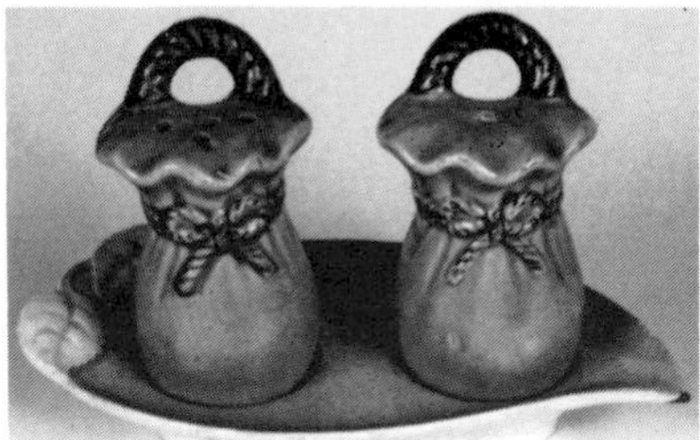

Cruet
Sacks **£15-20** *BEV*

Crown Devon cruets, marked, c1930, 6in (15cm) wide.
£20-40 each *DEC*

An XL ware cruet, c1950, 6½in (16.5cm) wide.
£15-20 *TS*

A Carlton Ware cruet set, c1950.
£25-30 *TS*

A foreign cruet, 4in (10cm) high.
£18-20 *CIR*

A fruit barrow cruet, 5½in (14cm) long.
£10-15 *MCA*

A cruet. **£5-7** *PAR*

An orange and green cruet, 9in (23cm) wide.
£18-20 *CIR*

Coffee Cans

A Susie Cooper coffee set with 6 cups and saucers, in pink and gilt design.
£200-225 *PAR*

An unmarked coffee can, c1937.
£20-25 *BCA*

Crown Staffordshire, supplied by Derry & Toms, Kensington, c1906. **£20-25** *BCA*

J. & G. Meakin coffee can, c1912.
£18-20 *BCA*

Coffee cans:

l. Bishop & Stonier, c1936. **£18-20** *BCA*

c. Aynsley, c1891+
£22-25 *BCA*

r. Paragon, c1920, damaged.
£2-5 *BCA*

Thos. Morris 'Regent' china coffee can and saucer, c1905, cup 2in (5cm) high. **£22-25** *BCA*

Royal Venton coffee can, 1926-38.
£20-25 *BCA*

Crown Staffordshire, c1906+
£20-25 *BCA*

Coffee can, Utzscheider & Co, Saargemünd, c1910. **£18-20** *BCA*

Crown Staffordshire, c1929.
£18-20 *BCA*

Bisto, England (Bishop & Stonier), c1936.
£22-25 *BCA*

Cups & Saucers

A Bloor Derby cup and saucer, with pink, gold and grey decoration, c1830, saucer 5½in (14cm).
£40-60 *FAN*

A Beleek cup and saucer, c1861, cup 2½in (6cm) high.
£60-80 *FAN*

A Fieldings Crown Devon cup and saucer, with blue and gold decoration, c1930, cup 2½in (6cm) high.
£10-20 *FAN*

A Grainger's Worcester cup and saucer, with jade and gold decoration, c1880, cup 2½in (6cm) high.
£40-60 *FAN*

A German import cup and saucer, c1900, cup 3in (7.5cm) high.
£10-15 *FAN*

A Zsolnay faience cup and saucer, Pecs, Hungary, c1870, saucer 5in (12.5cm).
£60-80 *FAN*

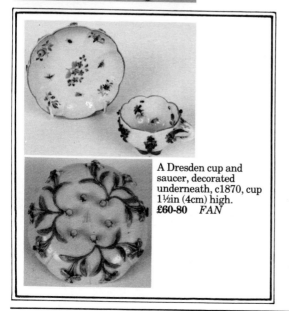

A Dresden cup and saucer, decorated underneath, c1870, cup 1½in (4cm) high.
£60-80 *FAN*

A Newhall cup and saucer, with pink, green and blue, c1815, cup 2½in (6cm) high.
£30-50 *FAN*

A Bishop & Stonier cup and saucer, in pink and gilt, c1877, cup 2½in (6cm) high.
£15-25 *FAN*

A Gardner of Russia cup and saucer, with gilt decoration, c1840, cup 2in (5cm) high.
£60-80 *FAN*

Gardner went to Russia and opened a factory there.

A Coalport cup and saucer, with gold and blue decoration, c1920, cup 2½in (6cm) high.
£25-35 *FAN*

A Cauldon ware cup and saucer, with pink and gilt decoration, c1900, cup 2in (5cm) high.
£20-30 *FAN*

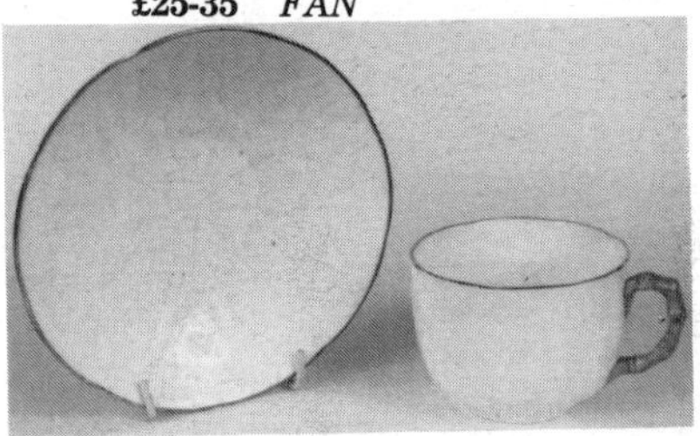

A Moore Bros. cup and saucer, in cream with pink handle and gilt rims, c1880, cup 2½in (6cm) high.
£15-30 *FAN*

A Japanese terracotta cup and saucer, cup 2½in (6cm) high.
£10-20 *FAN*

A Bristol cup and saucer, decorated in green and gilt, c1770, cup 3in (7cm) high. **£100-150** *FAN*

A Copeland cup and saucer, c1896, cup 3in (7.5cm) high.
£50-70 *FAN*

An Aynsley cup and saucer, decorated in gold and blue, c1891, cup 2½in (6cm) high. **£60-80** *FAN*

A Crown Staffordshire cup and saucer, cup 2½in (6cm) high.
£30-50 *FAN*

A Liverpool blue and white tea bowl and saucer, 18thC.
£300-350 *MAN*

Two Prattware transfer printed cups, 2½ and 3½in (6 and 9cm) high.
£45-50 each *RG*

A George Bowers cup and saucer, c1845, cup 4in (10cm).
£50-70 *FAN*

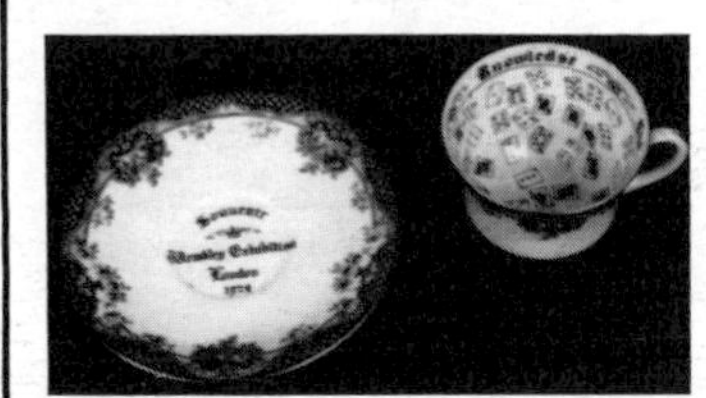

A fortune-telling cup and saucer, 1924.
£80-100 *PC*

A Brownfield cup and saucer, c1875, cup 2½in (6cm) high.
£30-60 *FAN*

A Ridgway cup and saucer, with blue and gilt decoration, c1850, saucer 6in (15cm).
£40-60 *FAN*

A Miles Mason cup and saucer in blue and white, with gilt border, c1810, cup 3in (7cm) high.
£50-70 *FAN*

A Liverpool Herculaneum cup and saucer, c1820, cup 2in (5cm) high.
£60-100 *FAN*

A Yates cup and saucer, with gilt and yellow shell pattern, c1820, cup 2in (5cm) high.
£50-70 *FAN*

A Hilditch cup and saucer, with blue and gilt decoration, c1830, saucer 6in (15cm).
£40-60 *FAN*

Staffordshire Dogs

A Staffordshire black and white dog, c1860, 10½in (26cm) high.
£65-85 *AA*

A Victorian Staffordshire dog jug, 8½in (21.5cm) high.
£60-80 *AA*

Staffordshire dogs, 19thC.
£165-195 per pair *AA*

A pair of Staffordshire dogs, 19thC, 12in (30.5cm) high.
£165-185 *AA*

Staffordshire dogs, 19thC.
£165-195 per pair *AA*

Staffordshire dogs, c1860, 9in (23cm) high.
£65-85 each *AA*

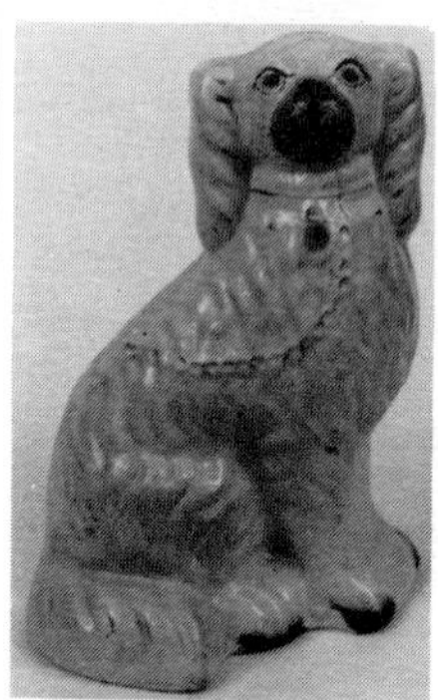

A Staffordshire dog, 19thC, 10in (25.5cm) high.
£70-90 *AA*

Staffordshire dogs.
£65-75
Restored **£30-40** *AA*

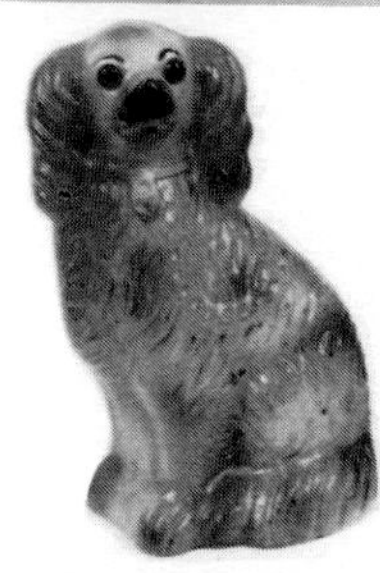

Two Staffordshire dogs, 19thC.
£55-75 each *AA*

Two Staffordshire dogs 19thC, 10in (25.5cm) high. **£75-85 each** *AA*

Egg Cups

l. A gold and peach egg cup, probably Coalport, c1850.
£40-45
r. A crimson and gold egg cup, probably Worcester.
£15-20 *AA*

Dickens Figures

Bretby figures: Sam Weller, Mr. Pickwick and Tom Weller.
£150-180 each *AA*

A blue and white transfer ware egg cup, 4in (10cm) high.
£18-20 *AA*

A Willow pattern egg cup and saucer, c1820, maker unknown, 2½in (6.5cm) high.
£30-40 *SCO*

A blue and white porcelain egg cup, 3in (7.5cm) high.
£25-35 *AA*

A Victorian egg cup set.
£35-45 *PAR*

A Sylvan egg cup, c1948, 5in (12.5cm) diam.
£15-20 *AA*

Wedgwood egg cups, c1878, 2 to 2½in (5 to 6cm) high.
l. **£30-40**
r. **£15-20** *AA*

Worcester egg cups, c1906, 2 to 2½in (5 to 6cm) high.
£20-25 each *AA*

Willow pattern egg cups.
£16-20 each *AA*

A Cauldon blue and white egg cup, with gold rim.

A Chinese Export egg cup, 19thC.

£18-20 each *AA*

Two Coalport blue and white egg cups, 2in (5cm) high. c1900 **£18-20** c1891 **£25-30** *AA*

A Victorian toast rack with egg cups, white with gilt, 8in (20.5cm) diam.
£75-95 *AA*

Sandlands egg cups, c1955.
£6-8 each *AA*

l. A Royal Doulton green egg cup.
£8-10

r. A blue, orange and gold egg cup.
£10-12 *AA*

l. A Hammersley egg cup, c1880.
£20-25

r. A Coalport egg cup, c1900.
£25-30 *AA*

l. A Shelley egg cup, c1925.
£20-25

r. A Royal Copenhagen egg cup.
£8-10 *AA*

l. An Aynsley egg cup, c1891.
£30-35

r. A Royal Doulton egg cup, c1930.
£20-25 *AA*

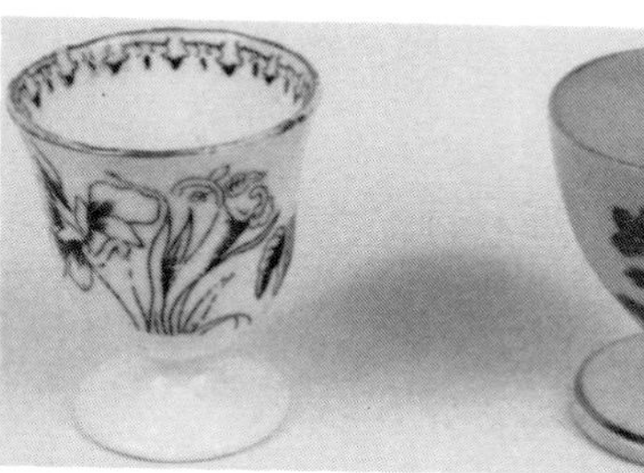

l. A black and white egg cup, c1860.
£30-40

r. A Satsuma egg cup.
£20-25 *AA*

l. A Victorian egg cup.
£15-20

r. A Paragon egg cup.
£15-20 *AA*

l. A mid-19thC egg cup with gold and crimson pattern.
£30-40

r. A floral and gilt egg cup.
£10-12 *AA*

l. A Victorian blue egg cup, with gilt rim.

r. A Paragon crimson floral egg cup, c1952.
£20-25 each *AA*

Egg cups on a plate, Birchwood, Made in England.
£10-20 *AL*

l. A Mason's egg cup.
£15-20
r. A 19thC Japanese egg cup.
£20-25 *AA*

A late Victorian egg cup.
£5-8 *OBS*

A blue and white egg hoop, possibly Spode, c1810.
£35-45 *BRE*

For duck eggs one side and hen eggs the other.

A selection of egg cups.
£2-4 *AL*

A white egg cup, with forget-me-nots and sunbursts.
£12-15 *AA*

A Spode egg cup holder, transfer printed in blue with the Net pattern, impressed mark, c1810, 9in (23cm) high.
£750-850 *WHI*

MAKE THE MOST OF MILLERS
Condition is absolutely vital when assessing the value of any item. Damaged pieces appreciate much less than perfect examples. However, a rare, desirable piece may command a high price even when damaged.

A Quimper egg cup set, 1950s, 10½in (26cm) diam.
£50-70 *MCA*

Jugs

A jug, printed on both sides with a bust portrait inscribed 'Daniel O'Connell, Esq., M.P. for the County of Clare', with wide copper and pink lustre band border, 5in (12.5cm) high.
£520-550 *Bon*

A Staffordshire jug, brown printed with a cartoon of Reformists, repaired, 6in (15cm) high.
£300-350 *Bon*

A Sunderland pink lustre 'Mariner's Compass' jug, 19thC, 6in (15cm).
£50-60 *PCh*

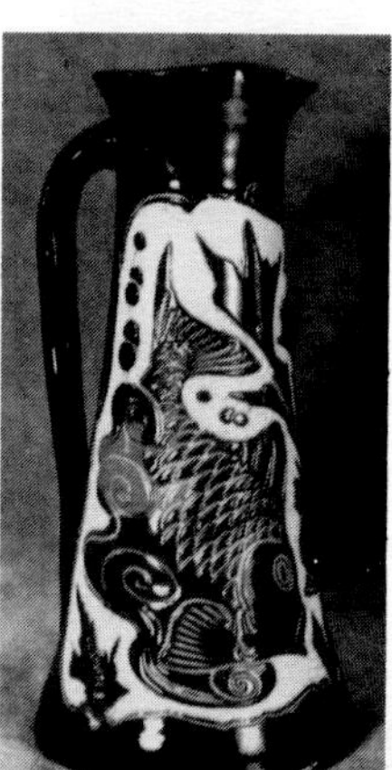

A Lauder Barum jug, decorated in coloured glazes with fish, 11in (28cm).
£80-100 *P(G)*

A French faience milk jug, c1880, 4½in (11cm).
£25-30 *MCA*

A French pottery jug, c1880, 3½in (9cm) high.
£30-35 *MCA*

A faience jug with End of Day pattern, c1870, 5½in (14cm) high.
£85-95 *MCA*

A jug, 19thC, 2½in (7cm) high.
£65-75 *MAN*

A pottery jug, printed with a portrait of 'Richard Oastler, the Friend of the Poor', holding a bill inscribed 'No Bastilles', 5½in (12.5cm) high.
£340-380 *Bon*

A small earthenware jug, 1920s.
£10-12 *COB*

A Staffordshire Toby jug, with lid, 19thC, 8in (20.5cm) high.
£110-120 *AA*

A French jug, c1870, 4in (10cm) high.
£25-30 *MCA*

Jackfield Ware

Jackfield ware is a type of black glazed pottery made at Jackfield, Shropshire, at a factory started by Maurice Thursfield, c1750. It has a brownish red biscuit earthenware body to which a lustrous cobalt glaze was applied by dipping. This was then fired in a kiln until jet black. Decoration in oil gilding was added although this has often worn off.

Wares of this kind were also made in Staffordshire by Astbury, Whieldon and Wedgwood in the late 19thC. This pottery sometimes known as japanned ware.

A jug with metal lid, 8in (20.5cm) high.
£27-35 *AA*

A Victorian jug, 6½in (16.5cm) high.
£15-20 *AA*

A coffee pot, 7in (18cm).
£20-25 *AA*

A jug, 5½in (14cm) high.
£10-15 *AA*

A commemorative jug, 6in (15cm) high.
£55-60 *AA*

A teapot, 7in (18cm) high.
£20-30 *AA*

Miniature Ceramics

A taper stick holder, with scattered rose decoration, foot rim damaged, c1850, 3in (7.5cm) diam.
£250-300 *BRE*

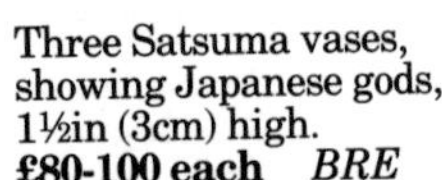

Three Satsuma vases, showing Japanese gods, 1½in (3cm) high.
£80-100 each *BRE*

A Minton pottery platter, c1850, 6in (15cm) wide.
£40-60 *BRE*

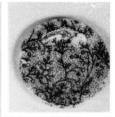

Plates by William Hackwood, 2 and 3½in (5 and 9cm) diam.
£30-50 each *MAN*

A Royal Crown Derby cream jug, pattern No. 6299, c1910.
£110-120 *BRE*

A Crown Staffordshire bough pot, with printed floral decoration, c1910, 3½in (9cm) long.
£130-150 *BRE*

A Derby porcelain pomade pot, cover and stand, in green with roses in panels, red mark, c1810, pot 2½in (6cm) high.
£150-200 *BRE*

Warming Plates

Children's warming plates, 8in (20cm) diam.
£25-30 each *PAR*

A warming plate with pewter base, 10½in (26cm).
£40-50 *PAR*

Cross Reference
Children's Ceramics

Staffordshire Peppers

A policeman, with coloured back, 6in (15cm) high.
£65-75 *AA*

Those with a coloured back were more expensive.

A set of 3 — pepper, vinegar and mustard, 1850-1900, 5½ to 6½in (14 to 16cm) high.
£200-220 each *AA*

Cross Reference
Ceramics — Cruets

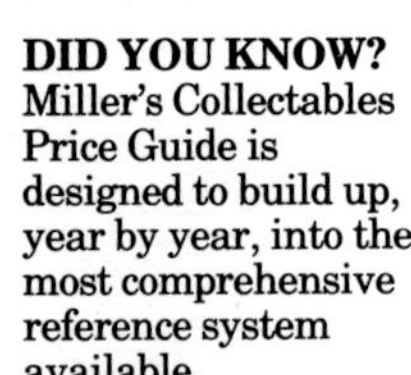

DID YOU KNOW?
Miller's Collectables Price Guide is designed to build up, year by year, into the most comprehensive reference system available.

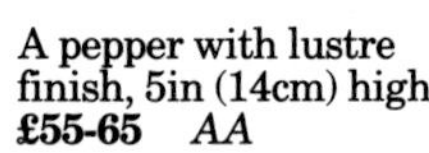

A pepper with lustre finish, 5in (14cm) high.
£55-65 *AA*

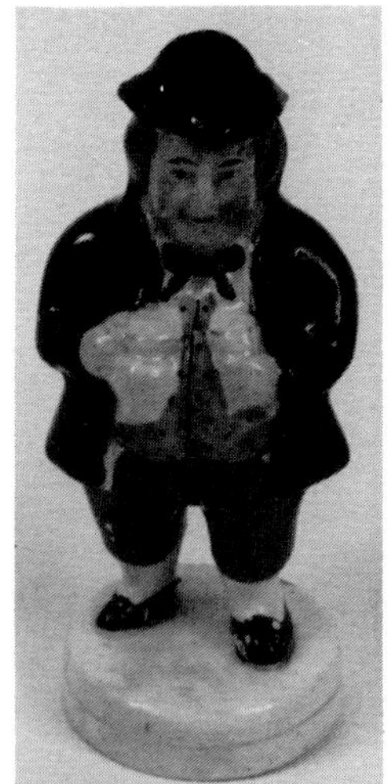

Staffordshire peppers, 6in (15cm) high. **£60-80 each** *AA*

Plates

A Lakin pottery plate, with perforated border, c1812, 8in (20.5cm) diam.
£100-120 *BRE*

Two Limoges plates depicting Picasso drawings, c1960.
£45-60 each *PC*

Limoges were licensed to reproduce Picasso pictures in limited numbers.

A Pountney of Bristol pottery plate, impressed mark, 9½in (24cm) diam.
£40-45 *BRE*

A Bristol charger, decorated in blue, yellow, green and orange, restored, 13½in (34cm) diam.
£225-250 *MIC*

A Delft blue and white plate, 18thC, 9½in (24cm) diam. **£70-90** *PCA*

A Chelsea porcelain dessert plate, damaged, Red Anchor mark, 8½in (22.5cm) diam. **£150-200** *HSS*

A Continental plate, signed Johnston c1890.
£60-100 *CAC*

Political Ceramics

Home Rule for Ireland, Staffordshire earthenware plates.
£150-180 *Bon*

A Hummel type match holder, commemorating the General Strike of 1926, 5½in (14cm) high.
£160-200 *Bon*

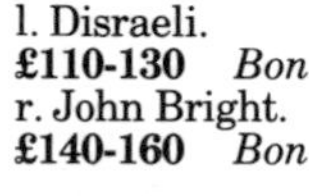
l. Disraeli.
£110-130 *Bon*
r. John Bright.
£140-160 *Bon*

A West Country bone china plate, printed with portrait medallions to commemorate The Formation of the Social Democratic Party in 1981, 11in (28cm) diam.
£25-30 *Bon*

A Staffordshire pottery jug, transfer printed with a portrait of R. Rushton, Bradford, 6in (15cm).
£120-140 *Bon*

Toothbrush Holders

Pinocchio characters, c1940.
£80-90 each *BEV*

Pigs, c1930.
£70-80 *BEV*

Teapots

A Welsh lady teapot, made in Germany, 1920s.
£85-100 *PGA*

A white stoneware moulded teapot, attributed to Mexborough, c1810.
£300-350 *PGA*

A souvenir of the Great War character teapot, c1916.
£85+ *PGA*

A Wedgwood 3-colour jasper dip teapot, 19thC.
£375-400 *PGA*

Cross Reference
Ceramics/Majolica

A Delft blue and white teapot, based on a Meissen pattern of early 18thC. **£450-500** *PGA*

A Foley Intarsio teapot and cover, printed factory marks, 8in (20.5cm) wide.
£350-400 *CSK*

A Wedgwood creamware teapot, with black transfer print of J. Wesley, by Sadler & Green of Liverpool, lid missing, c1780.
£200-250 *PGA*

A majolica Isle of Man three-legged teapot, Brownfield's Colbridge works, made for Broughton's of Douglas.
£350+ *PGA*

A Lingard 'Mary Had A Little Lamb' teapot, c1930.
£85-100 *PGA*

A Novelty teapot.
£35+ *BEV*

An extremely rare Minton fish teapot, c1875.
£2,200-2,500 *PGA*

A Staffordshire cockerel teapot, Tony Wood, 7in (18cm) high.
£30-40 *BEV*

A Royal Worcester Aesthetic Movement teapot, signed Budge, inscribed on base 'Fearful Consequences through the laws of natural selection and evolution of living up to one's teapot', c1880.
£1,200+ *PGA*

An extremely rare Minton coconut teapot with mushroom forming the lid, impressed marks.
£1,500+ *PGA*

A Staffordshire majolica fish teapot, late 19thC.
£300+ *PGA*

An Isle of Man three-legged teapot.
£250+ *PGA*

A teapot from the Pixie set, c1926, 6in (15cm) high.
£225-250 *BEV*

A commemorative teapot, George V and Queen Mary.
£45-55 *PGA*

Wall Vases

A Clarice Cliff wall planter, printed mark, 9in (23cm) high.
£220-250 *CSK*

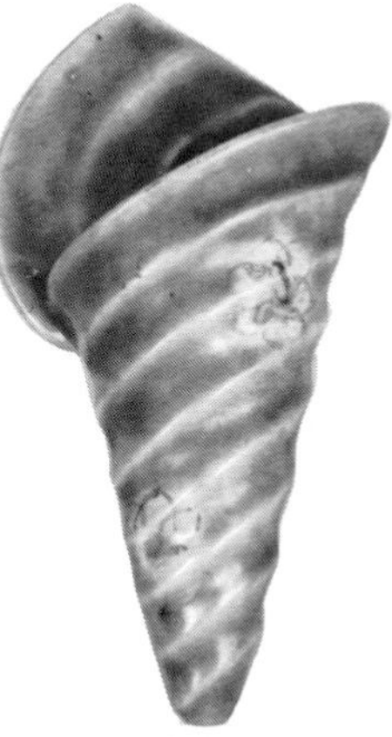

A Beswick wall pocket, 8½in (22cm) high.
£20-25 *STU*

A Beswick wall pocket, with palm tree design, 10in (25.5cm).
£35-45 *STU*

A pair of Carlton Ware wall vases, 9½in (24cm) high.
£125-165 each *BEV*

Cross Reference
Goss and Crested China

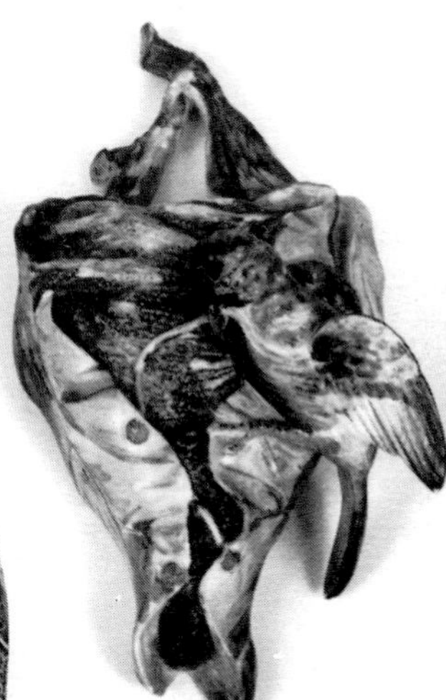

A pair of wall vases, probably Continental, c1890, 12in (30.5cm) high.
£150-200 *OD*

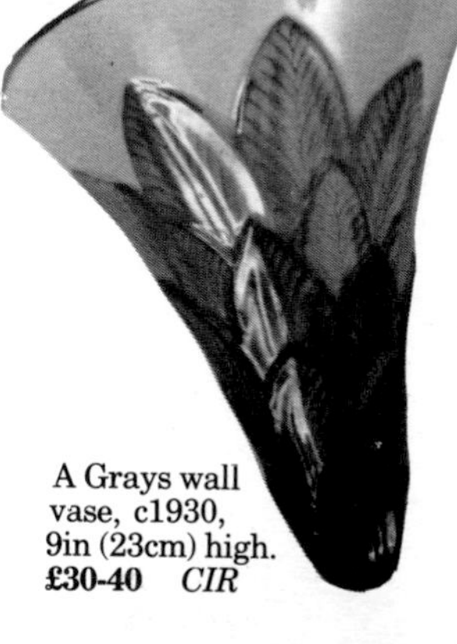

A Grays wall vase, c1930, 9in (23cm) high.
£30-40 *CIR*

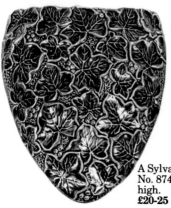

A Sylvac wall vase, Reg No. 874070, 7½in (19cm) high.
£20-25 *OD*

A Clarice Cliff wall planter, printed mark, 9½in (24cm) high.
£240-260 *CSK*

A Shorter ware hand painted galleon wall planter, mid-1930s, 7½in (19cm) high.
£40-50 *PC*

A Shorter ware hand painted wall pocket, late 1930s, 8½in (22cm) high.
£20-25 *PC*

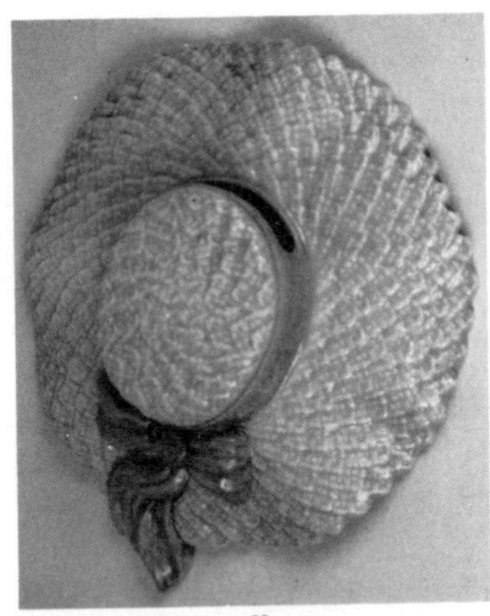
A Falcon Ware wall vase, 10in (25.5cm) diam.
£25-35 *CIR*

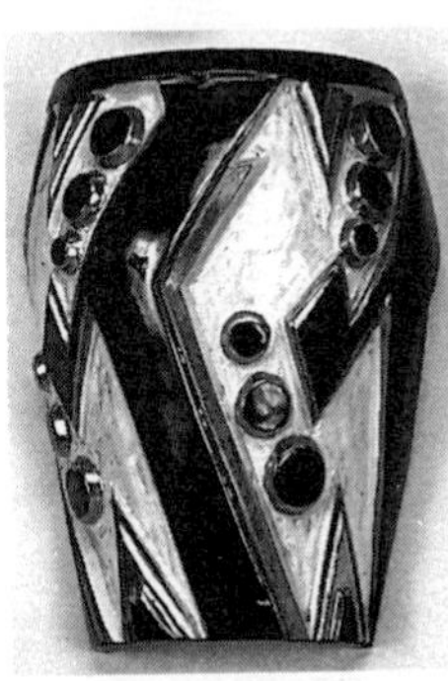
A Bizarre sgraffito wall vase, restored, lithograph mark, 8½in (21.5cm) high. **£300-350** *CSK*

A 'Marlene' wall pocket, unmarked, 7in (18cm) high. **£80-100** *CSK*

A Crown Devon wall vase, 10in (25.5cm) wide.
£15-20 *OD*

Vases

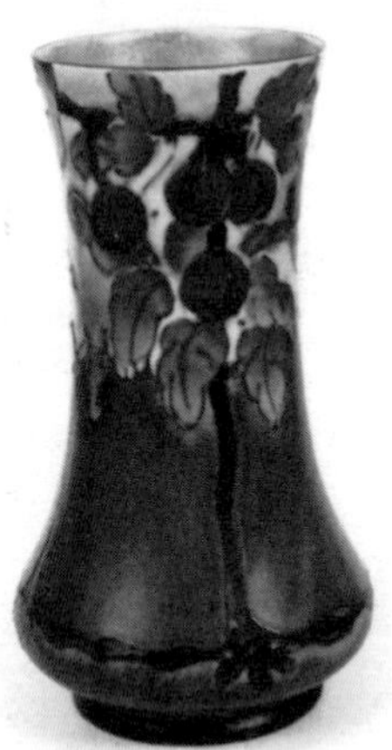
A Crown Devon vase, with Cherry Tree pattern, 8in (20cm).
£55-65 *JAZ*

A Wesuma pottery vase by Lemon, painted with kingfisher decoration, glaze flaw, c1910, 8in (20cm).
£75-80 *BIA*

Wesuma is shortened form of Weston-super-Mare.

A Copeland and Garrett trumpet shaped vase, with floral decoration on a green ground, 6in (16cm) high.
£50-55 *PCh*

A Chameleon ware vase, from Clews & Co, c1930, 11½in (29cm).
£100-120 *JAZ*

Coca-Cola

A cardboard shop sign, late 1950s.
£10-15 *COB*

A small advertising mirror, 1970s.
£5-6 *COB*

A quart promotional Coca-Cola can, c1979, 24in (61cm) high.
£10-12 *PC*

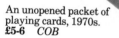

An unopened packet of playing cards, 1970s.
£5-6 *COB*

Bottle Radio

A battery radio, 1970s.
£10-15 *COB*

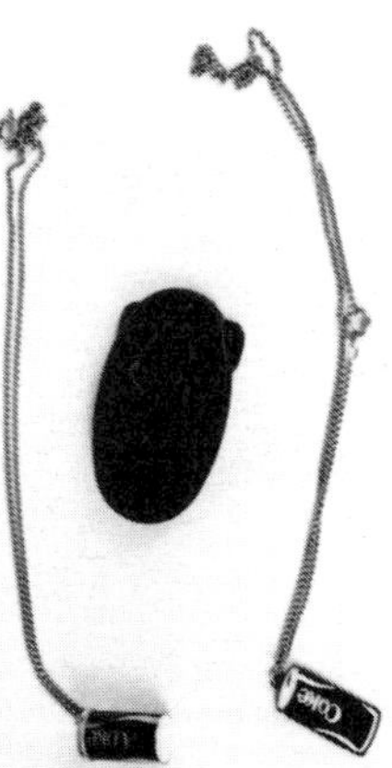

Two necklaces and a buckle, c1970.
Necklaces **£3-4 each**
Buckle **£7-8** *PC*

A porcelain clock, 1970s.
£30-35 *COB*

A cribbage board, c1950.
£8-10 *PC*

The history of Coca-Cola, published 1974.
£15-18 *COB*

Two cans, c1960.
£5-8 each *COB*

Two tin trays, probably copies made in 1960s.
£15-20 each *PC*

Dolls

The doll market has remained buoyant during the past year. Quality bisque headed examples, particularly the noted French manufacturers Jumeau, Bru and Descamps are sought after, with the German manufacturers, notably Heubach, Kammer & Reinhardt and Simon & Halbig, now commanding similar prices.

Original clothing, general condition and overall originality are the main factors affecting prices.

Bisque

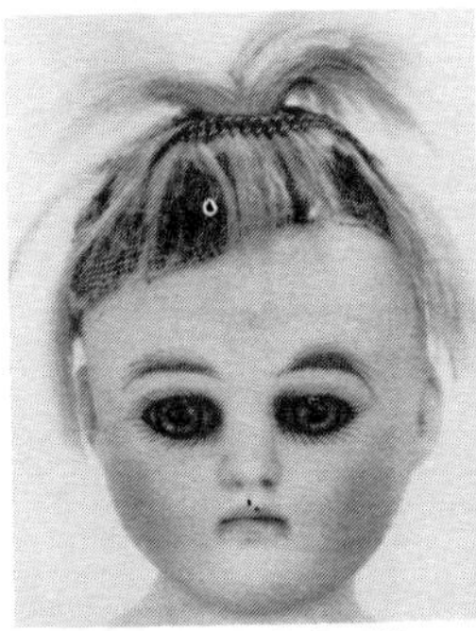

A bisque domed shoulder headed doll, the kid body dressed in white, marked 4.
£350-400 *CSK*

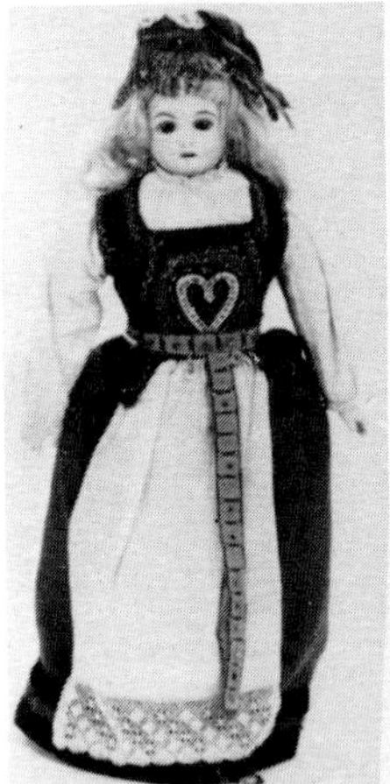

A bisque shoulder headed doll, with stuffed body, bisque hands and wearing bridal costume, Hardanger region of Norway, 16½in (42cm).
£170-200 *CSK*

A white bisque headed clown doll, with bisque arms, mounted on a box with musical movement, 15½in (39cm).
£400-500 *CSK*

A bisque figure of a lady, dressed in original net tu-tu, mark and number under clothes, 7in (18cm).
£250-300 *CSK*

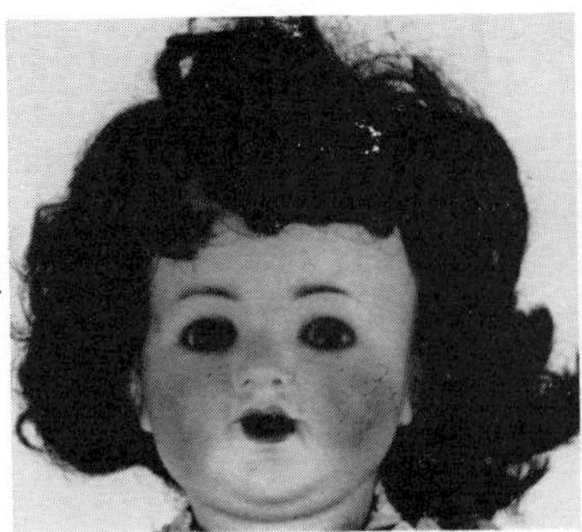

A bisque headed doll, with bent limbed composition body dressed in puce velvet, marked K*R Simon & Halbig 126 9, 21in (53cm) high.
£160-200 *CSK*

A bisque headed child doll, the jointed wood and composition body with walking mechanism and voice box, dressed in original white shift, marked Armand Marseille, in original box, 25in (63.5cm).
£260-300 *CSK*

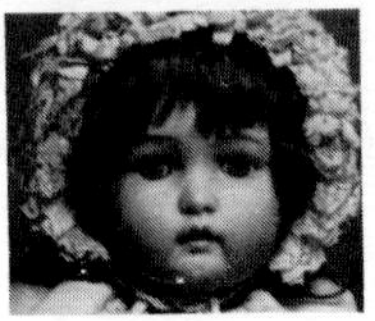

A bisque headed character doll, with jointed composition body, marked 1299 Halbig S&H8, 20in (50cm) high.
£1,000-1,200 *CSK*

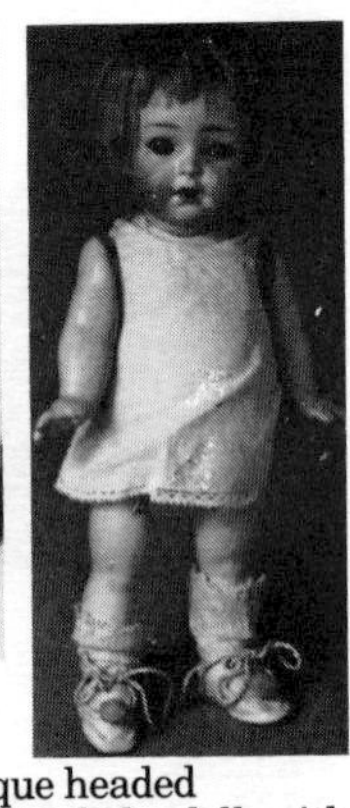

A bisque headed character baby doll, with composition body, marked Simon & Halbig 126 43, 10in (25.5cm) high.
£300-400 *CSK*

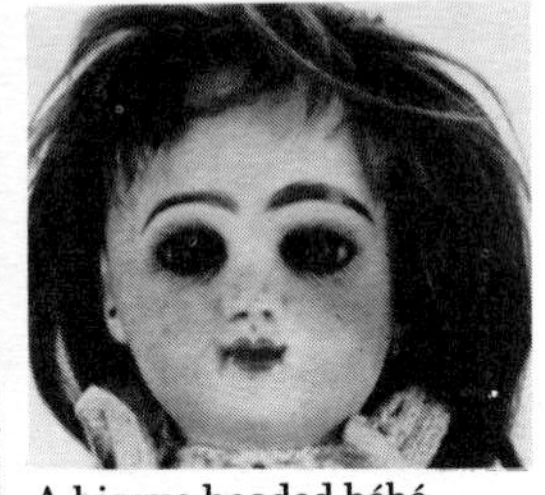

A bisque headed bébé, with jointed wood and composition body, hairline crack across face, marked Deposé Tête Jumeau on head and Jumeau Medaille D'or Paris on body, 13in (33cm).
£550-600 *CSK*

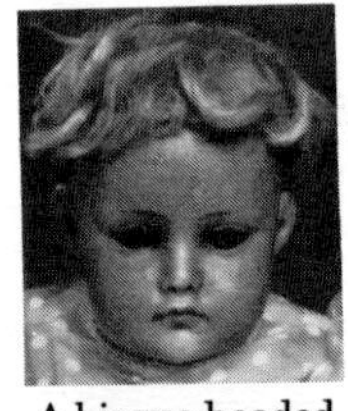

A bisque headed character baby doll, marked 700 4/0 by Armand Marseille, 10in (25cm) high.
£600-700 *CSK*

A brown bisque headed baby doll, with bent limbed composition body, marked Heubach Koppelsdorf 399.4/0.
£260-300 *CSK*

A bisque headed bébé, dressed in cream silk dress, hairline crack on forehead, marked Jumeau, 26in (66cm) high.
£1,000-1,500 *CSK*

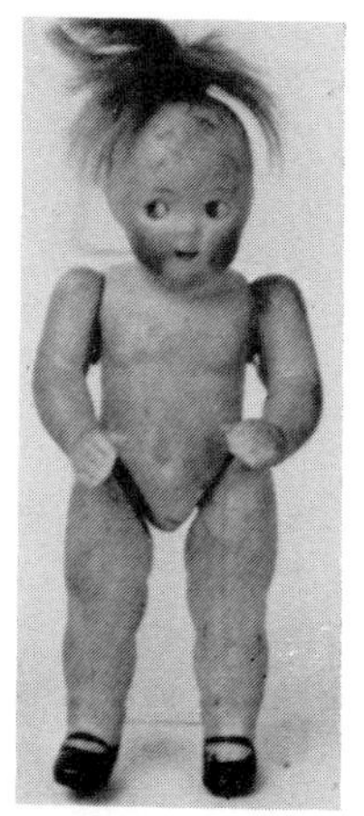
An all bisque googlie eyed doll, marked 179 5/0, 4in (10cm) high.
£200-250 *CSK*

A bisque shoulder headed doll, the kid body dressed in white, 18½in (47cm) high.
£700-750 *CSK*

DID YOU KNOW?
When popular magazines published patterns of Jumeau clothes, women readers copied them for themselves.

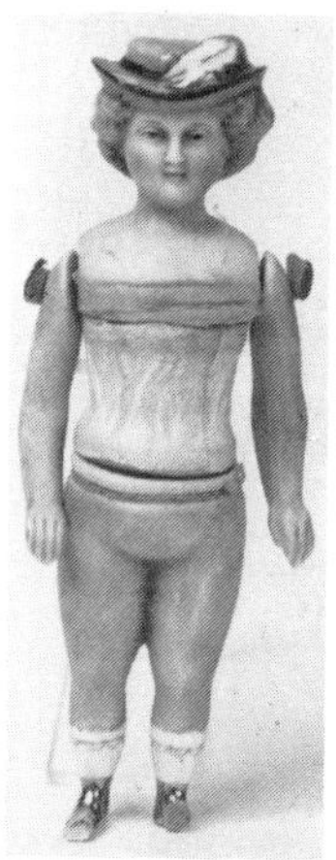
An all bisque doll, the torso with squeaker, small chips to hat and boots, 6½in (16cm) high.
£500-600 *CSK*

A bisque headed doll, dressed in original blue silk outfit with white underwear, 6in (15cm) high.
£200-250 *CSK*

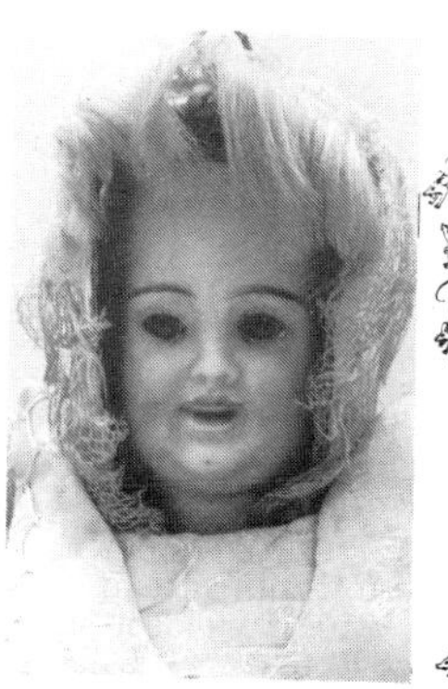

A bisque three-faced doll, with cloth body, in original lace outfit, underwear and shoes, hairline to crying face, marked C.B. for Carl Bergner, c1900, 12½in (32cm).
£300-350 *CSK*

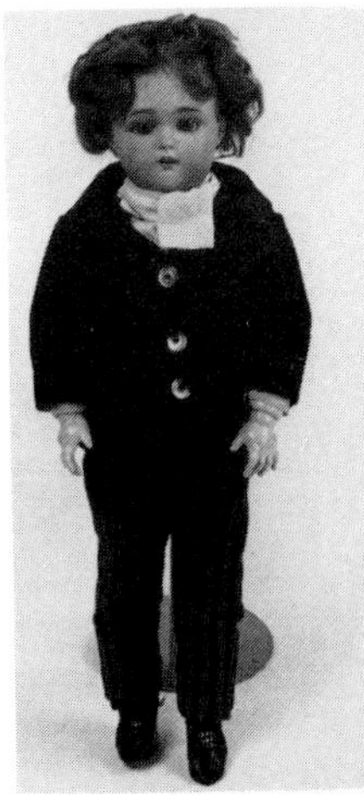

A bisque headed child doll, marked Simon & Halbig K*R 43, 17in (43cm) high.
£450-550 *CSK*

A bisque headed doll, Simon & Halbig.
£250-300 *HCH*

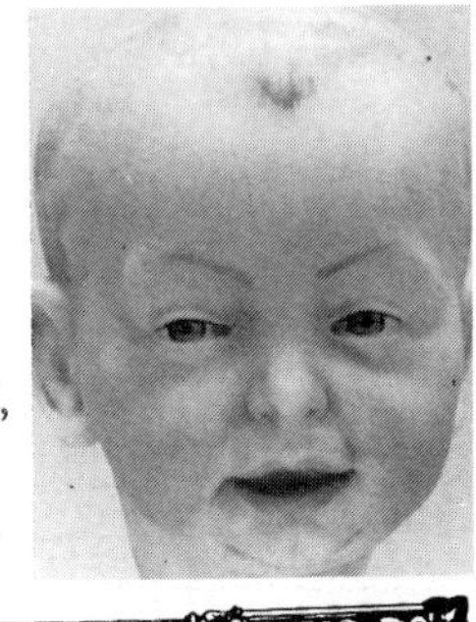

A bisque headed doll, with bent limbed composition body, marked 36 K*R 100.
£450-500 *CSK*

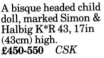

A bisque headed doll, dressed in original white cotton and lace dress and bonnet, marked 21 FS & C 1250/3/0, 12in (30.5cm).
£500-550 *CSK*

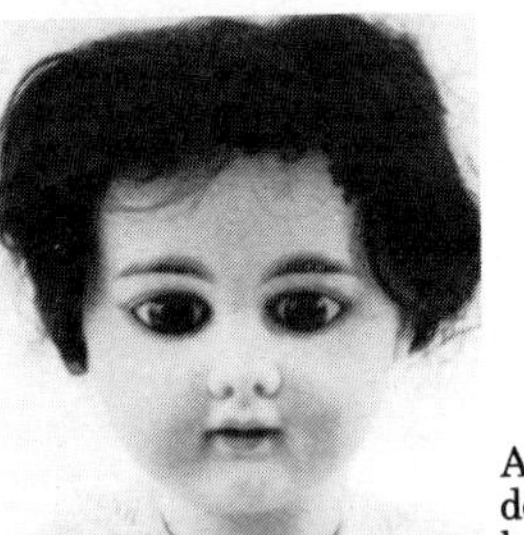

A bisque headed child doll, with fixed brown eyes and jointed body, marked AM12 DEP, c1893, 23in (58cm).
£400-500 *CSK*

A bisque headed doll, Armand Marseille Kopplesdorf, 1330 A7M, 17½in (45cm).
£50-80 *ALL*

A bisque swivel headed doll, with cloth body and bisque arms, marked S H 1039 3 DEP, 15½in (39cm).
£400-500 *CSK*

A S.F.B.J. Paris doll, c1910, 18in (45cm).
£425-450 *SA*

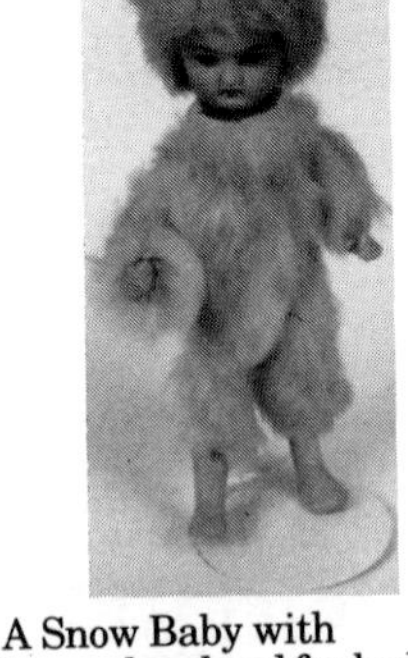

A Snow Baby with bisque head and fur body, 9½in (24cm).
£150-180 *PAR*

A painted bisque doll, 'Princess Elizabeth', impressed A.H., stamped Germany, 21in (53cm).
£300-350 *PAR*

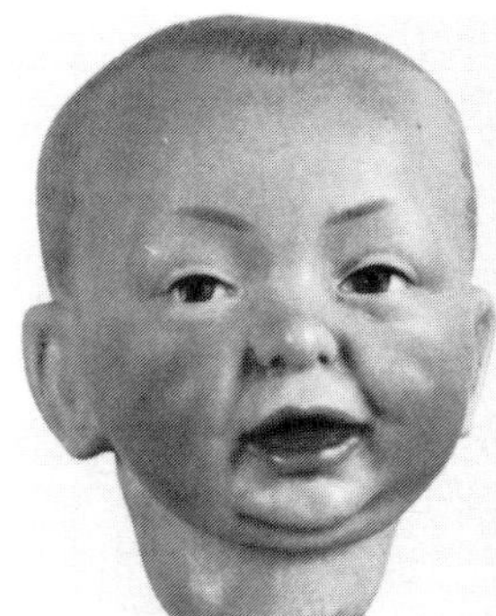

A bisque doll's head, marked K*R 100, 4½in (11cm).
£240-260 *CSK*

A doll by Simon & Halbig, 23in (58cm)
£400-500 *DOW*

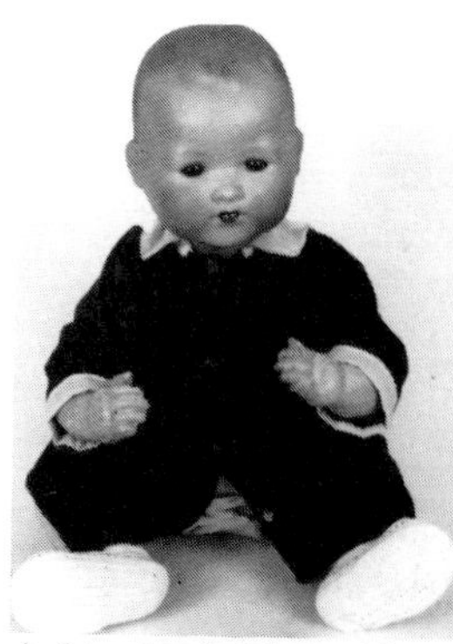

A china headed doll, with composition body and bent limbs, Armand Marseille, c1915, 19in (48cm) high.
£200-220 *SA*

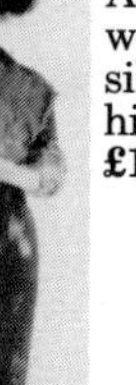

A bisque figure of a woman, with original silk dress, 7½in (19cm) high.
£170-200 *CSK*

A bisque domed shoulder headed doll, the stuffed body with bisque arms and legs, 15½in (39cm) high.
£400-450 *CSK*

A bisque headed doll, impressed S.F.B.J., Paris, 5, 18in (45cm).
£450-500 *PAR*

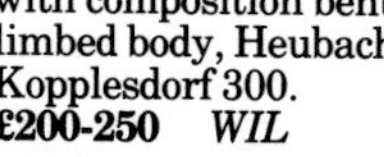

A bisque headed doll, with composition bent limbed body, Heubach Kopplesdorf 300.
£200-250 *WIL*

A bisque headed doll, impressed Simon & Halbig K * R 62, 25in (63cm).
£550-600 *PAR*

A bisque headed character baby doll, dressed in white, marked 971 A3M D.R.G.M. 267/1, 14½in (37cm).
£300-350 *CSK*

A bisque headed bébé, the jointed wood and composition body dressed in gold velvet, marked 3, 12in (30.5cm).
£450-500 *CSK*

An Armand Marseille doll in a wicker cot, 341/3K, 12in (30cm).
£300-350 *DOW*

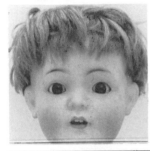

A bisque headed character baby doll, marked 1294 Simon & Halbig 40, 17in (43cm) high.
£260-300 *CSK*

A doll by Strobel Wilkins, 16in (40cm).
£200-300 *DOW*

A china headed baby doll, in original clothes, Armand Marseille, c1900, 15in (38cm) high.
£225-250 *SA*

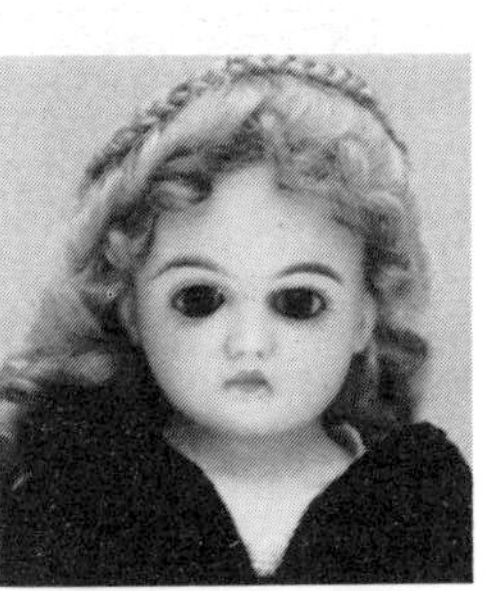

A bisque shoulder headed doll, the cloth body with bisque hands, dressed in black velvet jacket, marked Kling & Co., 167, 14in (35cm).
£350-400 *CSK*

A bisque headed bébé, impressed J. Steiner Bte, S.G.D.G., FLRE, A15, 23in (58cm).
£4,000-4,500 *PAR*

A bisque headed doll, the composition straight limbed body dressed as Ruprecht in fur costume, 8½in (22cm) high.
£220-250 *CSK*

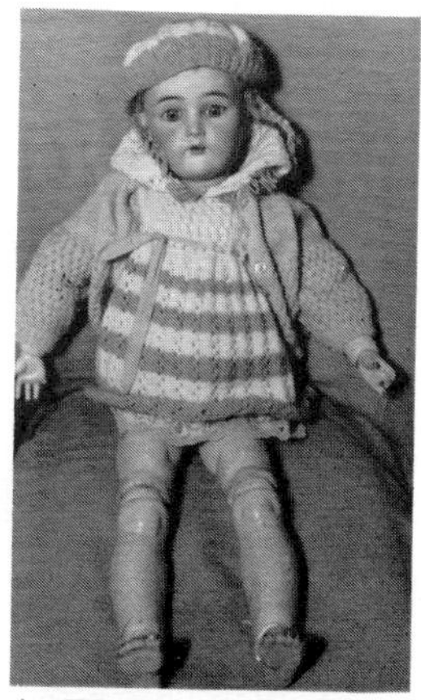

An Edwardian bisque headed doll, with jointed composition body, by Simon & Halbig, K & R.
£170-200 *MGM*

A bisque headed bent limbed baby, impressed Simon & Halbig K * R 126, 20in (50cm).
£450-500 *PAR*

A bisque headed doll with a kid body, AM370, 24in (60cm).
£450-500 *PAR*

A Schoenau & Hoffmeister doll, c1909, 17in (43cm).
£200-250 *DOW*

l. An all original French bisque headed boy doll, impressed 8/0, 12½in (33cm).
£200-250 *PAR*
r. An all original bisque headed girl doll, impressed AM390, A 6/0 M.
£200-250 *PAR*

DID YOU KNOW?
Miller's Collectables Price Guide is designed to build up, year by year, into the most comprehensive reference system available.

Celluloid

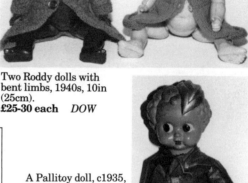

Two Roddy dolls with bent limbs, 1940s, 10in (25cm).
£25-30 each *DOW*

A Pallitoy doll, c1935, 14in (35cm).
£60-65 *DOW*

Wax

A wax headed doll, with blue glass eyes, original clothes, 17in (43cm).
£400-450 *PAR*

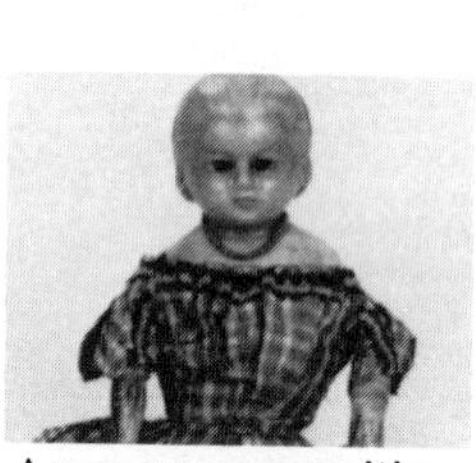

A wax over composition headed doll, the stuffed body with wooden limbs, dressed in blue and white silk dress, with additional clothing, c1865.
£350-400 *CSK*

A poured wax doll, with blue eyes and blonde inset hair, 13½in (34cm).
£450-500 *CSK*

Papier Mâché

Two papier mâché shoulder headed dolls as the Bisto Kids, 12in (30cm).
£150-200 *CSK*

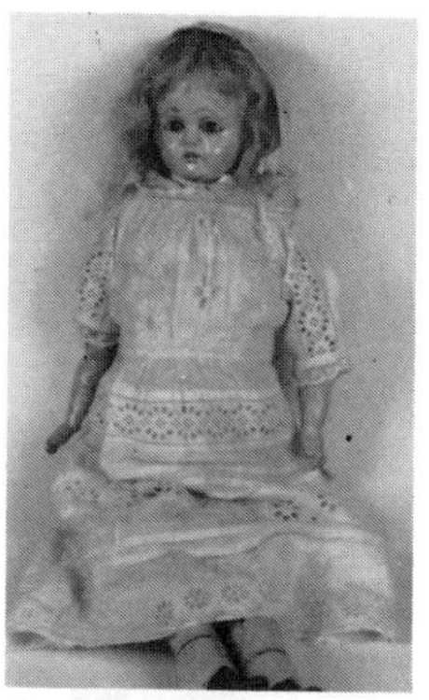

A papier mâché headed doll with stuffed material body, painted face, arms and legs, 27in (68cm).
£220-250 *PAR*

A Victorian doll in original clothes, German, 16in (40cm).
£225-250 *SA*

A painted felt headed doll, wearing a pink dress and tapestry coat, by Lenci, 20in (50cm).
£100-120 *CSK*

Miscellaneous

An English soft bodied doll, with moulded face and painted eyes, dressed in felt, 19in (48cm).
£30-40 *DOW*

Dean's doll, c1945, 20in (50cm).
£35-45 *SA*
These were sold in kit form.

An English doll with painted features and glass eyes, c1800.
£1,000-1,200 *Bon*

A Mulletta Oriental doll, c1945, 12in (30cm).
£125-150 *SA*

A Dutch soft-bodied doll with painted face, 1930s, 16in (40cm).
£15-25 *DOW*

A painted felt doll, dressed in a purple silk trimmed gown, some damage, marked Lenci on foot, 15in (38cm).
£250-300 *CSK*

A Victorian moulded head shoulder doll with soft body, 11in (29cm).
£110-120 *SA*

A French doll with composition head and painted eyes, 16in (40cm).
£40-60 *DOW*

A Norah Wellings all original brown velvet doll.
£90-100 *PAR*

FURTHER READING
Foulke, Jan, *The Ninth Blue Book of Dolls & Values,* Hobby House Press.
King, Constance Eileen, *The Price Guide to Dolls,* Woodbridge, Suffolk.

FRANK FEIGNWELL'S
ATTEMPTS
TO
AMUSE HIS FRIENDS.
EXHIBITED IN A SERIES OF CHARACTERS.
THE THIRD EDITION.
LONDON:

Frank Feignwell's Attempts to Amuse His Friends, a paper doll with 8 changes of costume, printed for S. and J. Fuller, 1810.
£250-300 *CSK*

Two Japanese carved wood and straw dolls late 19thC.
£100-150 *HCH*

Dolls Houses

A small Mettoy tin dolls house, with detachable garage, in mint condition.
£50-100 *WIL*

A painted wooden dolls house, probably by Silber & Fleming, re-painted, c1890, 24in (60cm) high.
£250-300 *CSK*

A wooden dolls house, painted to simulate stone and bricks, by Silber & Fleming, c1890, 27½in (69cm) high.
£250-300 *CSK*

Dolls House Furniture

A miniature upright piano in burr walnut, with brass candlestick holders and ivory keyboard, 15½in (39cm) high.
£1,000-1,200 *CSK*

A Georgian mahogany miniature bath tub, 7½in (19cm) and a Georgian style stool.
£165-185 *CSK*

A towel rail and stool.
£40-45 the pair *MCA*

A set of dolls house furniture.
£550-650 *CSK*

A dolls house bedroom suite.
£30-40 *CAC*

Dolls house armchair and settee, made from matchboxes, c1935.
£5-10 *MCA*

A French suite of furniture, with pink silk upholstery, chair arm missing, late 19thC.
£200-300 *P*

A dolls teaset in original box.
£15-20 *MCA*

A collection of dolls house furniture. **£800-1,000** *CSK*

A set of printed paper-on- wood dolls house furniture,
£500-550 *CSK*

A china early morning teaset, with scenes from the Florence K. Upton Golliwog books, German, marked R.E.G.425168-425172.
£200-250 *CSK*

A set of red painted cast metal and tinplate dolls house chairs, c1840.
£350-450 *CSK*

Hand-made dolls house furniture. **£40-50** *MCA*

A selection of Art Deco style furniture.
£30-40 *MCA*

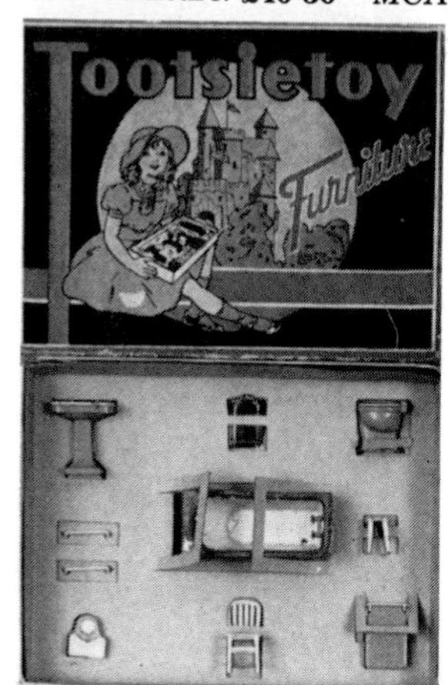

Tootsietoy Furniture Bathroom set, in original box, 1930s.
£80-100 *CSK*

Miniature dolls house furniture.
£200-300 *CSK*

Drinking

Advertising

A Carlton Ware figure, 10in (25cm) high.
£30-40 *BEV*

A Wade jug, c1960, 5½in (14cm).
£20-30 *STU*

A Doulton stoneware whisky jug, c1900, 10in (25cm).
£65-75 *RG*

Cross Reference
Ceramics
Stoneware

A jug advertising Castle Beers, 6in (15cm).
£30-35 *RG*

John Haig's Glenleven Whisky, 6in (15cm).
£55-60 *RG*

A green jug, Style & Winch Ltd, Maidstone, 4½in (11cm).
£50-60 *RG*

A Friary Ale jug in red and black, 4in (10cm) high.
£30-35 *RG*

A reproduction jug, with transfer printed pictures, Staffordshire pottery mark.
£10-15 *RG*

Two stoneware flagons, c1885, 8in (20cm).
£45-55 each *RG*

Two stoneware whisky jugs, 8in (20cm) high.
£55-75 each *RG*

Whitbread's match striker and ashtray, 4½in (11cm) high.
£40-50 *RG*

A Royal Doulton flask advertising Dewars Whisky, 8½in (21cm).
£180-200 *RG*

Guinness

A Carlton Ware toucan, adapted to a lamp, 9in (23.5cm) high.
£170-200 *BEV*

A Carlton Ware mug, c1960, 4in (10cm).
£20-25 *STU*

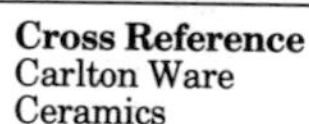

Cross Reference
Carlton Ware
Ceramics

A cruet, 2in (5cm) high.
£10-20 *CIR*

Carlton Ware flying toucans, with original box, c1950.
£200-250 *BEV*

These were not sold but given away in pubs.

Carlton Ware figures, 3½-4in (7.5-10cm).
£450-500 the set *BEV*

General

A neon sign advertising Budweiser, 1960s.
£15-20 *COB*

A mallet shaped whisky jug, embossed with Masonic emblems, c1870, 12½in (32cm) high.
£250-300 *RG*

Cocktails

A French travelling cocktail set, engraved with initials D.F.H., by G. Keller, Paris, late 19thC, 1,780gms.
£2,000-2,200 *C*

A glass cocktail shaker, c1930, 10in (25cm).
£35-45 *STU*

Optics

Optic measures, 1925-30.
£25-30 each *RG*

Corkscrews

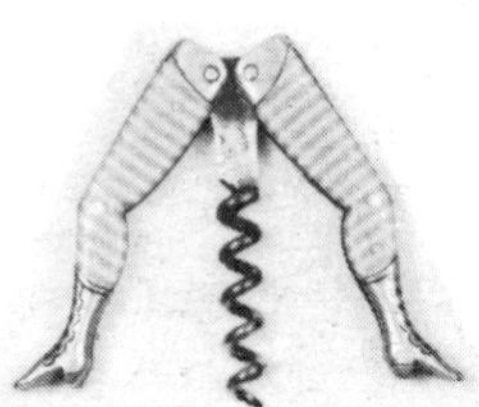

A corkscrew marked Registered Germany.
£120-150 *CSK*

A wooden handled corkscrew, 4½in (11cm) long.
£8-10 *CBA*

A hand-coloured lithograph poster, En Reconnaissance, by E. Montaut, copyright MM, Paris, 30 by 15in (75 by 38cm). **£500-600** *C*

l. to r. Four Lalique glass car mascots: A dragonfly, a cockerel, a ram's head and a greyhound. **£1,000-2,000 each**
A Red Ashay clear glass devil, slightly chipped, 5½in (14cm) high. **£300-400** *C*

A hand-coloured lithograph poster, Un Match Moderne, by E. Montaut, 32 by 16in (80 by 40cm). **£600-800** *C*

A gouache poster, Monaco Grand Prix 1957, Fangio in the Maserati, by Nicholas Watts, signed, 32 by 29in (80 by 74cm). **£2,000-2,500** *C*

A bronze Spirit of Ecstasy showroom display, signed Charles Sykes and No. 28, 20½in (52cm) high. **£8,000-9,000** *C*

A bronze showroom display figure, the base inscribed Susse Frs. Ed. Paris, Cire Perdue and signed Ch. Soudant, 21in (52cm) high. **£4,000-5,000** *C*

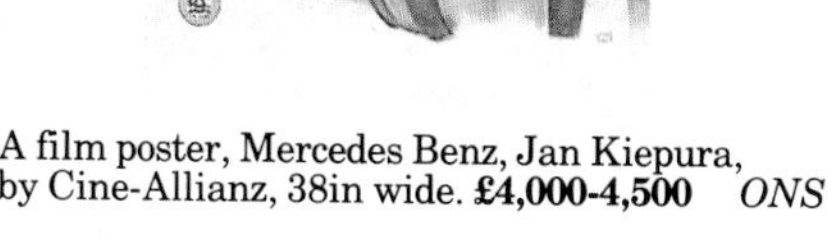

A film poster, Mercedes Benz, Jan Kiepura, by Cine-Allianz, 38in wide. **£4,000-4,500** *ONS*

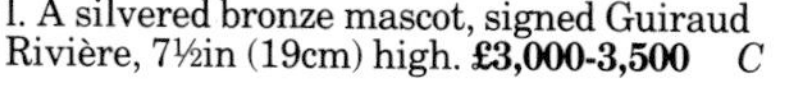

l. A silvered bronze mascot, signed Guiraud Rivière, 7½in (19cm) high. **£3,000-3,500** *C*

A pair of opera glasses.
£40-50 *AD*

A pair of opera glasses, by Chodburns Ltd.
£130-150 *DP*

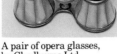

A brass fountain sign, c1910.
£30-35 *COB*

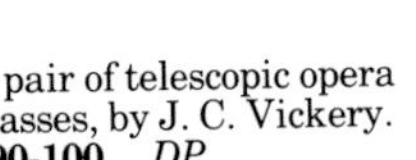

A pair of telescopic opera glasses, by J. C. Vickery.
£90-100 *DP*

A metal advertising clock, 1960s, 24in (61cm) diam. **£70-75** *COB*

An enamel Coca-Cola sign, 1953, 60 by 24in (152 by 61cm). **£60-70** *COB*

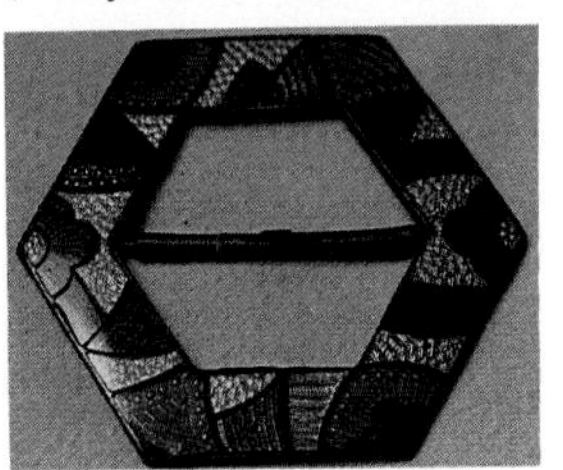

An Art Deco enamelled dress buckle. **£6-7** *OBS*

A Vauxhall glass buckle, 19thC. **£70-80** *DF*

An Ilford Advocate white enamel F45 Dallmeyer camera, 5½in (14cm) wide.
£100-120 *FT*

An enamel buckle, 19thC.
£200-250 *DF*

l. A Goerz Tenax Tropical camera, c1920.
£500-600 *FT*

A set of 6 Victorian cut steel and painted enamel buttons. **£30-40** *OBS*

Macintyre cup and saucer, c1902.
0-80 *FAN*

A Minton cup and saucer, c1865.
£40-60 *FAN*

Derby plate, c1825.
200-250 *PCh*

A George Jones cup and saucer. **£50-70** *FAN*

A Sèvres style plate, 19thC. **£160-200** *PCh*

Carlton crested match holder. **£65-70** *MGC*

A Linthorpe vase, c1880.
£400-500 *ASc*

Goss lustre ware 'Roman' vases. **£70-80 each** *MGC*

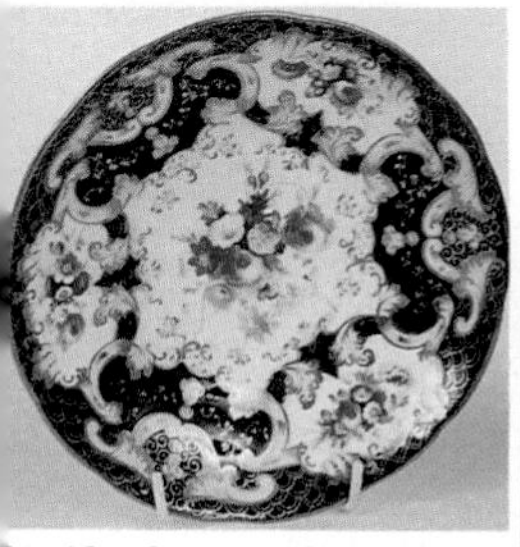

An Alcock cup and saucer, c1840. **£80-100** *FAN*

Willow Art, The Leominster Ducking Stool, 4½in (12cm). **£90-100** *MGC*

A Goss trio.
£65-70 *MGC*

A Shelley Bubbles pattern trio, c1921. **£40-45** *JAZ*

A Carlton Ware Buttercup pattern toast rack, grapefruit dish and mint jug.
£50-60 *BEV*

A Shelley Mabel Lucie Attwell cruet, c1928.
£200-250 *BEV*

A Keith Murray bowl and mug, c1935-36.
Bowl **£250-300** Mug **£35-45** *BEV*

r. A Shelley tulip vase, c1932.
£80-100 *BEV*

A Sadlers car teapot, c1932.
£75-100 *BEV*

A Keith Murray vase, c1935.
£150-180 *BEV*

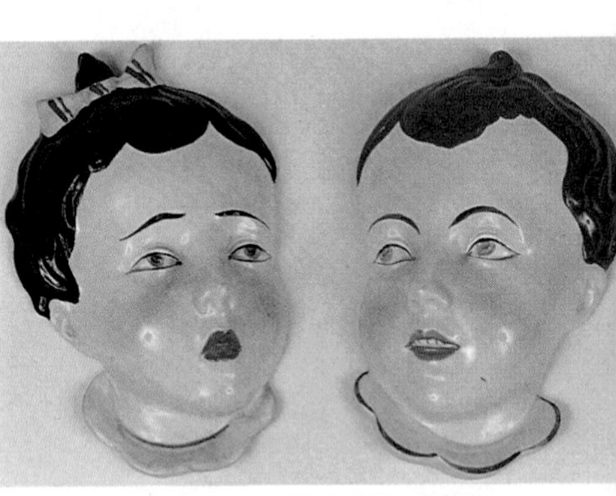

Royal Dux twins, c1933. **£200-250** *BEV*

Above and r. A 3-piece majolica set. **£375-400** *MCA*

A pair of Wade, Heath & Co., vases, c1935, 4in high. **£40-55** *AOS*

A Goebels head, c1930s. **£85-95** *BEV*

A Goebels wall mask, c1930s. **£125-150** *BEV*

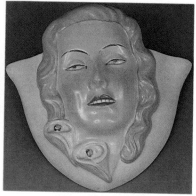

A face mask, c1930s. **£90-100** *BEV*

A Bennett vase, signed, c1930, 8½in (21cm) high. **£250-300** *JAZ*

A Royal Dux wall pocket, 1930s. **£150-170** *BEV*

Below. A Radford vase, c1930, 5in (13cm). **£45-50** *JAZ*

A Goebels head, 1930s. **£60-80** *BEV*

A Clarice Cliff Bizarre ginger jar, 3½in (9cm).
£350-400 *MAG*

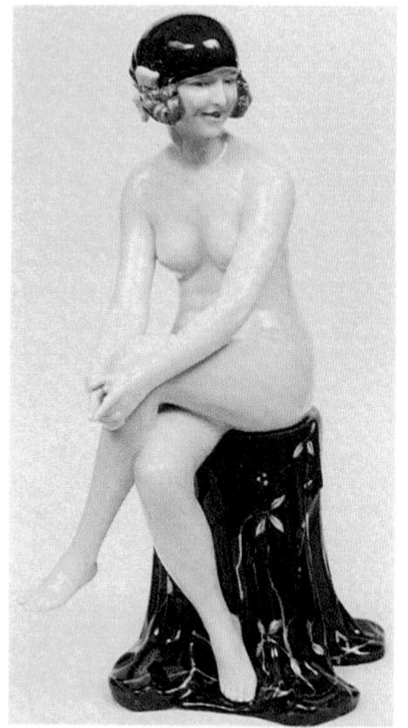

l. An Art Deco Royal Dux figure. **£450-650** *ASA*

r. A Goldscheider figure. **£300-400** *ASA*

A Charlotte Rhead vase, 1930s. **£200-250** *BEV*

A Clarice Cliff Lotus jug, c1930, 12in (30cm).
£1,500-2,000 *AOS*

A Clarice Cliff Orange Alpine plate, c1932. **£250-300** *BEV*

A Clarice Cliff Arklow pattern mug.
£120-150 *BIA*

A very rare pattern.

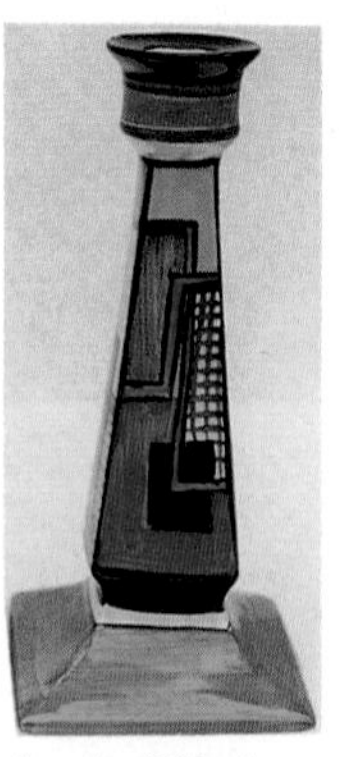

A pair of Clarice Cliff Bizarre candlesticks. **£500-550** *MAG*

A Grays plate, c1930.
£140-150 *JAZ*

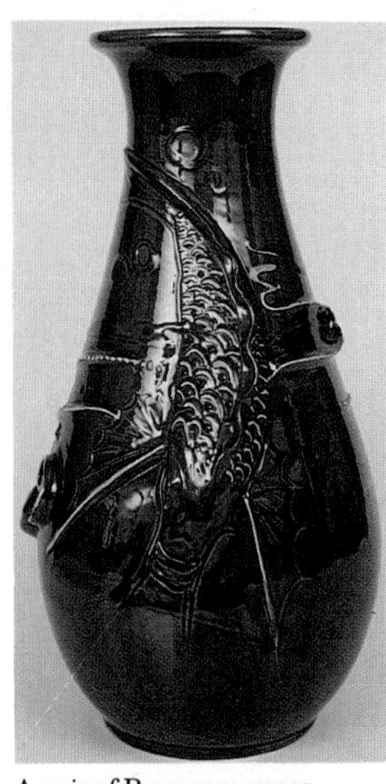

A pair of Brannam vases, c1890. **£400-450** *ASc*

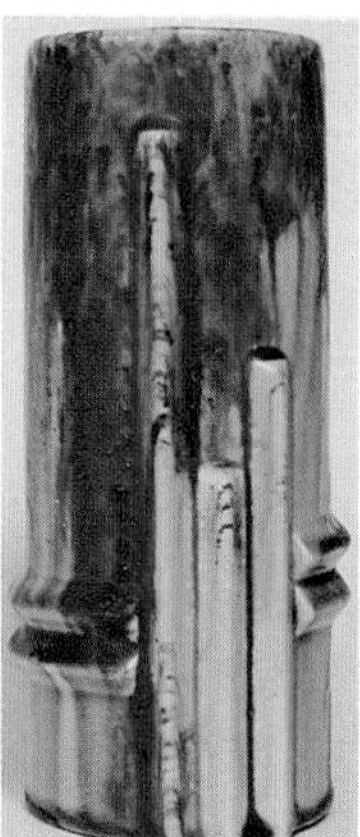

An Art Deco vase, c1930. **£45-55** *PC*

A Burmantoft vase, c1890, 9in (23cm). **£150-200** *ASc*

r. A Burmantoft bull frog, c1885. **£100-150** *ASc*

A Burmantoft firescreen by Neatby, c1890. **£250-300** *ASc*

A Father Christmas teapot, c1934. **£75-100** *BEV*

r. A Continental Art Nouveau ceramic centrepiece. **£400-450** *MAG*

A Burleigh vase, 1930s. **£40-50** *BEV*

A hand-painted teapot in the form of a pagoda, c1930. **£70-80** *PC*

A Poole Pottery Vase, c1930, 10in (25.5cm). **£250-300** *ASc*

A character jug, c1950. **£60-70** *PC*

Bernard Moore flambé ware, c1915, vases **£50-100** monkey **£200-400** *ASc*

Quimper pottery porringer and jug, c1900. **£35-75 each** *MCA*

A Crown Devon dish, c1930, 11in (28cm) wide. **£40-45** *JAZ*

A Crown Devon vase, Mattita design, c1930. **£250-300** *JAZ*

A Quimper pottery bowl, c1900, 6in diam. **£65-75** *MCA*

A Crown Devon coffee service for 6, c1930, coffee pot 8in (20cm) high. **£250-300** *JAZ*

A French faience pottery jug, 6½in (16.5cm) high. **£65-75** *MCA*

An Edward Radford painted jug, c1935, 10in (25cm) high. **£35-50** *AOS*

A Quimper cruet, c1930, 4½in (12cm) high. **£20-30** *MCA*

A French faience tobacco jar. **£140-150** *MCA*

A Quimper pottery plate, c1930. **£55-75** *MCA*

A footbath by Heathcote & Co, small hairline crack, c1825. **£1,500-1,800** *SCO*

A platter, Pountney and Allies, c1825. **£550-600** *SCO*

A pair of Royal Worcester swans, date mark 1875, 7in (18cm) wide. **£450-500** *BA*

A pair of Mason's Ironstone dessert dishes, impressed mark, c1815, 11in wide. **£450-500** *BEE*

A pap boat, c1850. **£40-60** *DBu*

A porcelain baby's feeding bottle, c1880. **£150-200** *DBu*

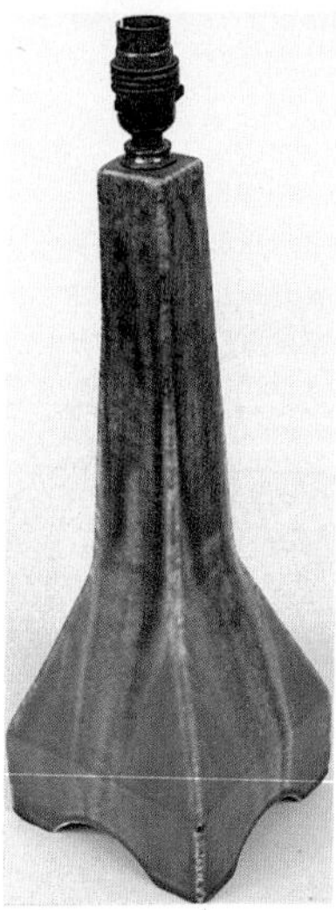

l. Ruskin Art Pottery lamp, 14½in high. **£190-200** *BA*

Majolica style hand-painted jugs, late 1920s, 8in (20.5cm) high. **£60-75** *PC*

Iayer pot lid, Strasburg, Io. 331, c1850. **£85-95** *BA*

A porcelain bowl, by Lucie Rie, impressed LR seal, 8in (20cm). **£3,500-4,000** *Bon*

A Pratt pot lid, Pretty Kettle of Fish, c1860. **£75-85** *BA*

A porcellaneous form by Gabriele Koch, ncised signature. **£800-900** *Bon*

A Wedgwood cup and saucer, Cadbury's Cup Chocolate, c1980. **£25-45** *FAN*

A Staffordshire pot lid, No. 226. **£65-75** *BA*

A Cauldon pot lid, No. 250, c1860. **£85-95** *BA*

A Pratt pot lid, No. 228, c1860. **£85-95** *BA*

Room in which Shakespeare was born, pot lid. **£65-75** *BA*

A Daniel cup and saucer, c1830. **£60-80** *FAN*

T. J. & J. Mayer, Bears on Rock, c1850. **£85-95** *BA*

A pincushion doll, 6in (15cm) high. **£180-220** *BEB*

A Heinrich Handwercke doll, c1895. **£750-850** *BEB*

A Simon & Halbig doll, c1919, 8in (20cm). **£180-250** *BEB*

A Simon & Halbig doll, c1890. **£600-700** *BEB*

H.M. The King, by Farnell & Co. **£120-150** *BEB*

A Christmas cake decoration, 3in high. **£20-70** *BEB*

A Steiff 'Micki', c1950, 10in. **£40-50** *BEB*

A Simon & Halbig doll. **£280-350** *BEB*

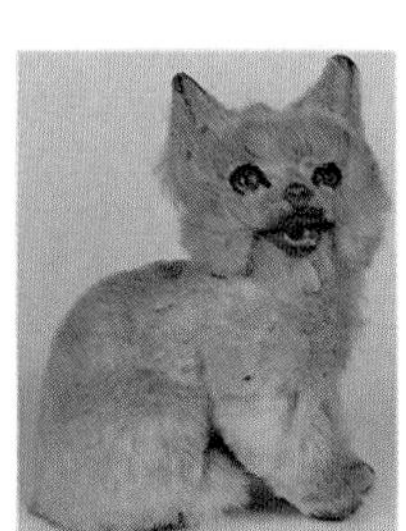

A Victorian cat, 3½in (9cm) high. **£30-40** *BEB*

A papier mâché pedlar doll, c1880, 17in high. **£1,200-1,400** *SA*

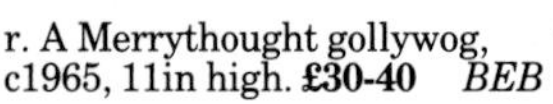

r. A Merrythought gollywog, c1965, 11in high. **£30-40** *BEB*

Pages from a Victorian Scrap album (see below).

A set of 14 Longmans, Green & Co. prints, Gollywog at War, c1899. **£50-80** *BEB*

A Victorian New Year card. **£8-12** *BEB*

A Victorian Valentine card. **£25-30** *BEB*

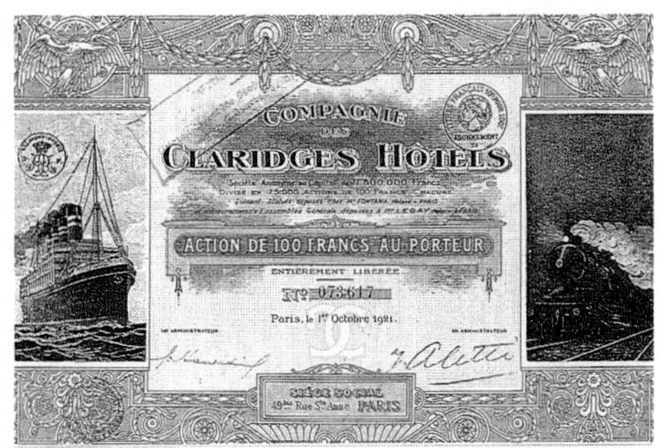

Certificate, Claridges, 1921. **£45-55** *GKR*

A Victorian Valentine card, 5½in (14cm) wide. **£5-10** *BEB*

Victorian Valentine card. **£15-20** *BEB*

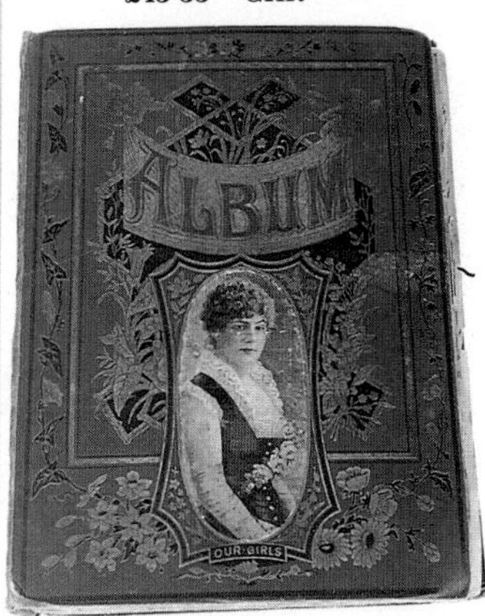

A Victorian scrap album. **£400-500** *(see top left) BEB*

5% Loan, £100 Bond, 1912,. **£50-60** *GKR*

A Victorian Christmas card, dated 1880. **£15-20** *BEB*

l. Share Certificate, Banque Industrielle de Chine. **£30-40** *GKR*

Raphael Tuck's unpublished Louis Wain mascot card, signed and sent by Wain. **£450-500** *VS*

A fan, c1870.
£100-150 *FF*

l. A money box, 1970s, 18in (45cm).
£15-20 *COB*

A mechanical Donald Duck, 5½in (14cm) high. **£800-850** *YC*

Fans:
Top. **£500-800**
Centre. **£150-200**
Bottom. **£40-60** *FF*

Mickey Mouse books, 1935-36.
£40-45 each *COB*

l. A French cockade fan, 1930s.
£10-20 *FF*
r. A Chinese Thousand Faces fan.
£600-650 *SR*

A Monart vase, 9in (23cm). **£120-150** *ASc*

A Strathearn glass vase, 7½in (19cm). **£65-85** *TS*

An Imperial Glass Co., U.S.A. bowl, c1915. **£60-70** *TS*

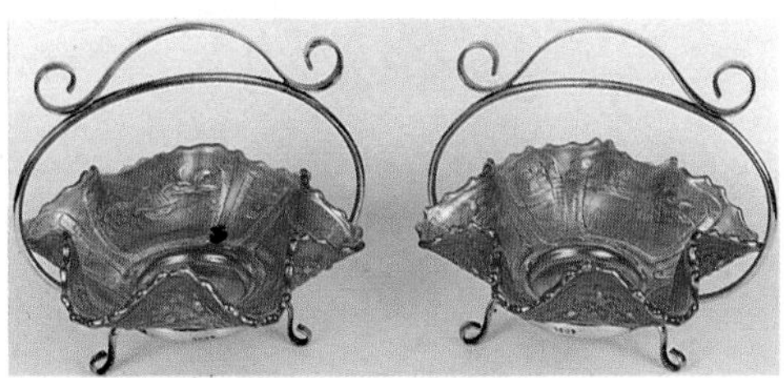

Fenton Art Glass sweetmeat baskets, c1915. **£50-60 each** *TS*

An Imperial Glass Co., bowl, c1915. **£55-65** *TS*

A Dugan bowl, c1915, 8½in (22cm) diam. **£60-70** *TS*

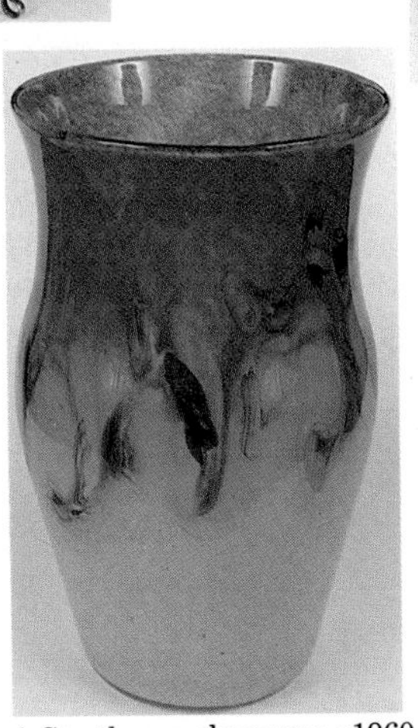

A Strathearn glass vase, c1960, 10in (26cm). **£85-100** *TS*

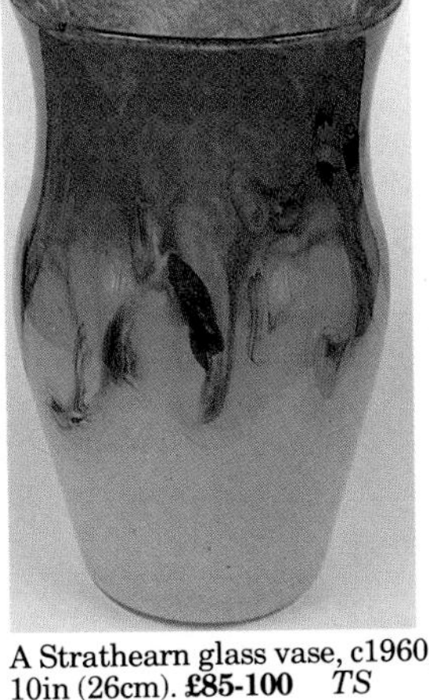

A Monart vase, 8in (20.5cm). **£100-125** *ASc*

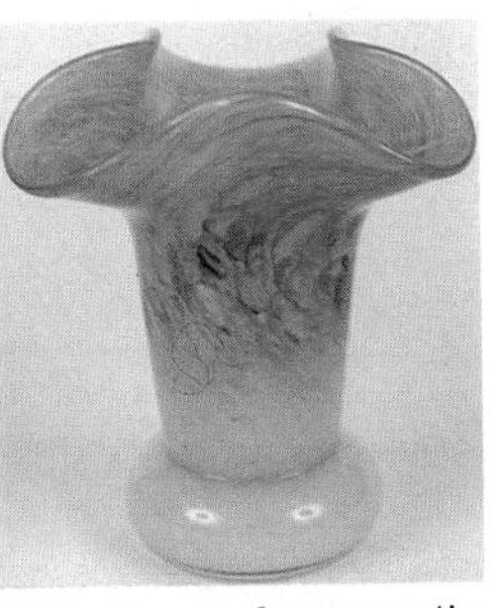

A Strathearn glass vase, 4in (10cm). **£20-25** *TS*

A Fenton Art glass bowl, U.S.A., 8½in (22cm) diam. **£45-50** *TS*

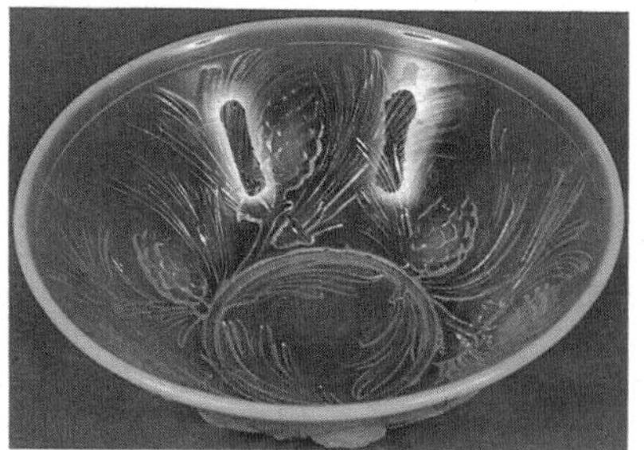

A Joblings glass bowl, with fir cone pattern, c1930s. **£35-45** *BEV*

Cloud glass bowls, by Davison, 1922-1938. **£15-20 each** *BEV*

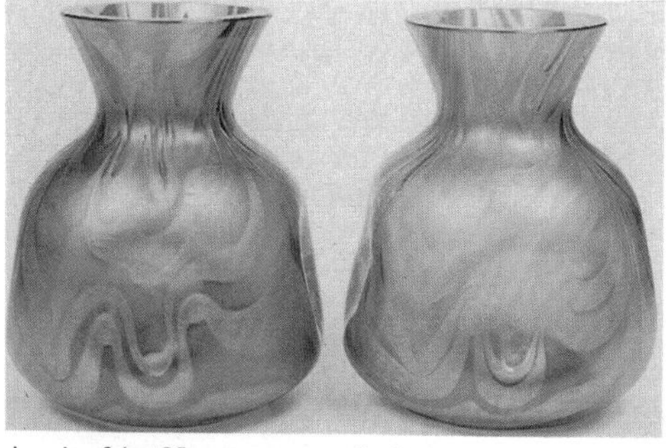

A pair of Art Nouveau vases, by Loetz, 4½in (11cm) high. **£300-400** *ASA*

A pair of Art Deco perfume bottles, 5½in (14cm) high. **£260-280** *Tri*

Two clear glass perfume bottles, 1920s, 5½in (14cm) high. **£95-120 each** *Tri*

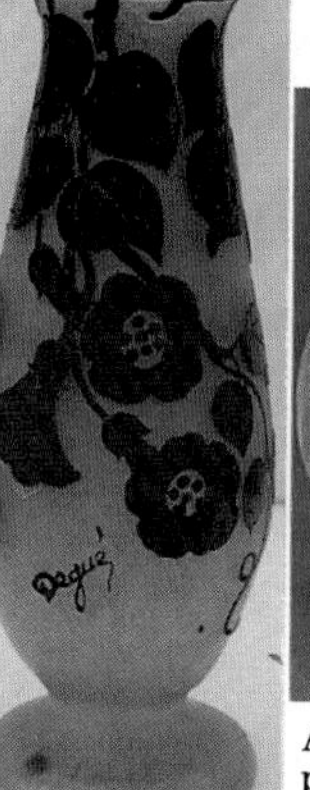

r. A cameo glass vase, decorated with flowers, 15in high. **£450-500** *MAG*

A Joblings glass bowl with shell pattern, c1930. **£40-50** *BEV*

A pair of Art Deco perfume bottles. **£120-130 each** *Tri*

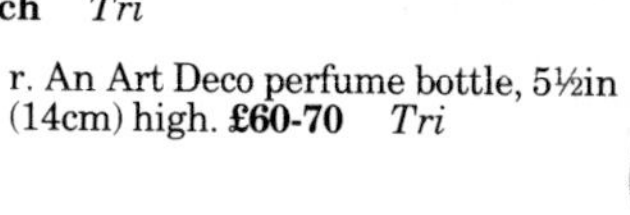

r. An Art Deco perfume bottle, 5½in (14cm) high. **£60-70** *Tri*

A Barbola mirror, c1930, 11in (28cm) diam. **£65-75** *MW*

A Victorian sword pin, 3in (7cm). **£12-18** *RA*

A heart-shaped mosaic brooch. **£15-18** *JH*

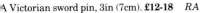

A Victorian bar brooch, 1½in (4cm) long. **£28-35** *RA*

A Victorian mosaic bar brooch, 1½in (4cm) long. **£15-20** *RA*

A millefiori mosaic brooch with turquoise background. **£20-30** *JH*

r. An Italian mosaic brooch, with pink background. **£20-25** *JH*

r. A Victorian mosaic brooch. **£15-20** *RA*

A Victorian mosaic violin brooch, 2in (5cm) long. **£10-15** *RA*

r. A millefiori mosaic brooch, with blue background, 2in (5cm) long. **£20-30** *JH*

A pair of folk carvings of doves, with original patina, c1840. **£600-700** *RYA*

A Victorian silver goblet, 4.5oz. **£150-180** *MAG*

A silver tea caddy with cover, hallmarked. **£150-200** *SAA*

A Victorian silver inkstand, by H. Lambert, hallmarked, 24oz. **£900-1,000** *MAG*

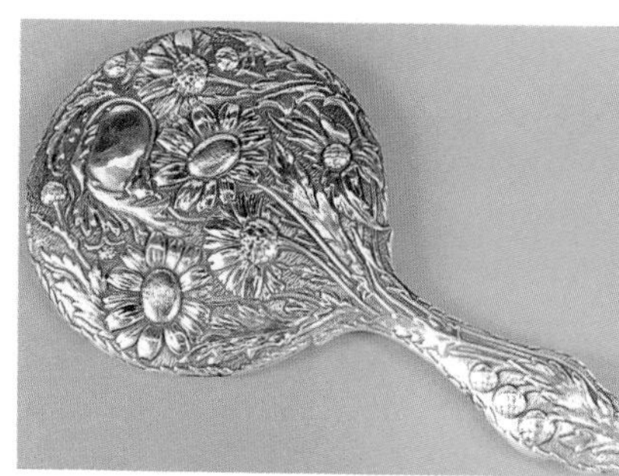

An Art Nouveau mirror, Birmingham 1904, 10in (25cm) long. **£160-180** *CLI*

A cast iron post box, c1905. **£140-160** *COB*

A silver purse, leather interior, Birmingham 1919. **£275-300** *CLI*

An Art Deco automaton clock. **£140-160** *SAA*

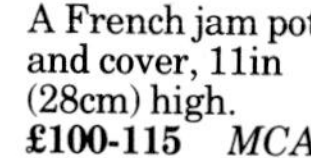

A French jam pot and cover, 11in (28cm) high. **£100-115** *MCA*

A copper tea kettle, c1920, 8½in (22cm) high. **£90-100** *MCA*

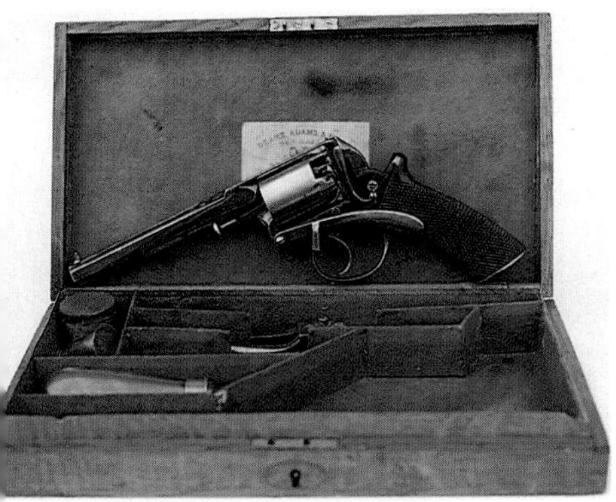

5-shot percussion revolver, by Deane, dams & Deane. **£550-600** *MAG*

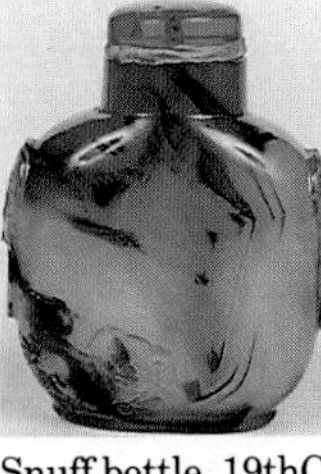

Snuff bottle, 19thC. **£350-400** *SR*

A Peking glass snuff bottle, c1820. **£350-400** *SR*

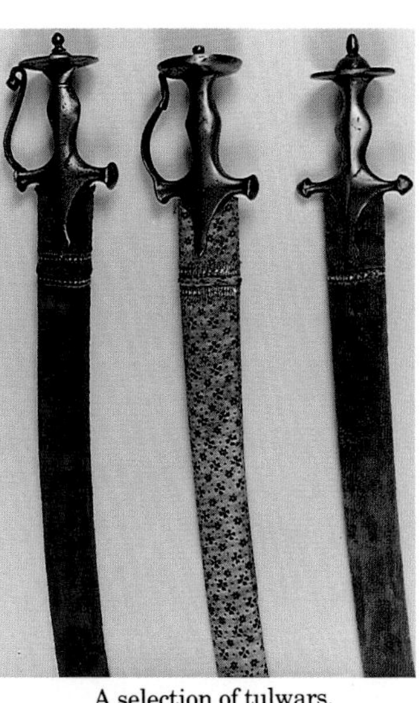

A selection of tulwars, c1800. **£35-120 each** *ARB*

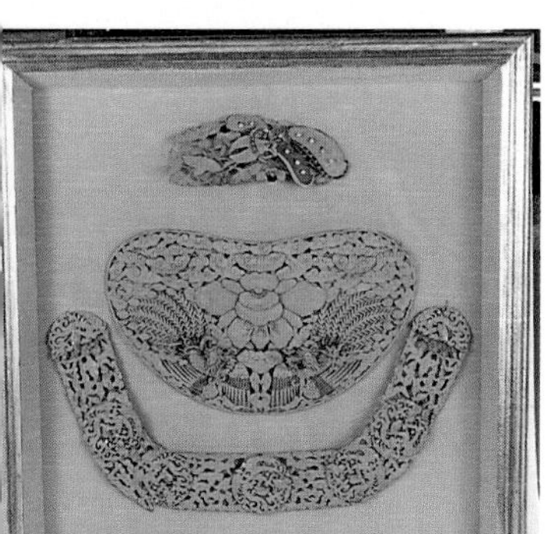

Mandarin kingfisher feather head-ess, early 19thC. **£3,000-3,500** *SR*

A Victorian 10-bore cannon, by Thomas Bland & Sons, marked. **£1,750-2,000** *ARB*

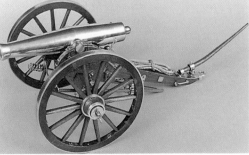

olour Sgt. B. Faulkner's edals. **£8,000-10,000** *C*

An American model, c1860. **£1,500-2,000** *ARB*

A Japanese ivory card case signed, 19thC. **£280-300** *SR*

A Japanese figure, 19thC, 6in (15cm) high. **£500-550** *SR*

Two Cantonese ivory card cases, 19thC, l. **£700-750** r. **£300-350** *SR*

'Le Blond' print No. 89, Snowballing.
£80-120 *BEE*

Led Zeppelin, John Bonham's Ludwig drum set, signed, c1978. **£3,000-4,000** *P*

A Baxter print, C.L.No. 353, The Day Before Marriage.
£140-180 *BEE*

A mechanical ladybird, 6in (15cm). **£30-35** *YC*

A Ferranti 145 radio, 1945. **£120-300** *RC*

A Bush DAC90A radio, c1950. **£55-115** *RC*

A Pye Model 'G' radio, c1932. **£75-325** *RC*

A Philco A637 radio, c1937. **£40-200** *RC*

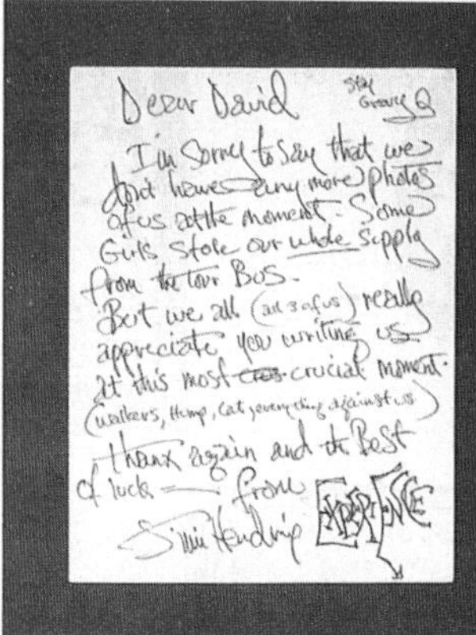

Dear David
Stay Groovy
I'm sorry to say that we don't have any more photos of us at the moment. Some Girls stole our whole supply from the tour Bus.
But we all (all 3 of us) really appreciate you writing us at this most crucial moment.
(writers, thump, cat, everything against us)
Thanx again and the Best of luck — from
Jimi Hendrix EXPERIENCE

A handwritten letter from Jimi Hendrix to a member of the Universal Autograph Collector's Club, c1967. **£1,500-2,000** *P*

A Spanish armillary sphere, 19thC. **£1,800-2,000** *CSK*

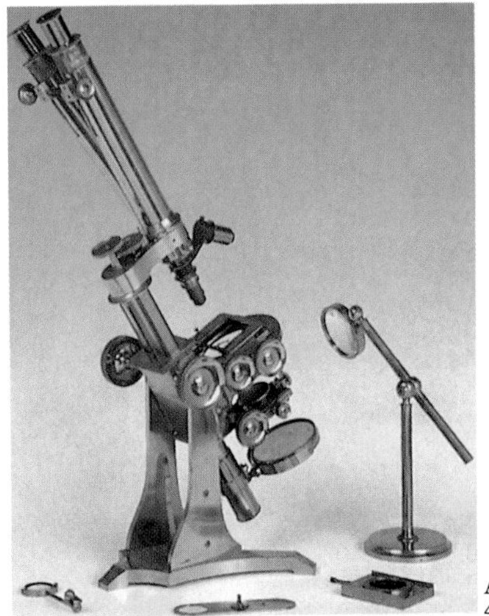
A Ross compound binocular microscope, 19thC. **£2,200-2,500** *CSK*

A refracting telescope, 19thC, 45½in long. **£2,200-2,500** *CSK*

A reflecting telescope, signed Bate, 19thC, body 24½in long. **£2,500-3,000** *CSK*

Cunard Line poster. **£450-500** *ONS*

Cunard poster, by Frank H. Mason. **£2,500-3,000** *ONS*

Red Star Line poster, by H. Cassiers. **£250-350** *ONS*

Cunard poster, Aquitania, by Odin Rosenvinge. **£450-500** *ONS*

A Cunard Line poster, Anon. **£750-850** *ONS*

Orient Line poster.
£400-500 *ONS*

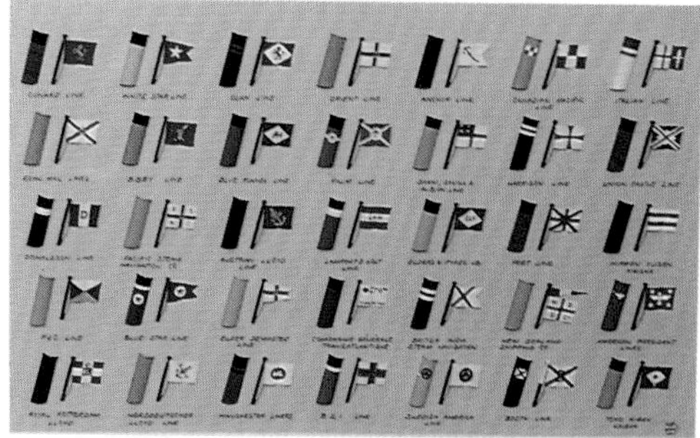
Hand-painted flags and funnels by David Brown, 1980s. **£75-90** *COB*

Cunard Line poster, by Kenneth Shoesmith.
£2,500-3,000 *ONS*

Cunard Line poster, by W. S. Bylitipolis.
£700-800 *ONS*

White Star Line poster, by Montague B. Black.
£800-900 *ONS*

Cunard Company magazines, 1922-23.
£15-18 each *COB*

Royal Mail Line brochures, 1936.
£5-15 each *COB*

Cunard poster.
£750-800 *ONS*

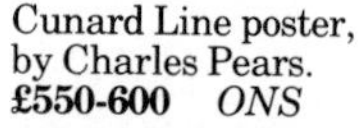

Cunard Line poster, by Charles Pears.
£550-600 *ONS*

American line poster, by Montague B Black.
£400-500 *ONS*

Cunard Line poster.
£900-1,200 *ONS*

Hand-painted and enamelled steamship medallions, 1980s. **£15-18 each** *COB*

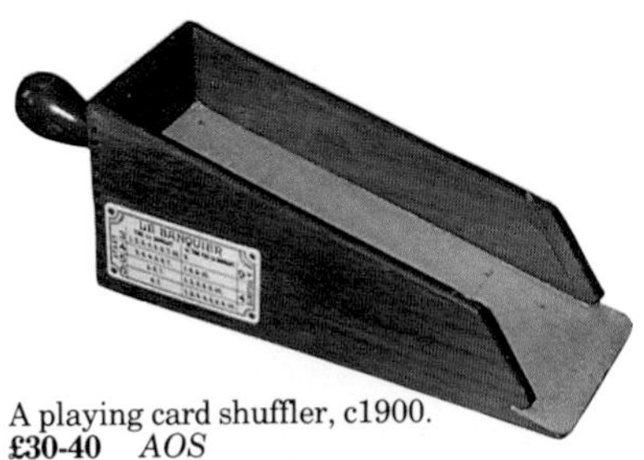

A playing card shuffler, c1900.
£30-40 *AOS*

A tin money box, 6in (15cm) high.
£35-45 *YC*

Noddy's car, c1962, 8in (20cm).
£90-100 *BAD*

A money box, 4in (10cm) high. **£6-8** *YC*

A silver plated and glass cruet, c1920. **£180-220** *CLI*

A French striking mantel clock, 19thC. **£180-200** *SAA*

A mahogany medicine chest, 19thC. **£2,000-2,500** *CSK*

A pair of French Provincial boxes. **£650-675** *MCA*

A Dutch toffee tin, c1930.
£265-285 *BAD*

A tin wind-up African drummer, c1960. **£50-75** *PC*

Metal golfer, c1920.
£250-300 *BEV*

An Edwardian bag.
£30-35 *Tri*

An English bear, c1940.
£125-150 *SA*

Ceramic bottle stand.
£60-75 *K*

A Lutz clockwork paddle steamer, c1890.
£9,000-10,000 *CSK*

A Beswick water jug, 1930s.
£85-95 *BEV*

An American thermometer.
£4,000-4,500 *CSK*

A North American beaded pin cushion, c1870. **£60-70** *PP*

A zebra, 24in (61cm) high.
£300-350 *SSA*

l. A tin money box, 5½in high. **£25-30** *YC*
r. A German Noah's Ark, 280 inmates, 19thC, 25in long. **£2,000-2,500** *AH*

Oldsmobile sedan. **£430-450** *BAD*

Britains Set No. 149, Military Display and Game, damaged, c1907. **£1,200-1,500** *CSK*

A mechanical clown in a barrel, 8in (20cm) high. **£450-500** *YC*

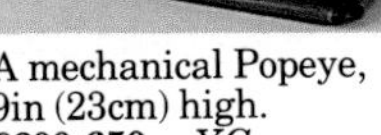

A mechanical Popeye, 9in (23cm) high. **£600-650** *YC*

A battery operated Pluto, 12in (30cm) long, original box. **£220-250** *YC*

l. A Victorian wooden horse and cart, 20in wide. **£80-90** *MCA*

l. Balloon Vendor, battery operated, 13in. **£130-175** *PC*
r. Charley Weaver, battery operated, 12in. **£80-130** *PC*

l. Good Time Charlie, battery operated. **£150-200** *PC*
r. Jocko, Drinking Monkey, battery operated. **£150-225** *PC*

Mr. McGregor, The Smoker, battery operated, 1962, 11in. **£100-150** *PC*

Chef Cook, battery operated, 10in. **£100-120** *PC*

Original boxes add greatly to the price.

Mambo, the Elephant Drummer, 10in. **£125-150** *PC*

Collection of Japanese wind-up toys, 1967, 5in. **£50-75 each** *PC*

l. Rock & Roll Monkey, battery operated, 12in. **£125-175** *PC*

Wind-up Bear with Camera, 7½in. **£50-75** *PC*

A Japanese friction powered ATC Asahi Chrysler Imperial car, 1962, 15in (38cm). **£12,500+** *MIN*

A Kibri & Co. news kiosk, c1930. **£1,250-1,500** *MIN*

Lehmann toys: l. 'Paddy and the Pig', c1910. **£1,750-2,000**
r. 'Captain of Köpenick', c1906.
£3,000-3,500 *MIN*

A Tipp & Co. clockwork delivery van, c1930, 9½in (24cm) long. **£6,750+** *MIN*

An F. Martin hand-painted clockwork toy, c1909.
£2,000-2,500 *MIN*

An Ingap 'Fiat' 2-door coupe, c1936, 12in (31cm). **£2,500+** *MIN*

An Ernst Plank steam driven 'tricylce', 1880, 8in (20.5cm). **£4,000+** *MIN*

A German clockwork dancing couple, late 19thC. **£2,000+** *MIN*

A Bing clockwork laundry van, c1908, 8in (20cm) long. **£8,000+** *MIN*

A Mettoy clockwork military motorcycle, c1939, 8½in (22cm). **£2,000-2,500** *MIN*

A Lehmann 'Tut Tut' car, c1901. **£2,500-3,000** *MIN*

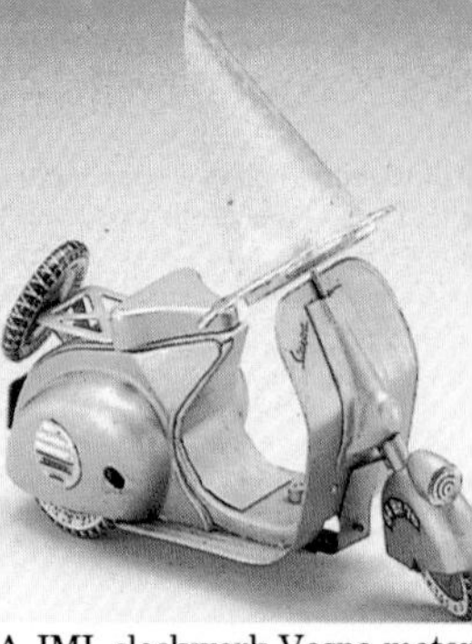
A JML clockwork Vespa motor cycle, c1950. **£400-450** *MIN*

An Aston Martin DB5, 11½in (29cm). **£300-350** *MIN*

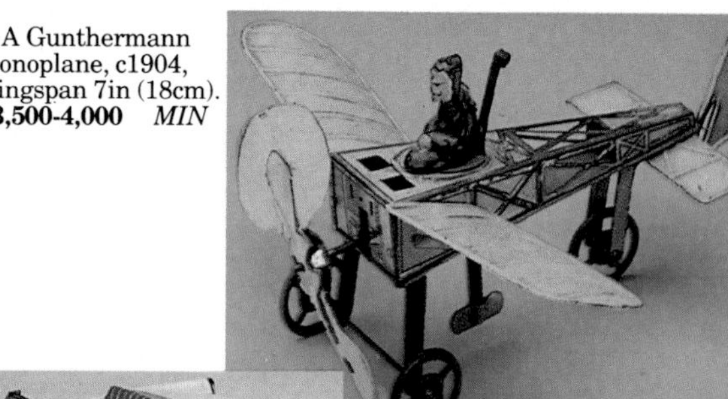
r. A Gunthermann monoplane, c1904, wingspan 7in (18cm). **£3,500-4,000** *MIN*

A Haji Ford Convertible, 1956, 12in (30.5cm). **£4,500-5,000** *MIN*

A Marklin clockwork limousine, 1922, 11in (28cm). **£20,000+** *MIN*

An Ernst Plank 4-sea tonneau, c1904. **£1,800-2,000** *MIN*

A JYE clockwork motor scooter/van, c1955, 7in (18cm). **£750-1,000** *MIN*

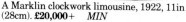

A Lehmann No. 645 clockwork duck, 7½in (19cm). **£1,200-1,500** *MIN*

r. A Carette clockwork 'Gordon Bennett' racing car, c1904. **£7,500+** *MIN*

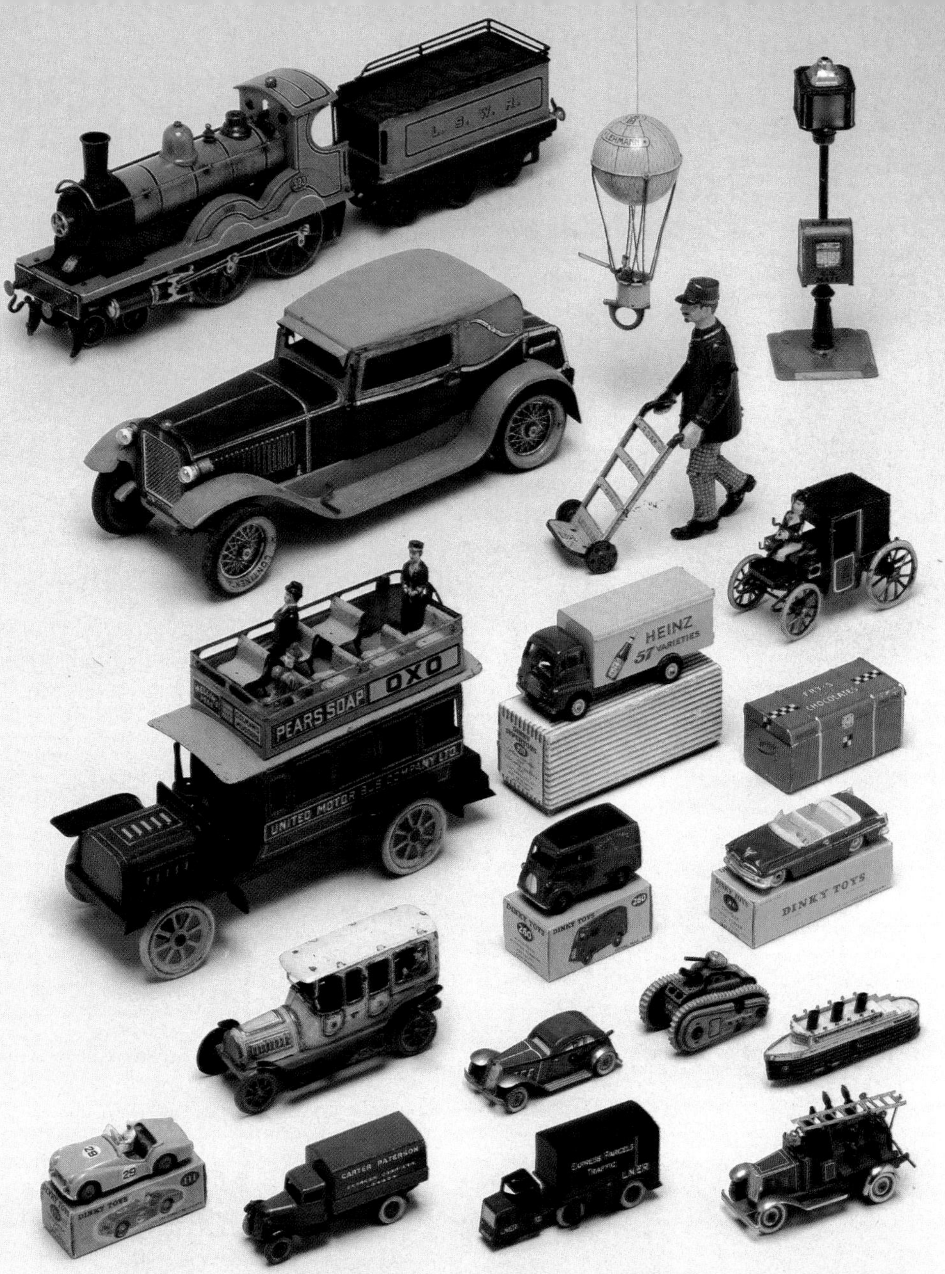

OXO
PEARS SOAP
UNITED MOTOR BUS COMPANY LTD
HEINZ
57 VARIETIES
DINKY TOYS

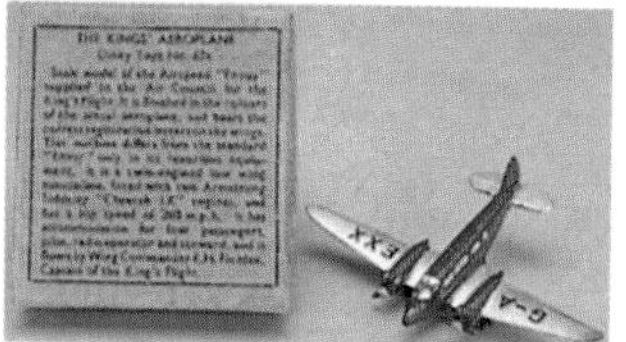

Dinky 62K 'The King's Aeroplane'. **£475-500** *MIN*

Corgi Chipperfield's Circus Truck. **£140-150** *MIN*

Dinky Leyland Esso Tanker. **£650-700** *MIN*

Matchbox 56 London Trolleybus. **£45-50** *MIN*

Dinky 772 British Road Signs. **£175-200** *MIN*

Dinky 108 MG Midget Sports. **£175-200** *MIN*

Corgi 327 MGB GT Coupe. **£65-75** *MIN*

Märklin 8021 VW Karmann Ghia. **£120-140** *MIN*

Dinky Austin Healey 100. **£175-200** *MIN*

Dinky 23J Racing Car. **£95-100** *MIN*

Dinky 44 AA Display Set. **£1,200-1,300** *MIN*

Dinky 105 Triumph TR2 Sports. **£150-180** *MIN*

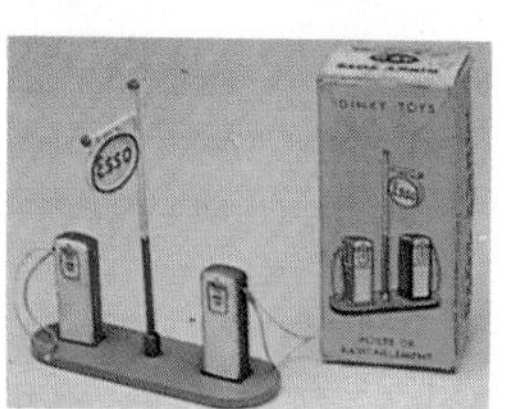

Dinky 45D Esso Petrol Pumps. **£75-100** *MIN*

Yesteryear Y12 Horse-Drawn Bus. **£65-75** *MIN*

Crescent Toy 1291, Aston Martin Racer. **£100-120** *MIN*

Solido 130 Aston Martin DB5 Vantage. **£125-150** *MIN*

Dinky Regent Tanker. **£650-700** *MIN*

Spot-On Presentation Set. **£850-900** *MIN*

r. Dinky Brockway Bridge Layer. **£250-260** *MIN*

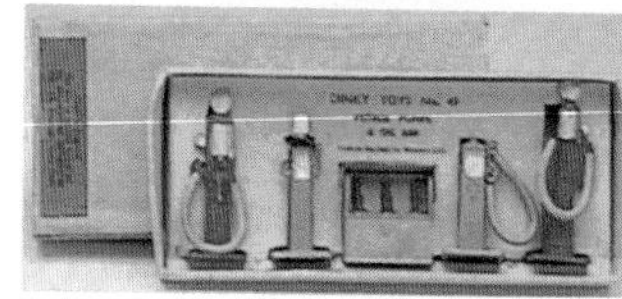

r. Dinky 49 Petrol Pump Set. **£275-300** *MIN*

A Bing lithographed tinplate station, 12in long. **£330-350** *CSK*

A Märklin steam vessel, c1910, 35in long. **£10,000-12,000** *CSK*

A lithographed tinplate biscuit tin. **£3,000-3,500** *CSK*

Lutz for Märklin, clockwork toy, 24in. **£12,000-14,000** *CSK*

A Märklin gauge I railway shed, c1904. **£450-500** *CSK*

Lighthouses by Bing and Doll, c1920. **£3,800-4,200 each** *CSK*

Märklin railway accessories, c1935. **£750-800** *CSK*

Clockwork toy by Bing, c1922, 39½in long. **£5,000-5,500** *CSK*

A Märklin gauge 0 model, c1921. **£600-700** *CSK*

A Märklin station, c1904, 29in long. **£12,000-14,000** *CSK*

A clockwork model by Märklin, c1900. **£12,000-13,000** *CSK*

A clockwork model by Bing, c1902. **£5,000-6,000** *CSK*

A Märklin electric model, c1909. **£5,000-6,000** *CSK*

A Märklin electric model, c1909, 47in long. **£35,000-40,000** *CSK*

l. A Märklin clockwork model. **£8,000-9,000** *CSK*
r. A Maltête et Parent, model. **£6,000-7,000** *CSK*

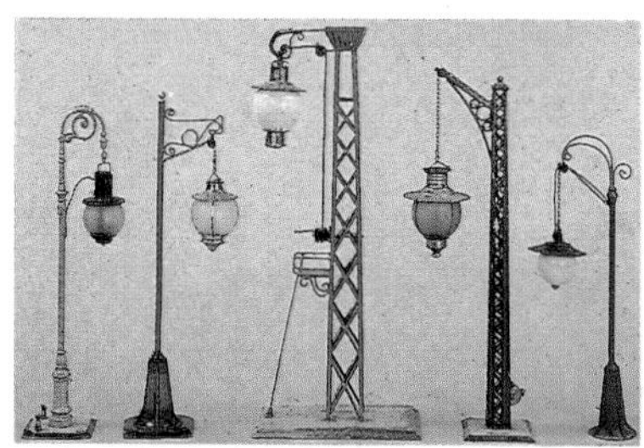
Bing lighting, 1914-25.
£1,200-1,500 *CSK*

A Bing steam train, replacement tender.
£1,800-2,000 *CSK*

A Märklin gauge 1 bridge, c1900.
£2,500-3,000 *CSK*

A Märklin gauge 0 station, c1926. **£1,750-2,000** *CSK*

A Märklin level crossing, 1935. **£250-300** *CSK*

A Märklin level crossing, c1912. **£500-700** *CSK*

Bing signals, c1914-25.
£450-500 *CSK*

A Märklin Toilette, c1909. **£1,000-1,500** *CSK*
r. Various signals, c1912-30. **£400-500** *CSK*

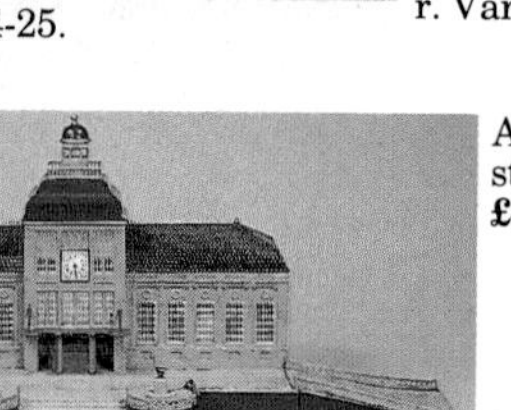
A Märklin gauge 0 station, c1921.
£4,500-5,000 *CSK*

Railway accessories, c1910-25.
£300-350 *CSK*

A Bing sleeping car and baggage car, c1904. **£2,500-3,000** *CSK*

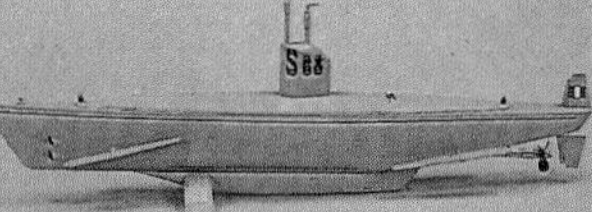
A Gil electric submarine, c1950. **£150-200** *CSK*

Various items.
£1,000-1,200 *CSK*

A Märklin clockwork train, c1908. **£4,000-5,000** *CSK*

A Bing steam engine, c1902.
£1,600-2,000 *CSK*

A Märklin station, c1920.
£3,000-3,500 *CSK*

The Red Arrow, a Hermann electric train.
£1,000-1,200 *CSK*
r. Bing signals, c1905. **£140-160** *CSK*

EPHEMERA
Autographs

David Lloyd George, photo slightly damaged, G.
£30-50 *VS*

A self portrait and autograph, by George Robey, poor condition, 1928.
£8-10 *COB*

Very common.

A page from an autograph book signed Rudolph Valentino, London Aug 2 1923, with photograph.
£200-300 *CSK*

Arthur Sullivan, signature cut from a letter, FR.
£40-50 *VS*

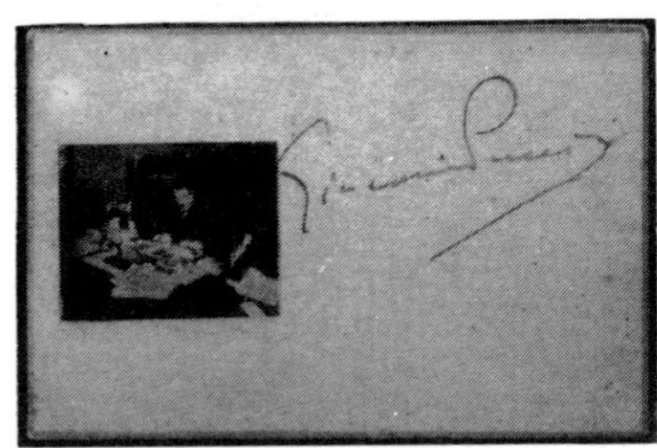

G. Puccini, signed card with photo, G.
£100-150 *VS*

Juan Peron, signed letter 16.2.1948, FR.
£80-120 *VS*

W. G. Grace, signed photo, VG. **£150-200** *VS*

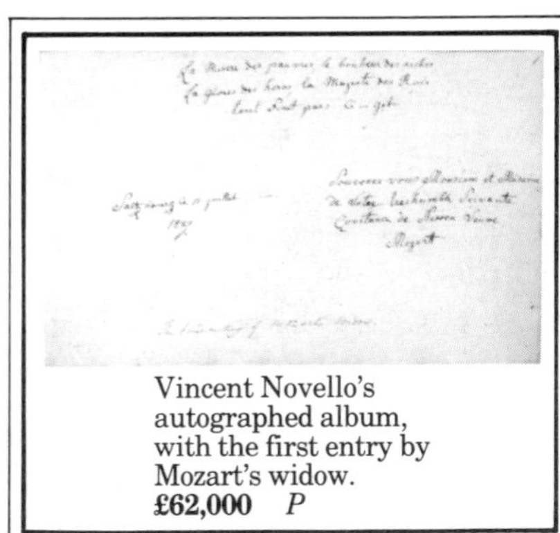

Vincent Novello's autographed album, with the first entry by Mozart's widow.
£62,000 *P*

Cross Reference
Colour section

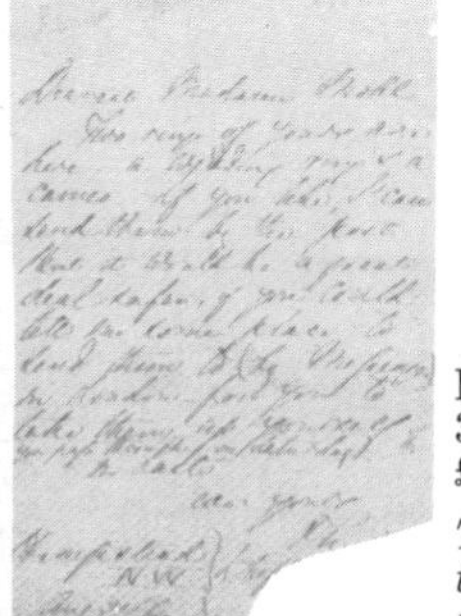

Florence Nightingale, 31st August 1864, P.
£30-40 *VS*

The value would be three times this if the signature was complete.

Arthur Sullivan, autographed musical note signed, dated 8th September 1869, VG.
£500-700 *VS*

Military

Dwight Eisenhower.
£50-80 *VS*

The mounting of signatures beneath photos like this is becoming popular amongst collectors and often falsely increase the price, i.e. without the photo this signature would only be worth £30-50.

Cross Reference
Militaria

Winston S. Churchill, signed piece, dated July 9th 1935, VG.
£200-300 *VS*

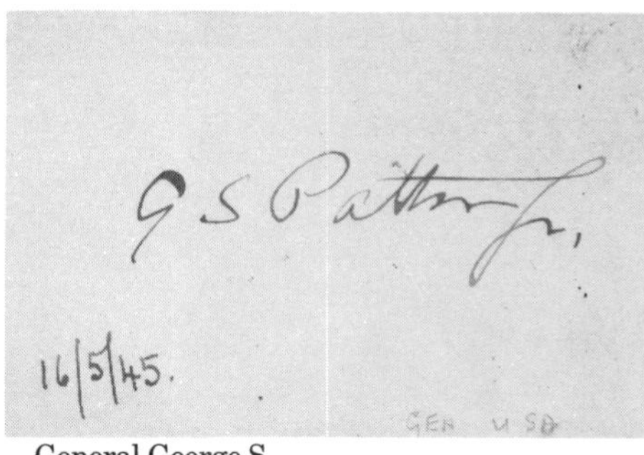

General George S. Patton, dated in another hand 16th May 1945, FR to G.
£250-350 *VS*

Colonel Gadaffi, signed colour picture, G. **£70-100** *VS*

Benito Mussolini, signed postcard, FR.
£250-350 *VS*

Erwin Rommel, signed postcard, FR.
£500-800 *VS*

Signed in indelible pencil. Rommel frequently did this as the desert winds evaporated ink.

Royalty

Queen Victoria's Diamond Jubilee, VG.
£80-120 *VS*

A 4-page letter signed by King George VI, to Viscount Gort, dated March 9th 1940, written at the height of the Finnish-Russian War. **£1,500-1,800** *VS*

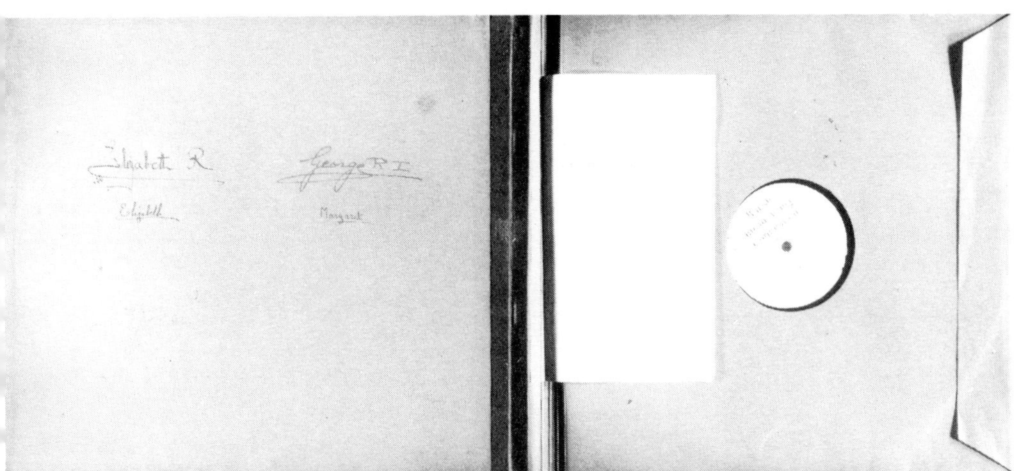

A set of 6 BBC records with various signatures of members of the Royal Family, in presentation album, G.
£500-600 *VS*

Very few issued.

Show Business

Elvis Presley, signed colour photograph, 1970s, EX.
£250-350 *VS*

Richard Burton, signed postcard, G.
£50-80 *VS*

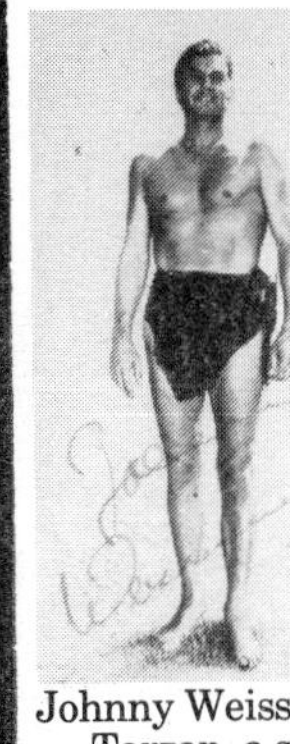

Johnny Weissmuller as Tarzan, a signed postcard, VG.
£60-100 *VS*

The Beatles, a signed newspaper photograph, FR.
£150-200 *VS*

Autographs by Chico Marx and Harpo Marx, G.
£50-80 each *VS*

A publicity photograph of Grace Kelly.
£80-120 *CSK*

Harry Houdini, signed postcard, FR.
£300-500 *VS*

Noël Coward, signed sepia photograph, 1941, FR **£40-60** *VS*

Kay Kendall, signed photograph, FR.
£80-100 *VS*

CRITICS' CIRCLE
FILM SECTION

Luncheon
to
Charles Chaplin Esq.

Empress Club, W.1 10-X-52

Charlie Chaplin, autographed menu.
£60-90 *CSK*

Errol Flynn, signed postcard, G.
£100-150 *VS*

Astaire and Rogers, signed colour postcard, VG.
£100-150 *VS*

Anna Pavlova, signed sepia postcard, G.
£150-200 *VS*

EX	Excellent
FR	Fair
G	Good
MT	Mint
P	Poor
VG	Very Good

Brigitte Bardot, signed photograph, VG.
£30-40 *VS*

Vivien Leigh, signed photographs.
l. 'Gone with the Wind', VG condition. **£300-350** *VS*
r. G condition **£100-150** *VS*

Children's Books

The Yellow Book, illustrated and produced by Aubrey Beardsley, 1890.
£25-35 *COB*

Little Wide-Awake, with illustrations, published by Routledge, 1890.
£25-75 *SAR*

Robinson Crusoe, illustrated by John Hassall.
£10-15 *RPM*

Friends of Field and Forest, 1930.
£15-20 *RPM*

Le Mair, by H. Willebeek, Le Mair written inside, 1913.
£35-40 *RPM*

The Story Wonder Book, published by Ward Lock & Co. **£12-15** *SAR*

A Popular School-Girl.
£6-8 *RPM*

Cross Reference
Toys
Disney

The Modern A.B.C., illustrated alphabet book, 1936.
£15-20
My A.B.C. Book, 1958.
£5-6 *COB*

A Song of The English, by Rudyard Kipling, c1914.
£15-18 *RPM*

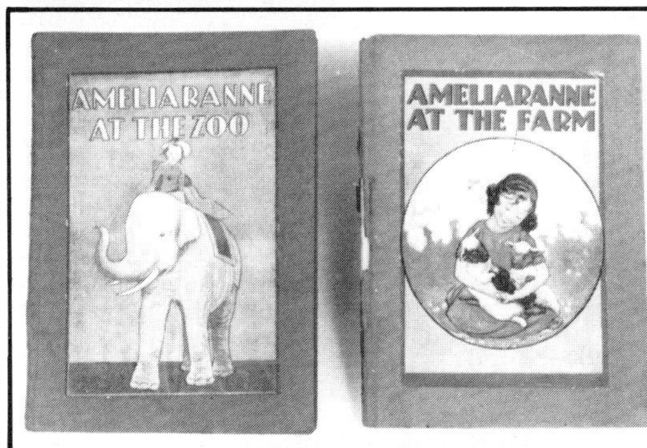

Ameliaranne books, 1936 and 1937. **£15-18 each** *RPM*

House at Pooh Corner, by A. A. Milne, First Edition published 1928.
£130-140 *RPM*

Alice's Adventures in Wonderland, by Lewis Carroll, published by Hodder & Stoughton.
£65-75 *SAR*

The All Story Wonder Book, published by Ward Lock & Co., 1929.
£30-35 *SAR*

The Modern Wonder Book For Boys, 1940.
£15-20 *SAR*

Boy's Own Annuals, 1932-37.
£28-30 each *RPM*

The Rose Book for Girls, well-known children's illustrations, c1915.
£10-12 *RPM*

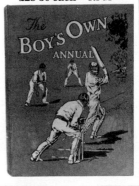

The Girl's Own Annual, c1889.
£28-30 *RPM*

The British Girl's Annual for 1920, published by Cassels.
£25-30 *SAR*

The Girl's Own Annual, 1927.
£22-25 *RPM*

Schoolboys' Bumper Book, published by Collins.
£8-10 *SAR*

Cigarette Cards

Although not as fashionable as in the past, cigarette card collecting has nevertheless a keen following with prices remaining steady. Condition is vital, even with otherwise rare cards and series, the value can be drastically affected by condition. Another factor to be taken into account is the fact that as cigarette cards are no longer produced, dealers have difficulty in replenishing their stocks.

The numbers detailed in the captions refer to the reference number in Albert's *The Guide to Cigarette Card Collecting*.

Actors & Actresses

J. Player, 1916, Players Past & Present, Ref. 216/25. **£9-18** *ACC*

J. Player, 1934, Film Stars, 1st series, Ref. 49/50.
£22-38 *ACC*

Cross Reference
Ephemera – Autographs

J. Player, 1925, Gilbert & Sullivan, 2nd series, Ref. 89/50.
£16-28 *ACC*

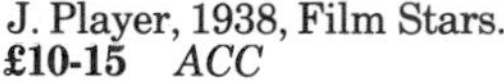

J. Player, 1938, Film Stars.
£10-15 *ACC*

J. Player, 1925, Gilbert & Sullivan, Ref. 190/50.
£20-40 *ACC*

Fauna

Grandee Cigars, 1980,
British Birds, Ref. 85/32.
£6-8 *ACC*

J. Player, 1931, Poultry,
Ref. 100/50.
£18-36 *ACC*

J. Player, 1929, Dogs
Heads, by Wardle, Ref.
PL139/50.
£20-40 *ACC*

J. Player, 1933, Aviary and Cage Birds,
Ref. 93/50. **£20-40** *ACC*

J. Player, 1932,
Butterflies,
Ref. 188/50.
£22-44 *ACC*

J. Player, 1935, Sea Fishes, Ref. 55/50.
£6-10 *ACC*

Military

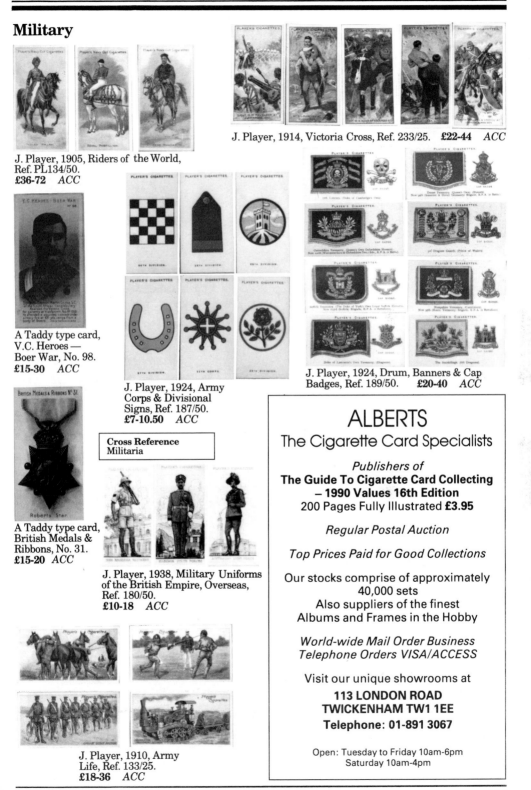

J. Player, 1905, Riders of the World, Ref. PL134/50.
£36-72 *ACC*

J. Player, 1914, Victoria Cross, Ref. 233/25. **£22-44** *ACC*

A Taddy type card, V.C. Heroes — Boer War, No. 98.
£15-30 *ACC*

J. Player, 1924, Army Corps & Divisional Signs, Ref. 187/50.
£7-10.50 *ACC*

J. Player, 1924, Drum, Banners & Cap Badges, Ref. 189/50. **£20-40** *ACC*

A Taddy type card, British Medals & Ribbons, No. 31.
£15-20 *ACC*

Cross Reference
Militaria

J. Player, 1938, Military Uniforms of the British Empire, Overseas, Ref. 180/50.
£10-18 *ACC*

J. Player, 1910, Army Life, Ref. 133/25.
£18-36 *ACC*

W. & F. Faulkner, Military Terms, 'Shoulder Arms', VG.
£14-28 *ACC*

J. Player, 1939, Uniforms of the T.A., Ref. 7/50. **£10-20** *ACC*

Royalty

J. Player, 1935, Kings & Queens of England, Ref. 182/50. **£18-36** *ACC*

J. Player, 1911, Ceremonial & Court Dress, Ref. 131/25.
£24-48 *ACC*

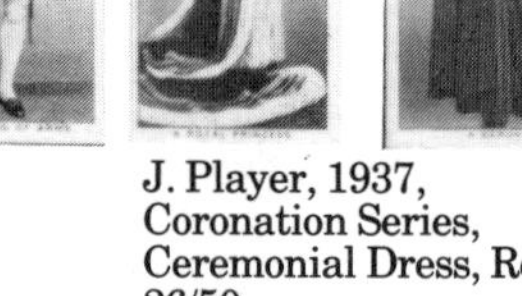

J. Player, 1937, Coronation Series, Ceremonial Dress, Ref. 26/50.
£7-10.50 *ACC*

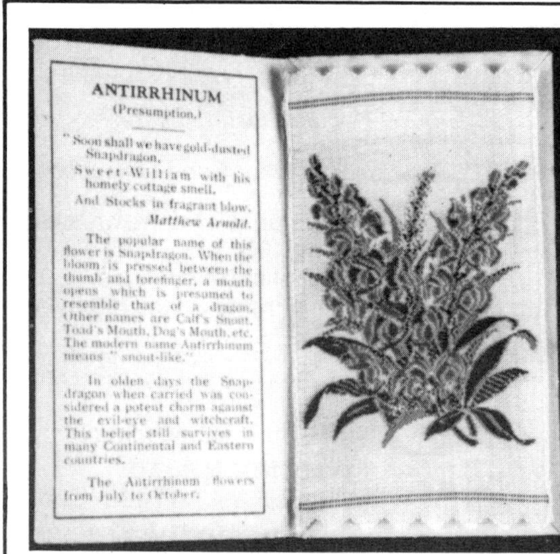

ANTIRRHINUM
(Presumption.)

"Soon shall we have gold-dusted Snapdragon,
Sweet-William with his homely cottage smell,
And Stocks in fragrant blow.
Matthew Arnold.

The popular name of this flower is Snapdragon. When the bloom is pressed between the thumb and forefinger, a mouth opens which is presumed to resemble that of a dragon. Other names are Calf's Snout, Toad's Mouth, Dog's Mouth, etc. The modern name Antirrhinum means "snout-like."

In olden days the Snapdragon when carried was considered a potent charm against the evil-eye and witchcraft. This belief still survives in many Continental and Eastern countries.

The Antirrhinum flowers from July to October.

Woven silks by Kensitas.
In cover **£3-4 each**
Without cover **No value** *ACC*

Sporting

J. Player, 1925, Racing Caricatures, Ref. 185/40.
£18-36 *ACC*

Cross Reference
Sport

J. Player, 1934, Hints on Association Football, Ref. 48/50.
£10-15 *ACC*

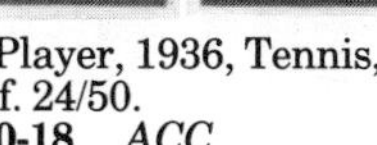

J. Player, 1936, Tennis, Ref. 24/50.
£10-18 *ACC*

J. Player, 1937, Speedway Riders, Ref. 23/50.
£22-38 *ACC*

Transport

J. Player, 1939, Modern Naval Craft, Ref. 178/50.
£7-12 *ACC*

An advertisement appeared in a British newspaper offering a high price for these sets. When brought to the attention of M.I.5 it was discovered that the prospective buyer was from German intelligence, who planned to issue them to their U-boat captains.

J. Player, 1937, Motor Cars, Ref. PL181/50.
£18-36 *ACC*

J. Player, 1936, International Air Liners, Ref. 59/50.
£8-14 *ACC*

J. Player, 1935, Civil Aeroplanes, Ref. 47/50.
£14-21 *ACC*

J. Player, 1938, Aircraft of the R.A.F., Ref. 4/50.
£12-18 *ACC*

J. Player, 1939, Cycling, Ref. 2/50.
£10-15 *ACC*

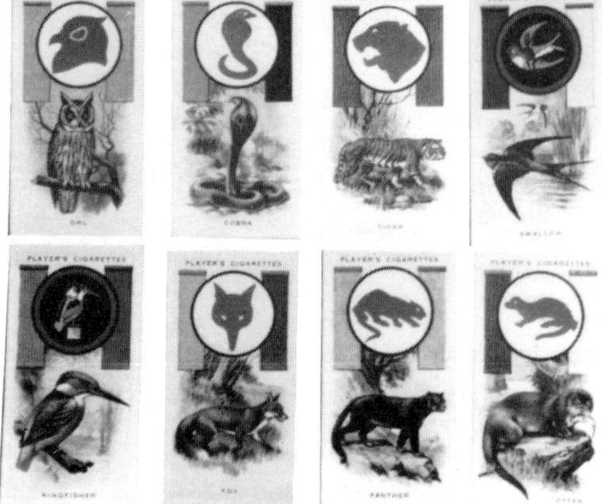

J. Player, 1933, Boy Scout & Girl Guide signs, Ref. 138/50.
£8-12 *ACC*

General

J. Player, 1911, Polar Exploration, Ref. 183/25.
£18-36 *ACC*

J. Player, 1923, Characters from Dickens, re-issued, Ref. 88/50.
£35-70 *ACC*

Doncella Country Houses and Castles, 1981, Ref. 80/32.
£4-5 *ACC*

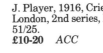

J. Player, 1916, Cries of London, 2nd series, Ref. 51/25.
£10-20 *ACC*

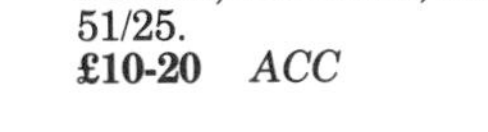

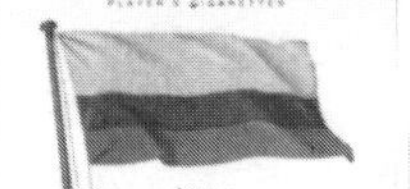

J. Player, 1928, Flags of the League of Nations, Ref. 92/50.
£8-12 *ACC*

FURTHER READING
McCulloch, Lou W., *Card Photographs, a Guide to their History and Value,* Millbank Books U.K.

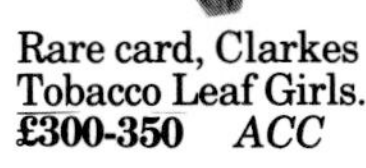

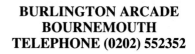

Rare card, Clarkes Tobacco Leaf Girls.
£300-350 *ACC*

Rare card, Faulkner, Police Terms, 'Police Court'.
£25-30 *ACC*

Comics

The American comic market has boomed in the U.K. over the last 3 years. It is a very fashion-based industry with characters becoming popular overnight, e.g. the prices for Batman comics have recently trebled.

Reprints of newspaper strips, such as Flash Gordon, were the first American comics. Superman, in 1938, was the start of the popular comic and these are, in fact, now being reprinted.

Distribution of American comics in the U.K. started in December 1959 but prior to that, they were brought over by American servicemen and even used as packing material!

They were rare before 1945 because of the paper shortage during the war.

Very few comics from the 1970s are collected, but those from the 1960s and before are always in demand.

Pristine condition is essential as far as value is concerned.

Fantastic Four, January 1988. **40-60p** *GCo*

Logan's Run, 1976. **30-50p** *GCo*

Cat Woman, April 1989. **£1-1.50** *GCo*

Tarzan, July 1984. **40-60p** *GCo*

Strange Adventures, No. 153, June 1963. **£2-3** *GCo*

Fantastic Four, April 1967. **£2-3** *GCo*

World's Finest, No. 115, February 1961. No. 119, August 1961. **£10-12 each** *GCo*

Captain America, No. 204, December 1976. **30-50p** *GCo*

The Flash, No. 219, January 1973. **£3-4** *GCo*

The Incredible Hulk, Series 178, August 1974. **£1-1.50** *GCo*

DID YOU KNOW?
Miller's Collectables Price Guide is designed to build up, year by year, into the most comprehensive reference system available.

Action Comics, No. 283, December 1961.
£12-14 *GCo*

The No. 1 issue in mint condition is thought to be worth over £17,000.

The Punisher, November 1987.
£1-1.50 *GCo*

The 'Nam, No. 36.
£1-1.50 *GCo*

The first issue coincided with the 5th anniversary of the start of the Vietnam war.

007, A James Bond comic, 1989.
£2-3 *GCo*

Batman, January 1989.
£2-3 *GCo*

Justice League, December 1987.
60p-£1 *GCo*

Groo the Wanderer, December 1987.
70p-£1 *GCo*

Batman, December 1988.
£6-8 *GCo*

Cut-Out Postcards

Greek and Italian Soldiers costume, Italian edition, G.
£20-30 *VS*

Jolly Jumbo, published by Pearson, 1921, G.
£45-60 *VS*

Toy Town, published by Mack, Pussy in Peace and War, G. **£20-30** *VS*

A Victorian découpage vase. **£125-150** *PAR*

This vase illustrates one of the uses for cut-out 'scraps', turning a plain vase into a wonderful 'collectable'.

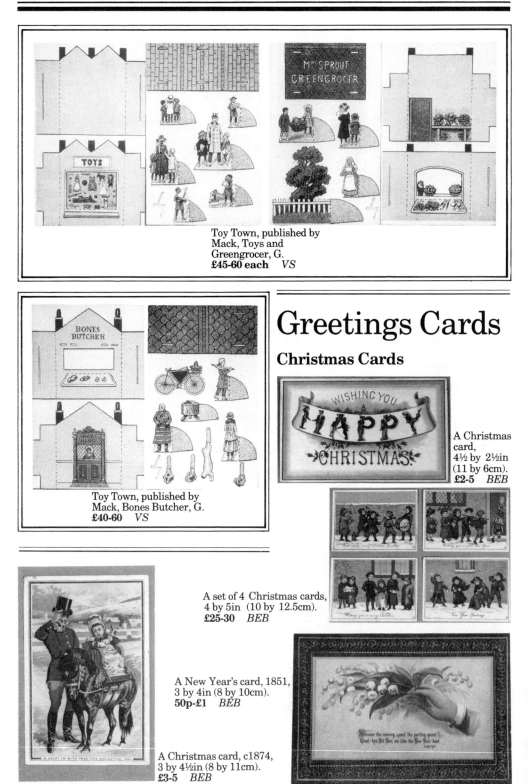

Toy Town, published by Mack, Toys and Greengrocer, G.
£45-60 each *VS*

Toy Town, published by Mack, Bones Butcher, G.
£40-60 *VS*

Greetings Cards

Christmas Cards

A Christmas card, 4½ by 2½in (11 by 6cm).
£2-5 *BEB*

A set of 4 Christmas cards, 4 by 5in (10 by 12.5cm).
£25-30 *BEB*

A New Year's card, 1851, 3 by 4in (8 by 10cm).
50p-£1 *BEB*

A Christmas card, c1874, 3 by 4½in (8 by 11cm).
£3-5 *BEB*

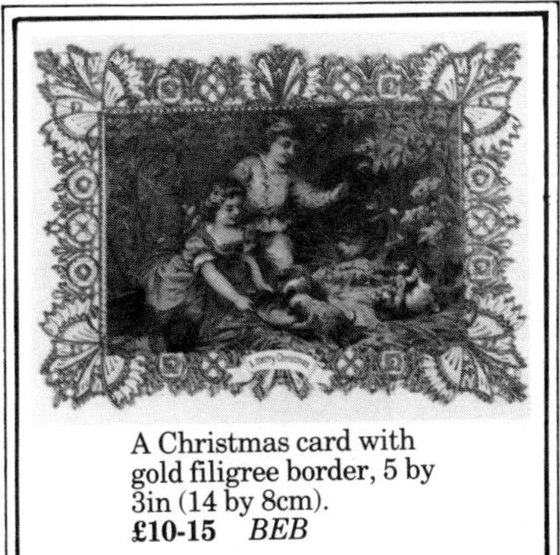

A Christmas card with gold filigree border, 5 by 3in (14 by 8cm).
£10-15 *BEB*

A Christmas card, 1879, 4 by 3in (10 by 7cm).
£2-5 *BEB*

A Christmas card.
£10-15 *BEB*

Valentines

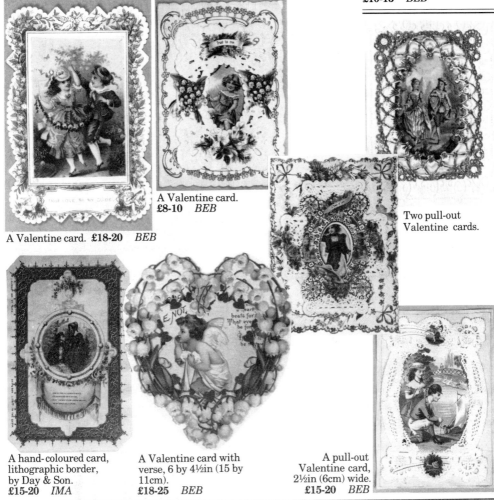

A Valentine card. **£18-20** *BEB*

A Valentine card.
£8-10 *BEB*

Two pull-out Valentine cards.

A hand-coloured card, lithographic border, by Day & Son.
£15-20 *IMA*

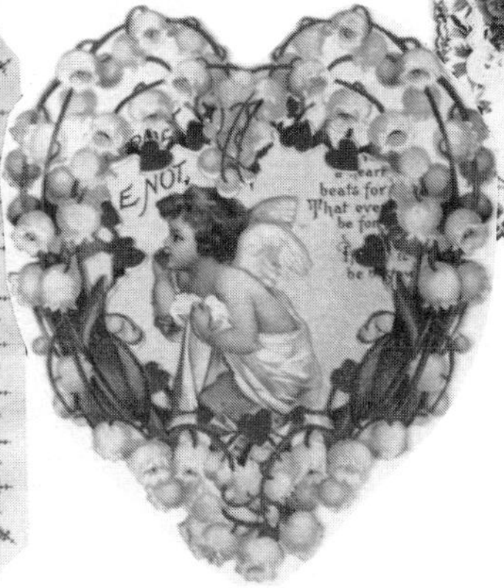

A Valentine card with verse, 6 by 4½in (15 by 11cm).
£18-25 *BEB*

A pull-out Valentine card, 2½in (6cm) wide.
£15-20 *BEB*

A selection of Valentine cards.
£5-10 each *BEB*

DID YOU KNOW?
For home made Valentines, 'Cupid's Annual Charter' and the 'Ladies Polite Valentine Writer' (6d) supplied stanzas for every sentiment.

A selection of Valentine cards.
£6-12 each *BEB*

Birthday Cards

Two birthday cards.
£4-10 each
BEB

General

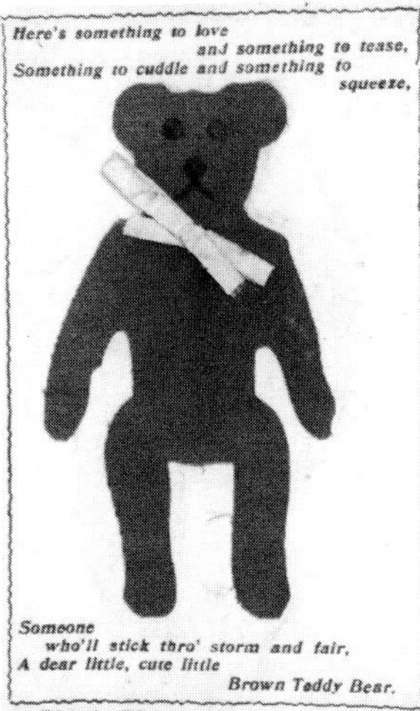

Here's something to love
and something to tease,
Something to cuddle and something to
squeeze,
Someone
who'll stick thro' storm and fair,
A dear little, cute little
Brown Teddy Bear.
H.B. London, W.C.
Fully Protected.

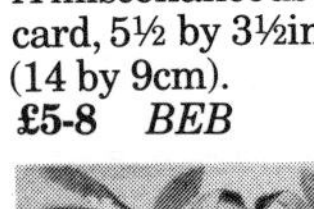
A miscellaneous card, 5½ by 3½in (14 by 9cm).
£5-8 *BEB*

78 Tarot cards, VG.
£30-35 *VS*

MAKE THE MOST OF MILLERS
Condition is absolutely vital when assessing the value of any item. Damaged pieces appreciate much less than perfect examples. However, a rare, desirable piece may command a high price even when damaged.

A novelty Kaleidoscope card, pub. by E.A.S., G.
£55-60 *VS*

Kaleidoscope clock card.
£30-35 *VS*

A mechanical card, day, date and month, G.
£16-20 *VS*

A mechanical card, moving day, date and month, VG.
£20-25 *VS*

Prints by Longmans, Green & Co., Gollywog at War, c1899. Refer Colour Section *BEB*

Advertising Postcards

These copies of popular advertisements and posters continue to be a very popular field, both for collectors of postcards and ephemera.

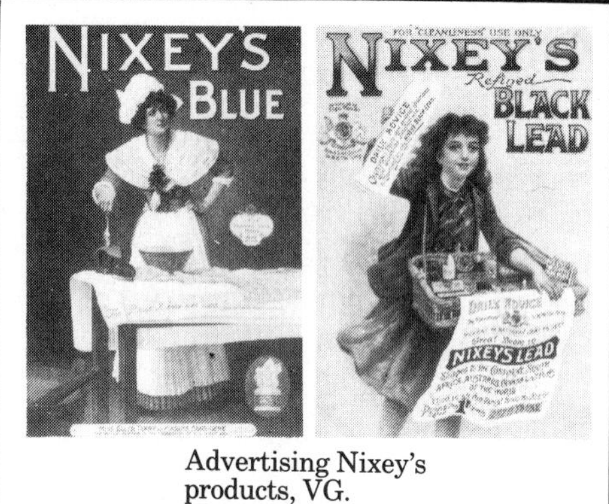

Advertising Nixey's products, VG.
£20-30 each *VS*

Raphael Tuck

Poster advertising Milkmaid Milk, G.
£30-40 *VS*

Advertising poster, Barker & Dobson's Walnut Toffee, VG.
£30-40 *VS*

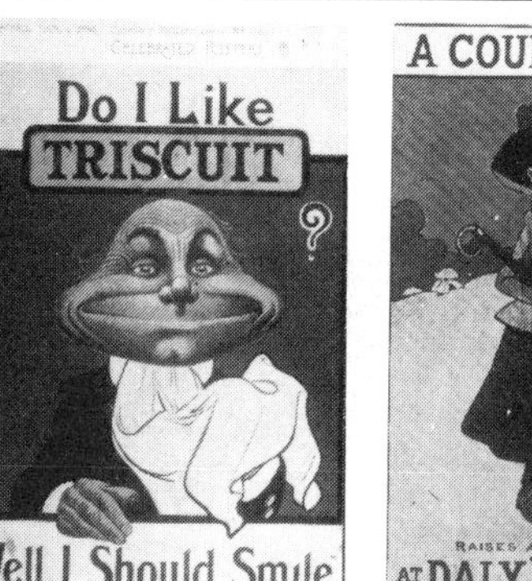

Poster for Triscuit, by Weiner, VG.
£30-40 *VS*

Advertising A Country Girl, at Daly's Theatre, VG.
£30-40 *VS*

Advertising Pear's Soap, G to VG.
£18-25 *VS*

Advert for Cachou Lajaunie, VG.
£30-50 *VS*

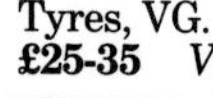

Advert for Palmer's Tyres, VG.
£25-35 *VS*

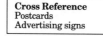

Cross Reference
Postcards
Advertising signs

Poster for Fry's Cocoa, VG.
£20-30 *VS*

Babbitt's Baby Soap card, 4½ by 3in (11 by 8cm).
£5-10 *BEB*

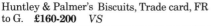

Huntley & Palmer's Biscuits, Trade card, FR to G. **£160-200** *VS*

Celebrated advertising posters, VG. **£40-60 each** *VS*

Beatrice Mallet, advert for Lion Noir boot polish, G. **£20-30** *VS*

Composite advert for GP Government Tea, VG. **£60-90** *VS*

Advert for Mazawattee Cocoa, G. **£30-50** *VS*

Posters

War Time

Feed the Guns with War Bonds.
£70-90 *ONS*

Buy War Bonds.
£100-150 *ONS*

Cross Reference
Railway posters
Shipping posters
Advertising postcards

Pick 'Em Up, by A. J. Owen, 20 by 15in (51 by 38cm).
£30-40 *ONS*

Save the Nation's Bread.
£70-100 *ONS*

Public Warning, 34½ by 22½in (87 by 57cm), 1915.
£300-400 *ONS*

Lend Your Five Shillings to your Country, D. D. Fries.
£20-30 *ONS*

Help to Buy an Aeroplane.
£100-150 *ONS*

Take It to the Salvage Dump, by C. L. Davidson, 20 by 15in (51 by 38cm).
£50-70 *ONS*

Serbia's Flag Day, published by Johnson Riddle, on linen.
£55-65 *ONS*

Belgian Red Cross, by Charles Buchel.
£30-50 *ONS*

Recruiting

Poles! Under the Polish Flag on to the Fight, on linen, 38 by 22in (97 by 56cm).
£40-60 *ONS*

Will you make a Fourth?
£100-120 *ONS*

Come Lad Slip Across and Help.
£60-80 *ONS*

When are the other boys Coming?
£80-100 *ONS*

Travel All Over the World.
£250-300 *ONS*

Fill Up the Ranks! No. 85c.
£70-80 *ONS*

Lend a Hand Boys, 29 by 13in (74 by 33cm).
£50-100 *ONS*

Join the Royal Engineers.
£85-100 *ONS*

The Navy Wants Men, stock poster, published by The Admiralty Recruiting Department.
£150-200 *ONS*

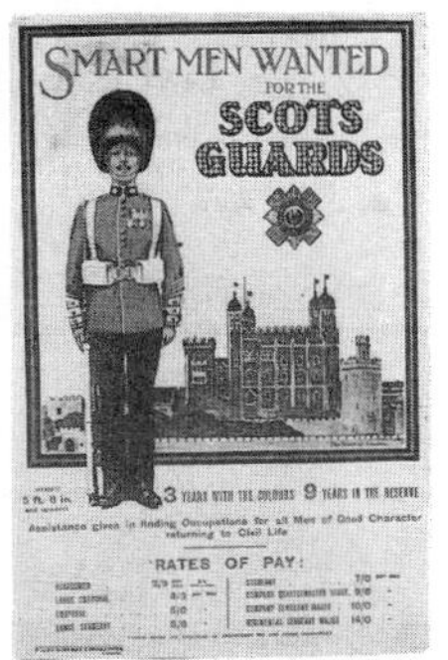

Smart men wanted. **£200-300 each** *ONS*

Film Posters & Ephemera

A polychrome film poster, Marilyn Monroe, 30 by 40in (76 by 101.5cm).
£180-300 *CSK*

A German polychrome film poster, James Dean, 33 by 23in (84 by 58cm).
£70-100 *CSK*

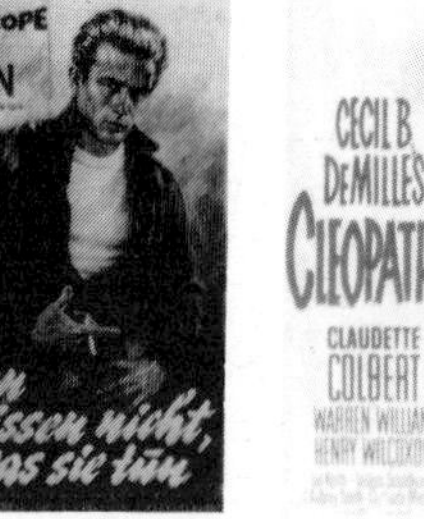

Twenty-three front of house stills, printed in U.S.A., 1950s, 7 framed and glazed.
£50-80 *CSK*

Eight American polychrome film posters, c1960.
£80-100 *CSK*

Law and Order and Tropic Zone, Ronald Reagan, Universal Productions and Paramount Pictures, 30 by 40in (76 by 101cm).
£300-700 *CSK*

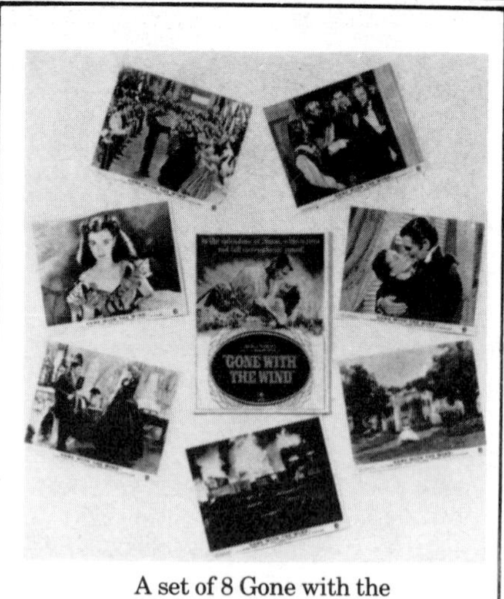

Wizard of Oz, individual signed pieces of Judy Garland, Ray Bolger, Jack Haley and Bert Lahr, 24 by 17in (61 by 43cm), framed and glazed.
£300-400 *VS*

Cross Reference
Autographs
Rock and Pop

A painted sign applied with cardboard cut-out letters, W. C. Fields, 30 by 40in (76 by 101cm).
£70-100 *CSK*

The Inn of the Sixth Happiness, 30 by 40in (76 by 101cm).
£40-60 *CSK*

A set of 8 Gone with the Wind front of house stills.
£50-100 *CSK*

Scripophily

City of Vienna 4% Loan, 200 crowns.
£15-20 *GKR*

Brazil Railway Co., Cap. $40m, 1910. **£20-25** *GKR*

Societe Generale des Cinematographes Eclipse, Bearer Share, 1906.
£35-45 *GKR*

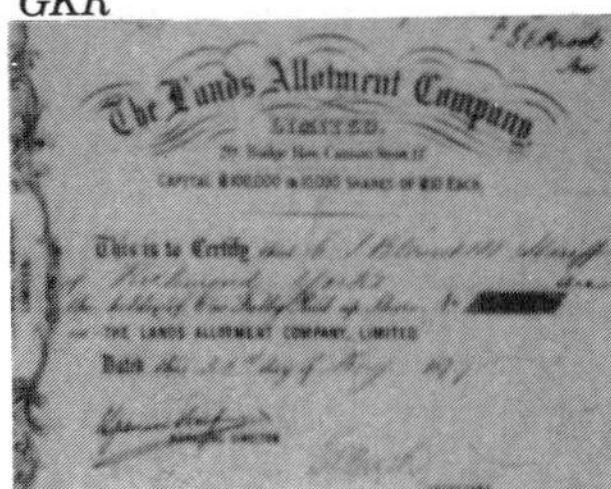

The Lands Allotment Co. Ltd., signed by Jabez Spencer Balfour, 1877.
£30-35 *GKR*

State of Louisiana, $500 Bond, 1892.
£20-25 *GKR*

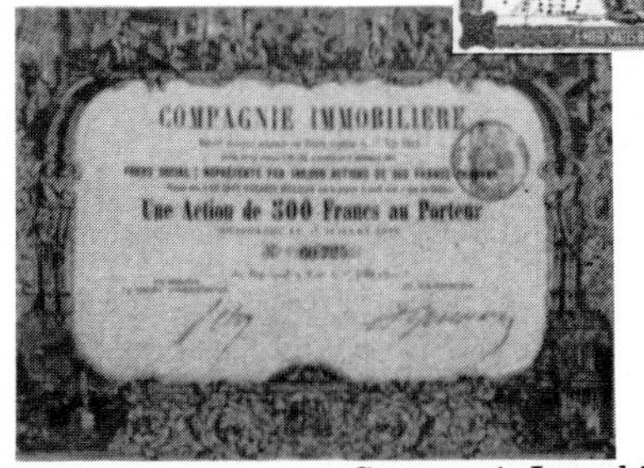

Compagnie Immobiliere, 500 Francs, 1863.
£15-20 *GKR*

City of Craiova, 5% Loan, 1930.
£15-20
GKR

Confederate States of America, 7% Cotton Loan, Bond for £100 Sterling or 2,500 Francs, or 4,000 lbs cotton, 1863.
£175-200 *GKR*

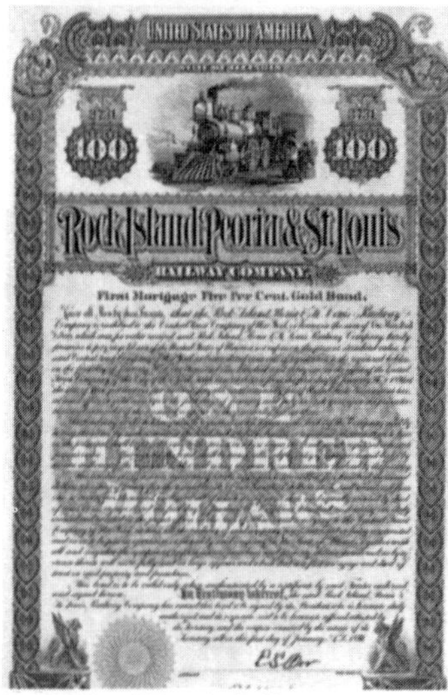

Rock Island Peoria & St. Louis Railway Co, 1st Mortgage 5% Gold Bond, 1891.
£40-50 *GKR*

Burlington & Missouri River, Nebraska, 1878.
£40-50 *GKR*

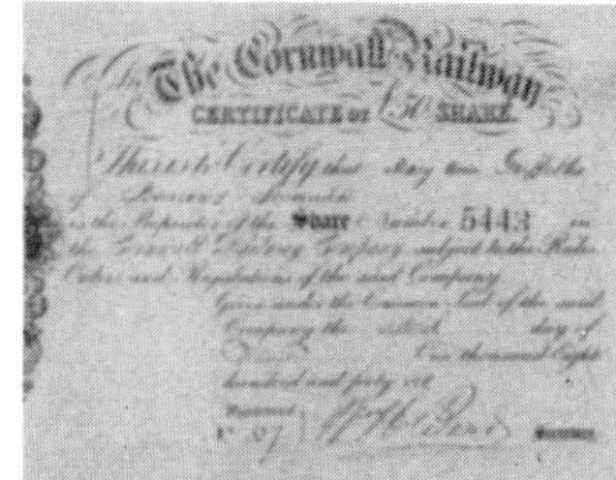

Cornwall Railway, £50 share, 1846. **£75-85** *GKR*

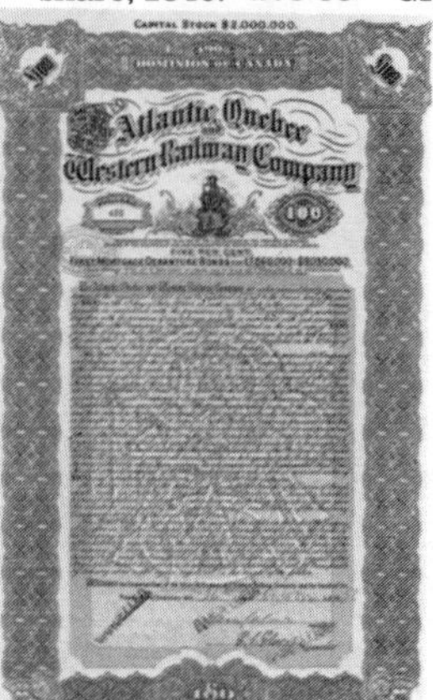

Atlantic Quebec & Western Railway Co, £100 Bond, 1906-10.
£20-25 *GKR*

City of St. Petersburg, 4½% Loan, 1901. **£15-20** *GKR*

City of Moscow, 5%, 1908.
£15-20 *GKR*

Chicago & Alton Railroad Co., $1,000 Bond, 1899.
£20-25 *GKR*

Last railroad robbed by Jesse James.

Imobiliara Soc. & Anon. Romana, Founders Share, 1906.
£25-35 *GKR*

New York, Ontario & Western Railway Co., 1930s.
£10-12 *GKR*

General Ephemera

Calendars

Unsigned calendar featuring the famous nude Golden Dreams photo of Marilyn Monroe, 1954, G.
£100-150 *VS*

Job, 1903 series, calendrier 1902, tobacco advert postcard, by Gervais, G.
£18-25 *VS*

Esquire Girl calendar, 1947.
£45-50 *COB*

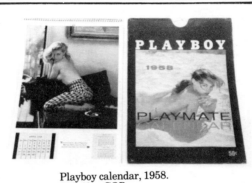

Playboy calendar, 1958.
£20-40 *COB*

A 3-section map of the River Thames, published by G. W. Bacon & Co, c1888, G to VG.
£200-300 *VS*

Maps

A ski map on linen, 1936.
£10-15 *COB*

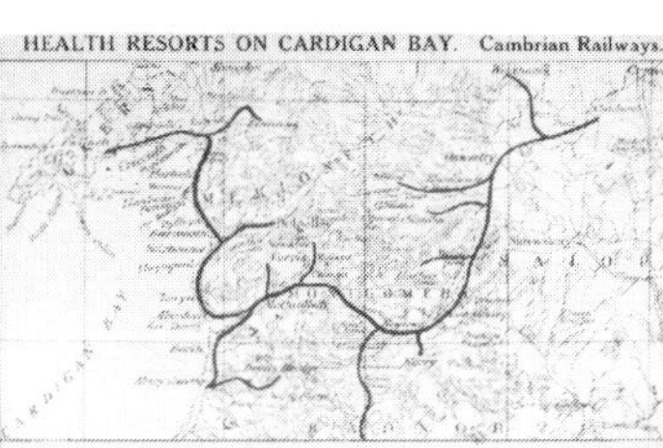

Cambrian Railway postcard, Health Resorts on Cardigan Bay, VG.
£30-40 *VS*

Ventnor, Isle of Wight Guide, 1949.
RAC linen road map of France, for Cyclists, c1930.
£15-30 each *WHA*

A map of London, c1935.
£15-30 *WHA*

Programmes

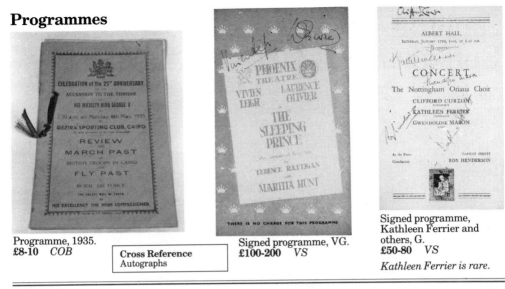

Programme, 1935.
£8-10 *COB*

Signed programme, VG.
£100-200 *VS*

Cross Reference
Autographs

Signed programme, Kathleen Ferrier and others, G.
£50-80 *VS*

Kathleen Ferrier is rare.

Magazines

Esquire, 361 issues.
£3,000+ *ONS*

London Mail, 390 issues.
£130-140 *ONS*

Cheerio.
£5-6 *ONS*

Greyfriars Herald, 30 issues.
£75-80 *ONS*

Razzle, 161 issues.
£40-45 *ONS*

Men Only, 372 issues.
£75-80 *ONS*

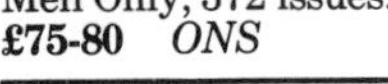

Miscellaneous

In Memoriam Print, Capt. Scott, 1913.
£25-35 *COB*

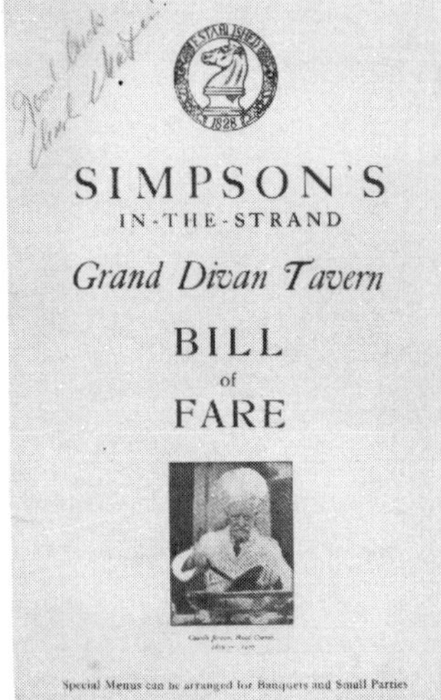

Charles Chaplin, signed menu, FR to G.
£60-90 *VS*

Fans

A black lace fan, with ebony sticks, c1885.
£20-40 *FF*

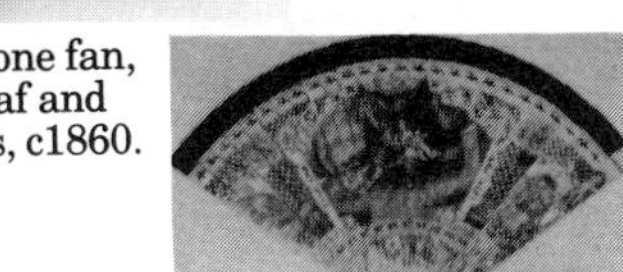

A Victorian abalone fan, with black net leaf and inset shell panels, c1860.
£100-150 *FF*

An ivory brisé fan, painted with Mercury and Venus, restored, early 18thC, 8in (20.5cm).
£450-500 *CSK*

A Victorian painted gauze fan, with gilded ebony sticks, c1860.
£40-60 *FF*

A Spanish painted paper leaf fan, with pierced mother-of-pearl sticks, c1870.
£100-150 *FF*

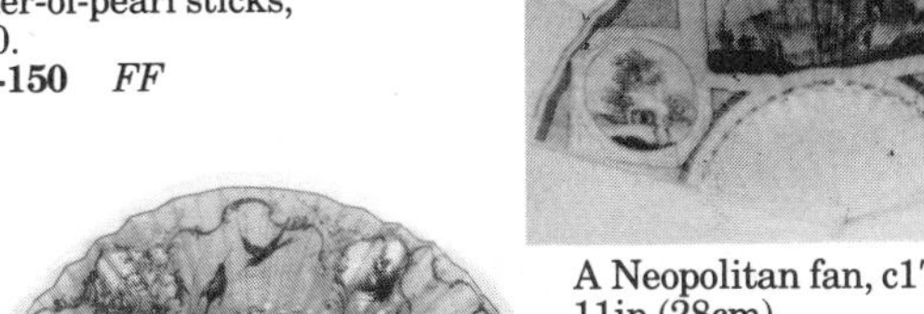

A Neopolitan fan, c1770, 11in (28cm).
£2,500-3,000 *CSK*

Two Victorian gauze leaf fans, with cedar wood sticks, signed Houghton, c1875.
£150-250 each *FF*

A Victorian painted silk leaf fan, with ivory sticks.
£80-100 *FF*

MAKE THE MOST OF MILLERS
Condition is absolutely vital when assessing the value of any item. Damaged pieces appreciate much less than perfect examples. However, a rare, desirable piece may command a high price even when damaged.

An Edwardian painted silk leaf fan, with wooden sticks, c1910.
£30-40 *FF*

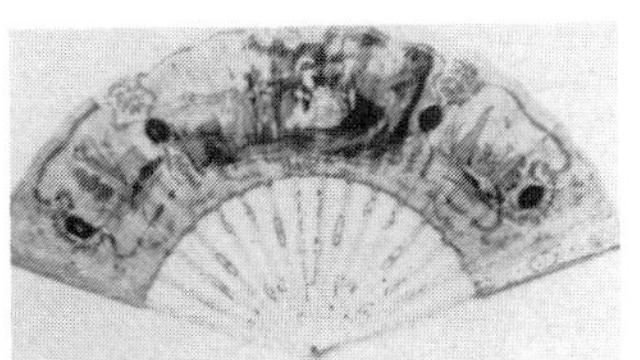

A fan, the silk leaf painted with 2 couples in a park, embroidered with sequins, the ivory sticks pierced and silvered, c1775, 11in (28cm).
£600-700 *CSK*

An ivory brisé fan, with shibayama decoration, silver ribbon loop and ivory Ojimi, c1860.
£1,200-1,500 *FF*

A French fan, with painted silk leaf and mother-of-pearl sticks, c1880.
£100-150 *FF*

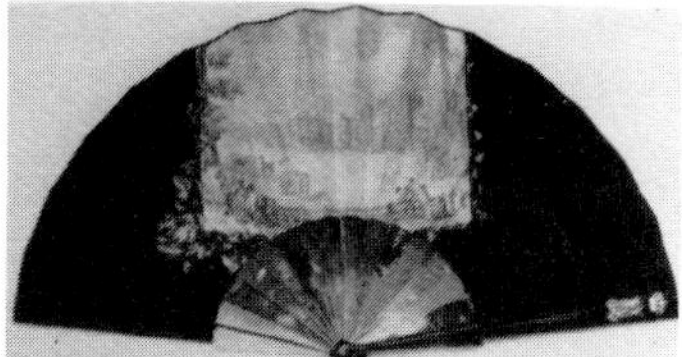

A black silk leaf fan, with tortoiseshell sticks, one guardstick set with monogram MR, crowned, early 20thC, 12in (30.5cm).
£500-600 *CSK*

This fan is believed to have belonged to H.M. Queen Mary.

A French Directoire period fan, with gauze leaf and horn sticks.
£80-100 *FF*

A fan, the leaf painted with the Family of Darius before Alexander, c1710, 11in (28cm).
£1,750-2,000 *CSK*

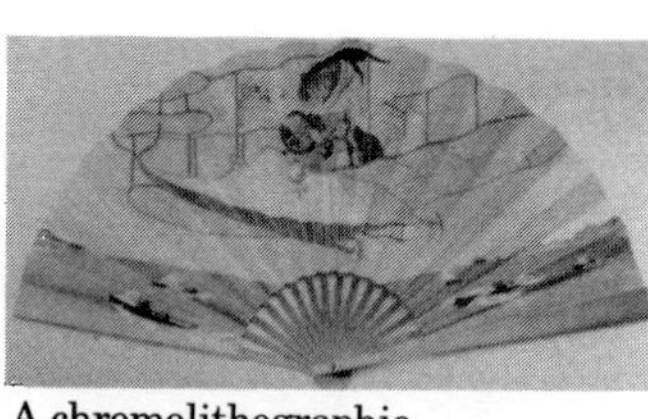

A chromolithographic fan, Parfum Pompeia, with wooden sticks, c1918, 9in (23cm).
£350-450 *CSK*

A French painted paper leaf fan, with pierced ivory sticks, c1760.
£200-300 *FF*

A European fan with applied embroidery on a net leaf, mother-of-pearl sticks, painted centre, c1860.
£150-200 *FF*

A painted silk leaf fan, with black and gold lacquered sticks, c1910, in glazed case.
£300-500 *CSK*

A Chinese silver filigree and enamel fan, c1840.
£200-300 *FF*

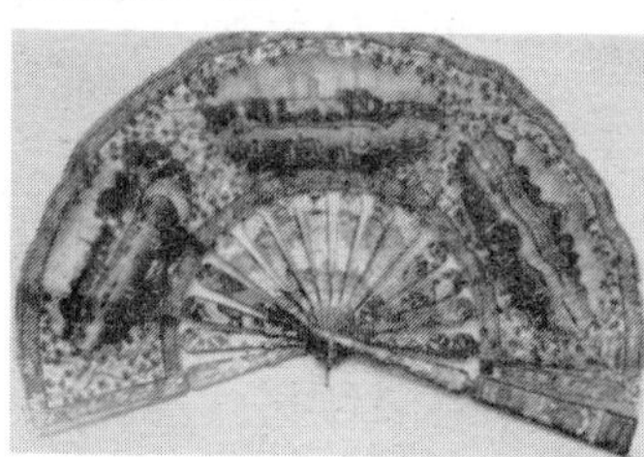

A Cantonese fan, with painted leaf and lacquer sticks, damage and repairs, c1860, in fitted box.
£1,500-1,800 *CSK*

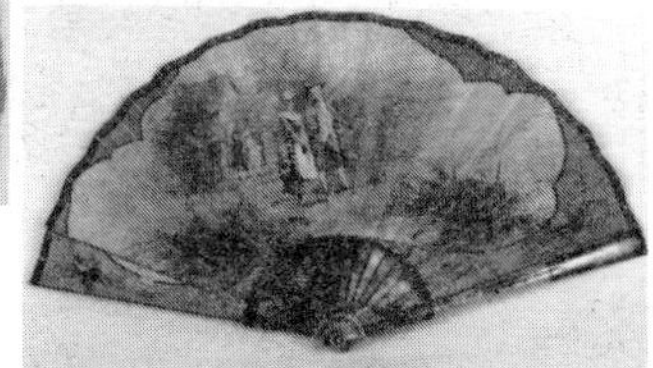

A painted paper leaf fan, with painted ivory sticks, c1740.
£300-400 *FF*

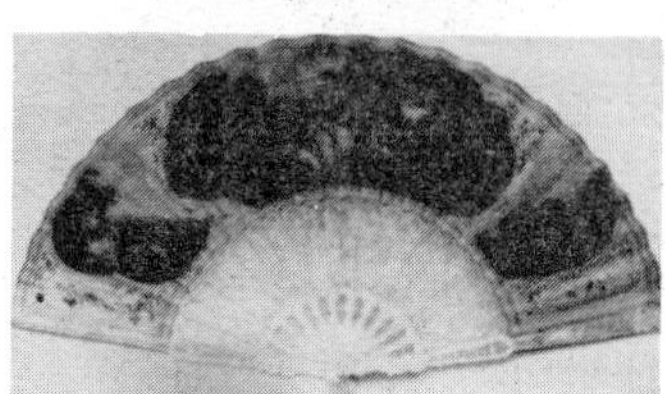

A fan, c1770, damage and repairs, 10in (25.5cm).
£500-600 *CSK*

A painted paper leaf fan, with pierced mother-of-pearl sticks, c1755.
£200-300 *FF*

Silk was not used until about the 1820s.

A Spanish painted paper leaf fan, with gilded mother-of-pearl, c1870.
£150-250 *FF*

An ivory brisé fan, the guardsticks applied with photographs of Czar Alexander III and his wife, c1881, 9in (23cm).
£700-750 *CSK*

An Italian fan, the leaf painted with Cleopatra, c1730, 11in (28cm).
£275-300 *CSK*

A fan, with ivory sticks, c1740, 10in (25.5cm).
£300-400 *CSK*

An ivory brisé fan, carved with the Return of a Hero, the guardsticks with a gold overlay, c1805, 5in (12.5cm).
£450-500 *CSK*

A Cantonese handscreen, with ivory handle, c1830, 15½in (39cm), in silk covered box.
£600-650 *C*

An ivory brisé fan, c1820, 7in (18cm).
£250-300 *CSK*

A painted fan, damage and repaired, c1750, 11in (28cm).
£300-350 *CSK*

A fan, possibly German, c1760, 11in (28cm).
£300-350 *CSK*

An English fan, slight repair, c1750, 11in (28cm).
£500-550 *CSK*

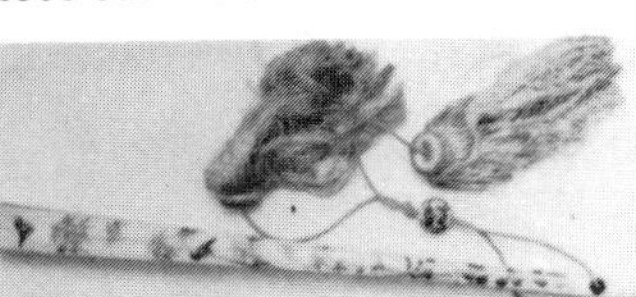

A Japanese fan, with hand-coloured woodcut snow scene leaf, some damage, late 19thC, 12in (30.5cm).
£150-200 *CSK*

A fan, the chicken skin leaf painted with an 18thC pastiche, embroidered with sequins, the mother-of-pearl sticks gilt, c1890, in glazed case.
£300-350 *CSK*

An Arts and Crafts fan, marked, c1890, in embroidered box.
£1,000-1,200 *CSK*

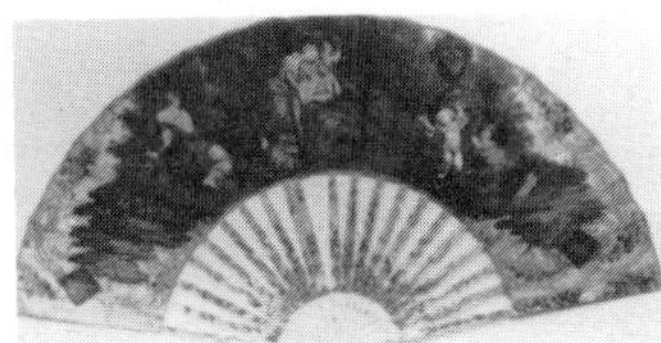

A fan, c1770, 10in (25.5cm).
£350-400 *CSK*

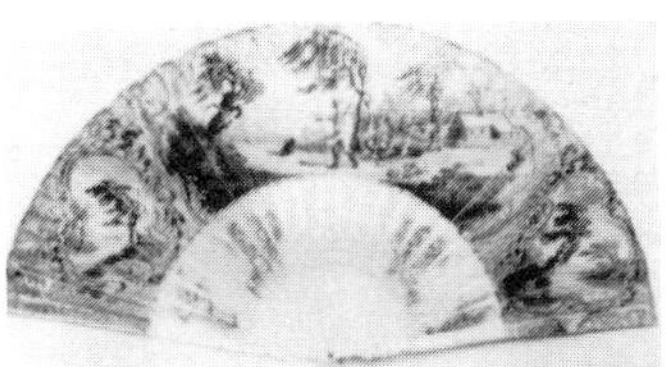

A fan, the ivory sticks carved with sheep and baskets of flowers and painted with musical instruments, c1750, 11in (28cm).
£700-800 *CSK*

A chromolithographic fan, commemorating the Chicago World Fair of 1893, the wooden sticks painted gold, worn and torn, 13½in (33cm).
£250-300 *CSK*

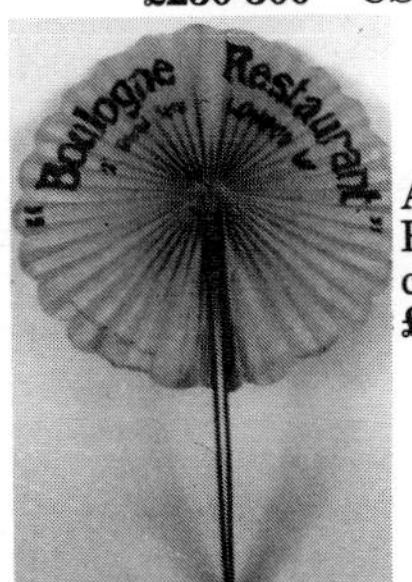

An advertising fan, Boulogne Restaurant, c1930.
£10-20 *FF*

A Canton tortoiseshell brisé fan, c1820, 7½in (19cm).
£650-700 *CSK*

An advertising fan, Reception of the American Fleet at Amoy by the Chinese Government, with menu, October 30th 1908.
£25-30 *FF*

A painted fan, c1730, 9½in (24cm).
£500-550 *CSK*

A fan, the leaf of Brussels point de Gaze, the mother-of-pearl sticks carved and pierced with classical urns, c1870, 11in (28cm), in satin box by E. Faucon.
£650-750 *CSK*

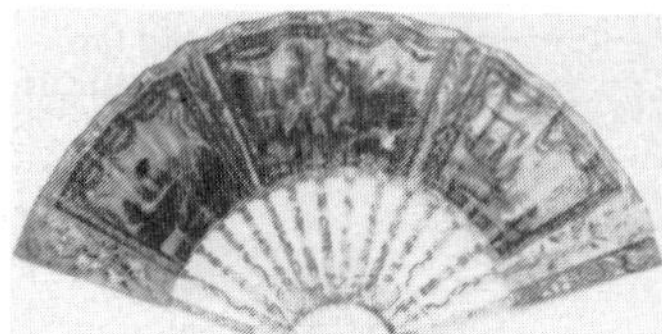

A French fan, worn, c1770, 10½in (26cm).
£300-350 *CSK*

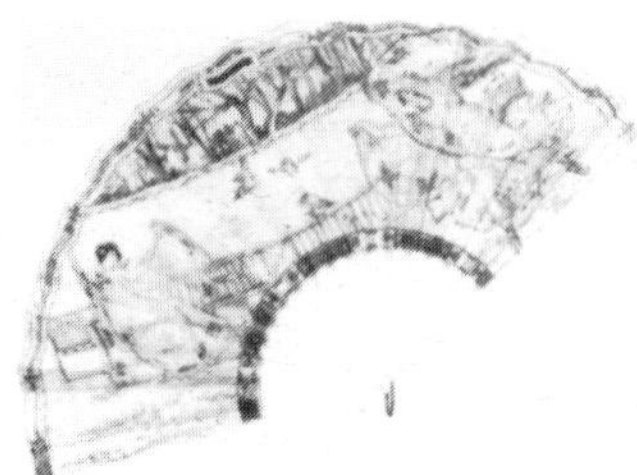

A painted fan, signed A. Klinger, with mother-of-pearl sticks, 1895, 14in (35.5cm).
£400-450 *CSK*

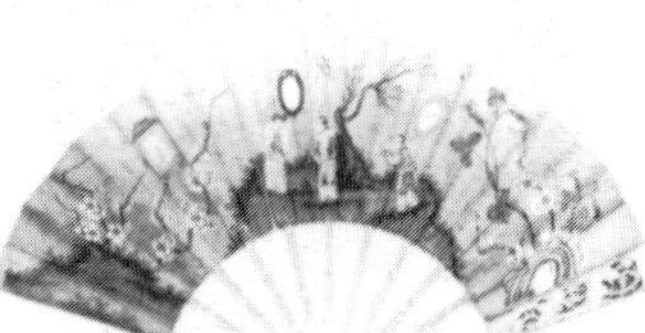

A fan, c1750, 11½in (29cm).
£1,000-1,200 *CSK*

A fan, painted with classical figures, the leaf mid-19thC, the sticks c1770, 10in (25.5cm).
£350-400 *CSK*

An unmounted fan leaf, painted with a Queen and a hero, c1730, 19in (48cm), mounted and glazed with passepartout.
£400-450 *CSK*

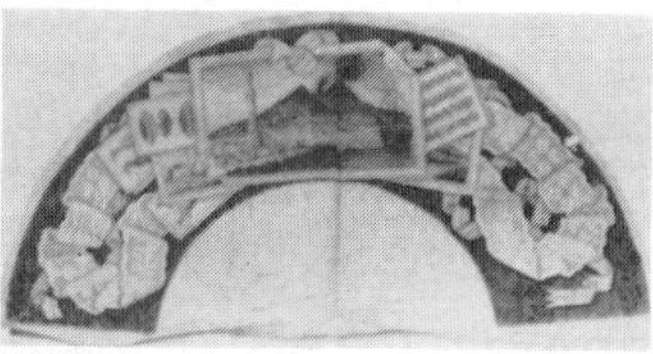

An Italian unmounted fan leaf on kid, damaged, c1770, 20in (51cm) wide.
£2,000-2,500 *CSK*

A Margate fan, published by Lewis Wells, leaf slightly torn, 1789, 10in (25.5cm).
£175-200 *CSK*

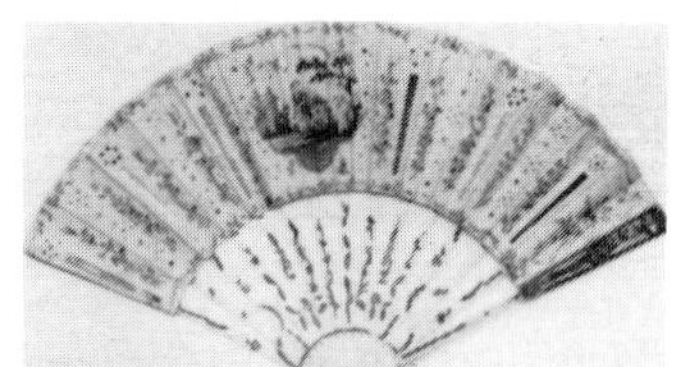

A painted fan, lacks pin, c1770, 10½in (27cm).
£120-140 *CSK*

A brisé fan, the upper half of ivory, the lower half and guardsticks of horn, c1790, 10in (25.5cm), in box.
£500-550 *C*

An autographed brisé wood fan, c1900.
£60-100 *FF*

A painted fan, damage and repaired, the leaf c1740, later sticks, in contemporary box.
£400-450 *CSK*

A pierced horn brisé double image fan, c1820, 6in (15cm).
£250-300 *CSK*

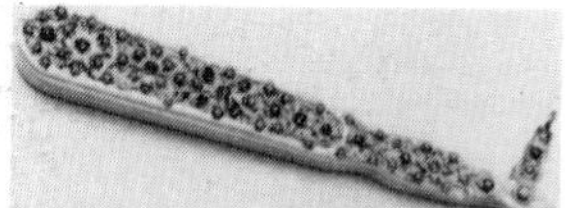

A ivory brisé fan, the guardsticks set with gilt filigree plaques, enamelled and set with garnets, turquoise and simulated pearls, c1870, 8in (20.5cm).
£900-1,000 *CSK*

A chromolithographic fan, inscribed Duvelleroy, Paris, c1910, 8in (20.5cm).
£800-1,000 *CSK*

A coloured lithographic advertising fan, published by La Cie. Fse. des Papiers Monnaie, 56 rue de la Victoire, Paris, c1890, 9½in (24cm).
£300-350 *CSK*

A painted fan, with mother-of-pearl sticks, repairs, c1750, 11½in (29cm), in contemporary box with 19thC Duvelleroy label.
£200-250 *CSK*

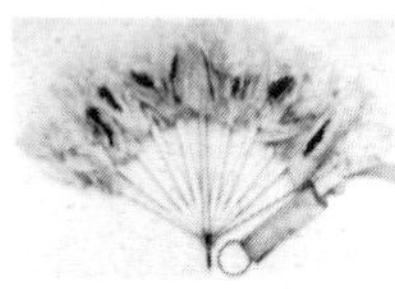

A novelty fan, closing in a circular manner to form a bunch of white silk poppies with green centres, stamped Bte S.G.D.G., c1897, 7½in (19cm).
£350-400 *CSK*

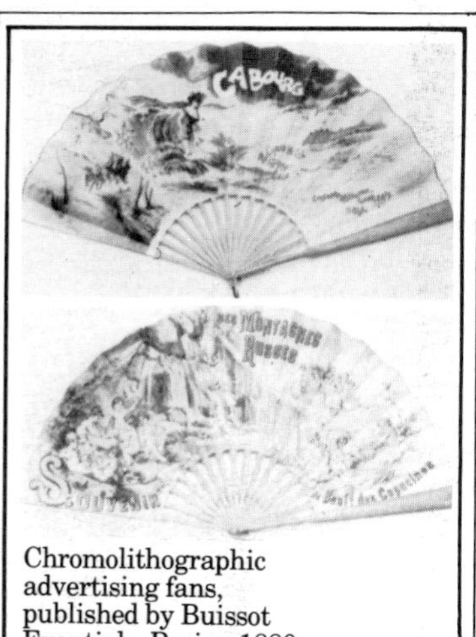

Chromolithographic advertising fans, published by Buissot Eventials, Paris, c1880, 12in (30.5cm).
£175-300 each *CSK*

Advertising fans, Paris, 1920s.
£30-50 each *FF*

MAKE THE MOST OF MILLERS
Price ranges in this book reflect what one should expect to *pay* for a similar example. When selling, however, one should expect to receive a lower figure. This will fluctuate according to a dealer's stock, saleability at a particular time, etc. It is always advisable, when selling, to approach a reputable specialist dealer or an auction house which has specialist sales.

Advertising fans for Duvelleroy at the 1851 Exhibition.
£150-250 each *FF*

Fishing

Reels

An ABU Cardinal 33, 1975-77.
£30-40 *JMG*

Now starting to be collectable.

A 5in Hardy sea Silex, 1930s.
£50-80 *JMG*

A 4in Longstone sea reel, poor condition.
£20-30 *JMG*

A 2⅞in Hardy Perfect, wartime model so now called the Spitfire model.
£60-100 *JMG*

A 3¼in Hardy Princess fly reel, first model with green handle and green finish back and front, restored, c1950.
£60-80 *JMG*

A 3½in Hardy Silex Multiplier, with brass oil pipe outside on the back, c1935.
£80-100 *JMG*

A 3½in Farlow, the Heyworth salmon fly reel.
£20-30 *JMG*

A 3⅜in Hardy St. George, 3-screw drum latch, 1920s.
£20-40 *JMG*

A 2½in Malloch of Perth Sun & Planet reel, internal gearing makes the spool and knob turn together, patented 1880.
£60-80 *JMG*

A 2½in Hardy brass faced Perfect, 1896 check.
£200-250 *JMG*

A 3½in Hardy Uniqua, wide drum for salmon, c1930.
£30-50 *JMG*

A 3¾in Allock Aerial, 1920s.
£20-30 *JMG*

A 3½in Hardy Perfect all-brass reel, 1896 check.
£200-300 *JMG*

A 3¼in Hardy Bouglé fly reel, restored, c1930s.
£300-400 *JMG*

Designed in 1903 by Louis M Bouglé of the Casting Club de France.

A 3⅜in Hardy Barton reel.
£600-800 *JMG*

Designed in the 1930s, is more expensive than the Perfect, only about 100 made, this wartime Spitfire model never before seen.

A 4in Hardy all-brass Perfect, No. 258 stamped foot, c1893.
£250-400 *JMG*

An unusual experimental model with a screw in the centre of the face.

A rare French Capta fixed spool reel, c1944.
£20-30 *JMG*

An ABU Record Flyer, No. 3000, 1950-57.
£50-70 *JMG*

A 4in Wallace Watson No. 3 centre pin spinning reel, patented 1931.
£20-30 *JMG*

A 5¼in Hardy Ebona sea reel, ebonite with nickel silver back fittings, World War I.
£100-150 *JMG*

A 2¾in Hardy Sunbeam, Bickerdyke lineguard, restored, c1930.
£20-35 *JMG*

MAKE THE MOST OF MILLERS
Condition is absolutely vital when assessing the value of any item. Damaged pieces appreciate much less than perfect examples. However, a rare, desirable piece may command a high price even when damaged.

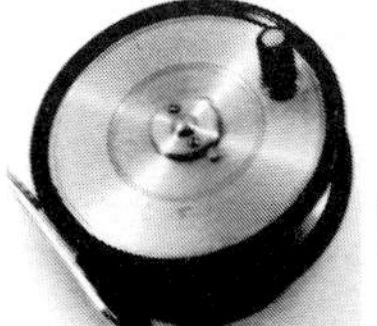

A 2½in Hardy brass crank-wind reel, c1890.
£30-50 *JMG*

A 3³⁄₁₆ Hardy, The Lightweight, restored, c1950.
£20-30 *JMG*

A French fixed spool reel, the Bretton, No. 804, post war.
£10-15 *JMG*

A 3¾in Hardy Super Silex, World War II.
£50-80 *JMG*

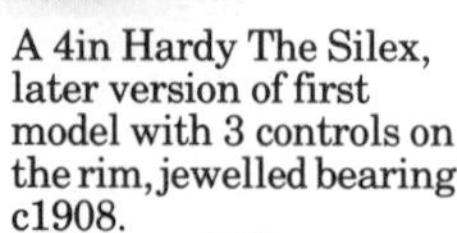

A 4in Hardy The Silex, later version of first model with 3 controls on the rim, jewelled bearing, c1908.
£50-70 *JMG*

A 3⅜in Hardy Perfect, ivorine handle, red agate lineguard, 1906 check.
£80-100 *JMG*

The only made version of the fixed spool reel, made by a Mr. Thorne, World War II.
£20-30 *JMG*

General

An ABU Ambassadeur 5000C De Luxe, in teak box with spare spool and tools, unused, c1980.
£100-140 *JMG*

A page from a 1934 Hardy tackle catalogue.
£20-25 *JMG*

A Hardy Multum-in-Parvo black japanned lure box, originated in 1928.
£15-20 *JMG*

A Hardy trace making and repairing black japanned box, with 3 tools, 1930s.
£20-40 *JMG*

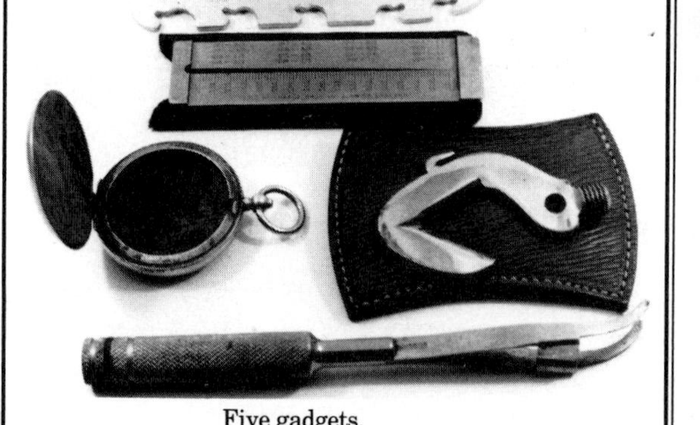

Five gadgets.
£5-30 each *JMG*

A Farlow aluminium alloy fly vice, as recommended 80 years ago by Frederic Halford.
£10-15 *JMG*

FURTHER READING

Maxtone Graham, Jamie, *Best of Hardy's Angler's Guides,* Peebles, Scotland 1982.
Maxtone Graham, Jamie, *To Catch a Fisherman,* Peebles, Scotland 1984.
Maxtone Graham, Jamie, *Fishing Tackle of Yesterday,* Peebles, Scotland 1989.

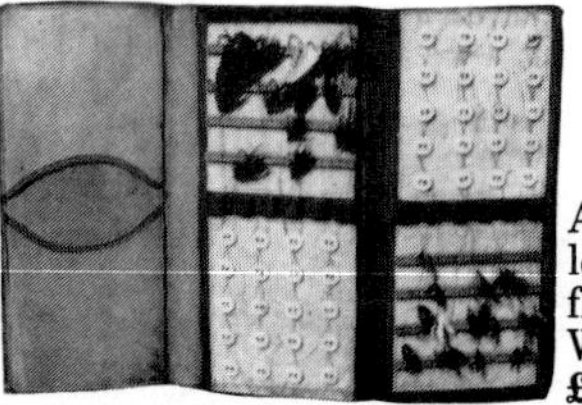

A Hardy patented leather wallet for trout flies tied to gut, cWorld War I.
£20-25 *JMG*

Carnival Glass

Carnival glass is a term used to describe the pressed moulded iridescent glass ware produced primarily in the U.S.A. between 1908-28. The glass was often hand finished, giving added interest to what was primarily 'cheap' glass. Marigold sprayed onto a clear glass base was the most popular colour, with shades of amethyst, green and blue also popular.

A large range of shapes were produced in the form of bowls, plates, water sets, punch sets and whimseys. Various patterns were depicted, predominantly with flowers and fruits and occasionally animals and birds. The value of any one item depends greatly on the quality of the mould pressing and iridescent finish, with pattern, colour and shape also playing an important part in the price. Damaged pieces are of little value to a collector.

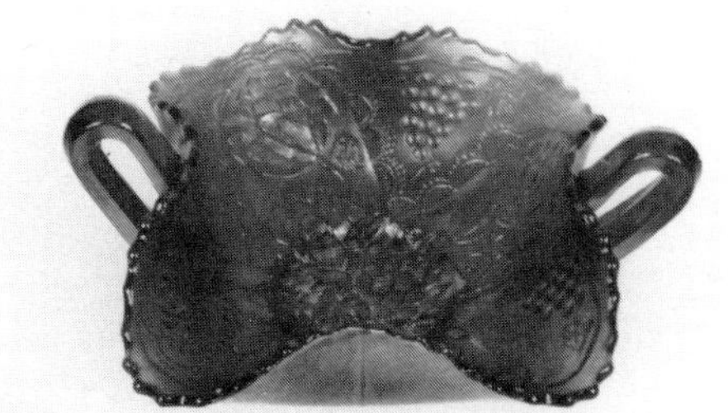

A Fenton Art Glass green lotus and grape bon bon dish, 7in (18cm) diam.
£55-60 *TS*

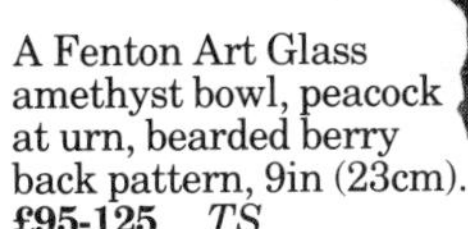

A Fenton Art Glass amethyst bowl, peacock at urn, bearded berry back pattern, 9in (23cm).
£95-125 *TS*

A Northwood stippled rays green bowl, basketweave back pattern, Northwood trademark in centre, 9in (23cm) diam. **£45-50** *TS*

An Imperial Glass Co. pansy bowl, arcs back pattern, helios green, 9in (23cm) diam.
£35-45 *TS*

A Northwood marigold bowl, grape and cable basketweave back pattern, 8in (20.5cm) wide. **£55-60** *TS*

A Fenton Art Glass blue orange tree bowl, bearded berry back pattern, 9in (23cm) diam. **£90-100** *TS*

A Northwood fruit and flowers dark purple bon bon dish, basketweave back pattern, 6in (15cm) diam.
£65-75 *TS*

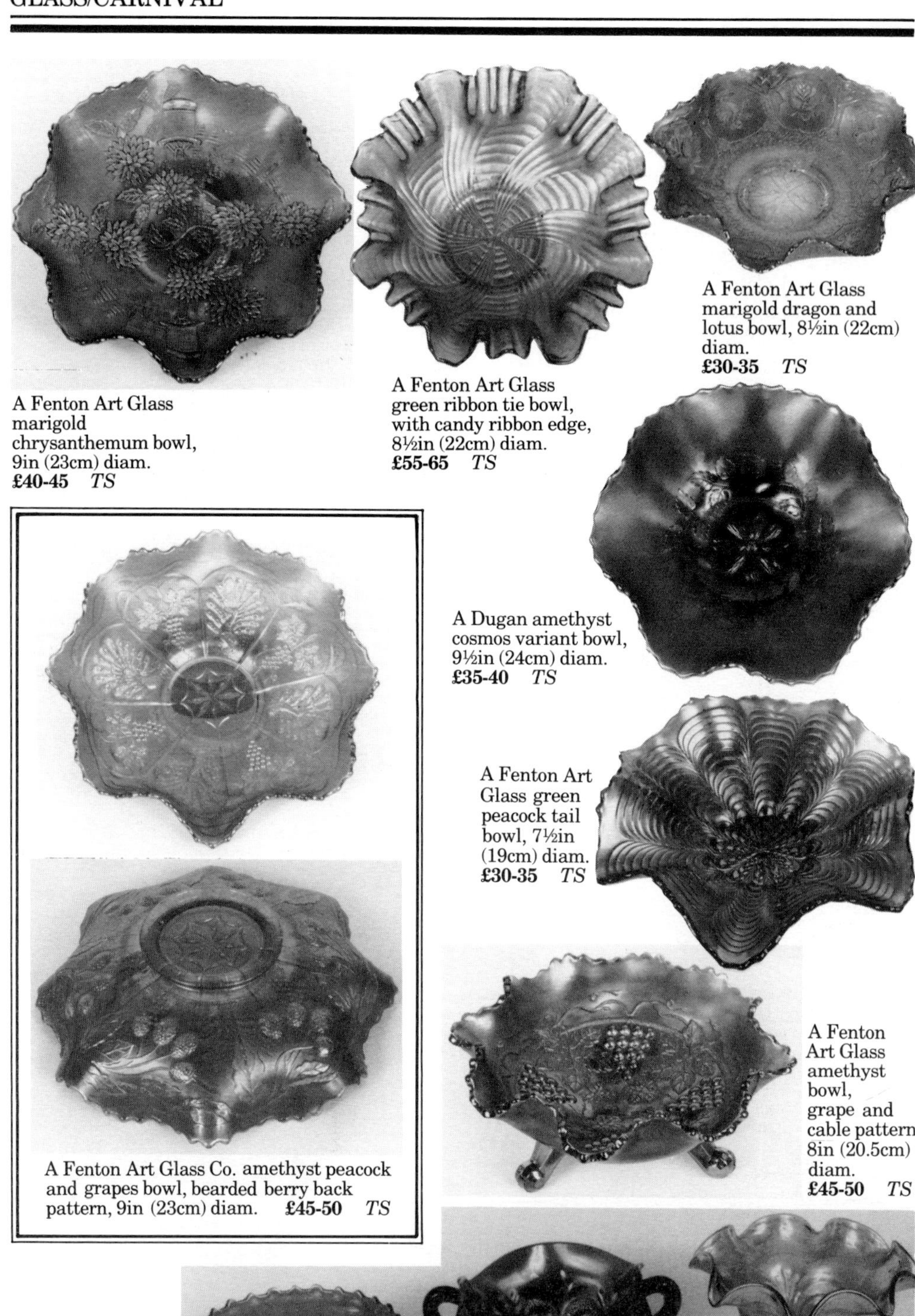

A Fenton Art Glass marigold chrysanthemum bowl, 9in (23cm) diam.
£40-45 *TS*

A Fenton Art Glass green ribbon tie bowl, with candy ribbon edge, 8½in (22cm) diam.
£55-65 *TS*

A Fenton Art Glass marigold dragon and lotus bowl, 8½in (22cm) diam.
£30-35 *TS*

A Dugan amethyst cosmos variant bowl, 9½in (24cm) diam.
£35-40 *TS*

A Fenton Art Glass green peacock tail bowl, 7½in (19cm) diam.
£30-35 *TS*

A Fenton Art Glass Co. amethyst peacock and grapes bowl, bearded berry back pattern, 9in (23cm) diam. **£45-50** *TS*

A Fenton Art Glass amethyst bowl, grape and cable pattern, 8in (20.5cm) diam.
£45-50 *TS*

Three pressed glass dishes.
£25-35 each *TS*

A Northwood marigold strawberry pattern bowl, with basketweave back pattern, Northwood trademark on base.
£40-45 *TS*

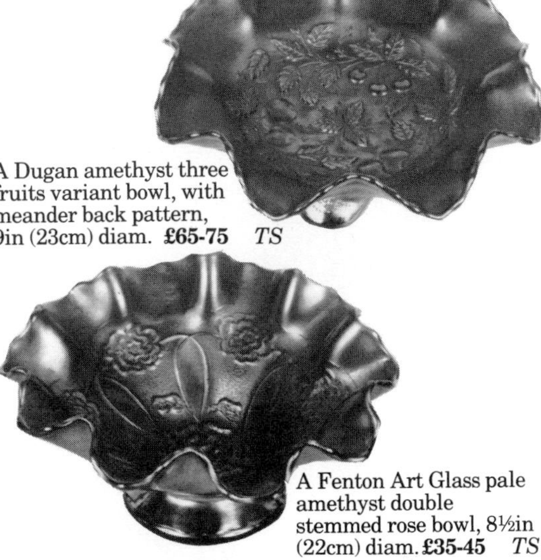

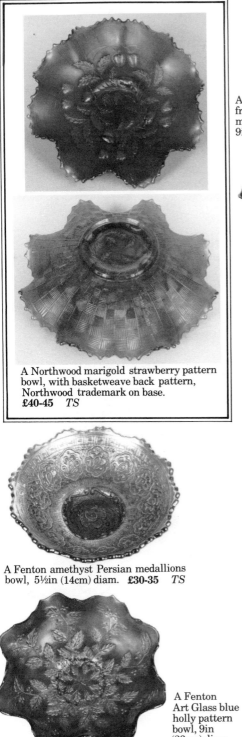

A Dugan amethyst three fruits variant bowl, with meander back pattern, 9in (23cm) diam. **£65-75** *TS*

A Fenton Art Glass pale amethyst double stemmed rose bowl, 8½in (22cm) diam. **£35-45** *TS*

DID YOU KNOW?
By the 1920s the original moulds were getting so worn that the mouldings were less crisp; a useful guide to dating carnival glass.

A Fenton amethyst Persian medallions bowl, 5½in (14cm) diam. **£30-35** *TS*

A Fenton Art Glass blue holly pattern bowl, 9in (23cm) diam.
£70-80 *TS*

A marigold compote, possibly Eda Works, Sweden, c1930, 9in (23cm) diam.
£30-35 *TS*

A foreign carnival glass button on original card, c1930. **£3-5** *TS*

Cross Reference
Buttons

A marigold chalice, Eda Works, Sweden, 8½in (22cm) high.
£40-45 *TS*

Marketed in Germany by Brockwitz.

A secondary marigold carnival glass bowl, c1930, 9½in (24cm) diam.
£15-20 *TS*

Secondary glass was given away at fairgrounds.

A marigold thistle vase, 6in (15cm) high.
£8-12 *TS*

An Imperial Glass marigold punch bowl set.
£140-150 *TS*

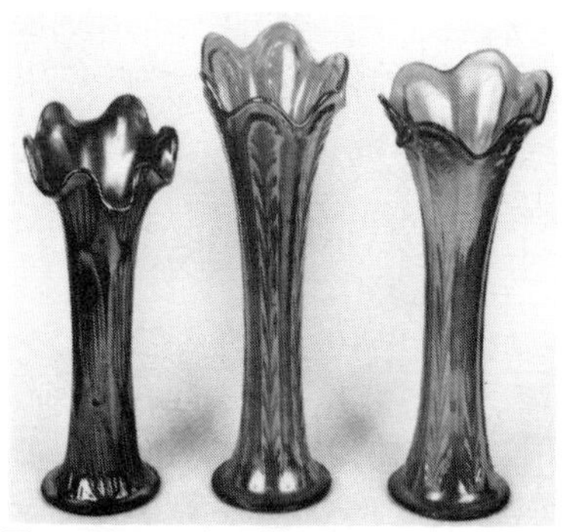

Three Fenton Art Glass vases.
£20-35 each *TS*

Czechoslovakian secondary carnival glass jewellery, c1930, 3½in (9cm). **£15-20** *TS*

Czechoslovakian necklaces.
£15-20 each *TS*

Cranberry Glass

A cranberry glass jug with trailed decoration, 5in (14cm) high.
£100-110 *PAR*

A cranberry glass wine jug, with ribbed handle, c1880, 8in (19cm) high.
£65-75 *Som*

A cranberry epergne, 15in (38cm) high.
£225-250 *PAR*

Nailsea Glass

A crown glass light green cream pan, with folded rim, c1800, 20in (51cm) diam.
£240-260 *Som*

A crown glass lacemaker's lamp, c1810, 5½in (14cm) high.
£160-180 *Som*

A bottle glass cream jug, c1800, 4½in (11cm) high.
£180-200 *Som*

A crown glass flagon, with applied loop handle, c1810, 7in (17cm) high.
£250-270 *Som*

Two light green crown glass inkwells, c1860, 2½in (6cm) high. **£70-80 each** *Som*

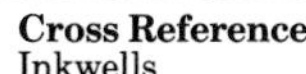

Cross Reference
Inkwells

Jobling Glass

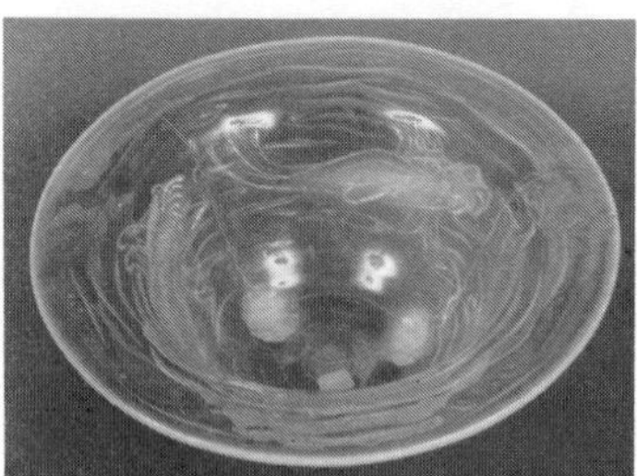

A fruit bowl, 11in (29cm) diam.
£95-100 *BEV*

A clear pink vase, 8in (21cm) high.
£75-85 *BEV*

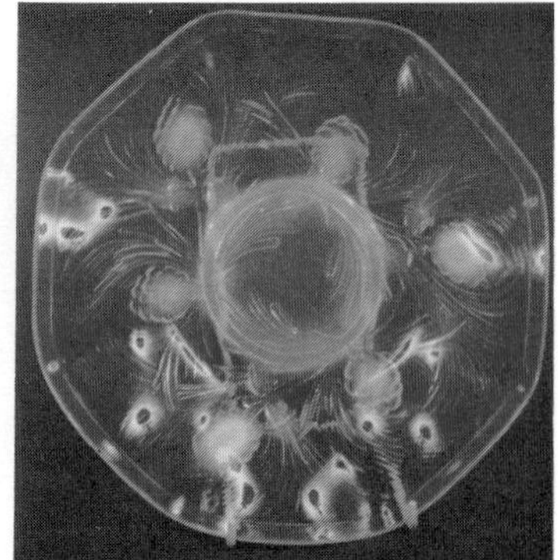

A bowl with wavy edge, 9½in (24cm) diam. **£40-50** *BEV*

Loetz Glass

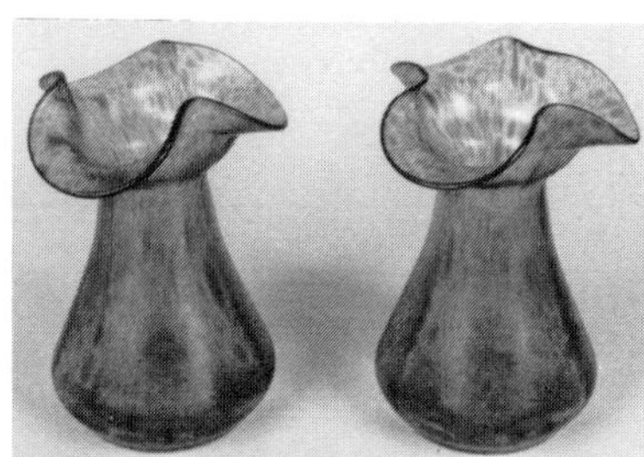

A pair of green vases, c1910, 6in (15cm) high.
£150-160 *SAI*

A pair of yellow candlesticks, possibly Loetz, 9in (24cm) high.
£135-145 *JAG*

A red powder bowl with black trim, 5in (14cm) diam.
£100-120 *JAG*

A red glass fruit bowl with black trim, 10in (25cm) diam.
£220-240 *JAG*

An Austrian Loetz style glass vase, c1900, 7½in (19cm) high.
£100-110 *WM*

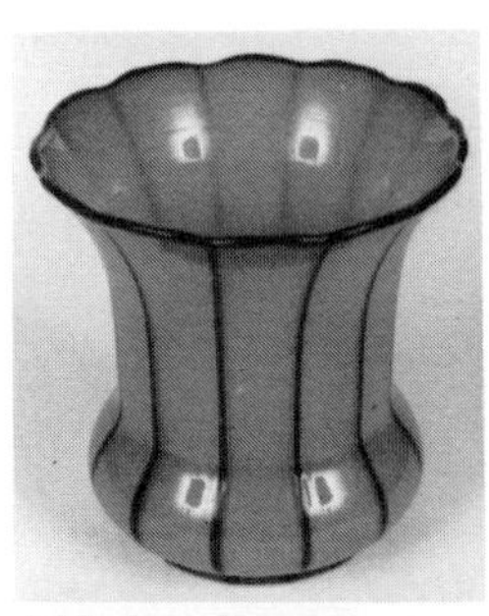

A black and orange striped vase, designed by Michael Powolny, 5in (14cm) high.
£260-280 *JAG*

A yellow bowl with black trim, 8½in (21cm) diam.
£90-100 *JAG*

DID YOU KNOW?
Miller's Collectables Price Guide is designed to build up, year by year, into the most comprehensive reference system available.

Powell Glass

The Whitefriars factory was established in the late 17thC but Powell glass was not produced by them until 1835 when James Powell joined the company. The factory moved to Harrow in the early 20thC and did not close until 1980.

An amber decanter with 6 glasses, c1910, decanter 8in (21cm) high.
£90-110 *SWa*

A vaseline glass vase with feather type design, 8in (20cm).
£65-75 *JAG*

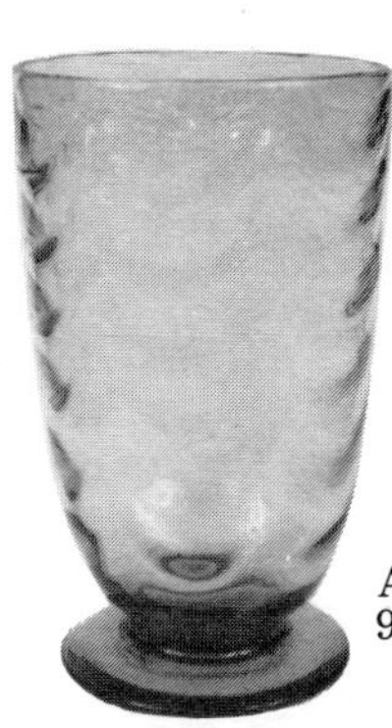

A green footed vase, c1933, 10in (25cm) high.
£50-75 *SWa*

A grey ribbed goblet, late 1930s, 9in (23cm) high. **£75-95** *SWa*

A glass bowl with blue trailing design, 9in (23cm) diam.
£100-110 *JAG*

A heavy blue glass bowl, c1932, 12in (30cm) wide.
£60-70 *SWa*

Three blue on blue applied glass vases, c1965, 7in (17.5cm) high. **£20-40 each** *SWa*

Three blue vases, c1965, tallest 8in (20cm) high.
£20-40 each *SWa*

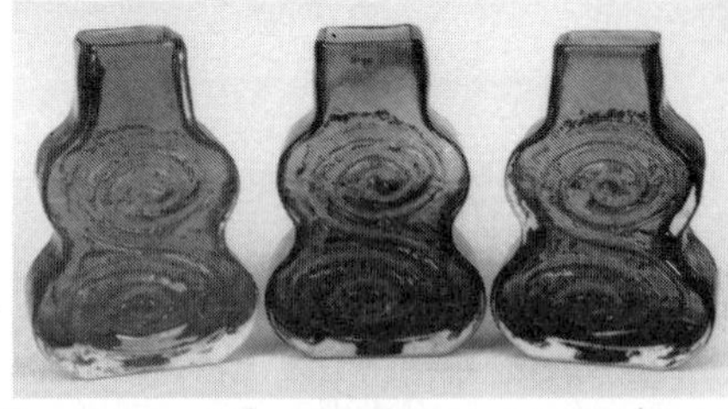

Three guitar style vases in green, tangerine and blue, c1965, 7in (17.5cm) high.
£20-40 each *SWa*

A blue brick vase, c1965, 8in (21cm) high.
£20-40 *SWa*

Three brick vases, c1965, 8½in (21cm) high.
£20-40 each *SWa*

Two clear glass vases and a bowl, with grey streaks, c1965, bowl 7in (17.5cm) diam.
£20-40 each *SWa*

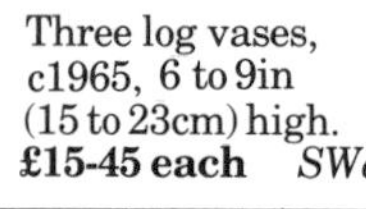

Three log vases, c1965, 6 to 9in (15 to 23cm) high.
£15-45 each *SWa*

Scandinavian Glass

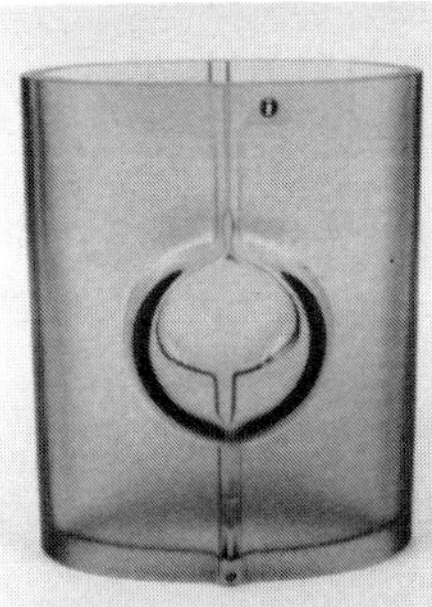

A grey glass vase, by Tapio Wirkkala, c1950, 7in (17.5cm) high.
£280-300 *WM*

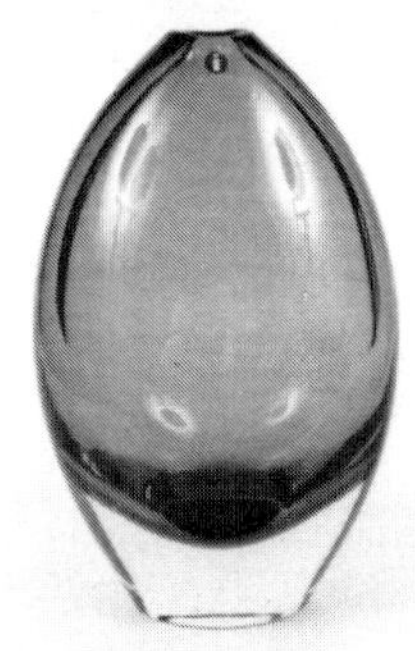

A blue glass vase, by Timo Sarpaneva, c1950, 7in (17.5cm) high.
£140-160 *WM*

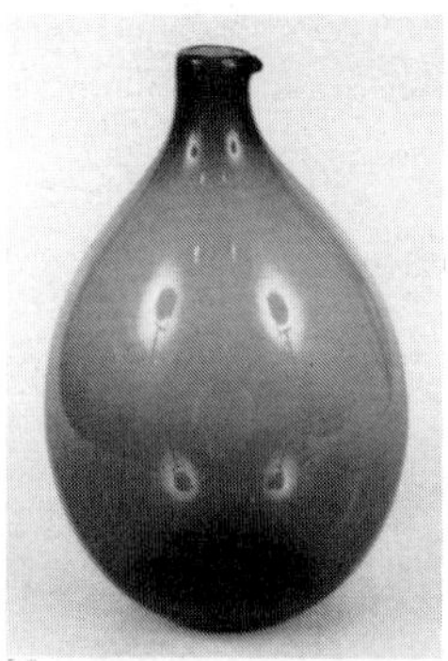

A grey/blue vase, by Timo Sarpaneva, c1950, 7in (17.5cm) high.
£75-100 *WM*

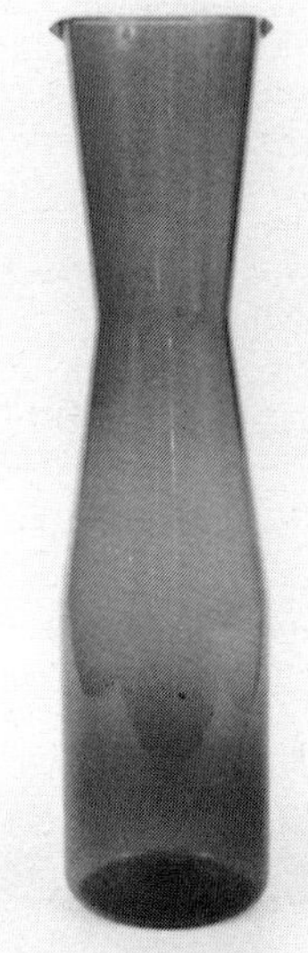

A grey/blue vase, by Timo Sarpaneva, c1950, 12½in (33cm) high.
£90-100 *WM*

Pressed Glass

Boots & Shoes

An opaque black posy holder, unmarked, c1880, 3in (7.5cm) high.
£20-25 *GH*

Two opaque black posy holders, unmarked, c1885, 4½in (11cm) long. **£25-35** *GH*

A Sowerby blue and white posy vase, marked, c1876, 5½in (14cm) long.
£55-65 *GH*

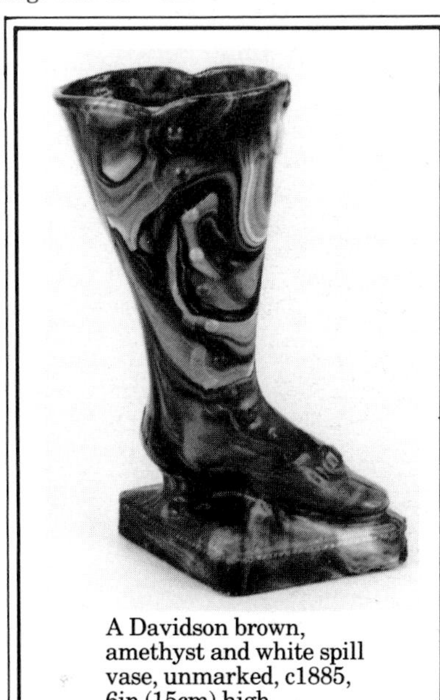

A Davidson brown, amethyst and white spill vase, unmarked, c1885, 6in (15cm) high.
£110-130 *GH*

Commemorative

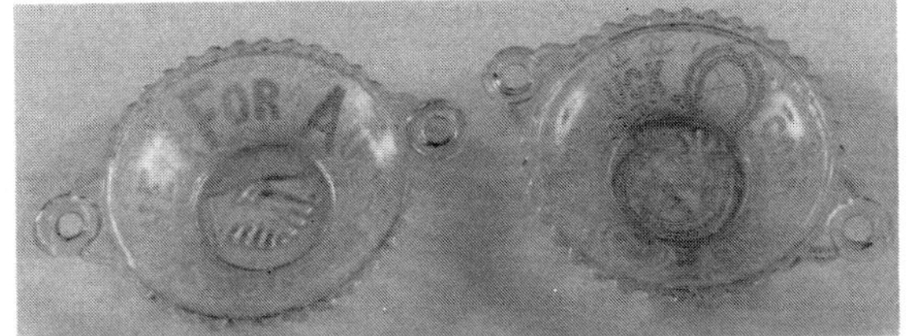

Two flint glass souvenir dishes, unmarked, c1883, 5in (14cm) diam. **£12-15** *GH*

A Greener flint glass commemorative plate, unmarked, 1887, 5in (14cm) diam.
£12-15 *GH*

A flint glass plate, attributed to Sowerby, unmarked, c1890, 10in (25cm) diam.
£20-25 *GH*

A flint glass commemorative plate, unmarked, 1888, 10in (25cm) diam.
£50-55 *GH*

Salts

A Thomas Kidd opaque black bust of Queen Victoria, unmarked, c1897, 3½in (9cm) high.
£170-200 *GH*

A pair of Sowerby blue malachite salts, marked, 1877, 2½in (6cm) high.
£55-65 *GH*

A pair of Greener flint glass salts, Reg. No. 218710, 1893, 5in (13cm) long.
£12-15 *GH*

A pair of Sowerby Queen's ivory ware salts, marked, 1878, 2in (5cm) high.
£130-140 *GH*

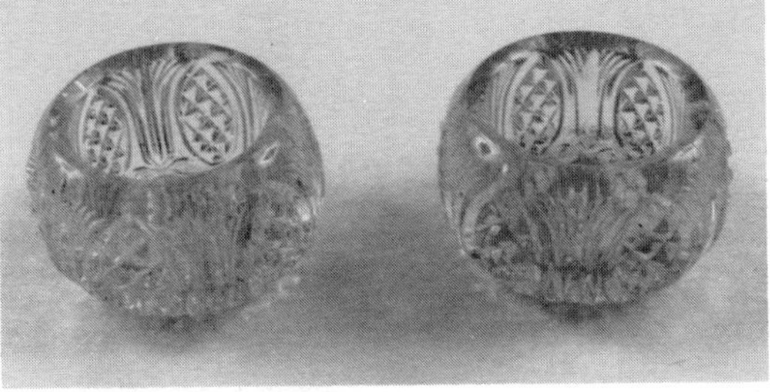

A pair of John Derbyshire flint glass salts, both marked, c1875, 3in (7.5cm) diam.
£15-20 *GH*

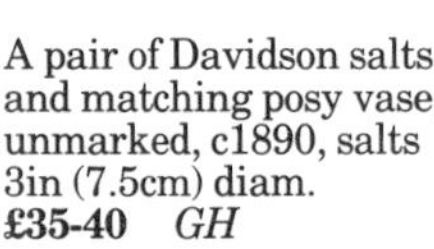

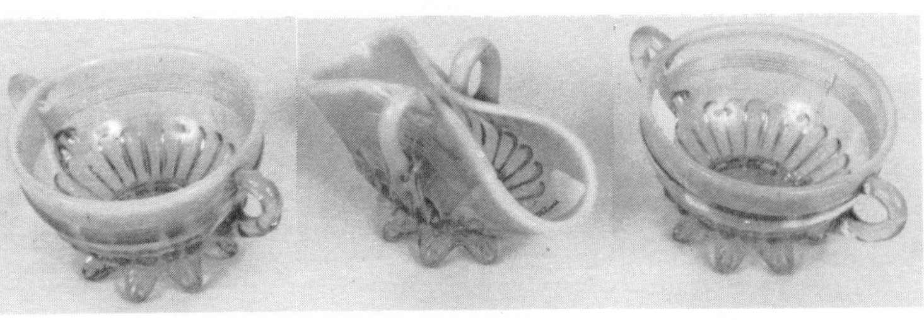

A pair of Davidson salts and matching posy vase, unmarked, c1890, salts 3in (7.5cm) diam.
£35-40 *GH*

Miscellaneous

A late Victorian pressed glass sugar basin, c1900, 5in (14cm) high.
£30-35 *EAS*

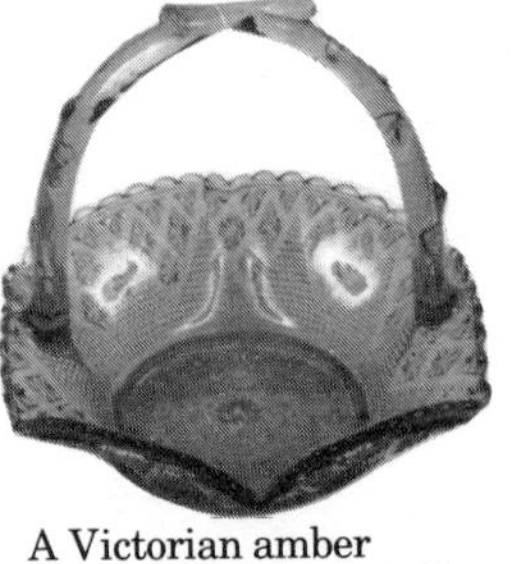

A Victorian amber pressed glass basket, 7in (17.5cm) high.
£25-30 *EAS*

A Sowerby Queen's ivory ware plate, marked, 1878, 9in (23.5cm) diam. **£85-95** *GH*

A Greener flint glass commemorative sugar basin and cream jug, marked, 1869, bowl, 4½in (11cm) high.
£50-60 *GH*

A Davidson amber pressed glass jug, c1885, 5in (13cm) high.
£20-25 *EAS*

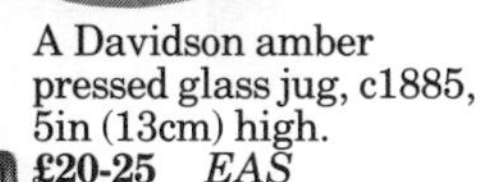

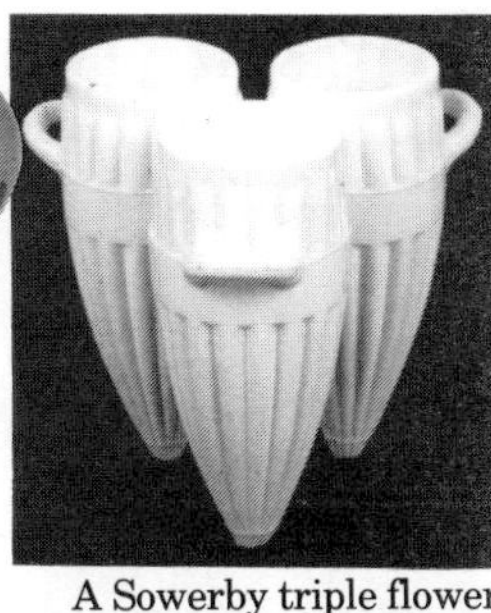

A Sowerby triple flower vase, marked, 1878, 3½in (9cm) high.
£45-50 *GH*

A Greener mid-blue night light, marked, 1891, damaged, 5in (13cm) high.
£40-45 *GH*

A Victorian amber pressed glass basket, 6½in (17cm) high.
£20-25 *EAS*

A blue and white tankard, attributed to Davidson, unmarked, c1890, 3in (7.5cm) high.
£25-35 *GH*

A G. Davidson coral pink pressed glass jug, 1896, 3in (7.5cm) high.
£16-20 *EAS*

A Davidson amber pressed glass sugar bowl, c1885, 5in (13cm) high.
£25-30 *EAS*

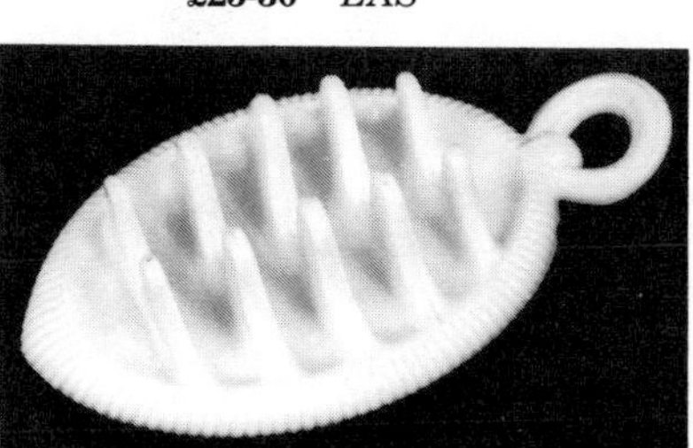

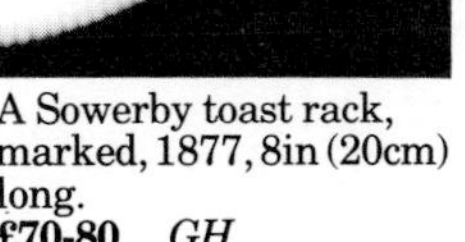

A Davidson spirit measure, unmarked, c1880, 2½in (6cm) high.
£30-35 *GH*

A Sowerby toast rack, marked, 1877, 8in (20cm) long.
£70-80 *GH*

A Molineaux Webb flint glass celery vase, marked, 1865, 10in (25cm) high.
£25-30 *GH*

Drinking Glasses

Rummers. **£55-65 each £110-125 pair** *Som*

Three rummers, with plain conical feet, early 19thC.
£35-45 each *Som*

A selection of dwarf ale glasses, early 19thC. **£30-40 each** *Som*

Four small wines, early 19thC. **£20-30 each** *Som*

A painted glass goblet, by Richard Redgrave, painted signature and registration mark for 25 October 1847, 8in (20cm) high.
£750-800 *C*

A Georgian glass, 5in (12.5cm) high.
£80-85 *SA*

A selection of small bucket wine glasses, c1825. **£25-35 each** *Som*

Door Stops

A Victorian green glass door stop, 5½in (14cm).
£125-140 *AA*

A pair of Nailsea door stops, c1860, 4½in (11.5cm) high.
£140-160 each *Som*

Victorian green glass door stop, 5 and 4in (12.5 and 10cm).
£85-100 *AA*

Two Victorian green glass door stops, 3½in (9cm) high.
£75-100 each *AA*

Handkerchief Vases

Two Venini handkerchief vases, c1945.
l. Small yellow and white, 3in (7.5cm) high.
£90-100
r. Large turquoise, 7in (18cm) high.
£380-400 *WM*

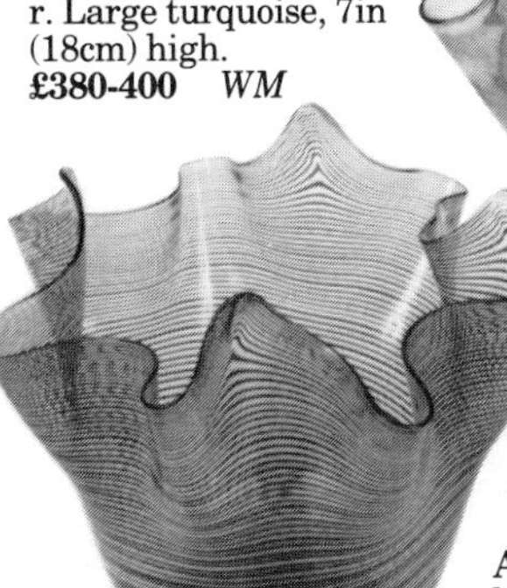

A Venini style handkerchief vase, with black trailing design, c1950, 5in (12.5cm) high.
£75-100 *JAG*

A Powell green glass handkerchief vase, 6in (15cm).
£45-55 *JAG*

Hats

A green glass hat, c1860.
£80-100

A Nailsea crown glass hat, c1830.
£60-80 *Som*

Hyacinth Vases

Three amethyst hyacinth vases, c1840.
£70-80 *Som*

A Victorian hyacinth vase, with cranberry base, 7in (18cm).
£45-50 *TS*

Perfume Bottles

A scent bottle, c1920, 7in (18cm).
£40-50 *AD*

A Bohemian red glass perfume bottle, 6in (15cm). **£50-55** *SA*

Two perfume bottles, with sterling silver neck rings, c1920.
£30-60 each *SA*

A silver shouldered scent bottle, London, 1900, 6in (15cm) high.
£380-400 *AD*

Three Victorian cut glass scent bottles, with silver neck bands, 3 and 4in (7.5 and 10cm) high.
£30-40 each *AD*

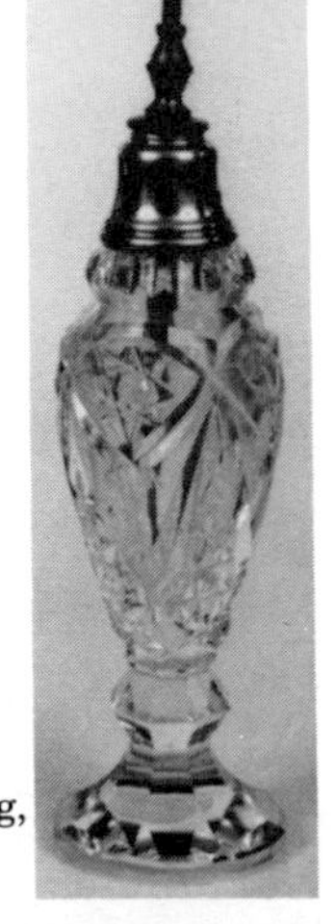

A perfume spray with sterling silver neck ring, c1920, 7in (18cm).
£45-50 *SA*

Two Victorian scent bottles, with silver tops.
£40-60 each *AD*

A pair of cut glass scent bottles with silver tops, c1905, 3in (7.5cm) high.
£150-160 *AD*

Opaline Glass

A Victorian blue glass vase, with enamelled decoration.
£40-50 *OBS*

A green glass lustre.
£45-55 *OBS*

A turquoise opaline glass vase, with painted and enamel decoration, 7in (18cm) high.
£20-25 *EAS*

A French Victorian opaline glass vase, 11in (28cm).
£45-55 *EAS*

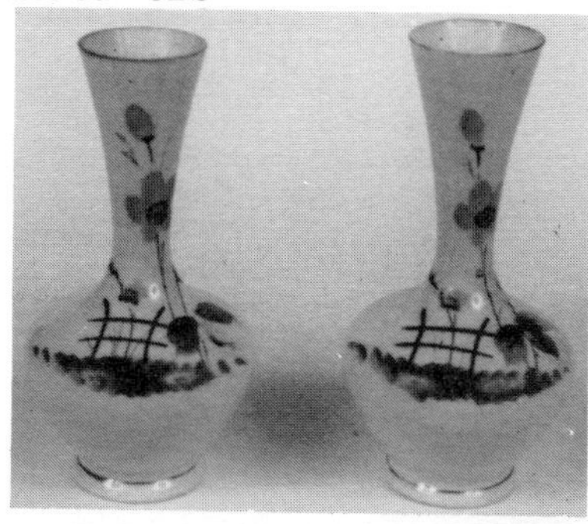

Two turquoise opaline vases, with painted decoration, 6½in (16.5cm).
£35-45 *EAS*

Two green opaline glass vases, with painted decoration, 8in (20.5cm) high.
£25-35 each *EAS*

Satin Glass

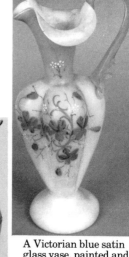

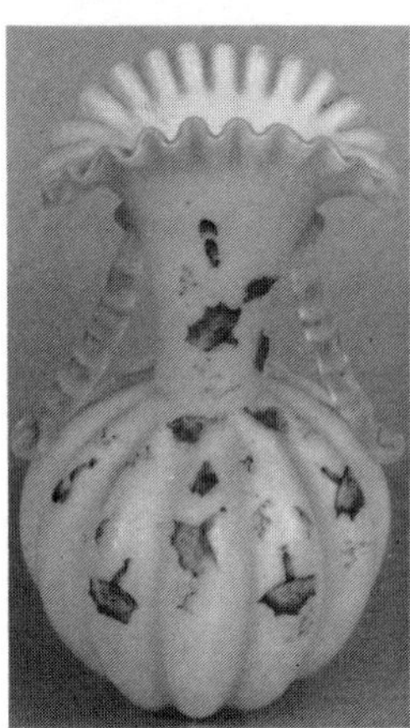

A Victorian pale green satin glass vase, with painted decoration, 7in (17.5cm) high.
£50-55 *EAS*

A Victorian green satin glass vase, tear pattern, 9in (23cm) high.
£60-70 *EAS*

An impressed peach tone vase, possibly Webbs, c1880, 8in (21cm) high.
£65-75 *TS*

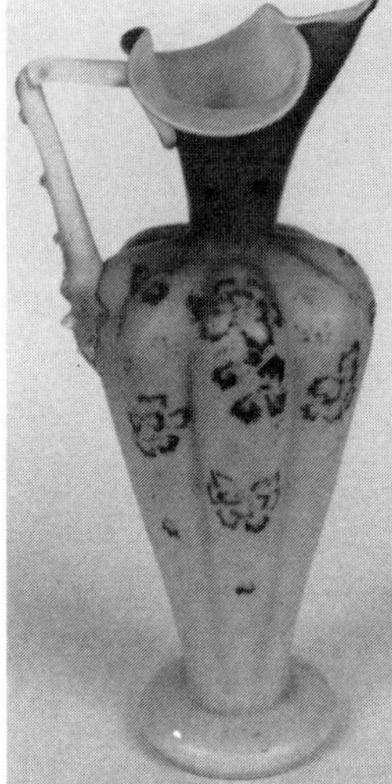

A pink satin glass ewer, with enamel decoration, 12in (30cm).
£90-95 *EAS*

A Victorian blue satin glass vase, painted and enamel decoration, 9in (23.5cm) high.
£50-55 *EAS*

Venini

A stylised glass fish, acid-stamped Venini, Murano, Italia, 13in (33cm) long.
£180-200 *C*

A mauve and pink glass egg-timer, signed, c1945, 7½in (19cm) high.
£375-400 *WM*

A pair of Venini style cocktail glasses, 5in (13cm) high.
£70-80 *JAG*

A coffee coloured decanter, signed, c1945, 11in (28cm) high.
£250-275 *WM*

General

A Webb glass bowl with Art Nouveau overlay decoration, signed, c1910, 9in (23.5cm) diam.
£160-180 *WIL*

Two Webb-Corbett amethyst vases:
l. c.1920, 6in (15cm) high.
£60-80 *FA*
r. With Liberty Tudric pewter stand, No. 5004, 9in (23cm) high.
£350-400 *FA*

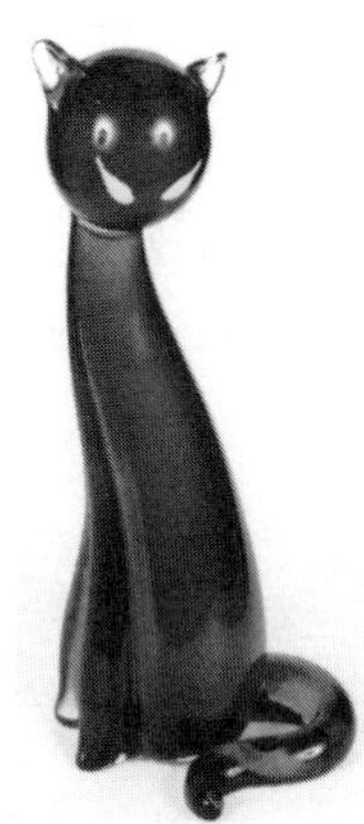

A Murano cat, c1955, 13in (33cm) high.
£130-140 *JAG*

An oil lamp in brass, with embossed glass shade, c1930.
£65-75 *OBS*

A glass bell shaped cover, 7½in (19cm) high.
£35-40 *MCA*

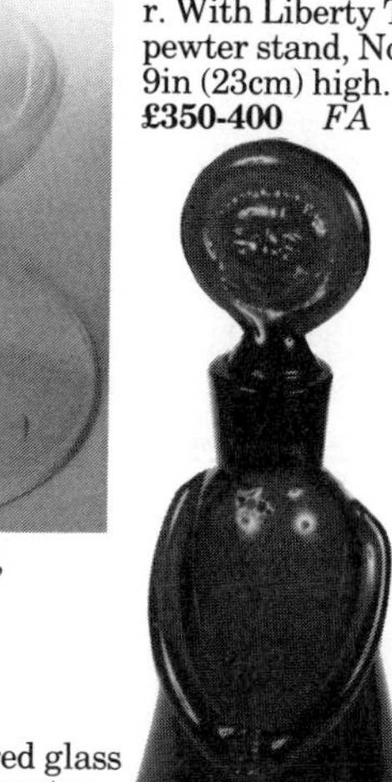

A Foreign dark red glass Aboda People decanter, with face on the stopper.
£65-70 *JAG*

A glass dome cover, 17in (43cm) high.
£70-80 *MCA*

A clear cased glass pig, with red, white and blue decoration, damaged, c1860, 5in (13cm) long.
£50-60 *Som*

FURTHER READING
Jones-North, Jacquelyne, *Commercial Perfume Bottles.*
Jones-North, Jacquelyne, *Perfume, Cologne and Scent Bottles,* Millbank Books, U.K.

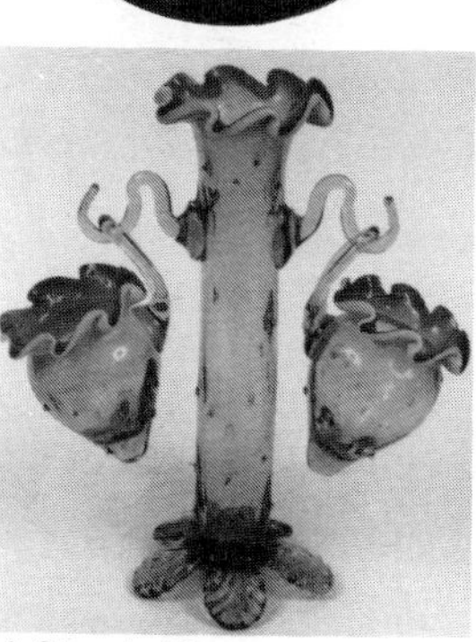

A Stourbridge green glass epergne, 8in (20cm) high. **£120-130** *AA*

A blue candlestick with flute cut knopped stem and plain conical foot, c1850, 8½in (21cm) high.
£48-55 *Som*

Horse Brasses & Harness

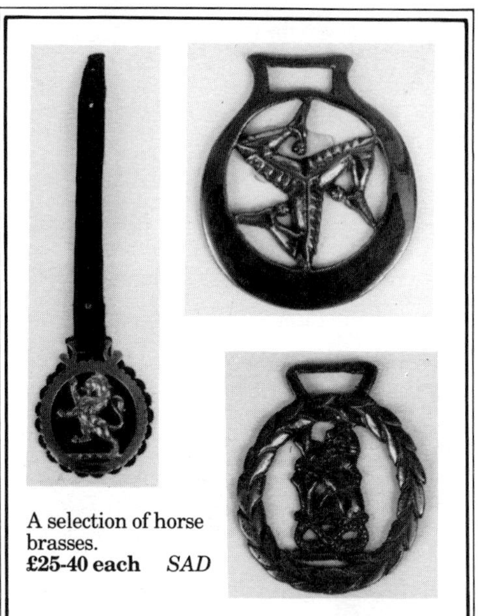

A selection of horse brasses.
£25-40 each *SAD*

A brass face piece.
£40-50 *SAD*

A brass face piece, with porcelain boss.
£50-60 *SAD*

A brass swinger on ebony base.
£25-30 *SAD*

A brass hame plate, 19thC.
£45-50
SAD

DID YOU KNOW?
A hame is a curved bar holding the traces of the harness attached to the collar of a draught animal.

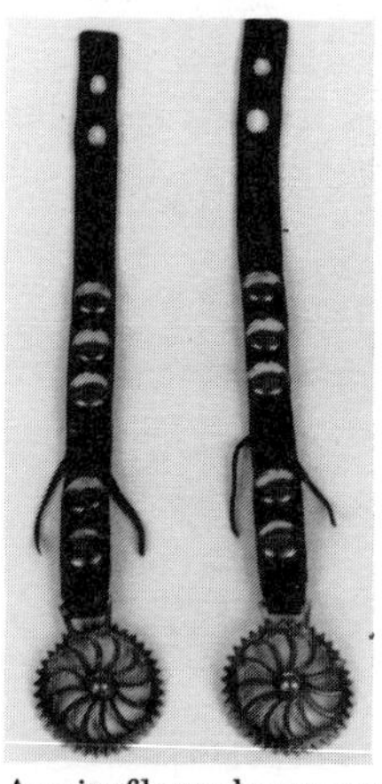

A pair of horse brasses on decorated straps.
£100-120 *SAD*

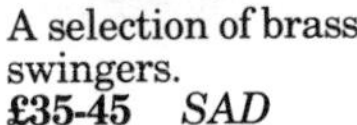

A selection of brass swingers.
£35-45 *SAD*

Inkwells

A silver inkwell, London 1917.
£220-250 *AD*

A Victorian glass inkwell, 2½in (6.5cm) high.
£90-100 *AD*

A Victorian glass inkwell, with silver top, London 1872, 3in (7.5cm).
£70-80 *AD*

An inkwell, 2in (5cm) high.
£30-35 *PP*

A Victorian cut glass inkwell, with silver top, 2½in (6.5cm) high.
£130-140 *AD*

A Victorian glass inkwell with brass top, 3in (7.5cm).
£50-60 *AD*

A grotesque mask stoneware inkwell, late 19thC, 3in (7.5cm) wide.
£110-125 *PCh*

A Victorian glass inkwell, with brass neck and mushroom top, 4in (10cm).
£150-160 *AD*

A glass inkwell with silver top, Birmingham 1919, 2in (5cm).
£80-90 *AD*

A Victorian glass inkwell, with brass neck, 3½in (9cm).
£140-150 *AD*

MAKE THE MOST OF MILLERS
Price ranges in this book reflect what one should expect to *pay* for a similar example. When selling, however, one should expect to receive a lower figure. This will fluctuate according to a dealer's stock, saleability at a particular time, etc. It is always advisable, when selling, to approach a reputable specialist dealer or an auction house which has specialist sales.

A selection of inkwells with brass tops, c1890, 2in (5cm) high.
£30-35 each *PP*

A Victorian inkwell, 2½in (6.5cm) high.
£35-40 *PP*

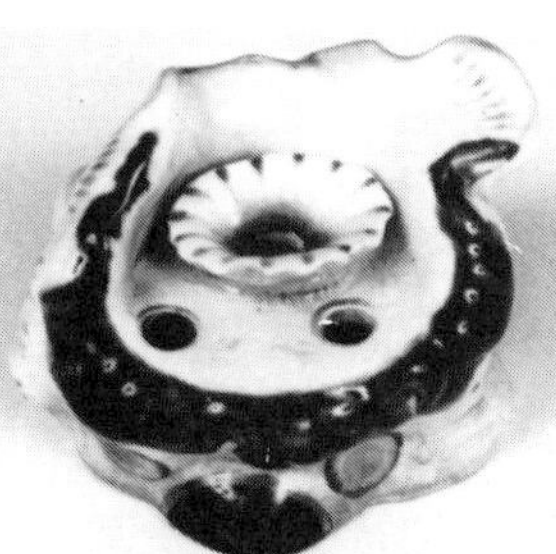

A Staffordshire inkwell, in the form of a shell, c1840.
£70-100 *JAS*

A brass inkwell, 3in (7.5cm).
£25-35 *BEV*

A Le Nove maiolica desk set, some damage, c1770, the tray 7½in (18.5cm) wide.
£1,000-1,200 *C*

An earthenware ink pot, c1830.
£230-250 *IW*

A Staffordshire inkwell, c1850, 4in (10cm).
£275-300 *HOW*

A Victorian plated ink pot, in the form of a ship's lantern.
£100-120 *JAS*

An old Sheffield plate inkstand, c1820.
£45-55 *JAS*

A Victorian inkstand.
£150-170 *AD*

An oak inkstand, the glass bottles with brass tops, 11in (28cm) wide.
£140-150 *AD*

A mother-of-pearl inlaid inkstand, with 2 glass inkwells, 11in (28cm).
£150-170 *PCh*

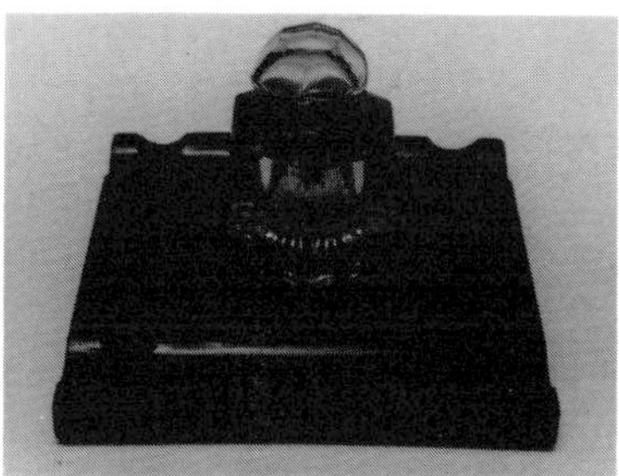

A Victorian glass inkwell on a wooden stand.
£70-80 *AD*

An Edwardian inkstand and pen tray, with 2 cut glass ink bottles, 11½in (29cm) wide.
£75-100 *PCh*

Cross Reference
Writing Accessories

A pen and inkstand, the ram's horns with plated mounts, bright cut decoration supporting a cut glass ink pot and pen rest, late 19thC, 6½in.
£80-100 *WIL*

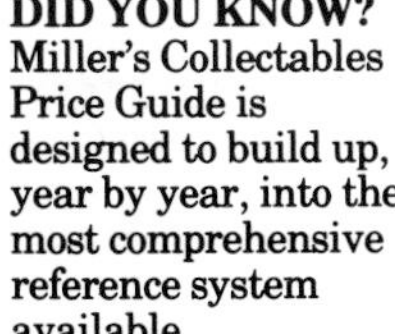

DID YOU KNOW?
Miller's Collectables Price Guide is designed to build up, year by year, into the most comprehensive reference system available.

A Victorian brass inkstand, 6in (15cm) wide.
£130-140 *AD*

Jewellery

Collectable jewellery is a large field in which we endeavour to feature both general and specific areas. This year we have highlighted Victorian 'mourning' jewellery, 'claw' jewellery and 'inspiration' jewellery made from old watch cocks.

Bakelite

A pair of Art Deco red and white earrings.
£25-30 *WWA*

A guitar.
£90-100
A necklace in cream and amber.
£85-95
A pair of green and chrome earrings.
£30-35 *WWA*

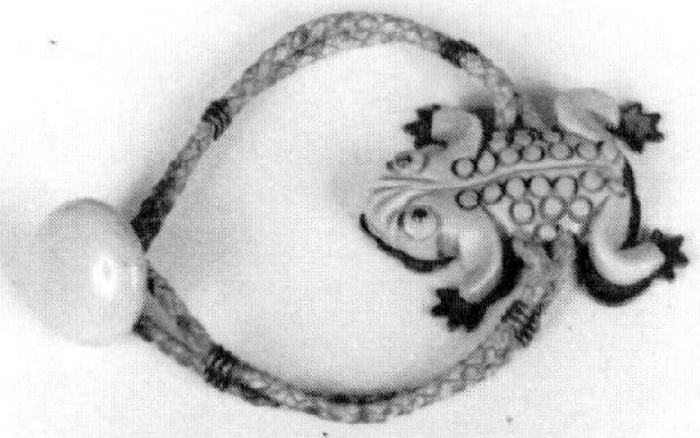

A frog bracelet, with woven leather strap.
£60-70 *WWA*

Three bangles.
£12-65 each
WWA
The wider ones are difficult to find, hence more expensive.

A green bracelet, 6½in (17cm) long. **£55-65** *WWA*

Bangles

An Oriental/Indian silver bangle.
£25-45 *ASA*

A silver plated bangle, 3in (7.5cm).
£10-15 *ASA*

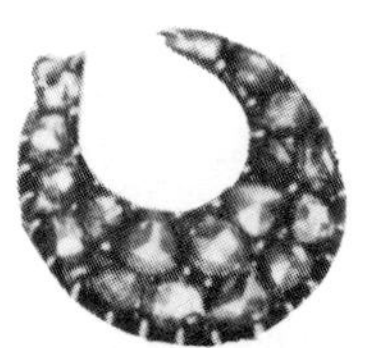

A rose diamond crescent brooch.
£160-180 *CSK*

An iron and Damascene stick pin, modelled as a soldier's head.
£100-150 *CSK*

A cameo brooch.
£140-160 *CSK*

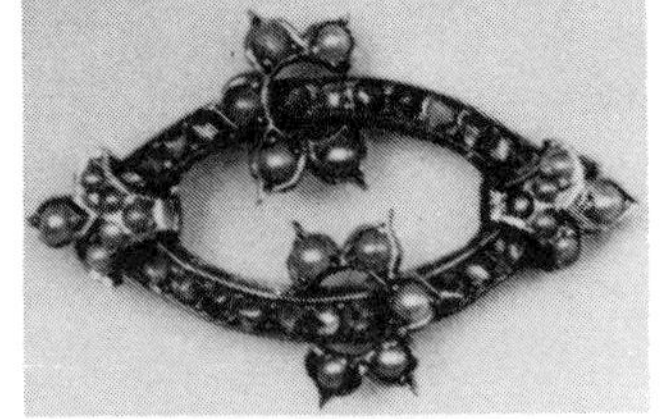

A rose diamond brooch with half pearl cluster motifs.
£150-180 *CSK*

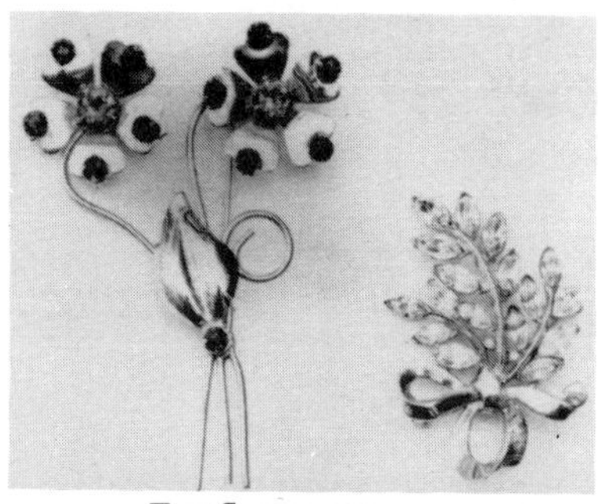

Two flowerspray brooches.
£15-20 each *CSK*

A silver and garnet brooch.
£35-45 *SAD*

An amethyst brooch with wirework border.
£130-150 *CSK*

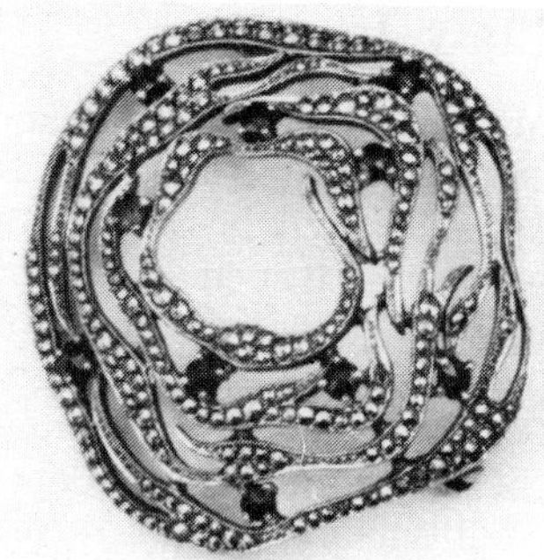

A garnet and marcasite openwork shaped brooch.
£40-50 *CSK*

An Etruscan style brooch. **£180-200** *CSK*

A cabochon garnet brooch.
£150-170 *CSK*

A white paste simulated pearl ladybird brooch, with simulated garnet body and green paste eyes, Nettie Rosenstein.
£70-80 *CSK*

Pendants

An Almeric Walter pâte-de-verre pendant, marked France on reverse.
£280-300 *P*

An Art Nouveau design half pearl and aquamarine brooch pendant.
£200-220 *CSK*

A Danish silver brooch.
£50-70 *ASA*

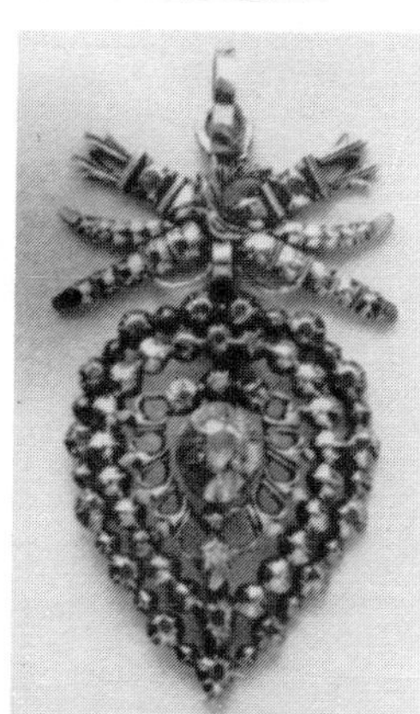

A rose diamond pear shaped cluster pendant.
£200-220 *CSK*

DID YOU KNOW?
Miller's Collectables Price Guide is designed to build up, year by year, into the most comprehensive reference system available.

Mexican silver pendants, marked.
£30-50 each *ASA*

Claw Jewellery

Man has always hunted and decorated himself with the trophies. During the 19thC he switched to decorating his woman with such adornments. Although they prove today to be reminders of the days of unnecessary slaughter, the skill of the jeweller cannot be denied. The value of these items is entirely dependent upon condition and the quality of the mounting.

A tiger's claw brooch set in silver.
£90-120 *PVH*

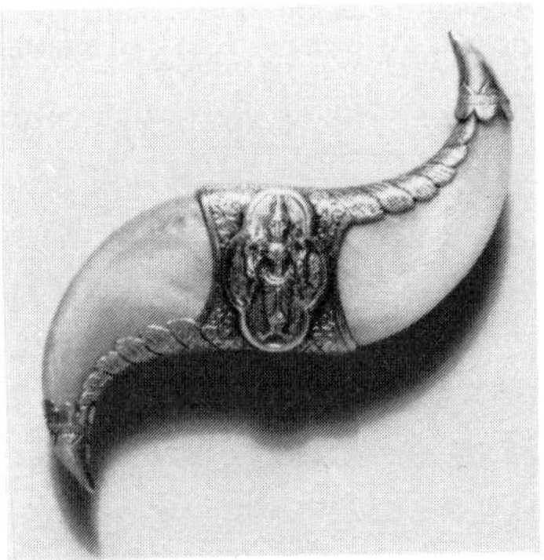

A tiger's claw brooch set in finely chased gold.
£85-95 *PVH*

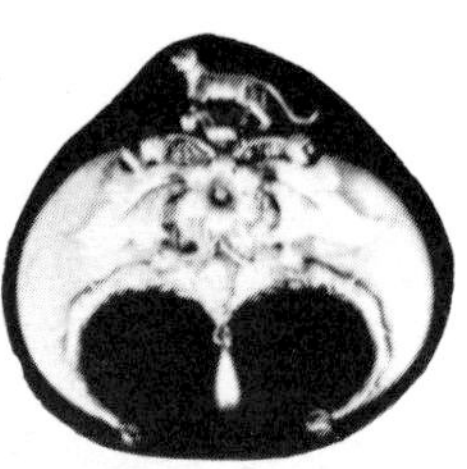

A tiger's claw brooch, set in gold.
£185-195 *PVH*

A tiger's claw set in hand engraved gold.
£75-95 *PVH*

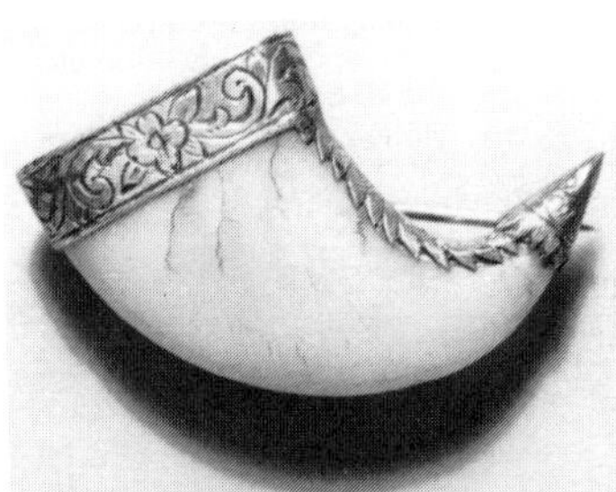

A lion's claw brooch set in engraved silver.
£65-85 *PVH*

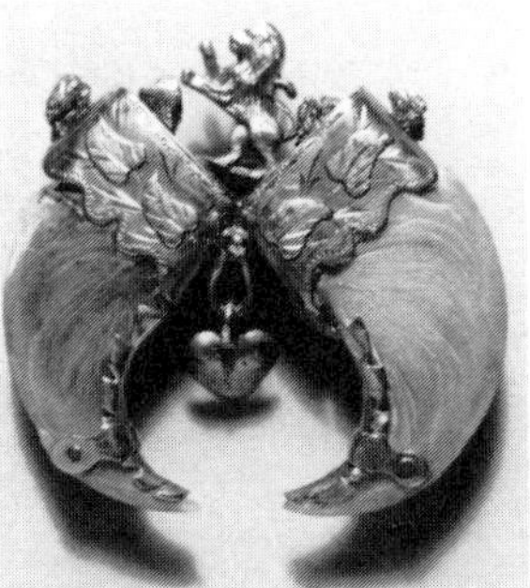

A lion's claw brooch, set in 3-colour gold.
£200-220 *PVH*

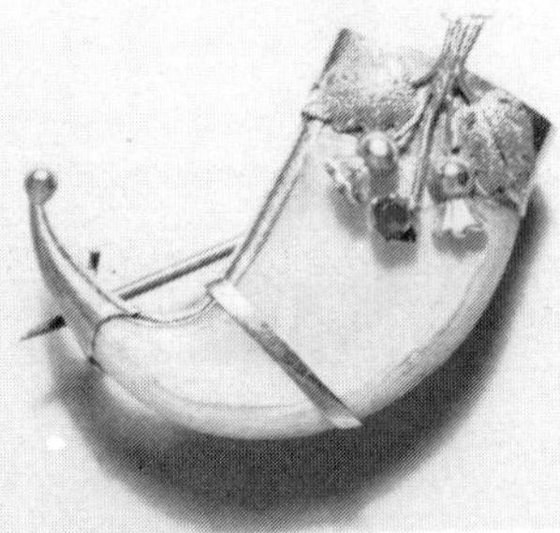

A tiger's claw brooch set in gold.
£100-150 *PVH*

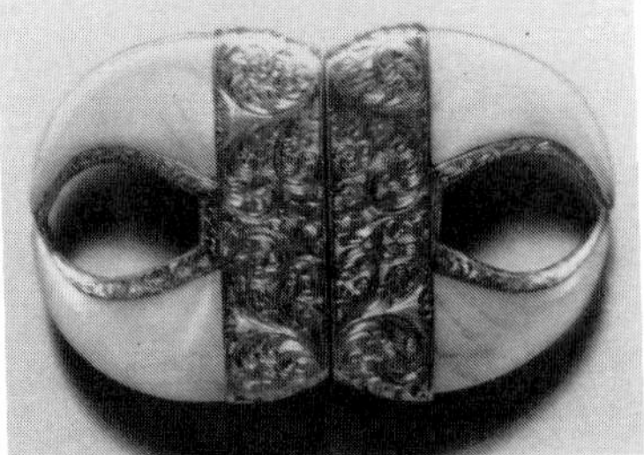

A tiger's claw buckle, set in hand engraved gold.
£220-250 *PVH*

Two pairs of tiger's claw earrings, set in gold.
£220-250 each *PVH*

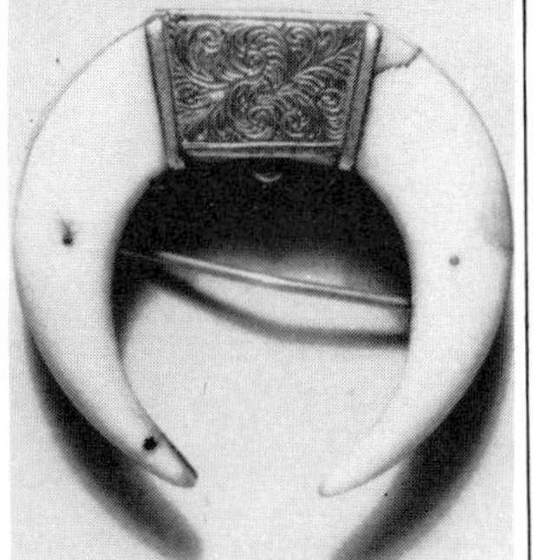

Boar's tusks brooch, set in engraved silver gilt.
£35-45 *PVH*

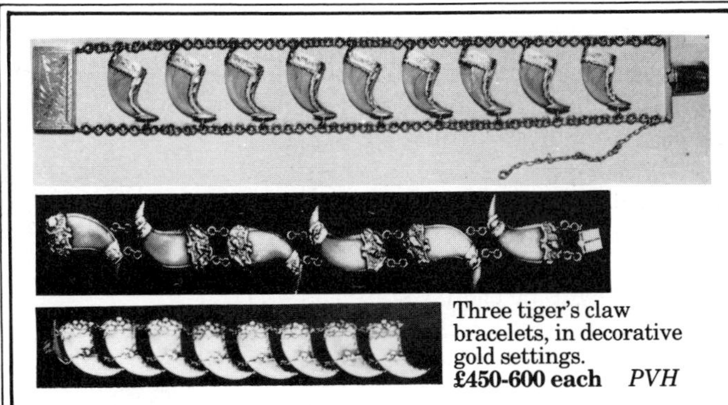

Three tiger's claw bracelets, in decorative gold settings.
£450-600 each *PVH*

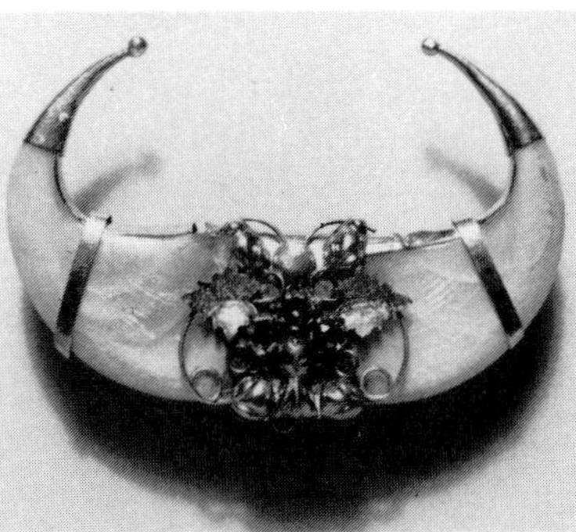

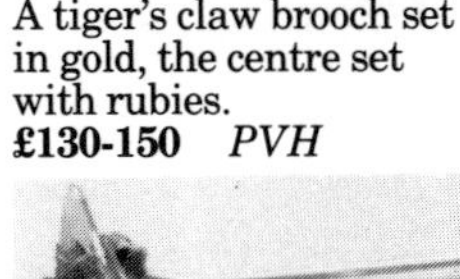

A tiger's claw brooch set in gold, the centre set with rubies.
£130-150 *PVH*

A gold mount for a lion's claw brooch, claws missing.
£135-155 *PVH*

A tiger's claw brooch set in gold with opals and rubies.
£90-120 *PVH*

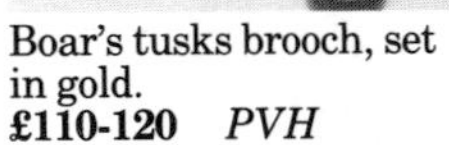

Boar's tusks brooch, set in gold.
£110-120 *PVH*

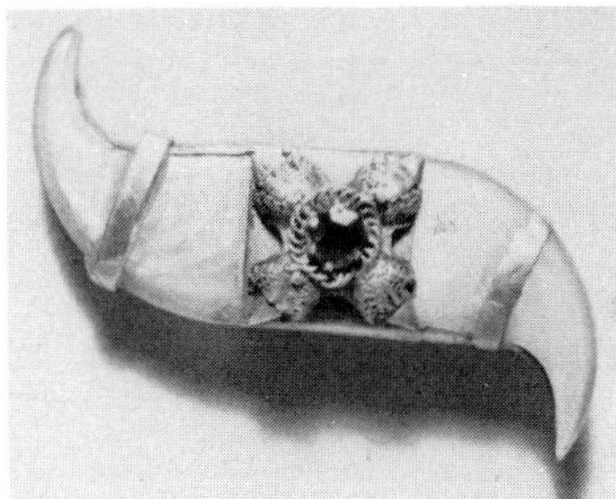

A tiger's claw brooch set in silver, with ruby in the centre.
£45-55 *PVH*

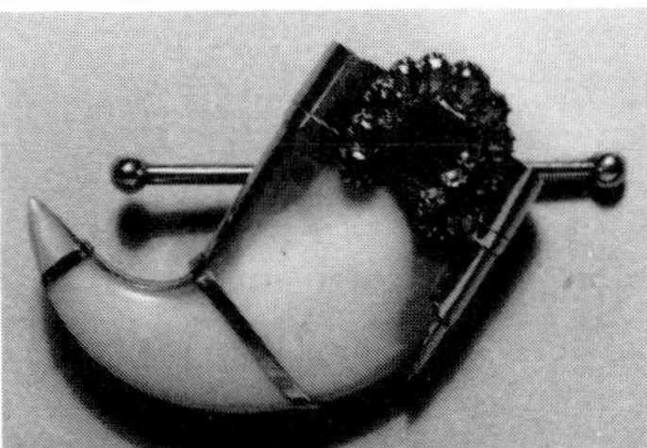

A tiger's claw set in gold, with 11 Burmese sapphires.
£275-300 *PVH*

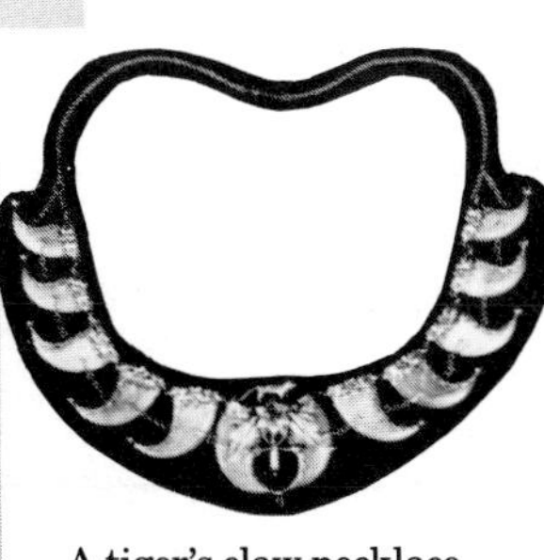

A tiger's claw necklace, set with gold flowers and a ruby.
£1,250-1,500 *PVH*

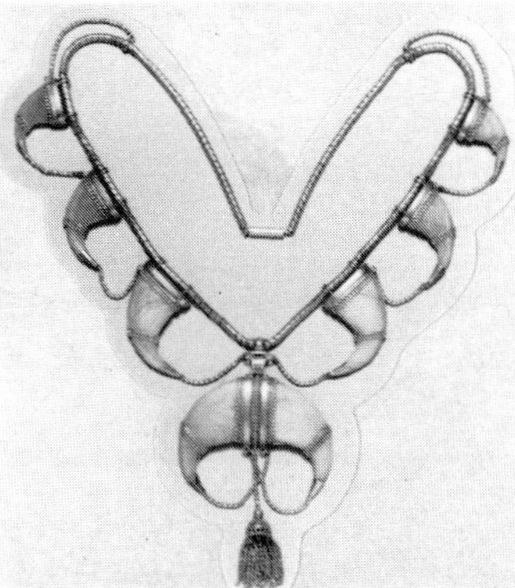

A tiger's claw necklace, set in gold.
£1,000-1,200 *PVH*

Jet Jewellery

Black became very fashionable following the death of Prince Albert. Black jewellery was used when in mourning during the Victorian period.

Real jet is a form of fossilised coal, mainly mined from an area around Whitby in Yorkshire. French jet is in fact glass and should be clearly stated as such as it is not jet.

A Victorian Whitby jet bracelet.
£200-250 *DF*

A Victorian Whitby jet shell cameo.
£90-100 *DF*

A Victorian Whitby jet fob.
£80-100 *DF*

A Victorian Whitby jet carved necklace.
£300-350 *DF*

A Whitby jet pendant.
£70-80 *DF*

A Victorian French jet bangle.
£150-200 *DF*

A Whitby jet cross.
£85-95 *DF*

A pair of French jet stud earrings.
£25-35 *DF*

A pair of Victorian French jet earrings, converted from buttons.
£35-45 *DF*

Rings

A square cut citrine eternity ring, 1940s style.
£175-200 *CSK*

An 18ct gold bloodstone signet ring, seal engraved with a lion rampant.
£220-250 *CSK*

A sapphire and diamond ring.
£140-160 *CSK*

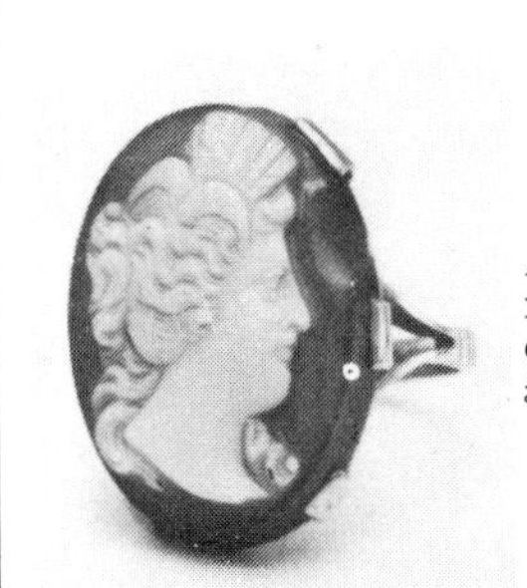

A hardstone cameo mounted as a ring, chipped.
£50-60 *CSK*

A rose diamond mourning ring, with central miniature under crystal.
£170-200 *CSK*

A sapphire and diamond cluster ring.
£140-160 *CSK*

A cut emerald single stone ring, with diamond shoulders.
£120-150 *CSK*

An 18ct gold opal and rose diamond marquise ring, engraved with initials and date 1901, opal chipped.
£200-220 *CSK*

A diamond cluster ring.
£120-140 *CSK*

Necklaces

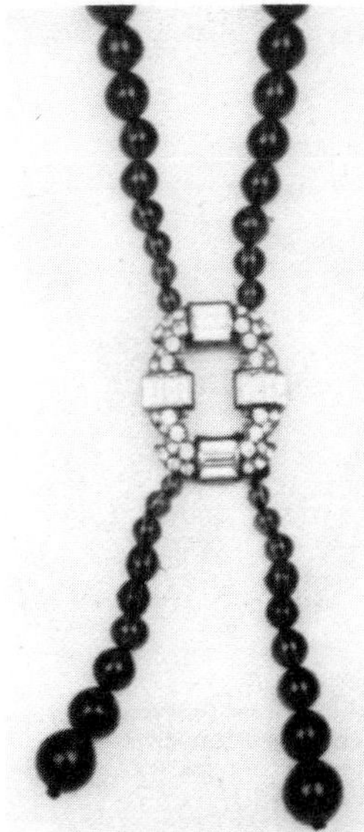

A simulated emerald glass bead necklace.
£50-80 *CSK*

A Norman Hartnell, blue, yellow and lilac pastel paste necklace with matching earrings.
£50-100 *CSK*

MAKE THE MOST OF MILLERS
Condition is absolutely vital when assessing the value of any item. Damaged pieces appreciate much less than perfect examples. However, a rare, desirable piece may command a high price even when damaged.

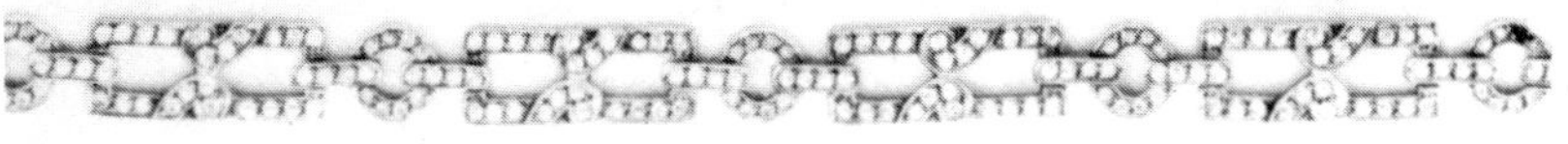

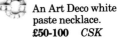

An Art Deco white paste necklace.
£50-100 *CSK*

Inspiration Jewellery

During Victorian times watch cocks were removed from watches and turned into all kinds of jewellery. Edward Good who owned 'Cameo Corner', New Oxford Street, London, collected many thousands of these little works of art and is responsible for a lot of this jewellery and inventing the name 'Inspiration' jewellery.

Watch cocks are an integral part of a spring driven watch used to protect the balance mechanism.

Six watch cocks made up as brooches, some set with various stones.
£5-15 each *PVH*

Watch cocks made into a necklace.
£65-75 *PVH*

A bracelet made up from mid-18thC watch cocks, some with various stones.
£110-120 *PVH*

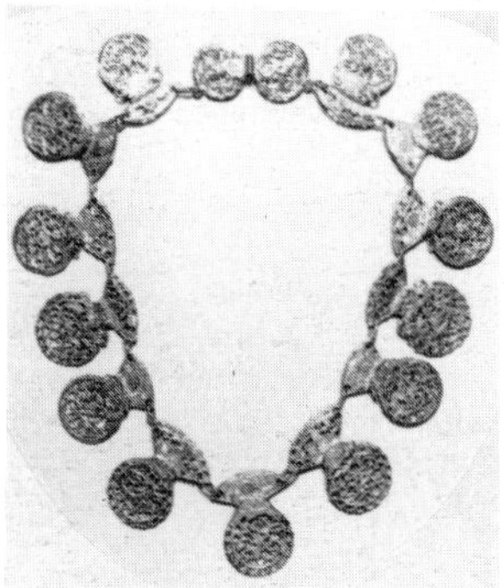

Watch cocks linked together to form a necklace.
£75-85 *PVH*

A verge watch movement with the watch cock in position.
£10-15 *PVH*

A gilded hand pierced watch fob with pocket watch key.
£10-12 *PVH*

A collection of pocket watch keys.
£2-4 each *PVH*

FURTHER READING
Lynnlee, J. L., *All That Glitters.*
Schiffer, Nancy, *Costume Jewellery, The Fun of Collecting.*
Schiffer, Nancy, *The Power of Jewellery.*
Kelley, Lyngerda, and Schiffer, Nancy, *Costume Jewellery, the Great Pretenders.*
Kelley, Lyngerda, and Schiffer, Nancy, *Plastic Jewellery,* Millbank Books, U.K.

Juke Boxes & Slot Machines

Juke Boxes

Edison record cylinder holders, American, c1890.
£20-25 each *NA*

A Roch-Ola stereo 100 juke box, American, c1961, 62in (157cm) high.
£700-1,000 *NA*

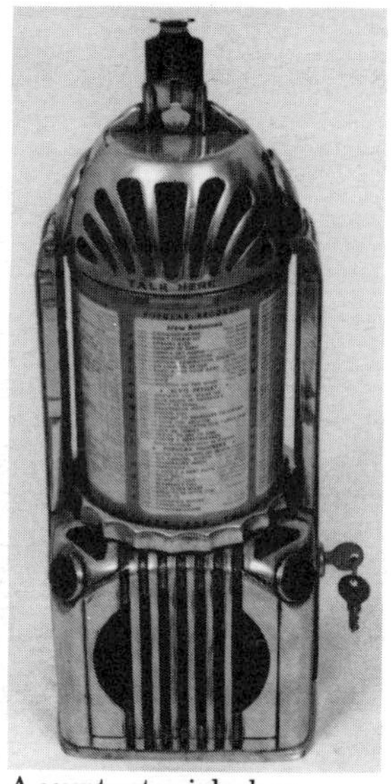

A counter top juke box, Shivers Multi-phone, American, 18in (46cm) high.
£400-500 *NA*

A Wurlitzer wall juke box, c1950, 13in (33cm) high.
£150-200 *NA*

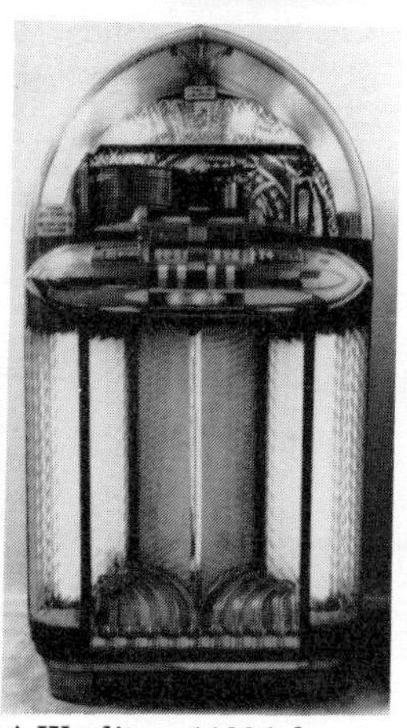

A Wurlitzer 1100 juke box, c1949, 52in (132cm).
£7,000-8,000 *NA*

A Bal-Ami Model 1 200 player juke box, c1957, 60in (152cm) high.
£2,000-3,000 *NA*

Used in the film Scandal.

Slot Machines

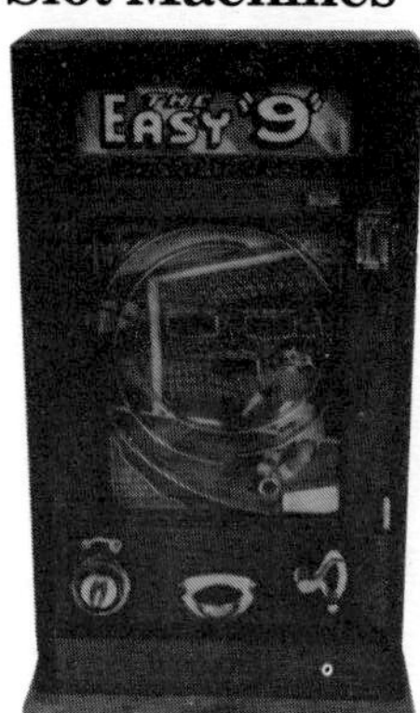

An Allwin Easy '9' amusement machine, c1950, 31½in (80cm) high.
£200-250 *NA*

Oracle Question and Answer machine, British, c1930.
£250-350 *NA*

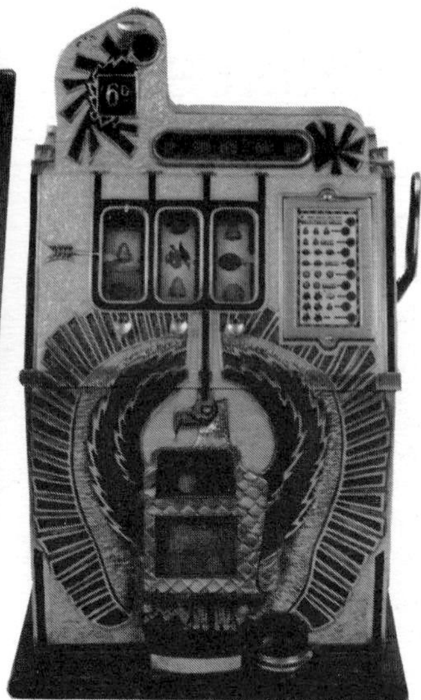

A Mills War Eagle one-armed bandit, American, c1930, 27in (68cm) high.
£800-1,000 *NA*

A chewing gum machine, 1960s, 36in (91.5cm).
£50-80 *NA*

Chrome serviette dispensing machines with 1 cent fortune telling cards, American, c1950, 6½in (17cm) high.
£100-150 each *NA*

The Violetta perfume spray machine, c1920, 22½in (57cm) high.
£350-400 *NA*

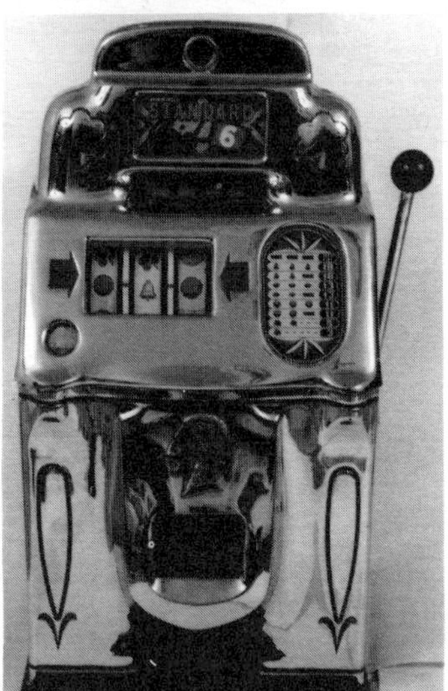

A Standard Chief one-armed bandit, c1946-47, 28½in (72cm) high.
£800-1,000 *NA*

Climbing the Alps amusement machine, c1940, 42in (106.5cm) high.
£200-250 *NA*

The Clown (Pickwick) slot machine, c1900.
£800-1,000 *NA*

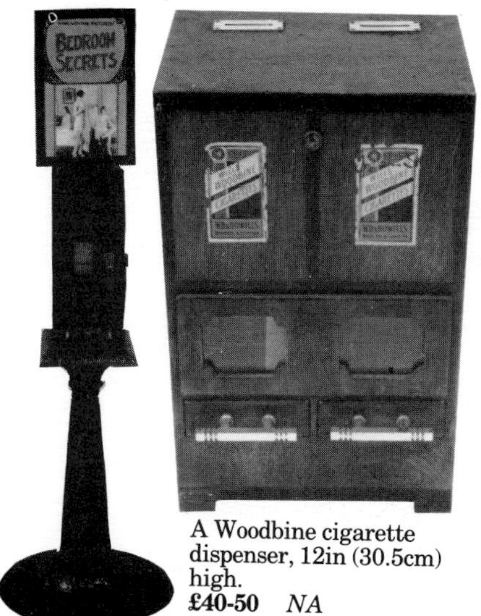

A Woodbine cigarette dispenser, 12in (30.5cm) high.
£40-50 *NA*

A Mutoscope 'What the Butler Saw' machine, c1890, 69in (175cm) high.
£2,000-3,000 *NA*

A Challenger shooting gallery, c1940.
£400-500 *NA*

A coin operated electric shock machine, battery operated, c1896.
£800-1,000 *NA*

A De Luxe Mercury one-armed bandit dispensing bubble gum, American, c1940.
£500-600 *NA*

This was an illegal gambling machine.

A Jusomat orange juice extractor, American, c1940, 9½in (24cm) high.
£80-100 *NA*

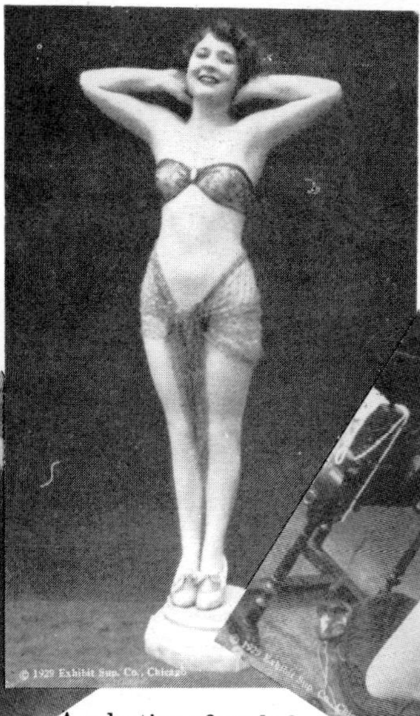

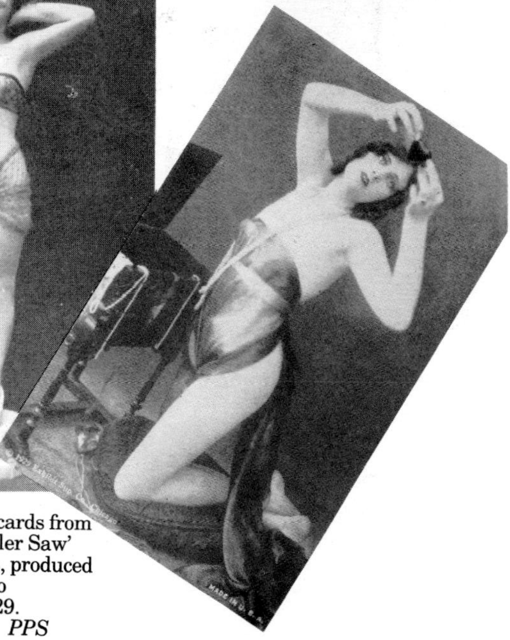

A selection of cards from 'What the Butler Saw' type machines, produced for the Chicago Exhibition 1929.
80p-£1 each *PPS*

KITCHENALIA

Bottle Openers

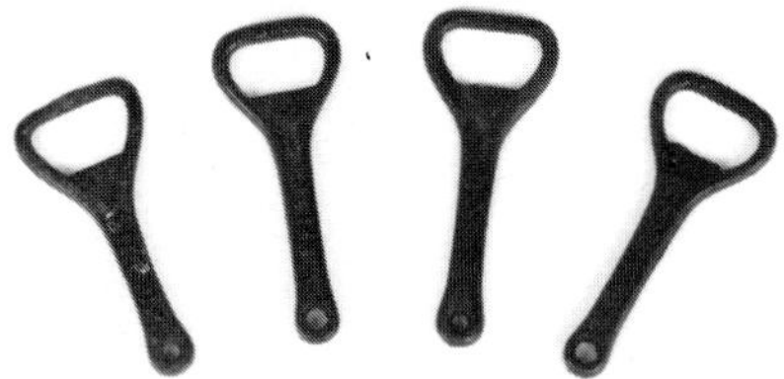

Advertising bottle openers, 4in (10cm) long.
50p-£1 each *DH*

Three bottle openers, 4½ to 5in (11 to 13cm).
£2-3 each *DH*

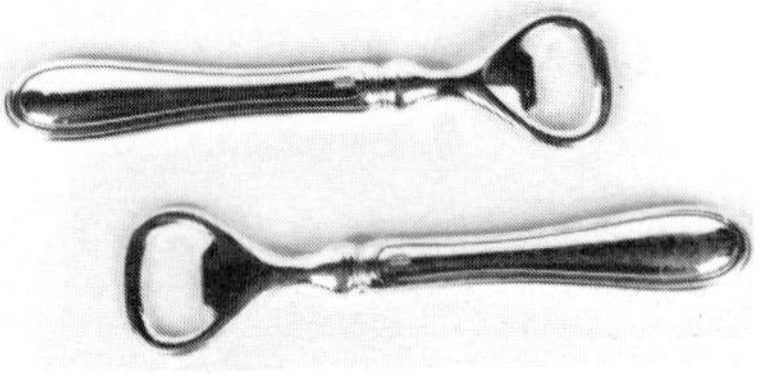

A pair of chrome bottle openers, 6in (15cm) long.
£1-2 *DH*

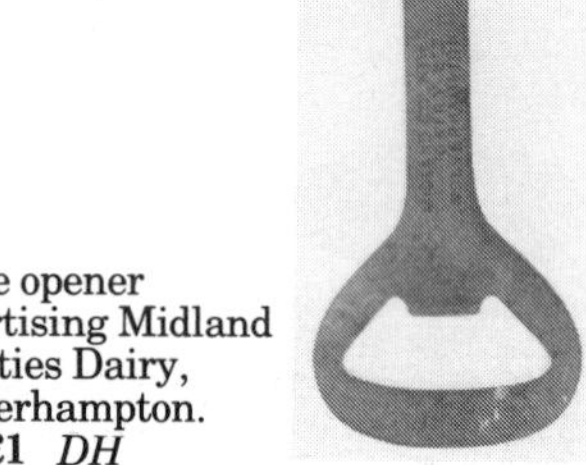

Bottle opener advertising Midland Counties Dairy, Wolverhampton.
50p-£1 *DH*

Ceramics

A Greens pottery egg separator.
£8-12 *AL*

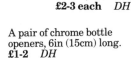

A tongue dish, 9½in (24cm) diam.
£25-30 *REL*

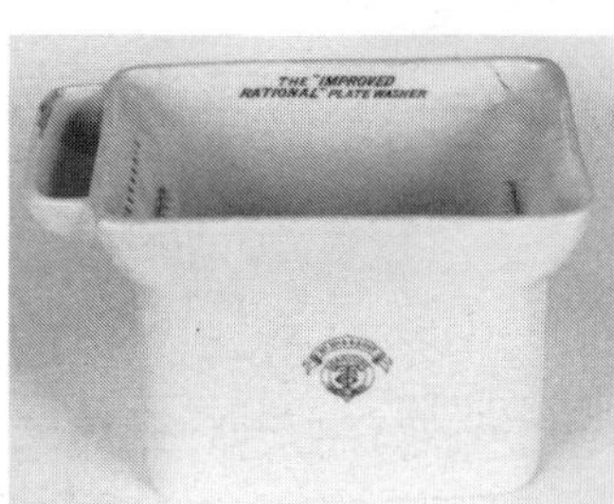

A plate washer, 6in (15cm) high.
£18-20 *REL*

Hemmings, Northampton, pie dish, 6in (15cm) wide.
£10-15 *AL*

A milk bowl, 7in (18cm) diam.
£50-70 *AL*

An earthenware inhaler, with original box, 10½in (26cm) high.
£12-15 *AL*

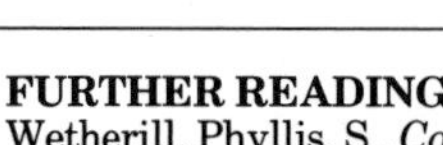

FURTHER READING
Wetherill, Phyllis, S., *Cookie Cutters and Cookie Molds: Art in the Kitchen.*
Kindig, Paul E., *Butter Prints and Molds,* Millbank Books, U.K.

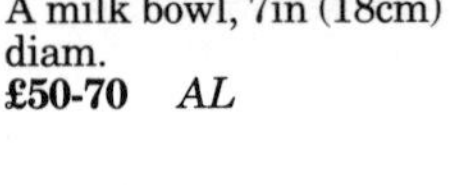

Cross Reference
Ceramics

Containers

A tin water or milk container, 5½in (14cm) high.
£5-6 *DH*

Possibly used on a barge.

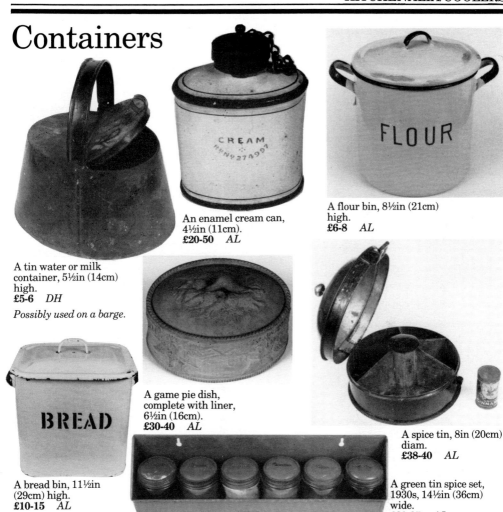

An enamel cream can, 4½in (11cm).
£20-50 *AL*

A flour bin, 8½in (21cm) high.
£6-8 *AL*

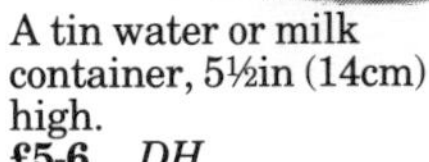

A game pie dish, complete with liner, 6½in (16cm).
£30-40 *AL*

A spice tin, 8in (20cm) diam.
£38-40 *AL*

BREAD

A bread bin, 11½in (29cm) high.
£10-15 *AL*

A green tin spice set, 1930s, 14½in (36cm) wide.
£20-25 *AL*

Coolers

Two terracotta butter coolers, 8½in (21cm) wide.
£10-12 each *AL*

A red clay butter cooler, 7½in (18cm) diam.
£12-15 *AL*

Coffee Grinders

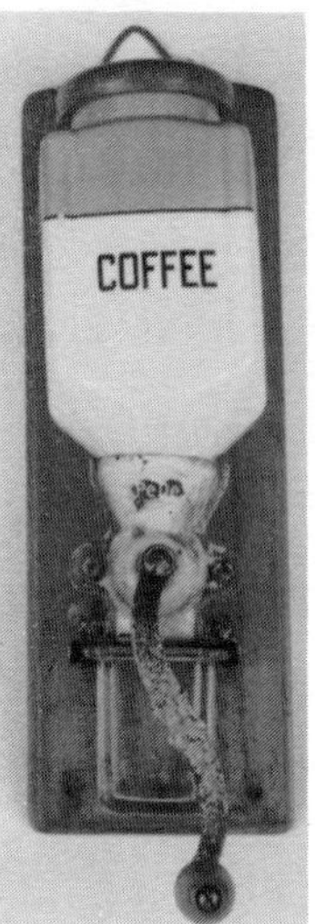

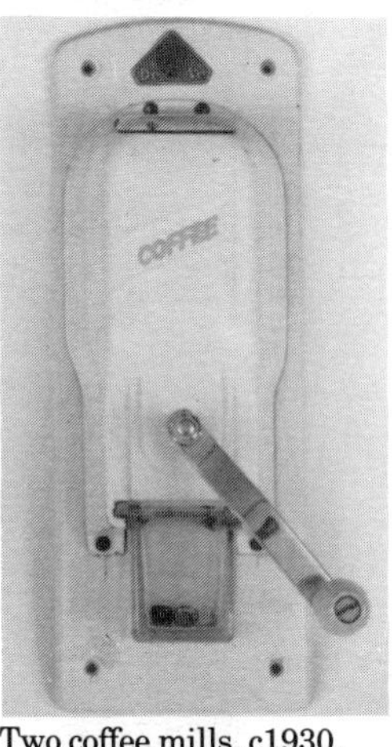

Two coffee mills, c1930, 13in (33cm) high.
£20-25 each *AL*

MAKE THE MOST OF MILLERS
Condition is absolutely vital when assessing the value of any item. Damaged pieces appreciate much less than perfect examples. However, a rare, desirable piece may command a high price even when damaged.

A coffee grinder.
£8-10 *WHA*

A food slicer.
£4-6 *WHA*

Cutters

Wood and bone pastry cutters.
£7-12 each *AL*

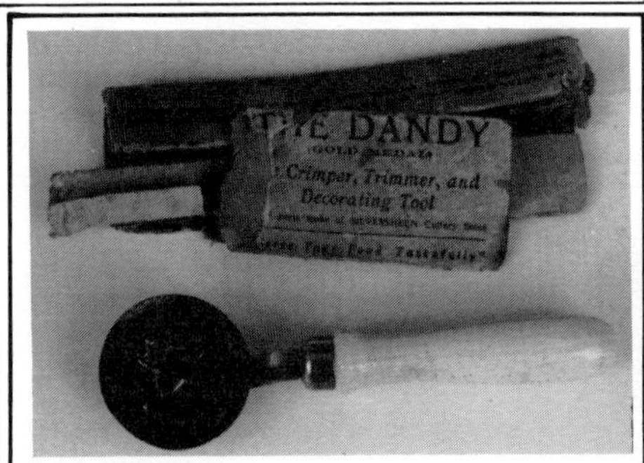

A silversheen pastry cutter and crimper.
£8-10 *AL*

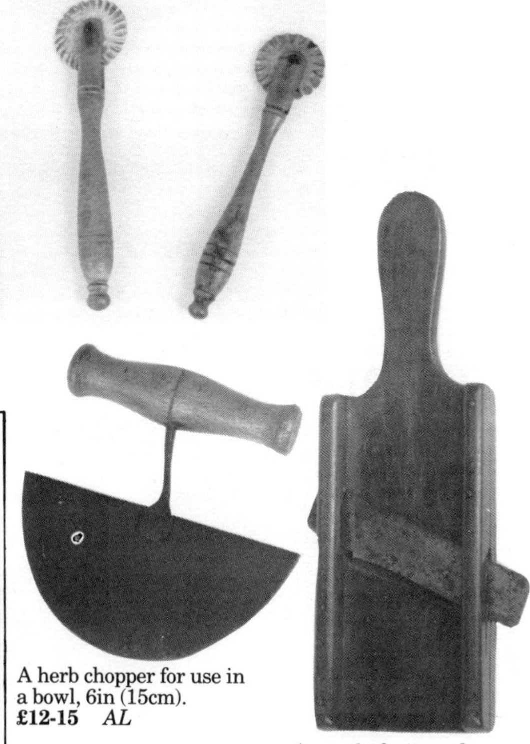

A herb chopper for use in a bowl, 6in (15cm).
£12-15 *AL*

An early fruitwood cucumber cutter, 9in (23.5cm) long.
£10-15 *AL*

Feeders

A ceramic feeder with green decoration, 2in (5.5cm) high.
£4-6 *AL*

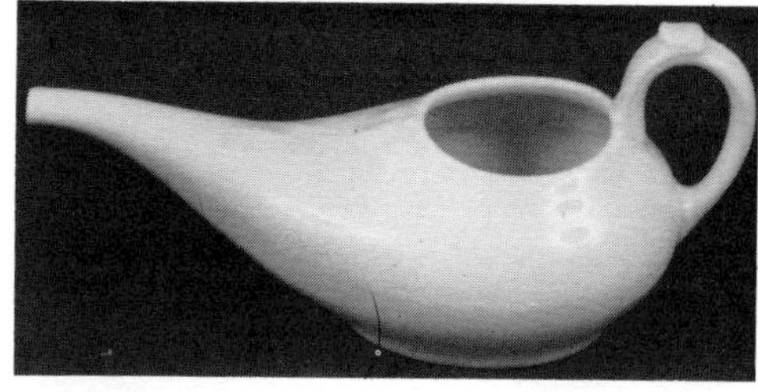

Ceramic feeder
£6-12 *AL*

Bread cutter, 18in (45cm) long.
£55-60 *MCA*

Gadgets

An American apple peeler and corer, used in a pie factory.
£50-60 *AL*

A spinning wheel, c1850, 33½in (84cm) high.
£230-250 *MCA*

A tin potato flourer, 12in (31cm) long.
£7-10 *AL*

Corn winders for making twine, 19thC.
£250-300 *MCA*

Both have to be used.

Glassware

A green pressed glass honey pot, 5½in (14cm) high.
£20-25 *AL*

A ham stand, 7½in (18cm) high.
£26-30 *AL*

Cross Reference
Glass

A glass biscuit jar, Meredith & Drew, 8in (20cm) high.
£22-25 *AL*

Irons

It is believed that the Chinese were the first people to use heat in the pressing process, a system not used in Europe until the 16thC. In the 19thC many new types of iron were invented to deal with new fashions; fluters, crimpers and goffering irons were used for pleating.

A selection of flat irons.
£15-30 each *AL*

A smoothing iron, 5in (14cm) long.
£3-5 *DH*

A charcoal iron.
£40-60 *PC*

DID YOU KNOW?
A Sadiron comes from 'sad' meaning heavy bodied, and was usually heated on cooking or laundry stoves.

An American petrol iron, late 19thC, 9in (23.5cm).
£60-80 *PC*

A box iron, 8in (20cm) high.
£10-15 *DH*

A wooden handled iron, with slug.
£32-35 *AL*

The slug was heated and placed inside the iron.

A travelling iron in original box, priced 3/11d.
£22-25 *AL*

A collection of flat irons, including charcoal, petrol, gas, sad and polishing irons.
£10-15 each *TM*

Two charcoal irons.
£40-60 each *PC*

Pepper Mills

An Italian wooden pepper mill, 3in (9cm) high.
£7-10 *AL*

A French brass pepper mill, 4in (10cm) high.
£20-25 *AL*

A French pepper mill in wood and copper, 3½in (9cm) high.
£15-20 *AL*

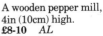

A wooden pepper mill, 4in (10cm) high.
£8-10 *AL*

Metalware

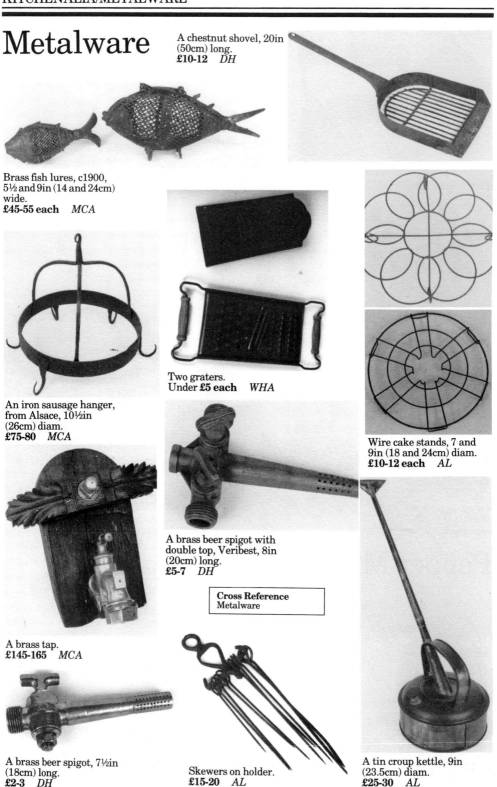

A chestnut shovel, 20in (50cm) long.
£10-12 *DH*

Brass fish lures, c1900, 5½ and 9in (14 and 24cm) wide.
£45-55 each *MCA*

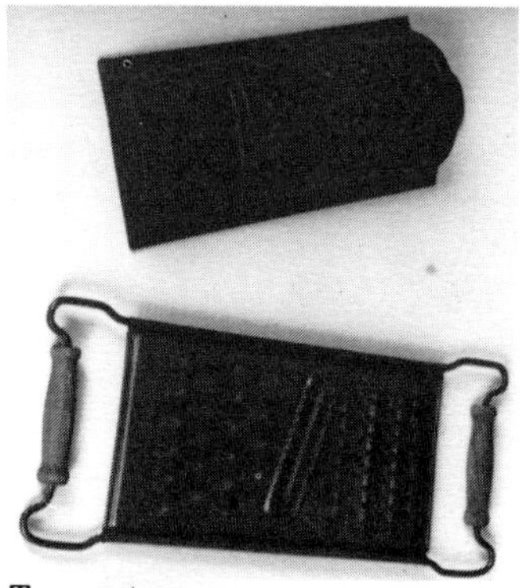

Two graters.
Under **£5 each** *WHA*

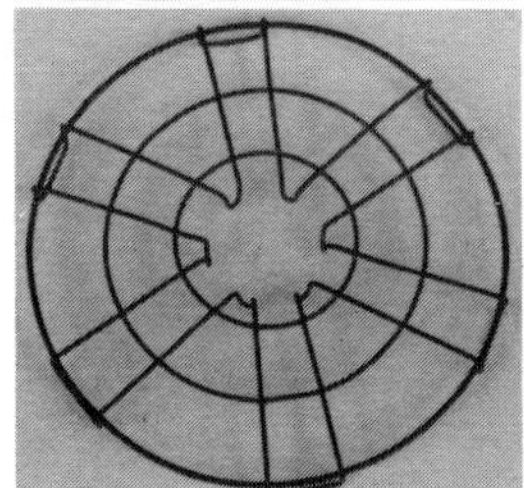

Wire cake stands, 7 and 9in (18 and 24cm) diam.
£10-12 each *AL*

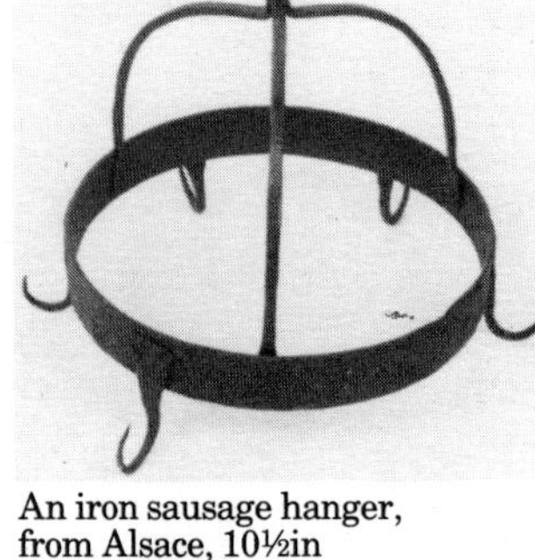

An iron sausage hanger, from Alsace, 10½in (26cm) diam.
£75-80 *MCA*

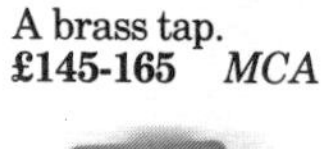

A brass tap.
£145-165 *MCA*

A brass beer spigot with double top, Veribest, 8in (20cm) long.
£5-7 *DH*

Cross Reference
Metalware

A brass beer spigot, 7½in (18cm) long.
£2-3 *DH*

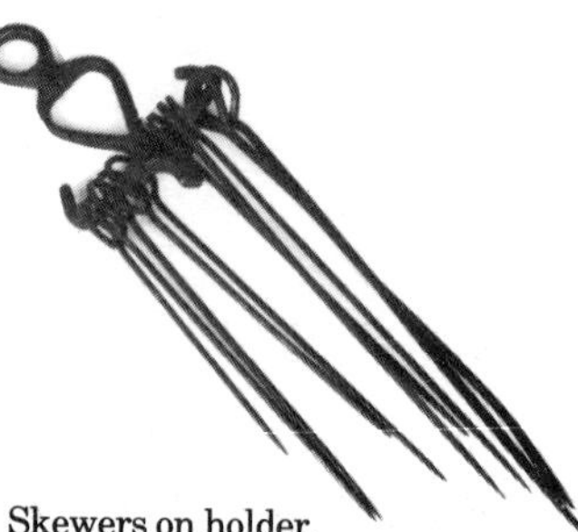

Skewers on holder.
£15-20 *AL*

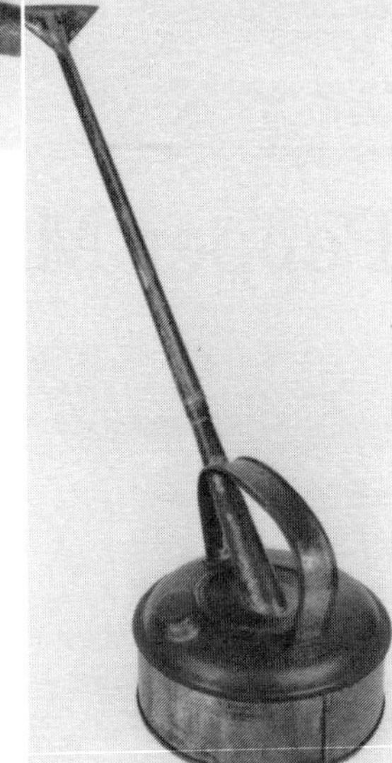

A tin croup kettle, 9in (23.5cm) diam.
£25-30 *AL*

Mincers

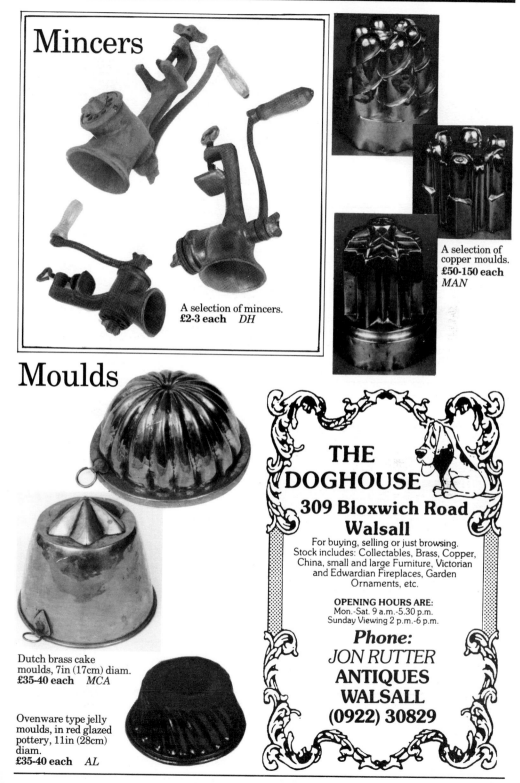

A selection of mincers.
£2-3 each *DH*

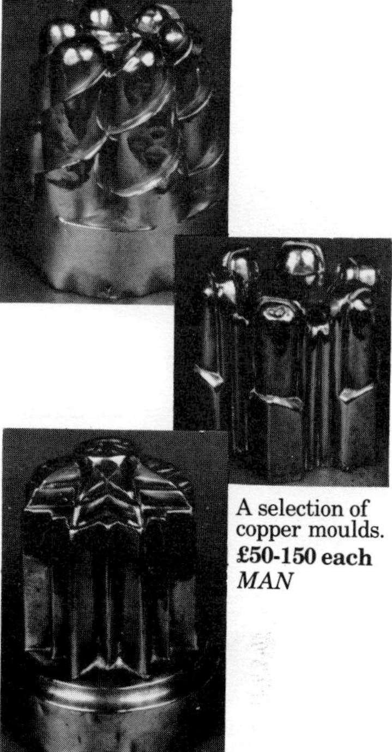

A selection of copper moulds.
£50-150 each
MAN

Moulds

Dutch brass cake moulds, 7in (17cm) diam.
£35-40 each *MCA*

Ovenware type jelly moulds, in red glazed pottery, 11in (28cm) diam.
£35-40 each *AL*

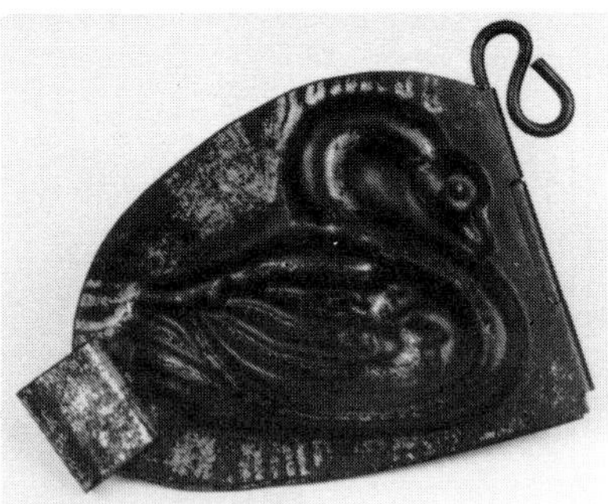

A tin mould of a swan.
£20-25 *AL*

A lead sweet mould, 3½in (9cm) diam.
£20-25 *AL*

A copper mould, 8in (20cm) long.
£50-55 *DH*

A tin Easter Egg mould, 5in (14cm) long.
£16-20 *AL*

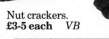

Metal nut crackers.
£2-4 each *VB*

Nutcrackers

Nut crackers.
£3-5 each *VB*

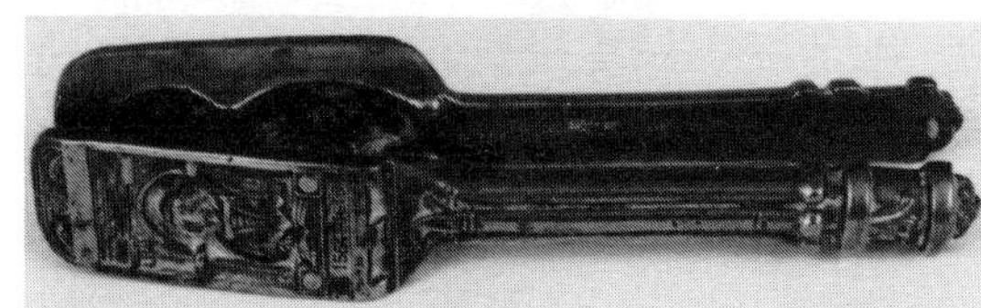

Brass nut crackers, 5½in (14cm) long.
£12-15 *AL*

Salts

Two salts.
£4-5 each *AL*

Glass salts.
£6-10 per pair *AL*

MAKE THE MOST OF MILLERS
Condition is absolutely vital when assessing the value of any item. Damaged pieces appreciate much less than perfect examples. However, a rare, desirable piece may command a high price even when damaged.

A pair of salts.
£7-8 *AL*

A ceramic sugar sifter with chrome top, marked Adams, England, 6in (15cm) high.
£16-20 *AL*

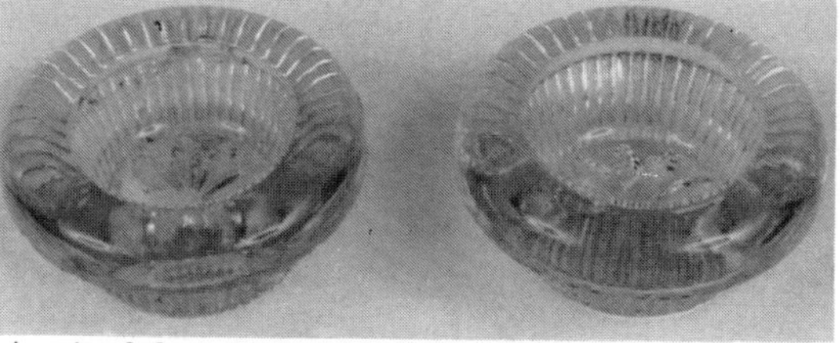

A pair of glass salts.
£6-7 *AL*

A chrome tea strainer, 7in (18cm) long.
£20-22 *AL*

Sifters & Strainers

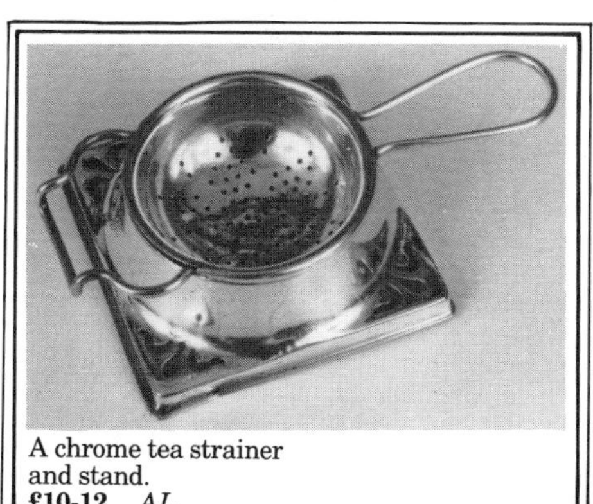

A chrome tea strainer and stand.
£10-12 *AL*

A tea strainer/maker, 6in (15cm).
£7-10 *AL*

A coffee strainer, 5½in (14cm).
£10-12 *AL*

Brass flour sifters, largest 5½in (14cm).
£50-60 each *AL*

A brass sugar shaker, 6½in (16.5cm) high.
£20-25 *AL*

A pewter tea strainer.
£12-15 *AL*

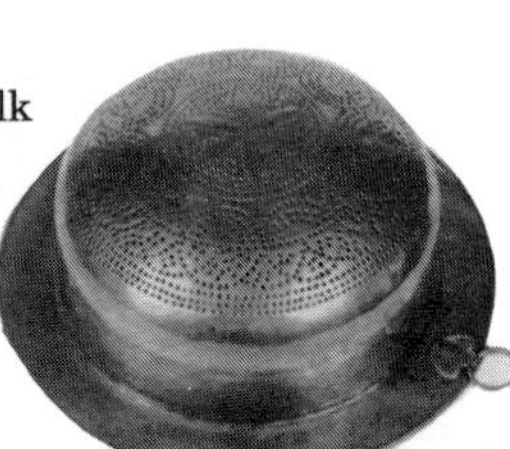

A brass milk strainer, 9in (23cm) diam.
£40-45 *MCA*

A sieve.
Under **£5** *WHA*

Squeezers

An amber glass squeezer.
£10-12 *AL*

A ceramic squeezer.
£10-12 *AL*

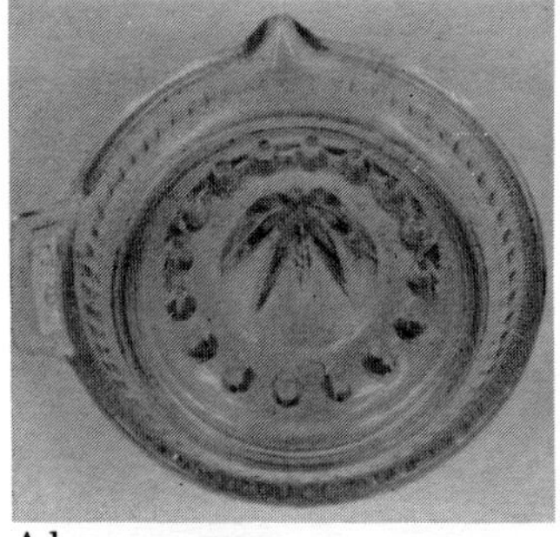

A lemon squeezer.
£2.50-3 *AL*

Two Bakelite lemon squeezers.
£7-10 each *AL*

Glass orange squeezers.
£4-7 *AL*

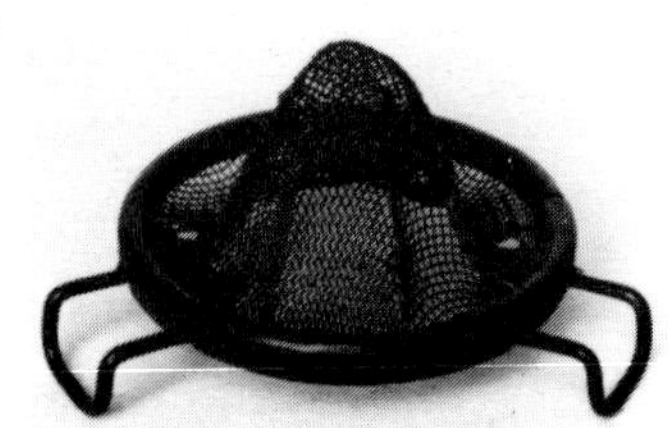

An orange squeezer.
£7-10 *AL*

Tin Openers

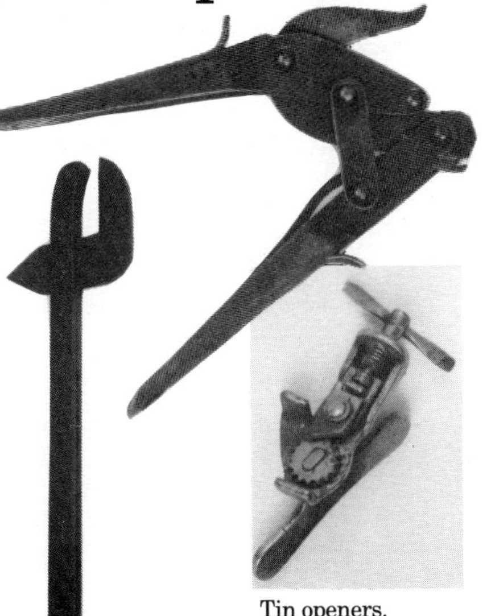

Tin openers.
£2.50-4 *AL*

A large iron can opener, 16in (40.5cm) long.
£12-15 *AL*

Wooden Items

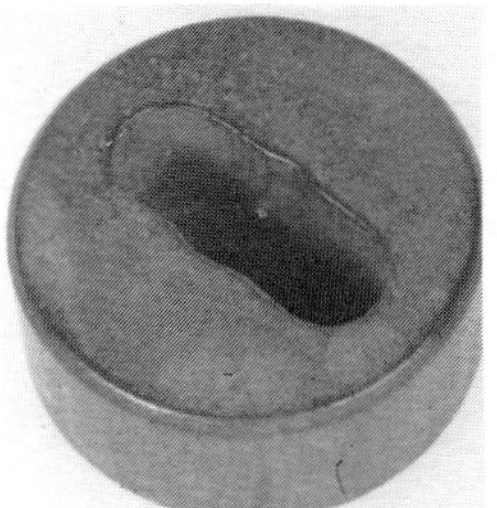

An opener for stopper bottles.
£1-2 *DH*

A dairy bucket.
£95-110 *MCA*

A fork, made from a natural tree branch, 19thC.
£25-30 *MCA*

Cross Reference
Treen

A French butter churn, 25½in (65cm) high.
£55-60 *MCA*

A pestle and mortar.
£18-20 *WHA*

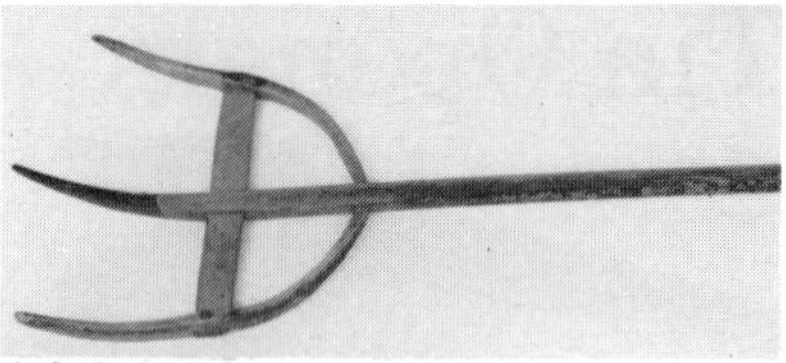

A fork with horn central prong, 19thC.
£55-60 *MCA*

A rolling pin, 18in (45.5cm) long.
£8-10 *DH*

A cheese board, 11in (28cm) diam.
£35-40 *MCA*

This wooden object was for pushing down the marble in a Codd type bottle.
£2-3 *DH*

A pine pestle and mortar shelf, 16in (40.5cm) high.
£75-80
Brass pestle and mortar.
£45-50 *MCA*

A wooden beer spigot, 8in (20.5cm) long.
£3-4 *DH*

A chopping board.
£45-55 *MCA*

Miscellaneous

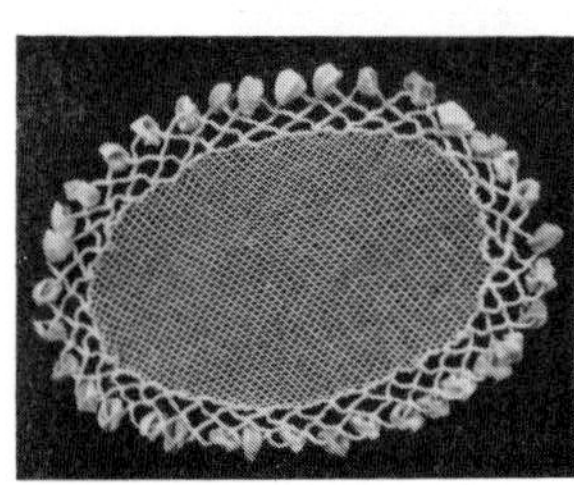

A net milk jug cover, edged with sea shells.
£10-12 *AL*

A Verwood pottery bread crock, damaged, c1830.
£35-40 *OBS*

A bottle basket.
£55-65 *MCA*

METALWARE

Brass

A naval brass mess tin, complete with tin liners, early 19thC, 13in (33cm) wide.
£250-300 *PCh*

A brass and copper cauldron, 9in (23cm) high.
£200-220 *MCA*

A brass trivet, 9½in (24cm) high.
£145-150 *MCA*

A brass Bachin, 18in (46cm) diam.
£175-185 *MCA*

A brass spittoon, 8in (20.5cm) diam.
£12-15 *DH*

A brass coal box, c1930.
£40-50 *OBS*

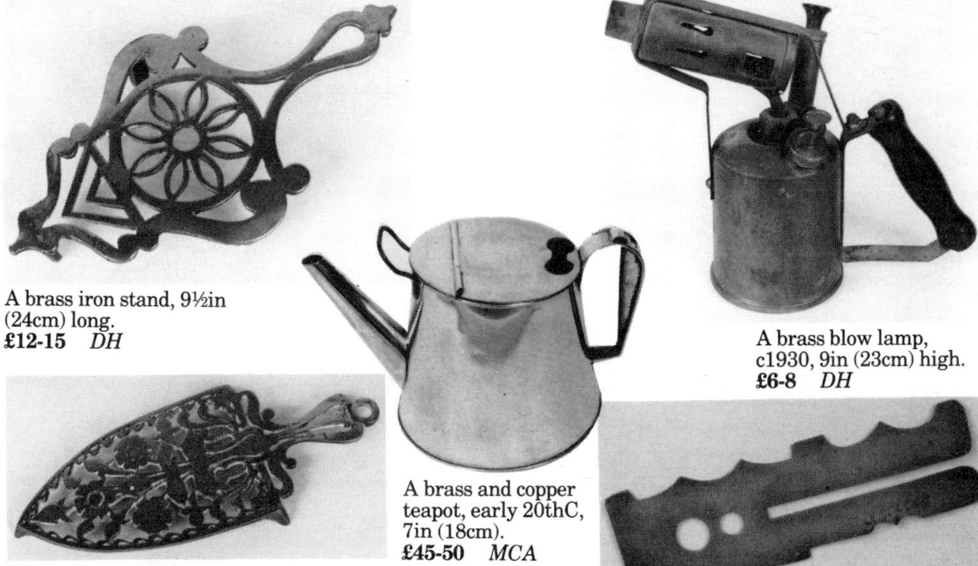

A brass iron stand, 9½in (24cm) long.
£12-15 *DH*

A brass blow lamp, c1930, 9in (23cm) high.
£6-8 *DH*

A brass iron stand, 19thC, 10½in (26cm) long.
£12-15 *DH*

A brass and copper teapot, early 20thC, 7in (18cm).
£45-50 *MCA*

A brass button cleaner, 6in (15cm) long. **£7-8** *AL*

A miniature brass chamber stick, 2½in (6cm) high.
£5-6 *DH*

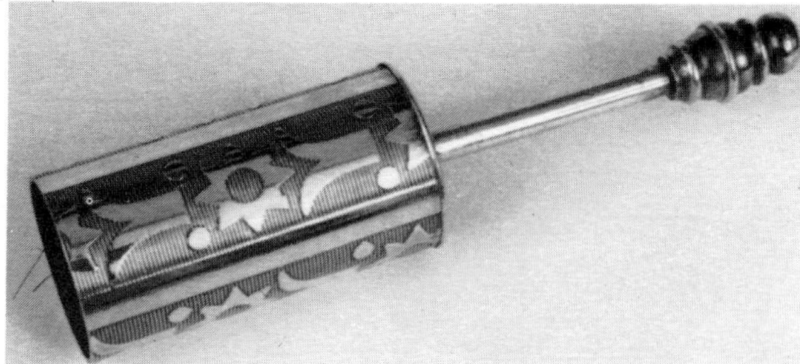

A brass crumb brush, 5in (12cm) long.
£10-15 *AL*

A brass soap dish, 4½in (11cm) wide.
£20-25 *AL*

A late George III brass fireguard, 20in (50cm) wide. **£55-60** *SAD*

Cross Reference
Candlesticks

A brass hearth brush, 11in (29cm) high.
£16-20 *AL*

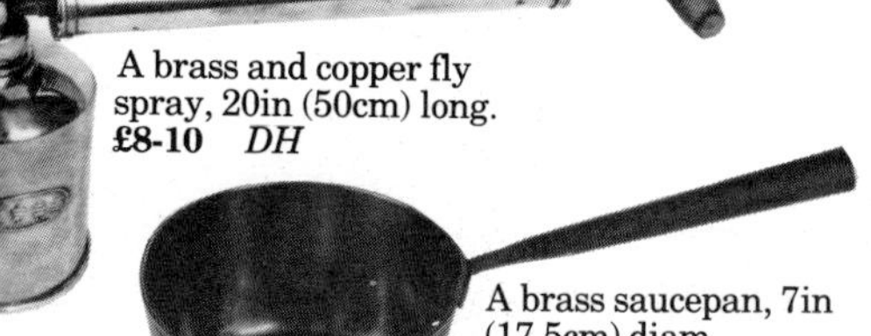

A brass and copper fly spray, 20in (50cm) long.
£8-10 *DH*

A brass saucepan, 7in (17.5cm) diam.
£25-30 *SAD*

A brass kettle stand, 18thC, 10in (25cm) high.
£55-60 *SAD*

A pair of miniature brass candlesticks, 2in (6cm) high.
£2-3 *DH*

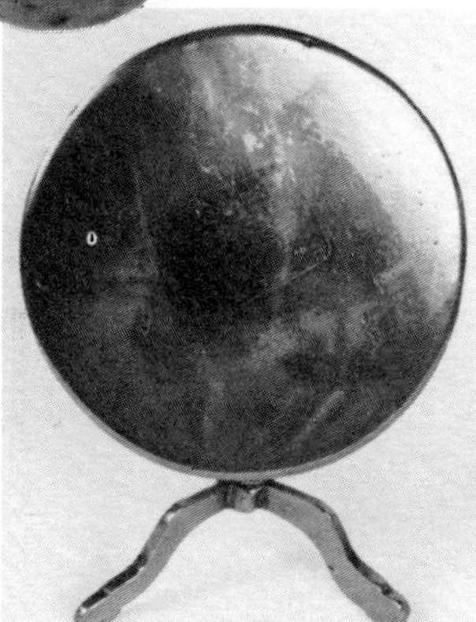

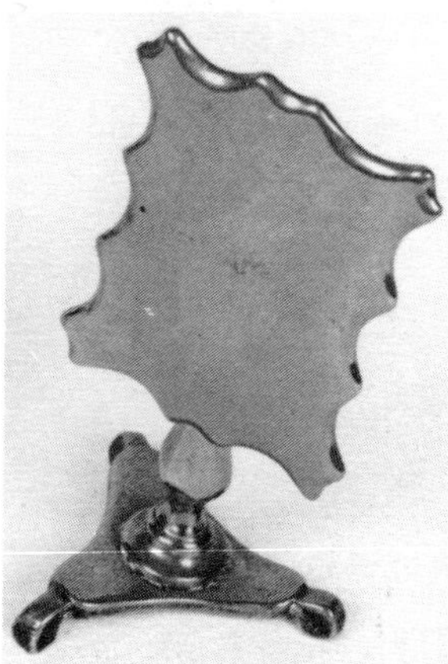

Two miniature brass tip-top tables, 4½in (11cm) high.
£10-12 each *DH*

Bronze

A pair of bronze fountain heads, modelled as dolphins, 17½in (44.5cm) wide.
£250-300 *CSK*

A bronze figure, cast from a model by Gregoire Calvet, 'L'Âme Antique', inscribed on base, 1899, 27½in (70cm). **£800-1,000** *P*

A bronze figure of a terrier, on marble plinth, 8in (20.5cm) high. **£100-120** *PCh*

An English bronze group of the Tarpeian Rock, signed and dated on the base 'G. Halse Sc.t London 1860', 25in (63cm).
£1,200-1,500 *C*

Copper

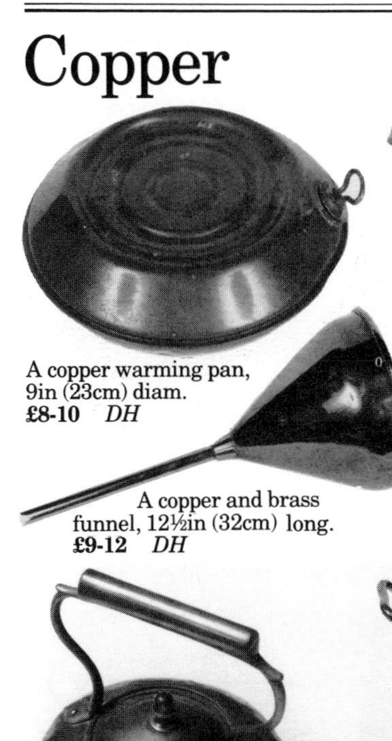

A copper warming pan, 9in (23cm) diam.
£8-10 *DH*

A copper and brass funnel, 12½in (32cm) long.
£9-12 *DH*

A copper tea urn, 20in (51cm) high.
£45-50 *DH*

A Georgian copper jug, 7in (18cm) high.
£75-85 *CAC*

A copper jam pan, early 20thC, 13in (33cm) diam.
£140-150 *MCA*

A Victorian copper kettle.
£45-50 *OBS*

A copper kettle, 9½in (24cm) high. **£35-40** *DH*

A copper pot with iron handle, mid-19thC, 12½in (32cm) high.
£145-150 *MCA*

A copper fish kettle with drainer, late 19thC, 20in (51cm) wide.
£375-400 *MCA*

A copper jug, 11½in (29cm) high.
£10-15 *DH*

An embossed copper tray, 6in (15cm) diam.
£10-15 *OBS*

A copper hot water bottle.
£18-20 *OBS*

A copper jardinière, 8in (20.5cm) high.
£25-30 *DH*

A copper kettle, c1900.
£30-40 *OBS*

A copper washing dolly, 40in (101.5cm) long.
£30-35 *SAD*

A Georgian copper pan lid, 12in (30.5cm) diam.
£35-40 *SAD*

A copper pot stand, with iron legs, 21in (53.5cm) wide.
£30-40 *SAD*

A copper coal scuttle, 9in (23cm) high.
£30-35 *DH*

A copper crumb tray, 12in (30.5cm) wide.
£20-25 *SAD*

A copper milk churn, converted to a stick stand, 14in (35.5cm) high.
£40-45 *DH*

A copper desk calendar.
£20-25 *AL*

A copper kettle, 19thC.
£100-120 *DH*

Iron

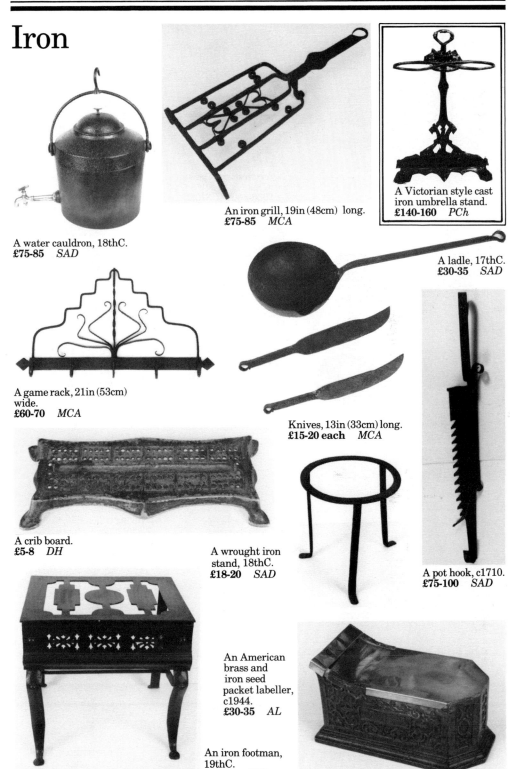

A water cauldron, 18thC.
£75-85 *SAD*

An iron grill, 19in (48cm) long.
£75-85 *MCA*

A Victorian style cast iron umbrella stand.
£140-160 *PCh*

A ladle, 17thC.
£30-35 *SAD*

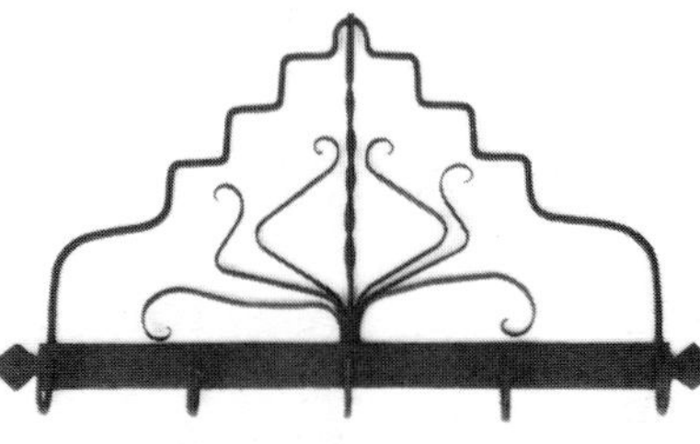

A game rack, 21in (53cm) wide.
£60-70 *MCA*

Knives, 13in (33cm) long.
£15-20 each *MCA*

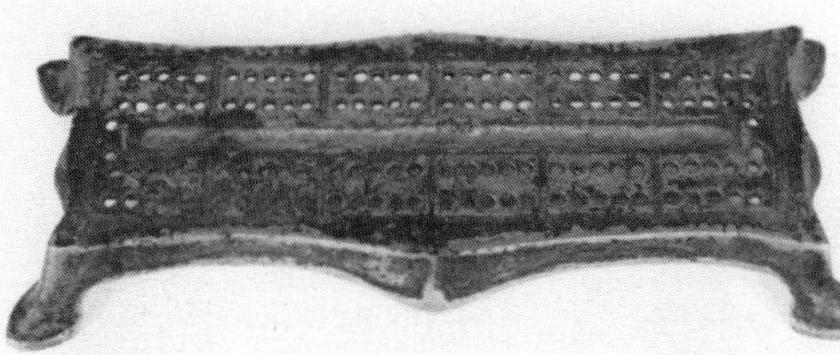

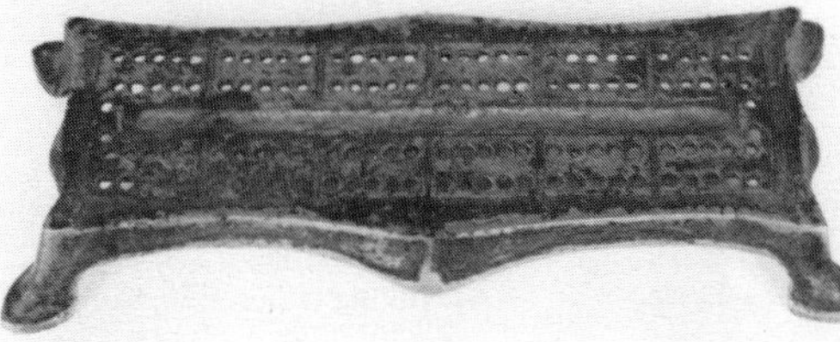

A crib board.
£5-8 *DH*

A wrought iron stand, 18thC.
£18-20 *SAD*

A pot hook, c1710.
£75-100 *SAD*

An iron footman, 19thC.
£45-55 *SAD*

An American brass and iron seed packet labeller, c1944.
£30-35 *AL*

Pewter

A pewter tray, 12in (30.5cm) diam.
£5-8 *DH*

A collection of pewter items.
£350-400 *CSK*

A ladle, c1770, with good touchmarks.
£175-200 *SAD*

A pair of pewter candlesticks, c1779, 6in (15cm) high.
£250-300 *SAD*

A Victorian tankard, 5in (12.5cm) high.
£55-65 *SAD*

Cross Reference
Candlesticks

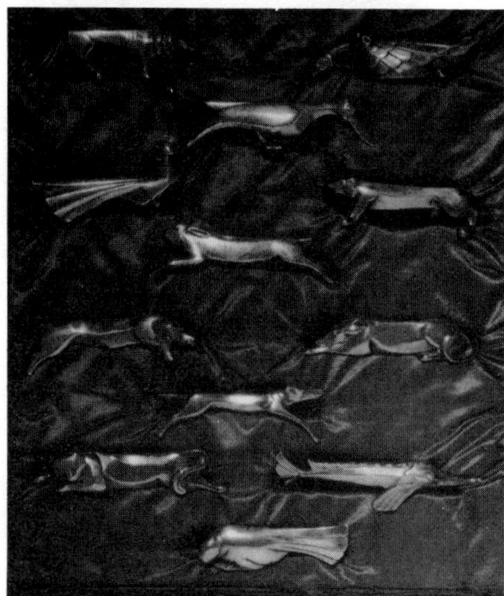

A set of 12 polished pewter knife rests, each stamped O. Gallia, with fitted case.
£1,000-1,500 *C*

A pewter candlestick, early 19thC, 6½in (16.5cm) high.
£175-200 *SAD*

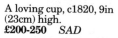

A loving cup, c1820, 9in (23cm) high.
£200-250 *SAD*

A pewter funnel, 6in (15cm) long.
£15-18 *AL*

Silver

A marrow scoop by Peter and Anne Bateman, c1797, 9in (23cm) long.
£150-160 *CLI*

Silver baskets.
£200-300 each
CSK

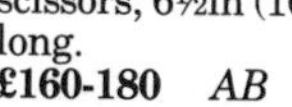

A pair of American sterling silver grape scissors, 6½in (16cm) long.
£160-180 *AB*

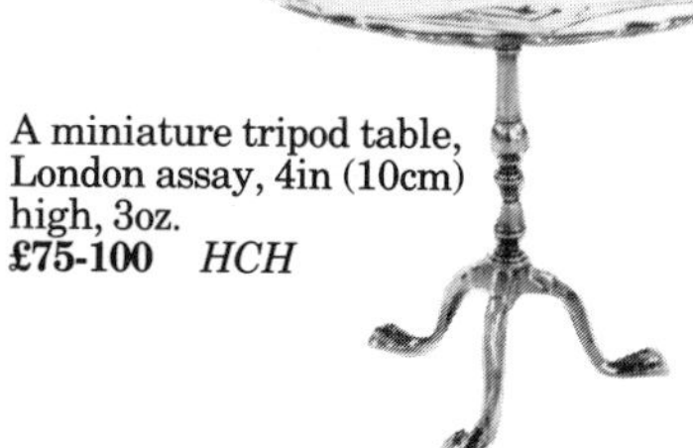

A miniature tripod table, London assay, 4in (10cm) high, 3oz.
£75-100 *HCH*

A ring box, Birmingham, 1909, 3½in (9cm) wide.
£140-150 *CLI*

A silver and tortoiseshell box, London, c1915, 2in (5cm) diam.
£140-150 *CLI*

Christening mugs, Sheffield, c1892, 2½in (6cm) high.
£125-200 each *CLI*

A matched pair of Georgian salts, c1760.
£240-260 *P*

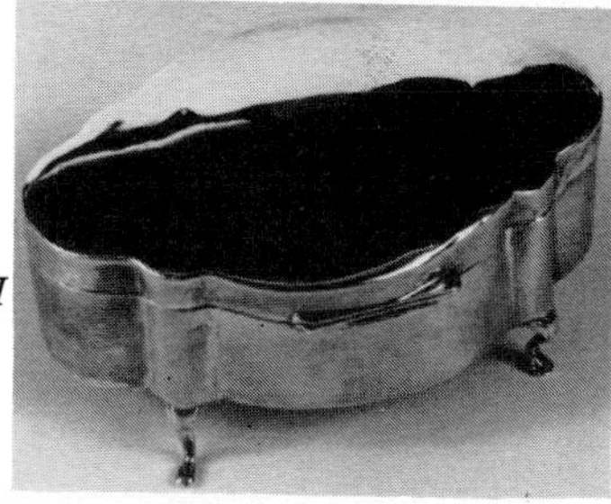

A ring box, Birmingham, 1921, 4½in (11.5cm) wide.
£120-140 *CLI*

A three-piece teaset, London, 1927, 40oz gross.
£380-400 *PCh*

Silver Plate

A figure riding a broomstick, La Sorcière, c1920, 5in (12.5cm).
£750-850 *C*

Cross Reference
Candlesticks

An oak salad bowl with plated mounts, and matching servers, early 20thC.
£240-260 *PCh*

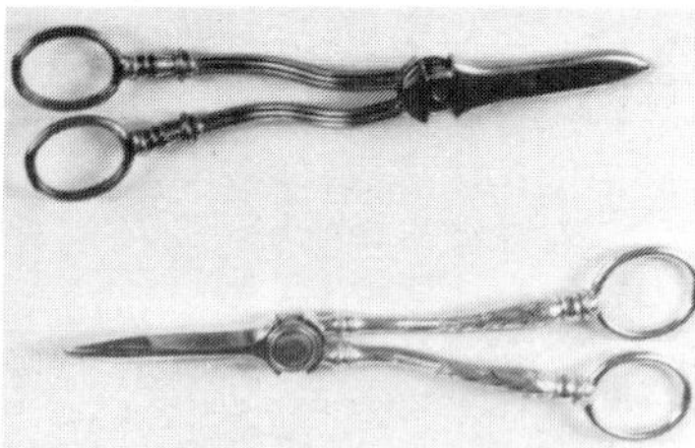

Grape scissors.
£50-75 each *CLI*

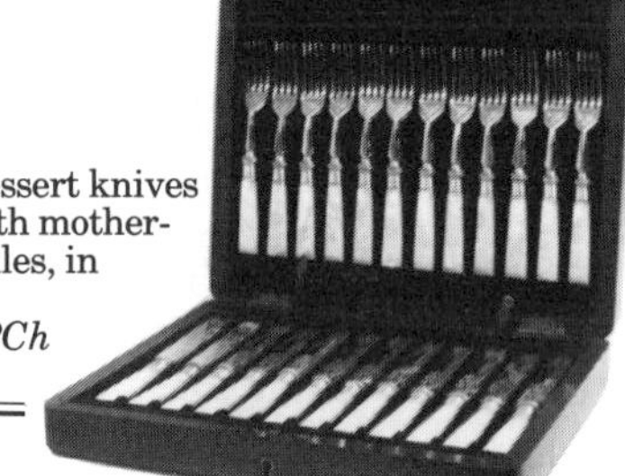

A set of 12 dessert knives and forks, with mother-of-pearl handles, in walnut case.
£150-180 *PCh*

Spelter

A late Victorian figure, 10in (25cm) high.
£25-30 *DH*

An Art Deco spelter group, mounted on an onyx base, 26½in (67cm).
£200-250 *P*

A pair of late Victorian figures, 22in (56cm) high.
£125-150 *DH*

Miscellaneous

A Britannia metal teapot, 6½in (16.5cm) high.
£15-20 *DH*

DID YOU KNOW?
Miller's Collectables Price Guide is designed to build up, year by year, into the most comprehensive reference system available.

Cross Reference
Ceramic Teapots

A tin hat box, 18in (46cm) diam.
£10-15 *DH*

Architectural Metalware

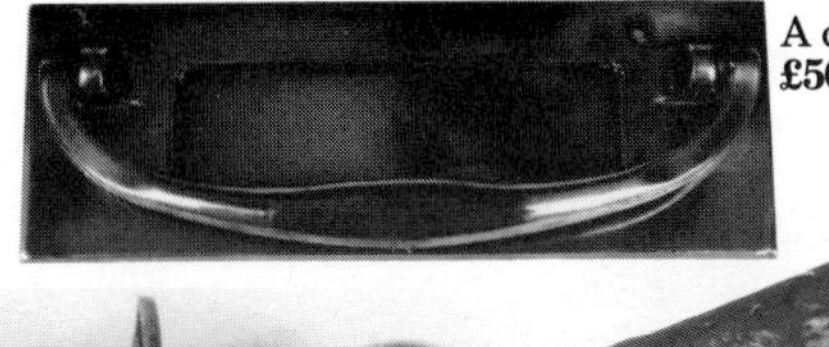

A copper letterbox.
£50-55 *CBA*

Bronze door handles, c1930.
£5-10 *DH*

An Art Nouveau style mild steel finger plate, originally coppered.
£5-20 *VF*

A Palace Motion door lock with brass handles.
£7-10 *DH*

Brass door handles.
£14-16 pair *CBA*

Bells

A brass hand bell.
£15-20 *AL*

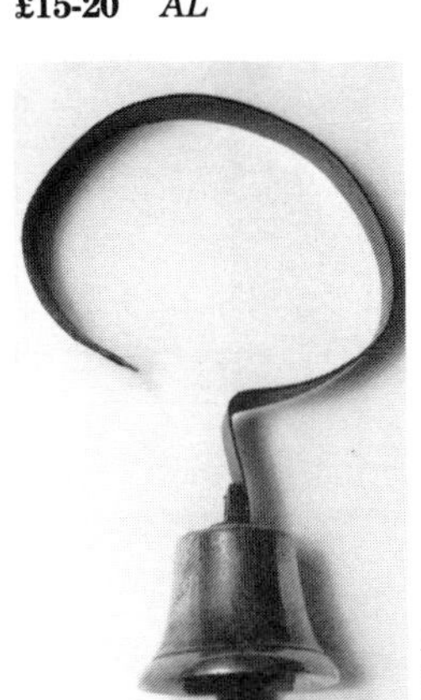

A Victorian bronze servants bell, with steel spring.
£18-20 *OBS*

A brass hand bell, 8½in (27cm) high.
£30-35 *AL*

A brass shop bell.
£18-20 *AL*

A brass shop bell.
£30-35 *AL*

A brass counter bell, c1880.
£12-15 *OBS*

Measures

A set of 8 measures with brass handles, from 1 gallon to ¼ gill.
£500-550 *AG*

Tin measures, 3 to 6in (7.5 to 15cm).
£15-20 each *AL*

Copper measures, from 2 to 8in (5 to 20cm).
£160-170 *PP*

Six Victorian bell metal tankards, from quart size to ½ gill.
£340-380 *WIL*

Toasting Forks

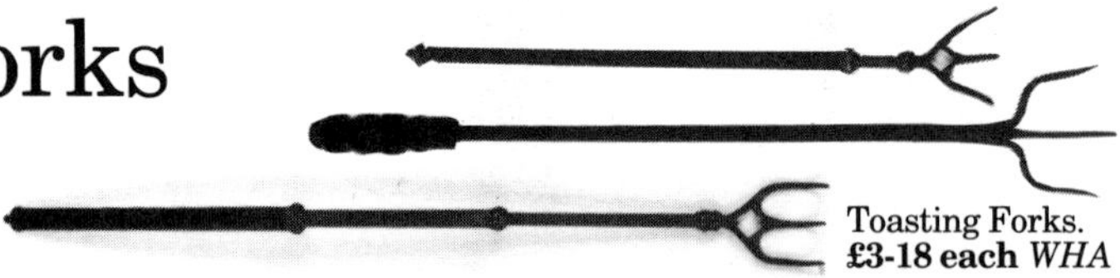

Toasting Forks.
£3-18 each *WHA*

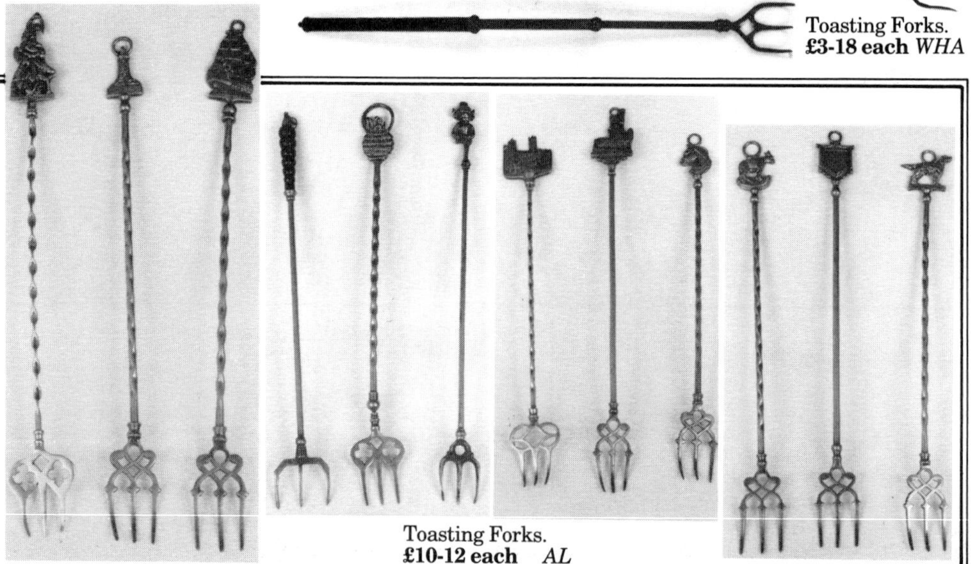

Toasting Forks.
£10-12 each *AL*

Air Pistols

An Abas Major air pistol, c1945.
£150-300 *VAG*

Only approx. 1,800 were made.

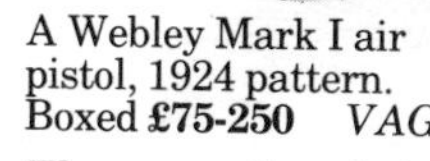

A Webley Mark I air pistol, 1924 pattern. Boxed **£75-250** *VAG*

There were 41 variations of this model.

A German Diana air pistol, 1920s.
£50-150 *VAG*

A German Tell II pre-war pistol.
£35-110 *VAG*

A Westley Richards 'Highest Possible' air pistol, c1907.
£250-500 *VAG*

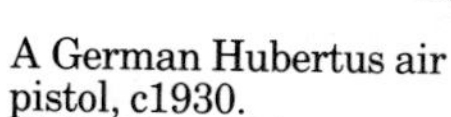

A German Hubertus air pistol, c1930.
£100-200 *VAG*

Difficult to date as records were lost during the last war.

A German Haenel model 28 air pistol, 1930s. **£75-175** *VAG*

Webley Senior slant grip pistols.
Pre-war **£75-150** *VAG*
Post-war **£50-150** *VAG*

A Webley Senior straight grip pistol, c1930.
£100-300 *VAG*

Air Rifles

A Webley Mark I air rifle, 1924 pattern.
£200-650 *VAG*

A Webley Mark II service air rifle, pre-war.
£150-750 cased *VAG*

An Oscar Will rifle, 1896 pattern.
£375-400 *VAG*

A rare Czechoslovakian VZ.36 prototype military training air rifle, c1936.
£950-1,250 *VAG*

A B.S.A. Improved model D rifle, c1910, 43½in (109cm).
£75-350 *VAG*

A B.S.A. light pattern, pre-war, 39½in (100cm).
£50-250 *VAG*

An Oscar Will bugle spanner, 1890-1920.
£250-300 *VAG*

A Lincoln Jefferies air rifle, c1908, cased, 43½in (109cm).
£150-750 *VAG*

A B.S.A. S pattern rifle, pre-war, 45½in (114cm).
£75-350 *VAG*

A German Haenil 4E repeater rifle, dated 12.11.36.
£400-650 *VAG*

Theoben Classic custom made field target rifles, stockwork by Kaboyashi, c1989.
£750-1,250 each *VAG*

Badges

A Victorian officer's gilt, silver and enamel cap of The Royal Fusiliers, damaged.
£50-80 *WAL*

A post-1902 officer's gilt and silver plated glengarry of The Black Watch.
£85-95 *WAL*

An Edward VII officer's gilt and silver plated forage cap badge of the Grenadier Guards.
£75-100 *WAL*

l. Royal Scots.
c. Cameron Highlanders.
r. Seaforth Highlanders.
£3-4.50 each *RMC*

The Lincolnshire Regiment.
£3-4.50 *RMC*

An other ranks white metal cap of the 2nd Volunteer Battalion The Lincolnshire Regiment.
£60-80 *WAL*

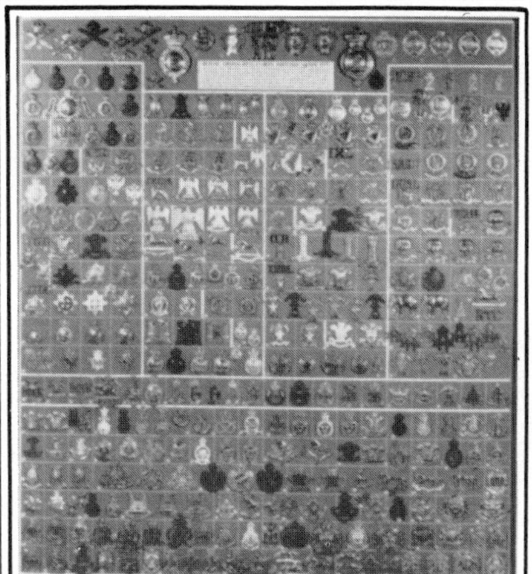

A collection of badges of Cavalry and Yeomanry regiments, mounted in a glazed case, 1939.
£2,500-3,000 *CSK*

An officer's gilt glengarry of The Kings Shropshire Light Infantry.
£100-120 *WAL*

A brass cap badge of the Tientsin British Municipal Volunteers, machine gun section.
£200-300 *WAL*

An other ranks white metal glengarry of the 5th Volunteer Battalion, The Royal Scots.
£40-50 *WAL*

An officer's silver cap of the Essex Regt, 1918.
£120-150 *WAL*

An officer's silver cap badge of the 9th Lancers, Birmingham, 1948.
£75-85 *WAL*

A post 1902 officer's gilt, silver plated and enamel cap of the Notts. and Derby Regiment.
£50-70 *WAL*

A post-1902 officer's gilt grenade glengarry of The Royal Scots Fusiliers, maker's plate of Anderson Edinburgh on back.
£40-50 *WAL*

An officer's gilt and silver plated forage cap badge of The Duke of Edinburgh, Wiltshire Regiment.
£75-100 *WAL*

The Royal Sussex Regiment.
£3-4.50 *RMC*

An officer's silver puggaree badge of The Hampshire Regiment, brooch pin, London, 1911.
£125-150 *WAL*

Various shoulder titles, collar badges, rank and trade badges.
50p-£2.00 each *RMC*

l. Royal Ulster Rifles.
£4-5 *RMC*
c. Alleyn's School O.T.C.
£8-10 *RMC*
r. Durham Light Infantry.
£3-4.50 *RMC*

An officer's silver cap of the 11th Battalion The Border Regiment, London, 1914.
£240-260 *WAL*

A piper's bonnet badge of the 5th Gurkha Rifles, worn 1931-47.
£40-50 *WAL*

The Dorsetshire Regiment.
£3-4.50 *RMC*

A late Victorian officer's silver coloured puggaree badge of The Hampshire Regiment, probably c1900.
£100-120 *WAL*

A silver cap badge of the Liverpool Pals, as given by Lord Derby to those joining before 16.10.14, London, 1914.
£75-100 *WAL*

Bayonets

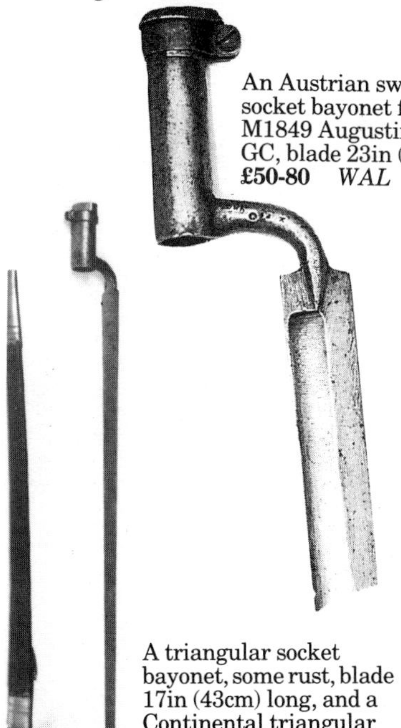

An Austrian sword socket bayonet for the M1849 Augustin rifle, GC, blade 23in (58cm).
£50-80 *WAL*

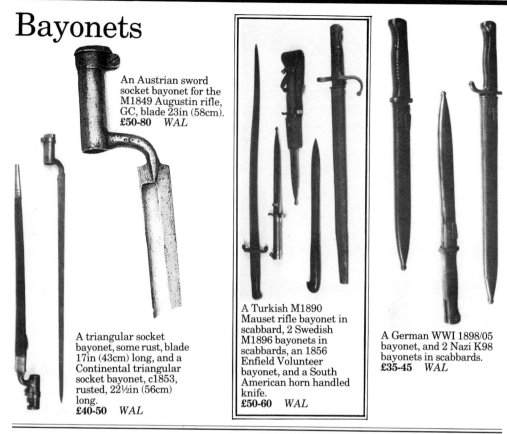

A triangular socket bayonet, some rust, blade 17in (43cm) long, and a Continental triangular socket bayonet, c1853, rusted, 22½in (56cm) long.
£40-50 *WAL*

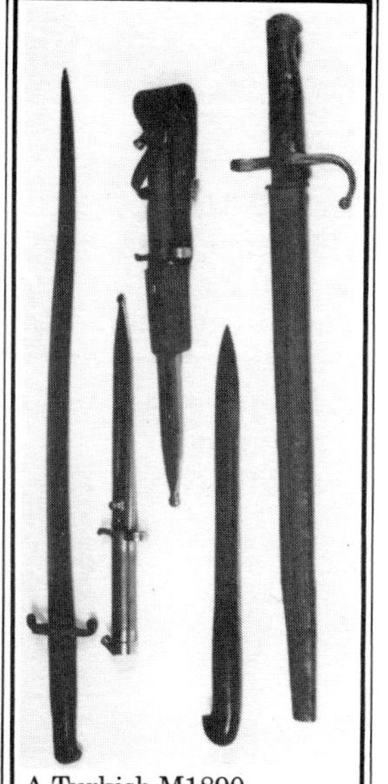

A Turkish M1890 Mauset rifle bayonet in scabbard, 2 Swedish M1896 bayonets in scabbards, an 1856 Enfield Volunteer bayonet, and a South American horn handled knife.
£50-60 *WAL*

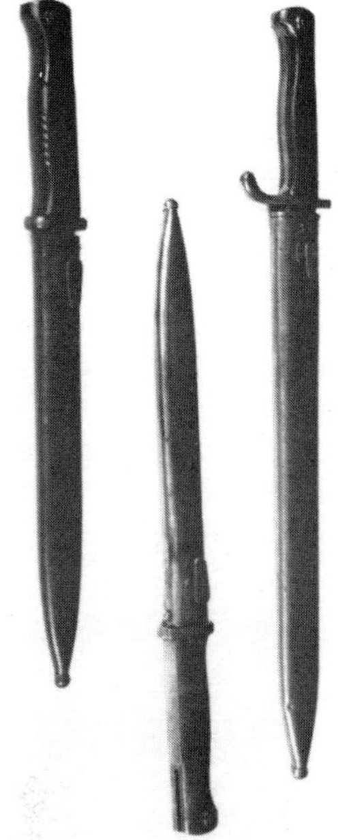

A German WWI 1898/05 bayonet, and 2 Nazi K98 bayonets in scabbards.
£35-45 *WAL*

Buckles

An officers waist belt clasp of the 2nd Admin. Bn. Forfar or Angus Rifle Volunteers, near VGC.
£60-80 *WAL*

A George V officer's full dress waist belt and plate of the 1st Royal Dragoons, some wear, GC.
£125-150 *WAL*

A Victorian Other Ranks white metal waist belt clasp of the 1st Lancashire Royal Engineers Volunteers, near VGC.
£80-100 *WAL*

A post-1902 officer's waist belt and clasp of the Calcutta Scottish Volunteers, near VGC.
£170-200 *WAL*

A pre-1881 officer's gilt and silver plated waist belt clasp of the 7th Royal Fusiliers, near VGC.
£70-80 *WAL*

A post-1902 officers waist belt and clasp, of the Royal Engineers Services, GC.
£80-100 *WAL*

Boer War

The following pages are representative of a unique collection of Boer War memorabilia. The collection encompasses every relevant area of collecting from ceramics to postcards. We have not cross referenced specific items as just about all of them could have been found in another section of this book. However, the collection is a marvellous example of 'theme' collecting, providing almost limitless areas for the collector to search.

Parian busts, c1900.
£50-80 each *PO*

Carlton Ware items with Ally Sloper's Half-holiday sketch.
l. **£35-50**
c. **£70-90**
r. **£120-150** *PO*

Ashtrays, depicting Field Marshall Lord Roberts and other Generals.
£35-60 each *PO*

A collection of silver brooches.
£8-30 each *PO*

A pair of French spelter lamps, by Rousseau, 26½in (67cm).
£500-600 *PO*

A terracotta plaque of General Sir Redvers Buller, by A. George.
£200-300 *PO*

Two tin vestas from a series issued with generals and 2 tin tape measures, most probably produced after WWI using old photographs.
£10-25 each *PO*

A selection of carved walking sticks.
£80-130 each *PO*

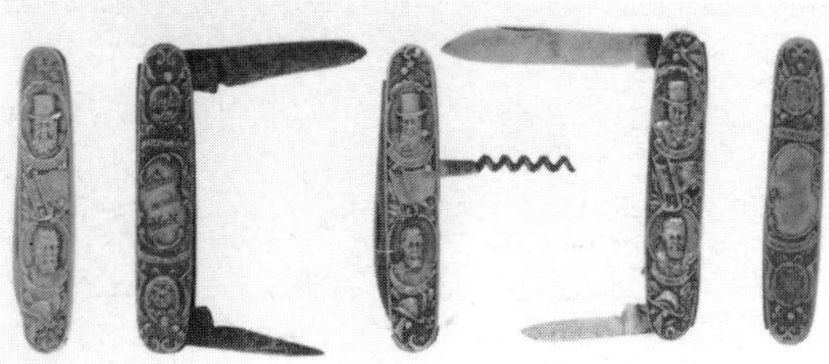

Knives.
£15-25 each *PO*

DID YOU KNOW?
Most soldiers carried pocket knives, many of which became collectors' items. Some carry names and initials, while others are unmarked. There were also scissors made with Boer War figures etched on them.

l. A caricature money box depicting President Kruger, 6½in (17cm) high.
£75-85
With pipe **£100-125**

r. A brass imitation reproduced and sold in the USA.
£15-25 *PO*

A medal.
£10-15 *PO*

Two gold rimmed plates with transfer printed battle scenes.
£40-60 *PO*

A note from Lord Kitchener on Transvaal Red Cross stationery.
£80-100 *PO*

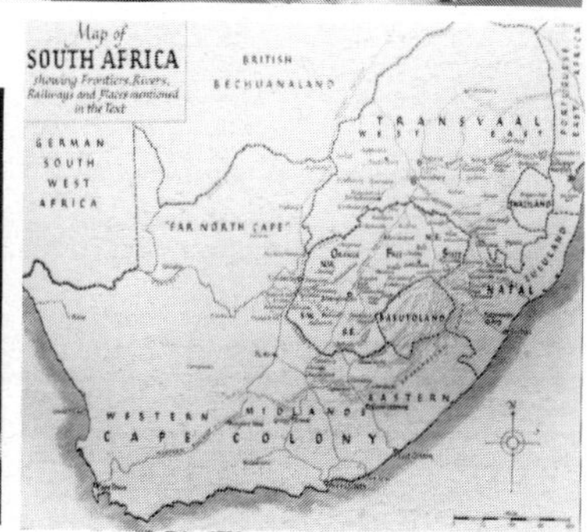

An ox cart made by a Boer prisoner-of-war.
£400-500 *PO*

A map of South Africa, c1900.
£15-25 *PO*

Two mugs and a match holder.
£30-45 each *PO*

Two pressed glass plates.
£20-30 *PO*

Examples of the music published during the Boer War.
£25-50 *PO*

Staffordshire figures.
£80-120 each *PO*

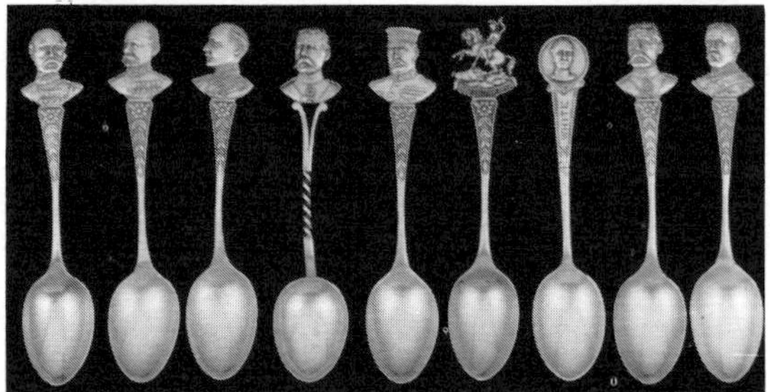

A selection of silver teaspoons.
£15-25 each *PO*

South African postcards.
£10-50 each *PO*

Embroidery.
£3-10 each *PO*

A set of Dutch plates depicting scenes from the Boer War.
£15-25 each *PO*

Various kinds of 'Gouvernements Noten' issued by the Zuid-Afrikaansche Republic, c1900.
£10-50 each *PO*

Condition is all important.

One of the most famous advertisements of the Boer War period.
£8-12 *PO*

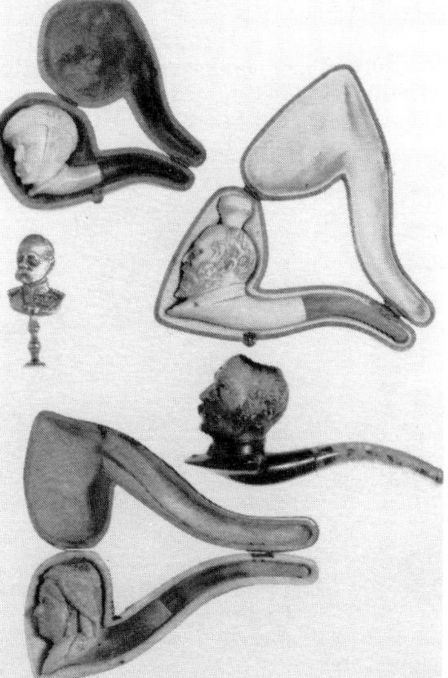

A collection of pipes and a pipe tamper.
£10-120 each *PO*

FURTHER READING
Oosthuizen, Pieter, *Boer War Memorabilia,* The Alderman Press, 1987.

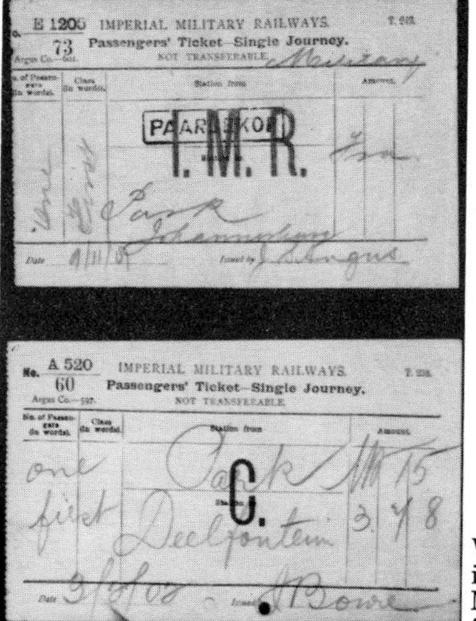

Wartime rail tickets issued by the Imperial Military Railways.
£5-10 each *PO*

A selection of silver items, c1900.
£25-60 each *PO*

Bugles

A Suffolk Regiment copper and brass bugle, W. Airedale.
£140-145 *MCA*

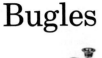

A Warwickshire brass bugle, C. Taylor.
£140-145 *MCA*

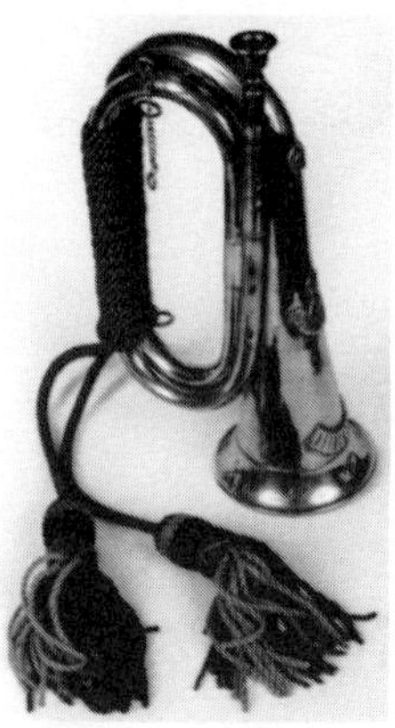

A Durham copper and brass bugle, E. Bennett.
£140-145 *MCA*

A Hampshire Regiment copper and brass bugle, Bugler Elder.
£140-145 *MCA*

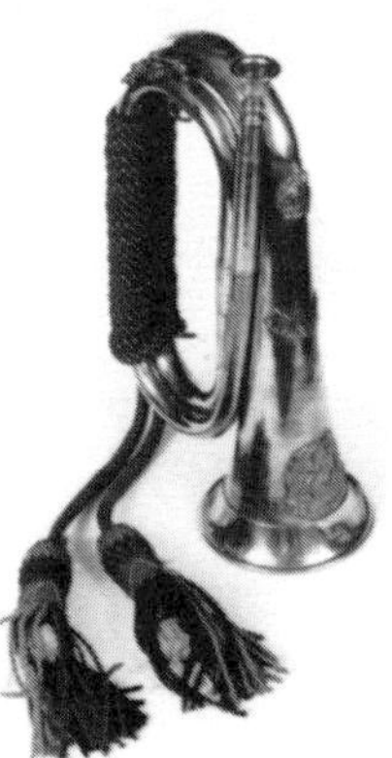

A West Yorkshire brass bugle, un-named.
£140-145 *MCA*

A Norfolk copper and brass bugle, S. Burns.
£140-145 *MCA*

Helmet Plates

The 14th Buckinghamshire Regiment, minor rubbing, GC.
£150-160 *WAL*

The 29th Worcestershire Regiment, GC.
£60-70 *WAL*

The Northamptonshire and Rutland Militia, GC.
£70-90 *WAL*

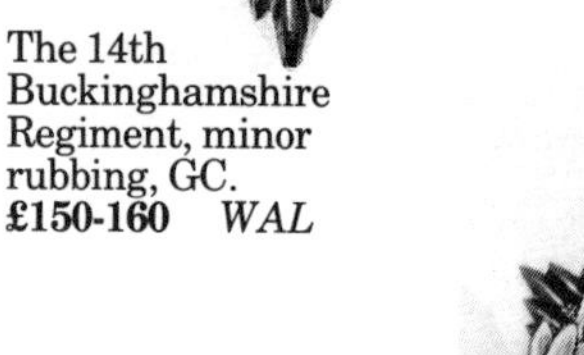

The North East Lancashire Vol. Infantry Brigade, in unissued state.
£90-100 *WAL*

The 3rd Vol. Bn. The Cheshire Regiment, VGC.
£90-100 *WAL*

2nd Royal Surrey Militia, Royal Crest in centre, GC.
£90-100 *WAL*

The 8th Lancashire Rifle Volunteers, GC.
£70-90 *WAL*

56th (West Essex) Regiment.
£200-220 *CSK*

65th (2nd Yorkshire North Riding) Regiment.
£200-220 *CSK*

Shoulder Belt Plates

The 72nd Duke of Albany's Own Highlanders.
£180-200 *WAL*

Argyll & Sutherland Highlanders.
£110-120 *CSK*

The Southwark (Princess Charlotte's Infantry) Volunteers, early 19thC.
£375-400 *CSK*

The 4th V.B. The Essex Regiment, unissued.
£180-200 *WAL*

A silver plated copper shoulder belt plate, GC.
£110-120 *WAL*

92nd Gordon Highlanders.
£110-120 *CSK*

Highland Light Infantry.
£100-120 *CSK*

The Manchester 2nd Vol. Battn. Regiment, GC.
£70-80 *WAL*

The 97th (Earl of Ulster's) Regiment, GC.
£170-180 *WAL*

Model Cannon

A Victorian brass model cannon, c1860, 9in (23cm) long.
£345-365 *ARB*

A brass model cannon, c1880.
£345-365 *ARB*

An iron cannon, c1760.
£200-250 *COB*

A model cannon in cast iron and brass, 8½in (21cm) long.
£110-120 *ARB*

A brass cannon, in shooting order, c1900, 6in (15cm) long.
£100-120 *ARB*

A Victorian gunmetal and oak model naval style carriage, 6in (15cm) long.
£300-350 *ARB*

DID YOU KNOW?
These collectors pieces were working scale models of the original cannon and were often used as ornaments.

A Victorian bronze, gunmetal model cannon, 10in (25cm) long.
£340-350 *ARB*

A Victorian desk model cannon, in shooting order, with gunmetal barrel, 6in (15cm) wide.
£300-350 *ARB*

A very rare sundial cannon for field artillery, in brass with steel fittings, 15in (38cm) long.
£4,500-5,000 *ARB*

These were placed on sundials and when the sun struck at a particular time, they fired. They can only operate accurately when used in France where it was designed.

Dirks

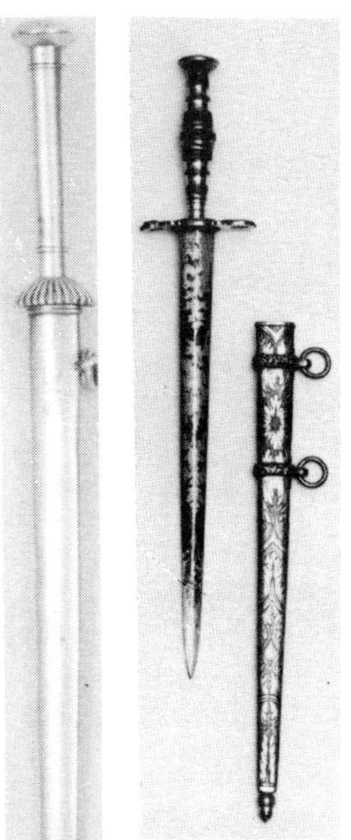

A small dirk with white metal hilt, etched blade 7in (18cm) long.
£100-120 *CSK*

A naval dirk with 9in (23cm) blade, in scabbard with 2 rings, c1820.
£350-400 *CSK*

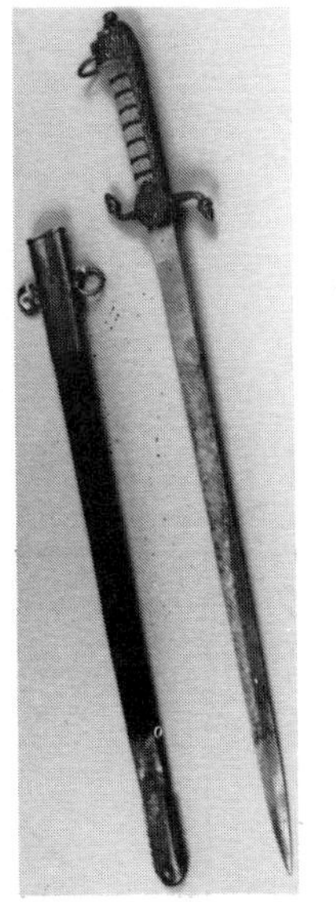

A Victorian Royal Navy midshipman's dirk.
£100-150 *PC*

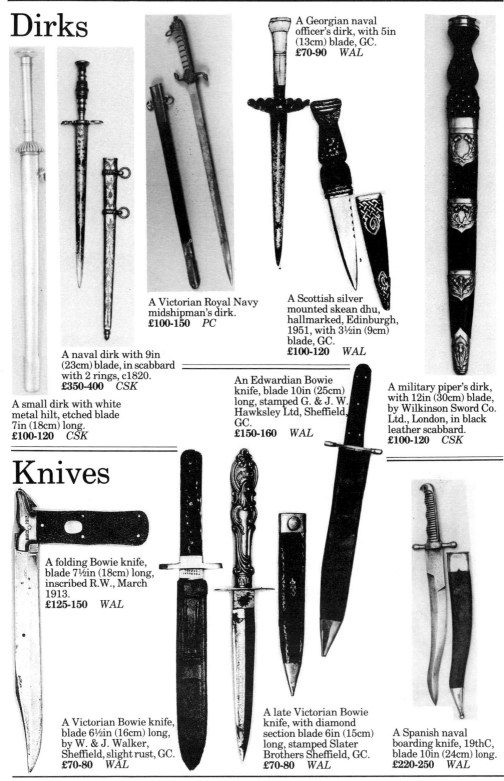

A Georgian naval officer's dirk, with 5in (13cm) blade, GC.
£70-90 *WAL*

A Scottish silver mounted skean dhu, hallmarked, Edinburgh, 1951, with 3½in (9cm) blade, GC.
£100-120 *WAL*

A military piper's dirk, with 12in (30cm) blade, by Wilkinson Sword Co. Ltd., London, in black leather scabbard.
£100-120 *CSK*

An Edwardian Bowie knife, blade 10in (25cm) long, stamped G. & J. W. Hawksley Ltd, Sheffield, GC.
£150-160 *WAL*

Knives

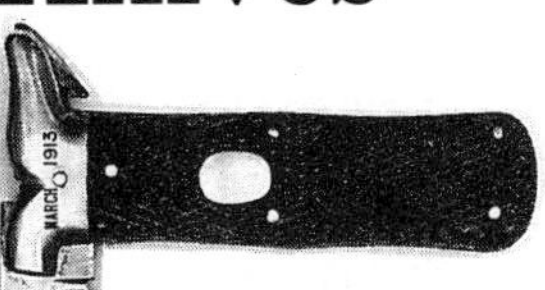

A folding Bowie knife, blade 7½in (18cm) long, inscribed R.W., March 1913.
£125-150 *WAL*

A Victorian Bowie knife, blade 6½in (16cm) long, by W. & J. Walker, Sheffield, slight rust, GC.
£70-80 *WAL*

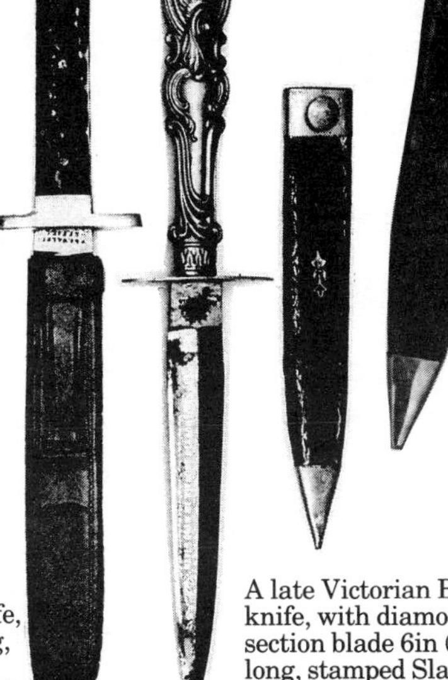

A late Victorian Bowie knife, with diamond section blade 6in (15cm) long, stamped Slater Brothers Sheffield, GC.
£70-80 *WAL*

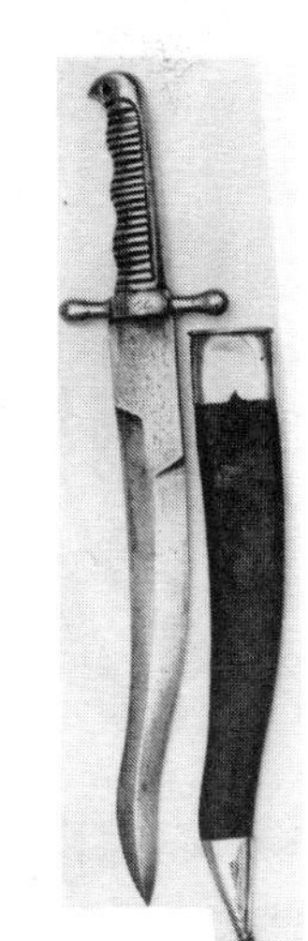

A Spanish naval boarding knife, 19thC, blade 10in (24cm) long.
£220-250 *WAL*

Medals

A Georgian engraved silver gilt Volunteer medal.
£350-400 *C*

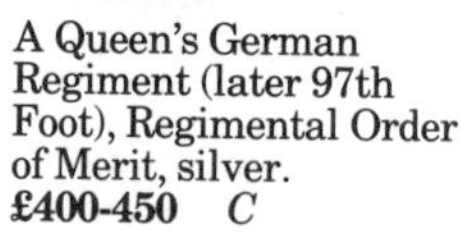

A Queen's German Regiment (later 97th Foot), Regimental Order of Merit, silver.
£400-450 *C*

The Queen's German Regiment Order of Merit was established to commemorate the re-capture of the Standard from Napoleon's Invincibles, Egypt 1801.

M.S.M. Victorian issue, impressed Quarter Master Sgt. J. V. McLaughlin, VF.
£110-140 *WAL*

A Naval General Service medal, 1793-1840, 1 bar Basque Roads, 1809, Pte. J. Preston, H.M.S. Gibraltar.
£400-450 *RMC*

Sutlej medal, for Moodkee 1845, 1 bar Ferozeshuhur, Bombr. J. Barmont, 3rd Brigade H. Ay.
£140-160 *WAL*

Punjab 1849, 2 bars Chilianwala, Goojerat, Chas. Cox, 14th Lt. Dragoons.
£140-160 *WAL*

Abyssinia medal, Pte. J. Board, 26th Regt.
£135-150 *RMC*

Three medals to Capt. G. Buchanan, 2nd Dragoons, Scots Greys, distinguished Officer of Scarlett's 'Three Hundred', Crimea, 1854-56, Balaklava, Inkermann, Sebastopol, officially impressed, Sardinia, Al Valore Militare, 1855-56, Turkish Crimea, Sardinian type, VF.
£1,500-1,800 *C*

China 1842, C/Sgt. S. Barnes, 98th Regiment.
£175-225 *RMC*

Indian Mutiny, 3 bars, Gnr. J. Callaghan, Bengal Horse Artillery.
£275-325 *RMC*

Indian Mutiny, 1 bar Lucknow, Thos Wheatley, 3rd Bn. Rifle Bde.
£70-80 *WAL*

Q.S.A., 2 bars, Dvr. H. Marsh, Army Service Corps.
£20-25 *RMC*

Hong Kong Jubilee medal, 1897, silver, inscribed Atwell Coxon.
£550-600 *C*
Of the highest rarity, apparently unrecorded in silver.

Indian GSM, 1854-1905, 411, J. Edwards, 80th Regt, 2/South Staffs, with bar, Bhootan.
£65-75 *RMC*

Army of India medal, 1799-1826, Gnr. George Allen, Artillery, with bar Ava.
£400-425 *RMC*

Q.S.A. 4 bars, KSA 2 bars, Pte. S. White, 2nd Btn. Royal Scots.
£40-50 *RMC*

D.C.M. Victorian, Afghanistan 1878/80, Egypt Bar El-Teb Tamaai, Khedive's Star 1884-86, Pte Hayes, 10th Hussars.
£1,300-1,500 *WAL*

l. Pte. J. F. Wright, 1st Btn. Duke of Cornwall's Light Infantry, Indian General Service Medal with bars, Punjab Frontier 1897-98, Tirah 1897-98.

r. Edward VII Long Service and Good Conduct medal.
£60-95 each *RMC*

Tptr. H. C. Pinn, 67th Co., 1899-1902, 18th Imp. Yeomanry City of London Sharpshooters, with 5 bars.
£80-95 *RMC*

Afghan War, 1878-80, 8 Bde/65 Pte. T. Moffett, 51st Regt. (K.O.Y.L.I.).
£40-45 *RMC*

Naval General Service, 1793-1840, 1 June 1794, Southampton 9 June 1796, St. Vincent, James Strachan, VF.
£2,500-3,000 *C*

Four 'Southampton 9 June 1796' clasps are shown on the official Admiralty clasp lists; 2 of these awards are known to exist, the medal to Private James Dallimore, held by The National Maritime Museum, Greenwich, and this one to James Strachan.

R.A.F. M.S.M. Geo. V coinage head, Flight Sgt. S. F. Bonnett.
£110-140 *WAL*

India General Service 1895, 1 bar, Q.S.A. 5 bars, K.S.A. 2 bars, Shoeing Smith N. Bawler, 10th Bty, Royal Field Artillery.
£75-95 *RMC*

A group of 7 to Lieutenant General J. Nash, late Bengal Army.
£5,000-5,500 *C*

Pte. W. H. Riles, Royal West Kent Regt, Indian G.S.M. 1908-35, with bar Afghanistan N.W.F., 1919.
£20-25 *RMC*

Voluntary Medical Services Long Service medal, Mrs. E. M. Shaylor.
£10-12 *RMC*

C.S.M. H. Elliott, 1/4th Bn. Kings' Own Scottish Borderers, T.F., Distinguished Conduct Medal, George V and group.
£125-225 *RMC*

Military medal to Sgt. M. Antoniszewski, Polish Army, with others.
£330-350 *WAL*

L. Cpl. C. D. Caird, Liverpool Regt, 1914-15 Star, British War medal and Victory.
£10-15 *RMC*

Special Constabulary Long Service medal, Walter G. Frost.
£3-5 *RMC*

Mne. J. H. Davison, Royal Marines, Naval G.S.M., with bar Cyprus.
£40-60 *RMC*

H. J. Balsdon, P.O. Distinguished Service Medal, George VI.
£175-225 *RMC*

Military Cross, 1914-15 Star, British War medal, Victory, Capt. S. Oswald, Army Cyclist Corps. and 2nd Traffic Control.
£190-230 *RMC*

Indian Army Long Service and Good Conduct, 505 Sowar Sheer Khan, 15th Lancers, Edward VII.
£20-25 *RMC*

Gnr. J. R. Sanders Royal Artillery Territorial Efficiency medal, George VI.
£10-15 *RMC*

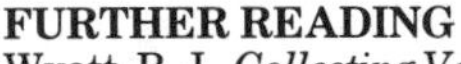

FURTHER READING
Wyatt, R. J., *Collecting Volunteer Militaria,* 1974.

Orders

The Commander of the Order of St. Michael and St. George (CMG), Afghan 1878-80 with bar Kabul, Surgeon T. H. Sweeney, 45th Bengal Native Infantry.
£300-400 *RMC*

The Most Honourable Order of the Bath, Knight Grand Cross, G.C.B., Military Division, miniature, c1816, 44 by 42mm.
£900-950 *C*

Stars of these dimensions are unrecorded.

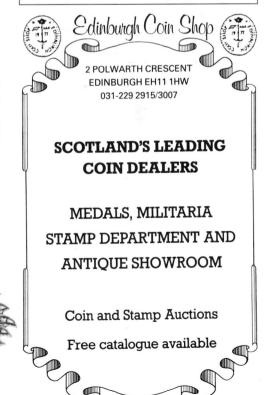

Nelson's Navy

These pages show a selection of militaria dating from the Napoleonic wars period. Some of the items shown are unique, others are readily available, but they all serve to remind us of the very harsh life that sailors endured. Naval items continue to be very collectable.

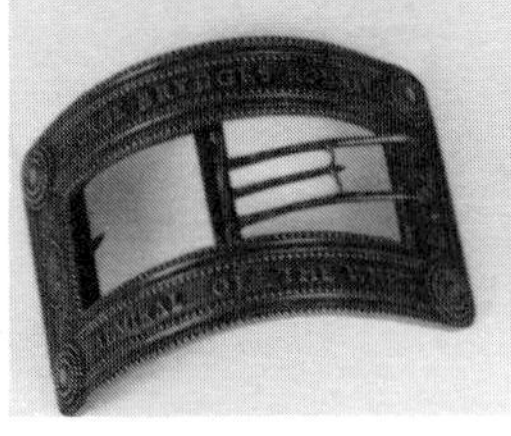

Lord Rodney's shoe buckles, 'Admiral of the White'.
Unique *WAL*

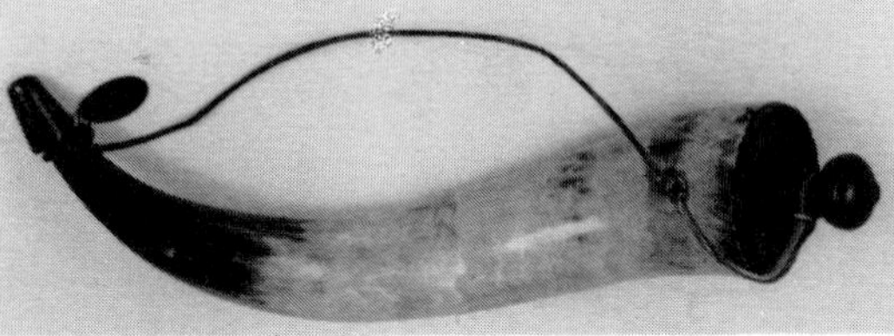

A master gunner's horn.
£200-250 *WAL*

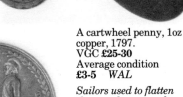

A cartwheel penny, 1oz copper, 1797.
VGC **£25-30**
Average condition
£3-5 *WAL*

Sailors used to flatten them under guns when they fired and gave them away as conversation pieces.

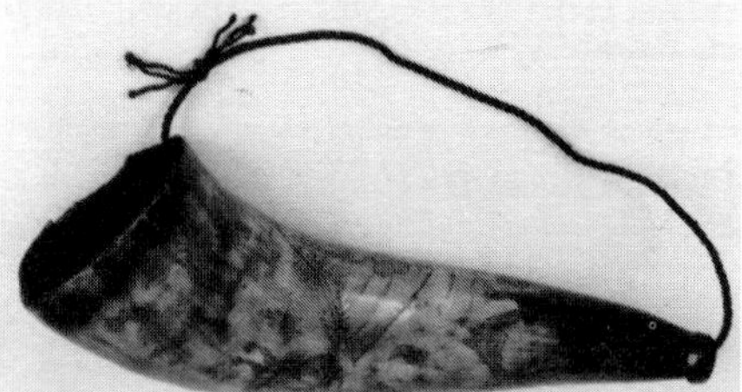

A 63rd Regiment scrimshaw horn.
£750-800 *WAL*

St. Vincent medal, given to all crew who didn't take part in the Spithead mutiny.
£400-450 *WAL*

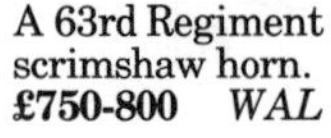

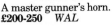

A Georgian press gang cosh.
£50-60 *WAL*

A print of Nelson, 9 by 6in (23 by 15cm).
£50-60 *WAL*

This print was produced immediately after the 'Nile', and Nelson was made Lord shortly after.

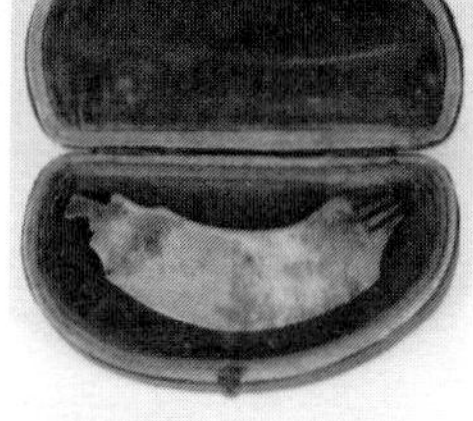

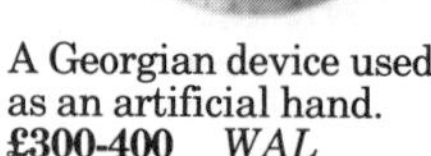

A Georgian device used as an artificial hand.
£300-400 *WAL*

Sailors very often lost more limbs than soldiers because of falling and splintering timbers. The left-hand edge was inserted into the wooden stump, thus enabling the victim to cut and eat his food.

A French prisoner-of-war double domino set.
£100-115 *WAL*

A bosun's starter.
£50-60 *WAL*

Hand grenades from HMS Vincent.
£450-500 each *WAL*

A brass deserter's stamp.
£1,000-1,200 *WAL*

Used to stamp a 'D' in fine needles under the arm.

DID YOU KNOW?
As faith in the currency dwindled at that time, George III decreed that a one penny coin would consist of one penny's worth of pure copper.

A naval officer's hanger, with green stained ivory grip, c1750.
£550-600 *WAL*

A naval General Service medal, with Trafalgar bar, issued 1849 to survivors.
£600-700 *WAL*

Trafalgar is a very scarce bar to this medal.

A naval flintlock 7-barrelled volley gun.
£2,500-3,000 *WAL*

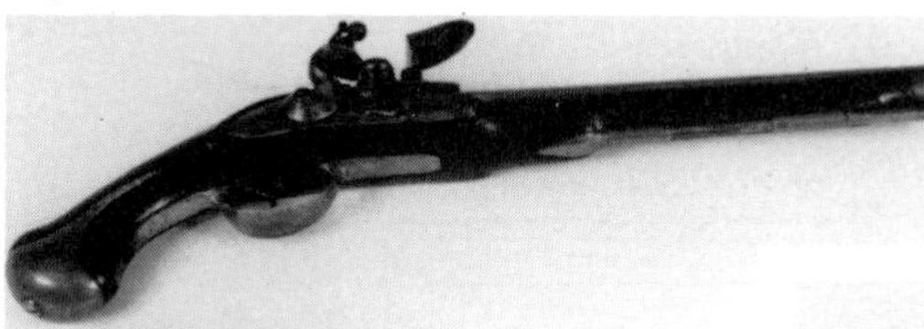

A naval flintlock pistol, bearing cypher of King Christian VII, probably captured at the Battle of Copenhagen, 1801.
£900-1,000 *WAL*

A naval flintlock cannon igniter.
£450-500 *WAL*

A Georgian Long Sea Service flintlock belt pistol, 1796 pattern.
Exceptional condition
£1,000+
Average condition
£400-500 *WAL*

A Georgian sailor's cutlass.
£150-200 *WAL*

A naval officer's flintlock boarding pistol, with spring bayonet.
£1,250-1,500 *WAL*

A 'Cat-O-Nine Tails'.
£200-250 *WAL*

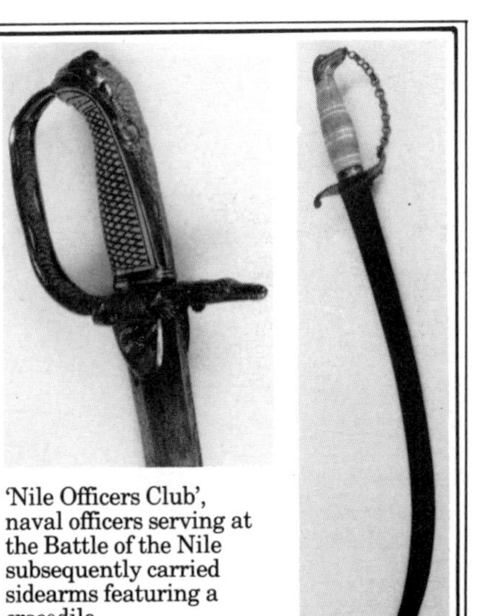

'Nile Officers Club', naval officers serving at the Battle of the Nile subsequently carried sidearms featuring a crocodile.
Sword **£600+**
Dirk **£250+** *WAL*

Pistols

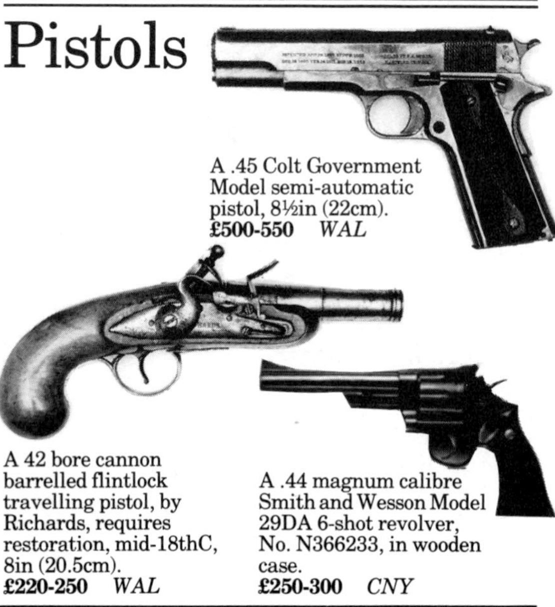

A .45 Colt Government Model semi-automatic pistol, 8½in (22cm).
£500-550 *WAL*

A 42 bore cannon barrelled flintlock travelling pistol, by Richards, requires restoration, mid-18thC, 8in (20.5cm).
£220-250 *WAL*

A .44 magnum calibre Smith and Wesson Model 29DA 6-shot revolver, No. N366233, in wooden case.
£250-300 *CNY*

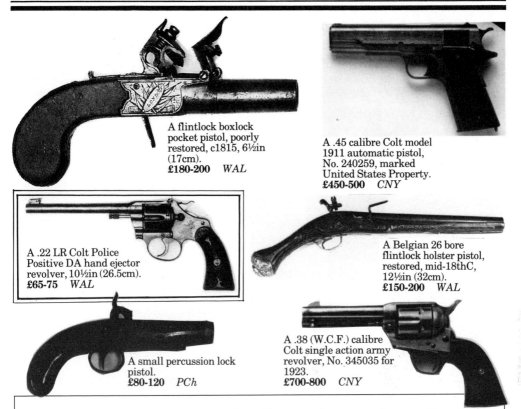

A flintlock boxlock pocket pistol, poorly restored, c1815, 6½in (17cm).
£180-200 *WAL*

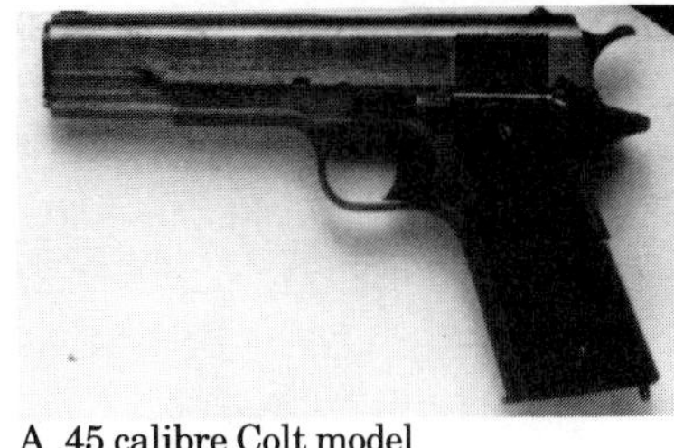
A .45 calibre Colt model 1911 automatic pistol, No. 240259, marked United States Property.
£450-500 *CNY*

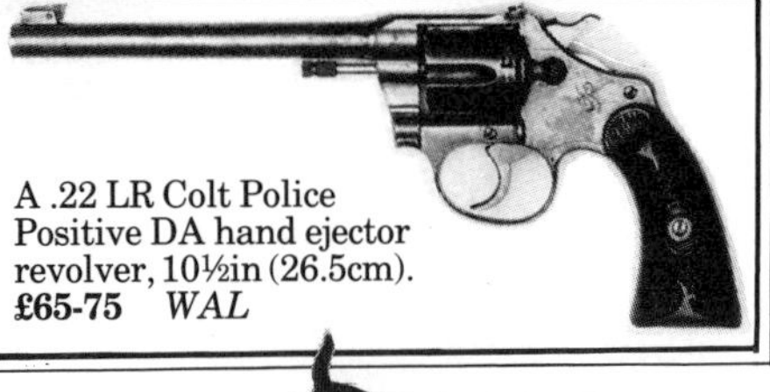
A .22 LR Colt Police Positive DA hand ejector revolver, 10½in (26.5cm).
£65-75 *WAL*

A Belgian 26 bore flintlock holster pistol, restored, mid-18thC, 12½in (32cm).
£150-200 *WAL*

A small percussion lock pistol.
£80-120 *PCh*

A .38 (W.C.F.) calibre Colt single action army revolver, No. 345035 for 1923.
£700-800 *CNY*

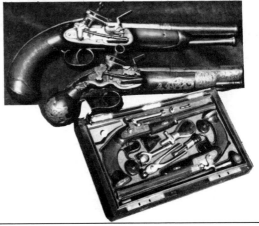

Powder Flasks

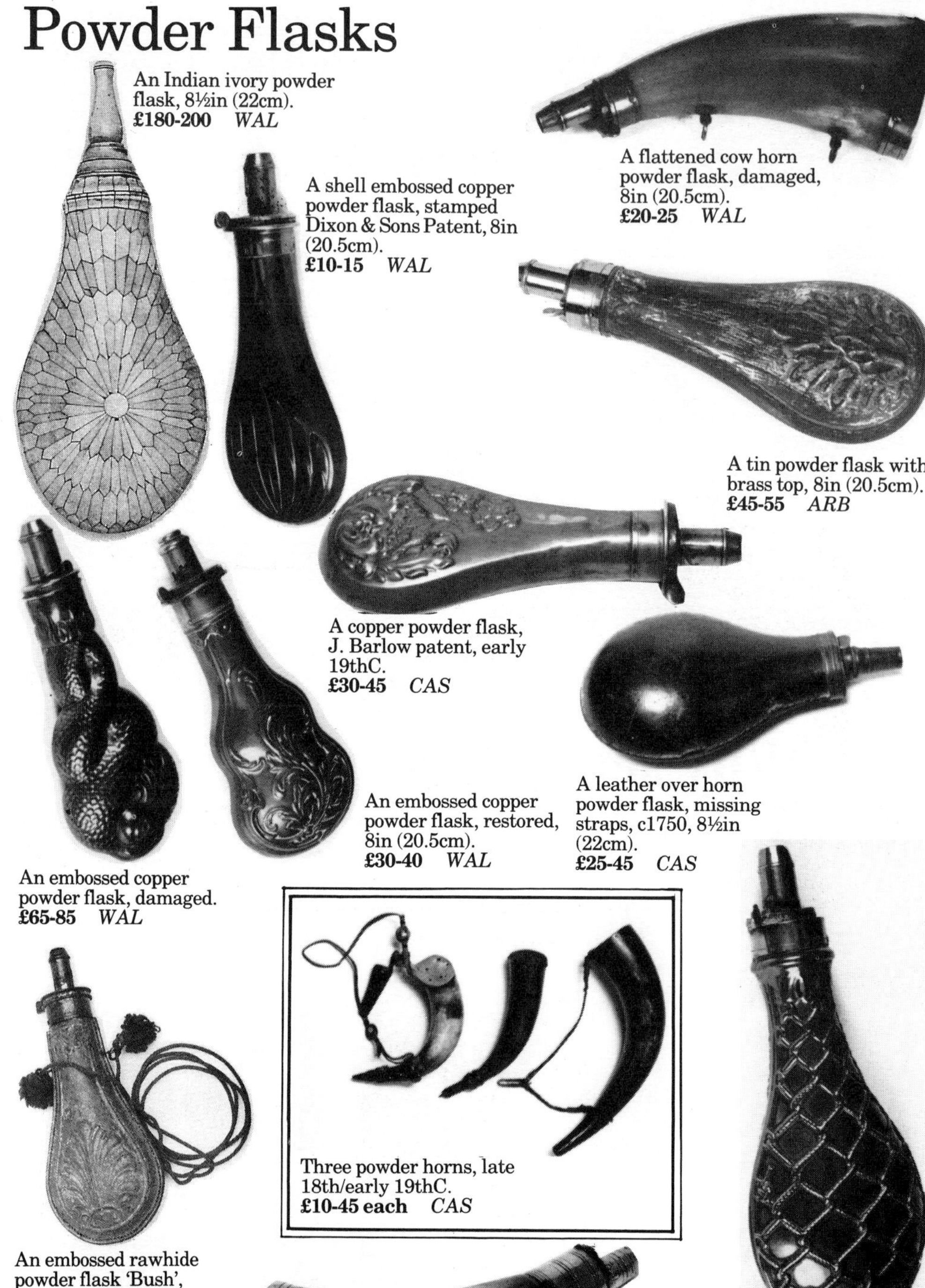

An Indian ivory powder flask, 8½in (22cm).
£180-200 *WAL*

A shell embossed copper powder flask, stamped Dixon & Sons Patent, 8in (20.5cm).
£10-15 *WAL*

A flattened cow horn powder flask, damaged, 8in (20.5cm).
£20-25 *WAL*

A tin powder flask with brass top, 8in (20.5cm).
£45-55 *ARB*

A copper powder flask, J. Barlow patent, early 19thC.
£30-45 *CAS*

An embossed copper powder flask, restored, 8in (20.5cm).
£30-40 *WAL*

A leather over horn powder flask, missing straps, c1750, 8½in (22cm).
£25-45 *CAS*

An embossed copper powder flask, damaged.
£65-85 *WAL*

Three powder horns, late 18th/early 19thC.
£10-45 each *CAS*

An embossed rawhide powder flask 'Bush', probably made by Franklin E. Darrow of Bristol, Connecticut, patent top stamped Mar 14th 1871, no spring, 8in (20.5cm).
£75-100 *WAL*

A powder horn, early 19thC.
£200-325 *CAS*

An embossed copper powder flask, damaged, 8in (20cm).
£20-25 *WAL*

Swords

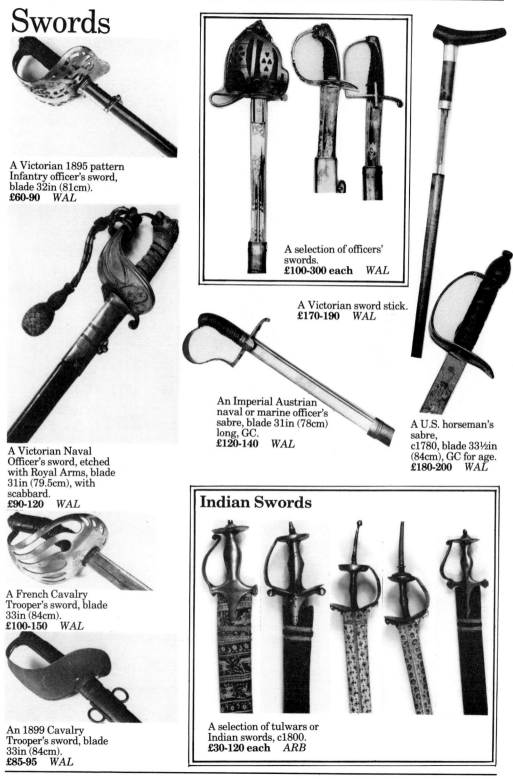

A Victorian 1895 pattern Infantry officer's sword, blade 32in (81cm).
£60-90 *WAL*

A Victorian Naval Officer's sword, etched with Royal Arms, blade 31in (79.5cm), with scabbard.
£90-120 *WAL*

A French Cavalry Trooper's sword, blade 33in (84cm).
£100-150 *WAL*

An 1899 Cavalry Trooper's sword, blade 33in (84cm).
£85-95 *WAL*

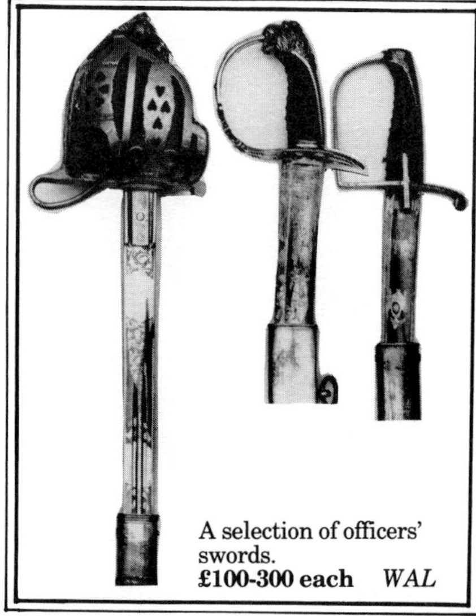

A selection of officers' swords.
£100-300 each *WAL*

A Victorian sword stick.
£170-190 *WAL*

An Imperial Austrian naval or marine officer's sabre, blade 31in (78cm) long, GC.
£120-140 *WAL*

A U.S. horseman's sabre, c1780, blade 33½in (84cm), GC for age.
£180-200 *WAL*

Indian Swords

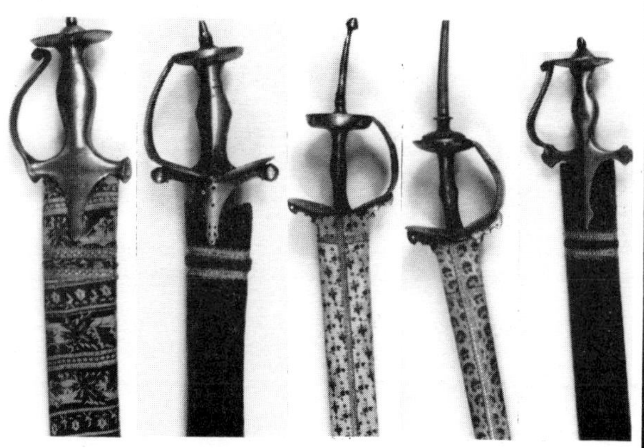

A selection of tulwars or Indian swords, c1800.
£30-120 each *ARB*

Uniforms

An officer's short-tailed scarlet coatee of Napoleonic Wars period,
£700-750 *CSK*

A Staff Major's SD khaki jacket, dated July 1918.
£100-150 *WAL*

A WWI Lieutenant's khaki SD uniform of the Women's Royal Air Force.
£550-650 *WAL*

A Victorian coatee and epaulettes of an officer of the Yeoman of the Guard.
£450-550 *CSK*

A Major's grey tunic of the Queen's Westminster Rifle Volunteers, GC.
£400-450 *WAL*

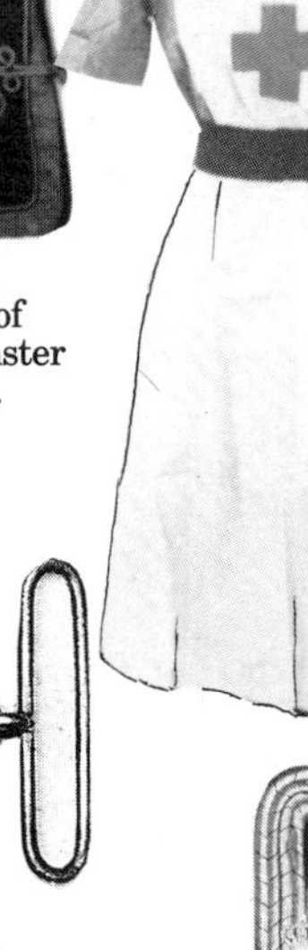

A British Red Cross V.A.D. outfit, c1939.
£220-250 *CSK*

A Victorian Volunteer Artillery officer's shoulder belt and full dress pouch.
£180-200 *WAL*

Imperial German Hanoverian officer's dress epaulettes.
£80-100 *WAL*

Head dress

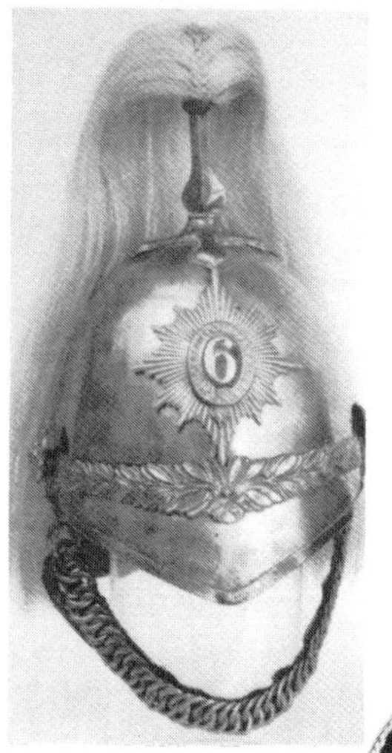

A 6th Dragoon Guards (Carabiniers) helmet with white plume, chin chain shortened.
£400-450 *CSK*

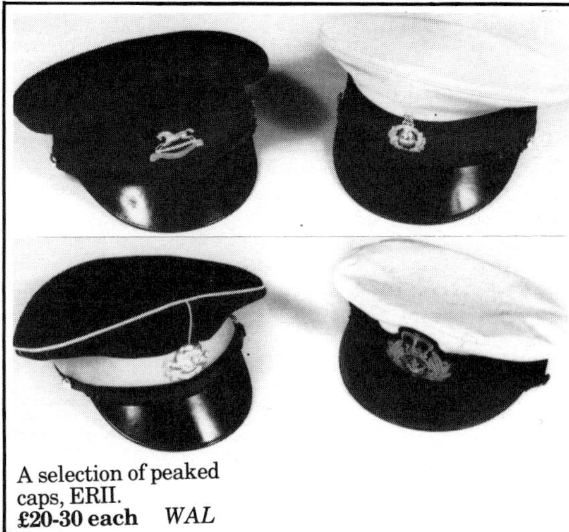

A selection of peaked caps, ERII.
£20-30 each *WAL*

A Victorian officer's blue cloth spiked helmet of the 2nd Vol. Battn. West Yorkshire Regiment.
£400-500 *WAL*

An Austrian officer's undress shako, with box.
£120-150 *CSK*

A Saxony Infantryman's pickelhaube.
£220-250 *WAL*

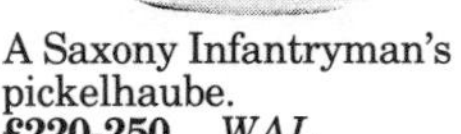

A rare Nazi Waffen SS officer's peaked cap.
£350-400 *WAL*

A French brass fireman's helmet, c1890.
£150-170 *COB*

A Victorian Trooper's lance cap (chapka), of the 9th (Queen's Royal) Lancers, no plume.
£300-350 *CSK*

General

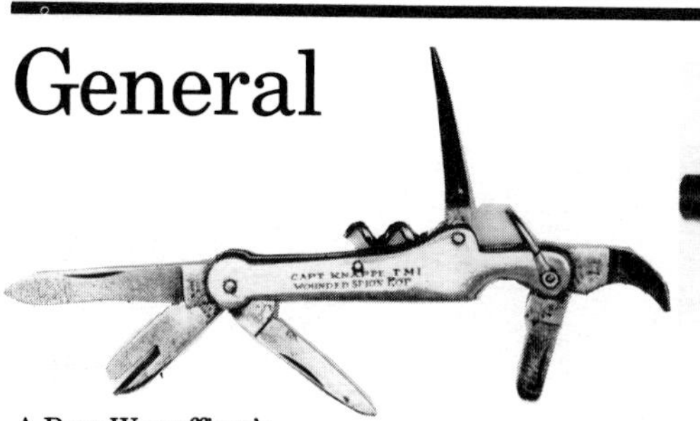

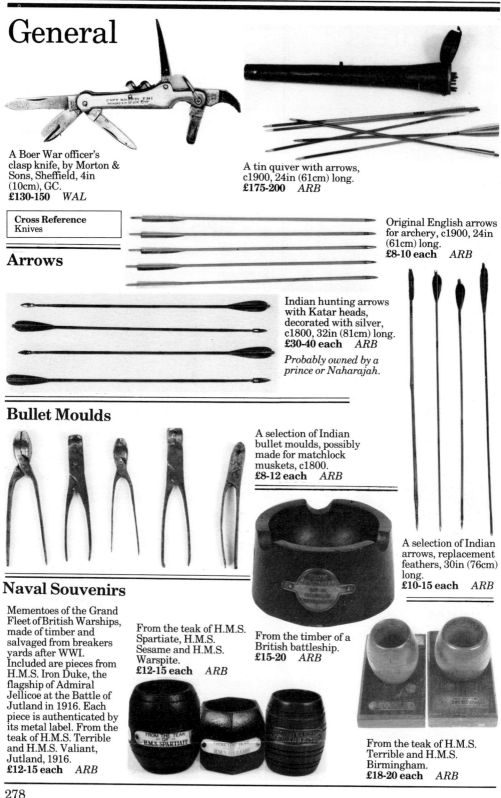

A Boer War officer's clasp knife, by Morton & Sons, Sheffield, 4in (10cm), GC.
£130-150 *WAL*

A tin quiver with arrows, c1900, 24in (61cm) long.
£175-200 *ARB*

Cross Reference
Knives

Arrows

Original English arrows for archery, c1900, 24in (61cm) long.
£8-10 each *ARB*

Indian hunting arrows with Katar heads, decorated with silver, c1800, 32in (81cm) long.
£30-40 each *ARB*

Probably owned by a prince or Naharajah.

A selection of Indian arrows, replacement feathers, 30in (76cm) long.
£10-15 each *ARB*

Bullet Moulds

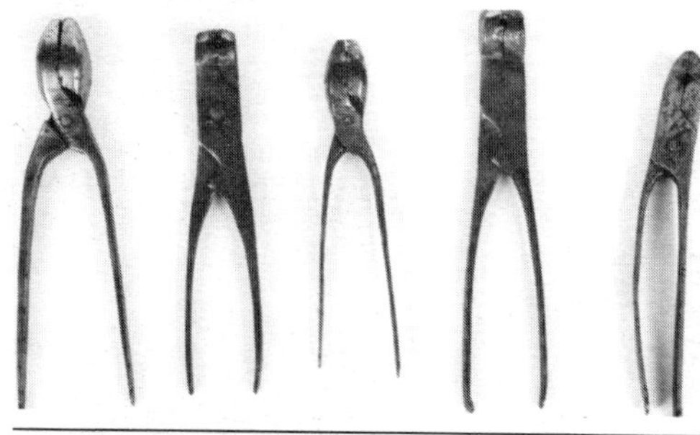

A selection of Indian bullet moulds, possibly made for matchlock muskets, c1800.
£8-12 each *ARB*

Naval Souvenirs

Mementoes of the Grand Fleet of British Warships, made of timber and salvaged from breakers yards after WWI. Included are pieces from H.M.S. Iron Duke, the flagship of Admiral Jellicoe at the Battle of Jutland in 1916. Each piece is authenticated by its metal label. From the teak of H.M.S. Terrible and H.M.S. Valiant, Jutland, 1916.
£12-15 each *ARB*

From the teak of H.M.S. Spartiate, H.M.S. Sesame and H.M.S. Warspite.
£12-15 each *ARB*

From the timber of a British battleship.
£15-20 *ARB*

From the teak of H.M.S. Terrible and H.M.S. Birmingham.
£18-20 each *ARB*

Miscellaneous

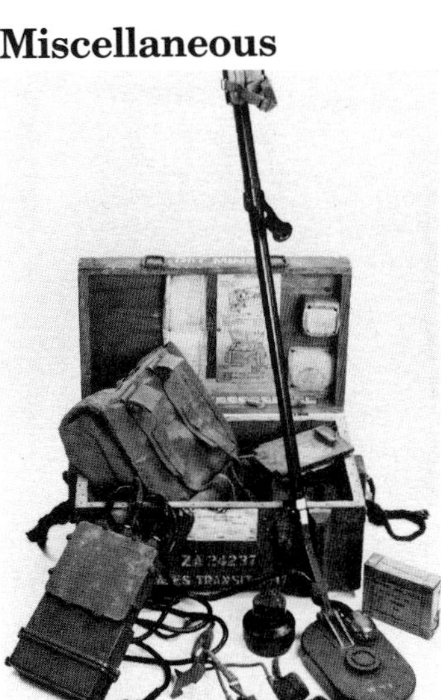

A mine detector, c1944.
£130-140 *CSK*

A bass drum of the Grenadier Guards, 2nd Battalion, by Henry Potter & Co., London.
£450-500 *CSK*

A hide shield, decorated with white metal plates, lined with leather, 21in (53.5cm) diam.
£350-400 *CSK*

An inflatable rubber dummy army lorry, in a canvas cover.
£550-600 *CSK*

A Free French flag, 1940s.
£15-18 *COB*

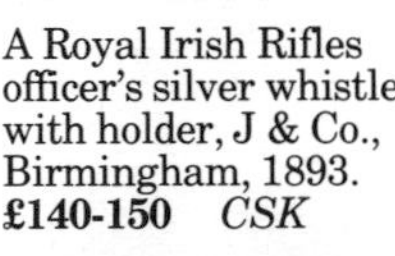

A Royal Irish Rifles officer's silver whistle with holder, J & Co., Birmingham, 1893.
£140-150 *CSK*

A flintlock lighter, with mahogany grip, 18thC, 8½in (22cm) long.
£280-360 *PCM*

A tin for a 1869 pattern shako, brass nameplate 'Warne Lemmon, Esq., 1st Surrey Militia', worn.
£25-35 *WAL*

A Russian flag, 1940s.
£25-30 *COB*

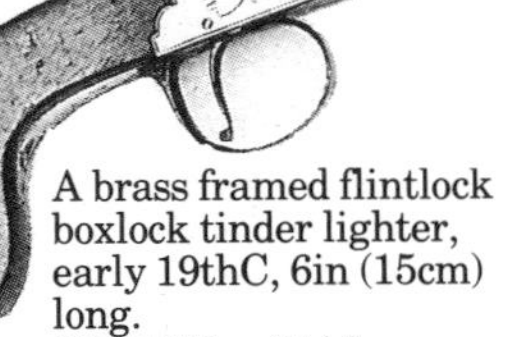

A brass framed flintlock boxlock tinder lighter, early 19thC, 6in (15cm) long.
£200-250 *WAL*

A brass framed hand ignited eprouvette, late 18thC, 7in (18cm).
£100-120 *WAL*

Musical

An Expert phonograph, with brass trumpet and oak case. **£300-350** *SAA*

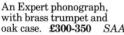

An H.M.V. table model gramophone.
£70-80 *COB*

An early Edison electric phonograph mechanism.
£1,200-1,500 *CSK*

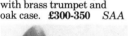

An H.M.V. Intermediate Monarch gramophone with mahogany case, soundbox replaced.
£750-800 *CSK*

A Columbia Regal Disc Graphophone, c1908.
£1,000-1,500 *CSK*

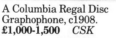

An H.M.V. Model 2 mahogany horn gramophone.
£850-950 *CSK*

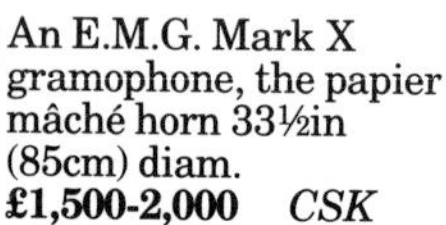

An E.M.G. Mark X gramophone, the papier mâché horn 33½in (85cm) diam.
£1,500-2,000 *CSK*

A Celestina 20-note organette.
£850-950 *CSK*

A Symphonion disc box with twin combs, 21 discs, 14in (35cm).
£1,000-1,400 *CSK*

Money Boxes

A Victorian black Sambo money box, 6in (15cm) high.
£95-100 *SAD*

Must be in good condition.

An Arthur Wood money box
£30-40 *STU*

A Victorian painted metal money box.
£10-15 *PC*

A money box issued for the Coronation, 1953, 4in (10cm) high.
£8-10 *DH*

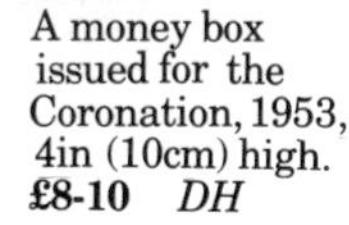

A tramp money box, Poor Tired Tim.
£90-100 *YC*

Cash Registers

A National cash register, 24in (61cm) high.
£500-700 *NA*

An Art Deco cash register, 18in (45cm) high.
£110-130 *DH*

A Victorian National cash register, brass back plate missing, 17in (42.5cm) high.
£250-300 *DH*

Oriental

A pair of Chinese lions.
£500-550 *RIP*

A pair of Chinese hardstone jardinières, containing shrubs of rose quartz and other agates, 12in (30.5cm) high.
£100-120 *WHB*

A niello buckle, 19thC.
£65-75 *DF*

A white metal model of a sailing ship and 12 small models. **£220-250** *MGM*

A raised silkwork and painted silk picture, 19thC, framed and glazed, 17 by 14in (43 by 35.5cm).
£225-250 *DBP*

A set of S.E. Asian opium scales, with wooden fitted box, 19thC.
£150-180 *DBP*

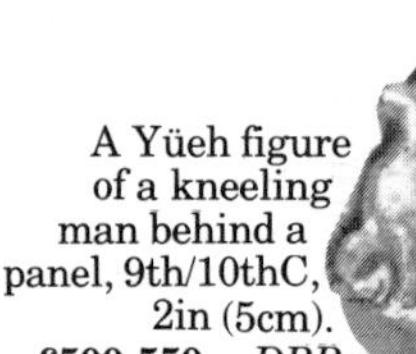

A Yüeh figure of a kneeling man behind a panel, 9th/10thC, 2in (5cm).
£500-550 *DBP*

Cross Reference
Scales and Balances

A Tibetan table prayer wheel.
£185-200 *DBP*

A carved balsa wood model of a Burmese temple, early 20thC, 17in (48cm) wide, in glazed case. **£320-350** *P(Ch)*

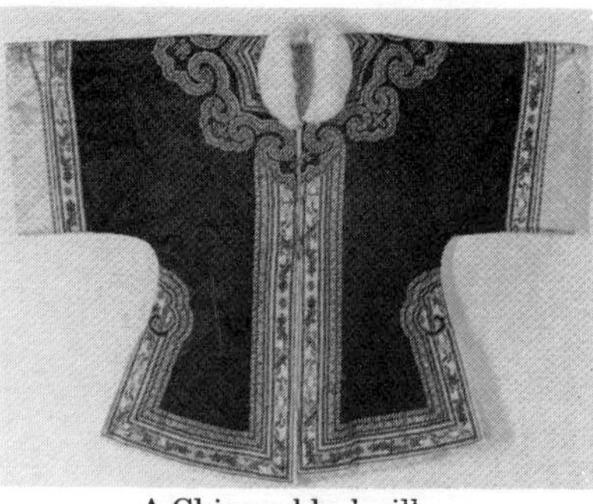

A Chinese black silk coat, embroidered in ivory silk, with white coney lining, 19thC.
£250-350 *P*

A Canton ivory silk shawl, embroidered with flowering vines, 60in (152cm) square.
£150-200 *CSK*

A carved ivory kiseruzutsu, signed Ren, 19thC, 8½in (22cm) long.
£500-550 *C*

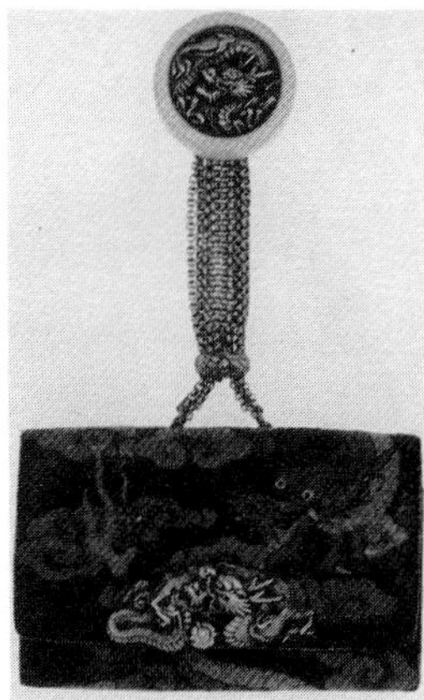

A Japanese purse, embroidered with coloured silks, lined with printed leather, 19thC.
£160-180 *P*

Tsubas

An ivory carving of 3 figures and a horse, 19thC.
£170-190 *GEN*

A bronze scroll holder, 3½in (9cm) long.
£90-100 *CBA*

An iron Shaomi school tsuba, unsigned, early 19thC, 3½in (8.5cm).
£400-500 *C*

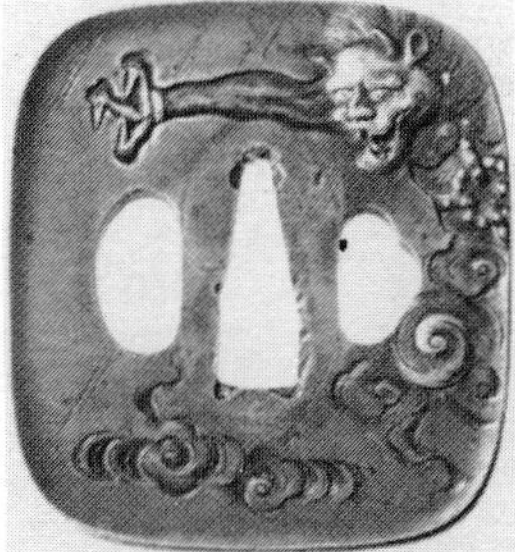

A Sentoku tsuba, unsigned, 19thC, 3in (7.5cm).
£250-350 *C*

A Japanese carved ivory figure of a flower seller, 19thC, 10in (25.5cm).
£160-200 *DEN*

A soapstone figure of a cow with a monkey, 3in (7.5cm).
£20-25 *CBA*

A pair of Japanese ivory and mother-of-pearl panels, in black lacquered and floral painted frames.
£320-350 *MN*

Netsuke

A staghorn netsuke as an oni, or little demon, holding a club, unsigned, 4cm high.
£45-55 *WAD*

An ivory netsuke as a recumbent goat, with inlaid eyes, signed, 5cm wide.
£60-70 *WAD*

An ivory netsuke as a coiled snake with inlaid eyes, signed, 5cm wide.
£90-100 *WAD*

An ivory netsuke in the form of an ox, signed, 5cm wide.
£70-80 *WAD*

An ivory netsuke in the form of a rooster, with inlaid eyes, signed, 5cm wide.
£65-75 *WAD*

An ivory netsuke in the form of a wild boar.
£65-75 *WAD*

DID YOU KNOW?
The ox was one of the 12 animals that hurried to Buddha's side when word went out that he was dying and, therefore, is assured a place of honour in the Oriental Zodiac.

An ivory netsuke as a crouching rabbit, with inlaid eyes, signed, 5cm.
£70-80 *WAD*

An ivory netsuke in the form of a recumbent cow and calf, with inlaid eyes, signed, 5cm wide.
£90-100 *WAD*

A staghorn netsuke as a kneeling Hotei, the God of Happiness, 3cm wide.
£65-75 *WAD*

A staghorn netsuke as a shi-shi temple dog, resting on a box, unsigned, 3cm wide.
£55-65 *WAD*

DID YOU KNOW?
The pig occupies last place in the 12 animals of the Oriental Zodiac, and is noted for rushing headlong into attack, looking neither right nor left. People born in the Year of the Pig are said to have a brave but reckless character.

Paperweights

Topographical paperweights provide an enormous scope for the collector. From Victorian times to the present day, just about every resort, historic building, major event and even popular characters had their own paperweights.

The most desirable are the early hand-painted Victorian examples, often painted on a mother-of-pearl base.

Folkestone War Memorial. **£12-15** *BEN*

Danzig, Frauengasse, 4½in (11cm) high. **£15-20** *BEN*

Town Hall, Preston. **£15-20** *BEN*

Weston-super-Mare, Winter Gardens. **£15-20** *BEN*

Danzig, Langebrücke. **£15-20** *BEN*

St. John's R.C. Church, Bath, early 20thC. **£35-40** *BEN*

Toad Rock. **£30-35** *BEN*

Three paperweights, 2in (5cm) diam. **£20-30 each** *BEN*

Two paperweights, Crystal Palace and Old Church, Bonchurch.
£25-30 each *BEN*

Bridge of Dee, Bala, 4 by 2½in (10 by 6cm).
£15-20 *BEN*

French views, Paris and Amiens, Vue Générale.
£25-30 each *BEN*

Arc de Triomphe.
£20-25 *BEN*

An unknown scene, 3½in (9cm) diam.
£20-25 *BEN*

Three English views.
£15-20 each *BEN*

The Marquis of Lorne.
£15-20 *BEN*

MAKE THE MOST OF MILLER'S
Condition is absolutely vital when assessing the value of any item. Damaged pieces appreciate much less than perfect examples. However, a rare, desirable piece may command a high price even when damaged.

Papier Mâché

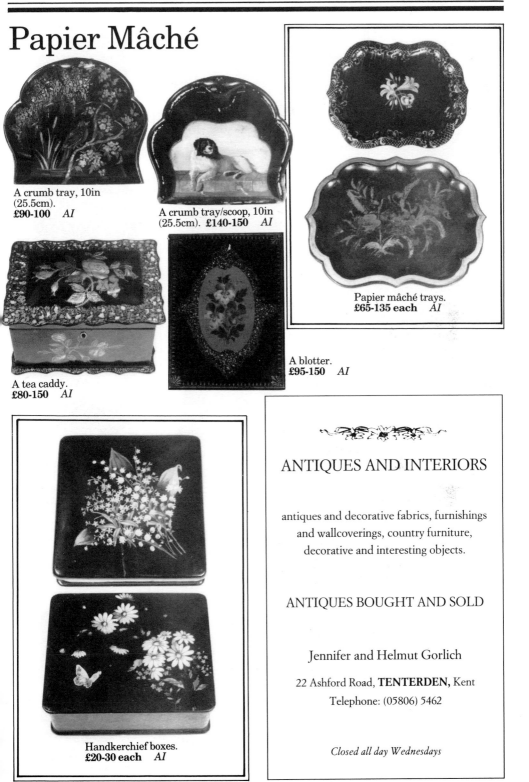

A crumb tray, 10in (25.5cm).
£90-100 *AI*

A crumb tray/scoop, 10in (25.5cm). **£140-150** *AI*

Papier mâché trays.
£65-135 each *AI*

A tea caddy.
£80-150 *AI*

A blotter.
£95-150 *AI*

Handkerchief boxes.
£20-30 each *AI*

Handkerchief boxes.
£20-25 each *AI*

An inkstand, 15in (38cm) wide.
£350-400 *AI*

A stamp box.
£25-45 *AI*

An inkstand.
£85-100 *AI*

A tea caddy.
£85-150 *AI*

A pen tray.
£20-30 *AI*

Papier mâché trays.
£35-65 each *AI*

Papier mâché boxes.
£20-35 each *AI*

Photographs

An albumen print, Charles Negre, Imperial Asylum, Vincennes, 1859.
£200-300 *CSK*

Patch Boxes

A South Staffordshire patch box, with gilt metal mounts, c1780.
£220-250 *C*

Victoria and Albert.
£60-80 *EUR*

An extensive selection of patch boxes is featured in Miller's Collectables Price Guide 1989-90, page 273.

A Victorian photograph in gilt and leather frame.
£15-18 *J*

A Victorian photograph in a padded frame.
£25-35 *J*

A Victorian photograph in a gilt frame.
£10-15 *J*

A Victorian tin type photograph, in leather bound frame, damage to frame.
£25-35 *J*

A stereoscopic daguerreotype, T. R. Williams, Still Life, mid-1850s.
£450-550 *CSK*

A stereoscopic daguerreotype, c1850.
£1,700-2,000 *CSK*

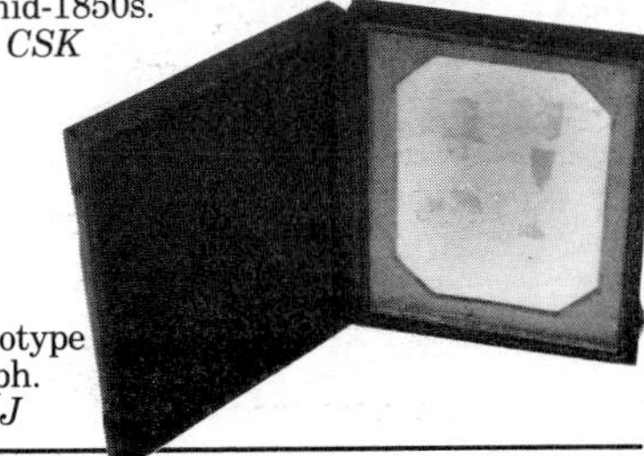

An Ambrotype photograph.
£30-40 *J*

Pincushion Dolls

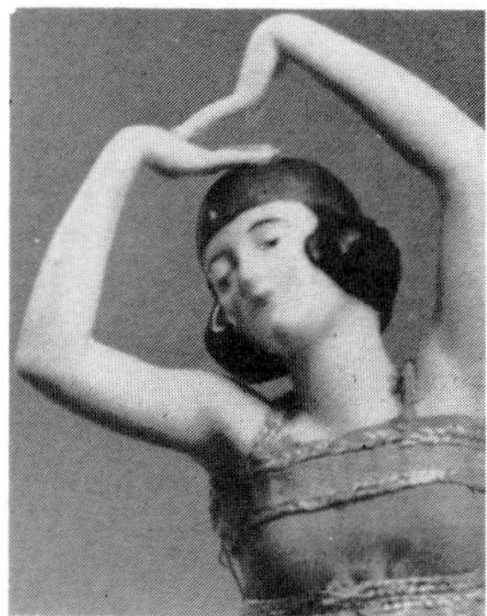

A china pincushion doll, 12in (30.5cm).
£80-100 *CSK*

A half figure of an English woman, with bisque face and glazed body.
£60-70 *CSK*

Two pincushion dolls.
£50-60 each *CSK*

A collection of figures.
£25-30 *PWA*

Playing Cards

A Luxus Rummy pack by Piatnik, c1940.
£12-15 *IC*

A Dosai Matching Game, a popular Japanese game, by Matsui Tengudo, hand printed, 1980.
£35-45 *IC*

An historical deck, designed by Prof. Olle Hjortzberg for Granbergs of Stockholm, 1930s.
£40-50 *IC*

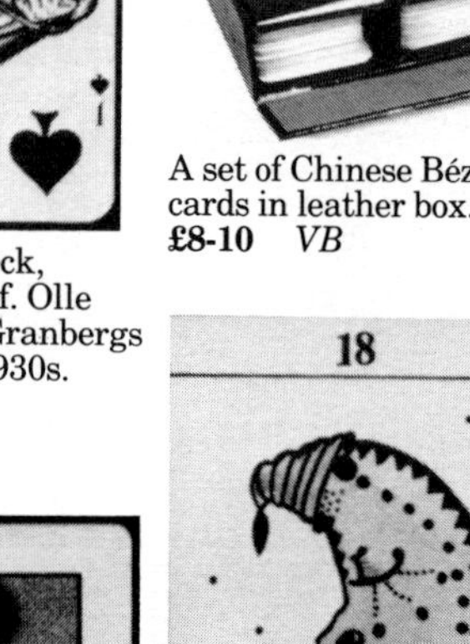

A set of Chinese Bézique cards in leather box.
£8-10 *VB*

An unusual Spanish deck, by Mingote for Fournier, 1969.
£10-15 *IC*

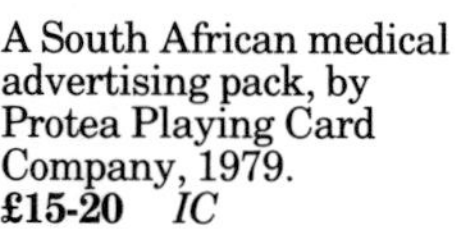

A South African medical advertising pack, by Protea Playing Card Company, 1979.
£15-20 *IC*

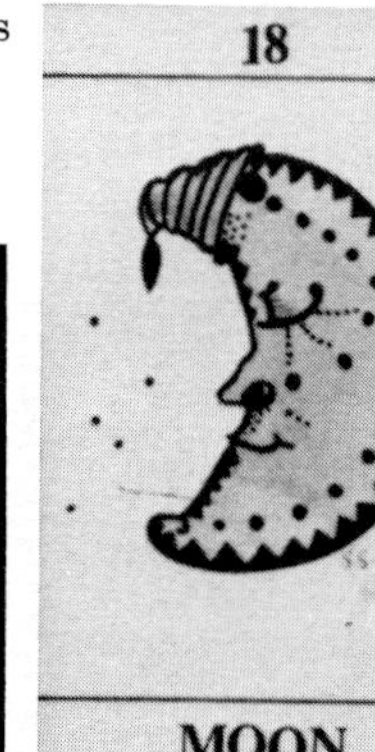

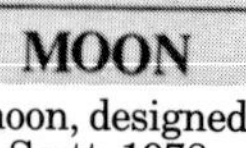

The moon, designed by Sarah Scott, 1978.
£15-20 *IC*

An Italian cartoon style pack, by Viassone, with teeth in addition to standard suit signs, known as the Junior Dental pack of 1979.
£10-15 *IC*

The Minchiatte, an Italian deck of 98 cards, trump No. 13 represents death in 1830s deck.
£450-500 *IC*

The Jack of Hearts from a Hunt & Son pack, early English.
£80-100 *IC*

A complete set of Fortune Telling cards, in original box.
£5-8 *PC*

A French export pack for Vietnam, known as To-Tom, consisting of 120 cards, c1900.
£8-10 *IC*

A Holmblad Saloman Tarot deck, consisting of 78 cards, Danish, published 1900.
£300-350 *IC*

Tarot is not just a fortune telling pack, but was used for various card games.

A Spanish Cavalier deck, 1880.
£30-40 *IC*

The Italians and Spanish use chalices, coins, swords and batons in their packs, which usually contain 48 cards, numbered from 1-12 with no queens.

The King of diamonds of Belgian Dynasty deck, depicting King Leopold, 1936.
£25-30 *IC*

An American Hobbydoctor calorie control pack, c1980.
£4-6 *IC*

Modern cardmakers endeavour to produce original ideas for packs.

A French Shipping Lines deck, depicting the French Merchant Navy, by Marie, commissioned in 1961.
£18-20 *IC*

The Four Corners of the World, by B. Dondorf of Frankfurt, Germany, c1910.
£150-200 *IC*

Jeu Grotesque, an early illusion pack with each card depicting 2-12 faces, 1813.
£280-300 *IC*

DID YOU KNOW?
Double faced cards with the indices on the top corners of cards were introduced after 1860.

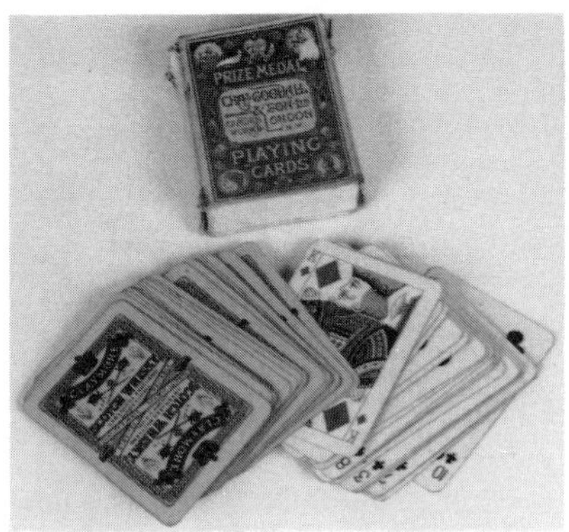

Advertising playing cards.
£8-10 *REL*

Dutch Pasquins Windkaart, uncut sheet.
£300-350 *IC*

An historical pack by Fournier, Discoverers and Colonizers of America, 1954.
£35-45 *IC*

An Austrian pack, the aces depict Italian scenes and the courts medieval costumes, 1927.
£20-30 *IC*

A German deck, 1870.
£110-120 *IC*

An Ecuadorian pack, Jack of coins, c1940.
£6-8 *IC*

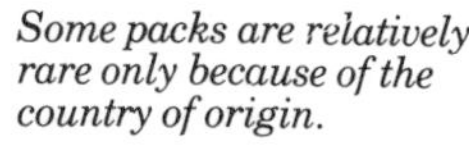

Some packs are relatively rare only because of the country of origin.

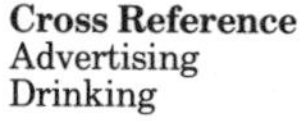

Cross Reference
Advertising
Drinking

A French deck, with court cards named, printed from wood blocks and stencil coloured by hand, c1820.
£45-55 *IC*

An Italian reproduction set, by Lissone, of an 1840 tarot deck, 1979.
£12-15 *IC*

Four French/English Prisoner-of-War cards, with hand made box.
£500-600 *IC*

A deck of cards.
£10-20 *CAS*

L.N.E.R. playing cards.
£8-10 *SAD*

Police

CITY OF COVENTRY.

The Watch Committee of the City of Coventry invite Applications from Parties desirous of undertaking the duties of

CHIEF SUPERINTENDENT

OF

POLICE

of this City, and INSPECTOR of WEIGHTS and MEASURES. Salary, £150 a Year, the Superintendent providing his own Residence and Clothing.

The Population of the City is about 40,000; the strength of the Police Force 40; the Area of the City 1,650 Acres.

Applications, in the handwriting of the Applicant, stating particulars of Age and Height, and accompanied by Testimonials, to be sent to my Office, on or before the FIRST day of MARCH NEXT.

THOMAS BROWETT,

Town Clerk.

February, 1862.

A police poster, dated 1862.
£100-140 *MIT*

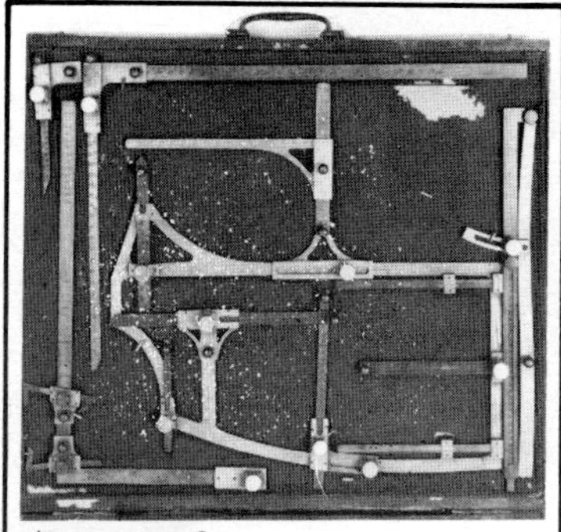

A rare set of anthropometric instruments, Bertillons Apparatus, for the measurement and classification of criminals, in fitted lined case, 19½in (49cm).
£700-750 *CSK*

A Special Constable's Faithful Service Medal, George IV.
£10-20 *MIT*

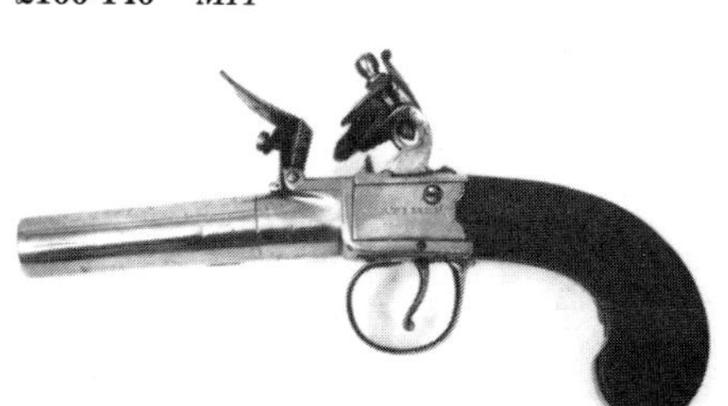

A Conductor's pistol of Thames River Police, marked Milwall No. 44, c1800.
£400-500 *MIT*

The City of London Marshall's sword.
£500-600
A belt buckle for his ceremonial uniform.
£125-150 *MIT*

Prior to 1839 and the City of London Police Force, the Marshall was responsible for law and order within the City boundaries.

A police hanger, complete with frog to scabbard and armoury number 53, blade engraved B in F Police (Barrow-in-Furness).
£200-250 *MIT*

The D-shape of the hilt dates this after 1850.

A Dolan patent bull's-eye lantern, c1850.
£30-40 *MIT*

A modern Chief Constable's hat.
£100-130 *MIT*

A Glamorgan Inspector's hat, some damage, c1915.
£30-40 *MIT*

MAKE THE MOST OF MILLERS
Price ranges in this book reflect what one should expect to *pay* for a similar example. When selling, however, one should expect to receive a lower figure. This will fluctuate according to a dealer's stock, saleability at a particular time, etc. It is always advisable, when selling, to approach a reputable specialist dealer or an auction house which has specialist sales.

A Wedgwood limited edition plate, commemorating the 150th anniversary of the Metropolitan Police.
£30-50 *MIT*

Tipstaffs & Truncheons

A rare tipstaff for Official of City of London, Guildhall, dated 1752.
£900-1,000 *MIT*

A selection of Magistrates staffs of Office, made from wood, brass, silver or ivory.
£500-1,000 each *MIT*

Values depend on condition, markings, inscriptions and materials.

Rare truncheons and tipstaffs for the High Constables of Hundreds.
£300-800 each *MIT*

Channel Islands tipstaffs.
£400-600 each *MIT*

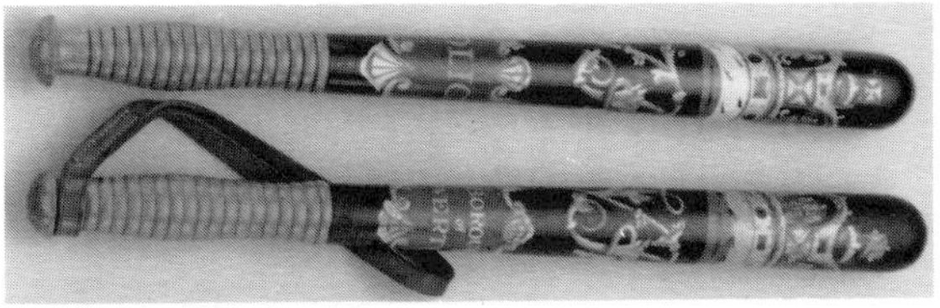

Parker Field pattern truncheons.
£200-300 each *MIT*

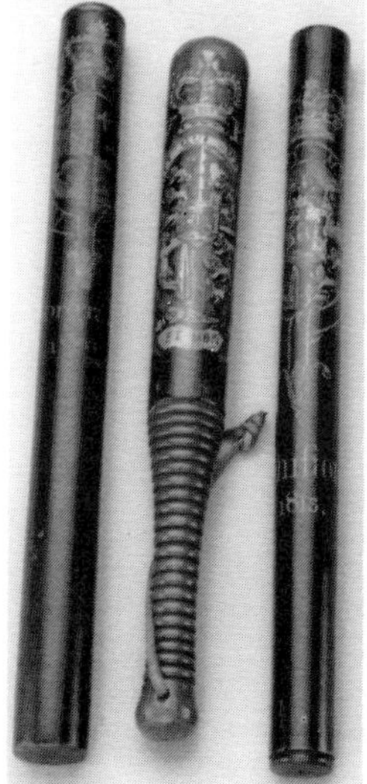

Three painted truncheons.
£200-300 each *MIT*

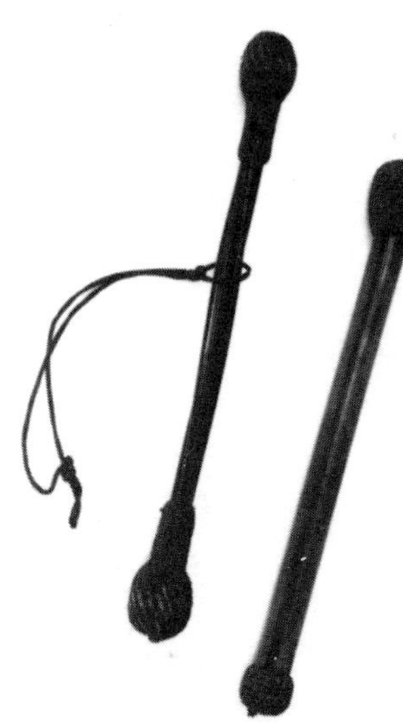

Early Victorian life preservers, lead weighted, as used by civilians.
£80-150 each *MIT*

A Victorian truncheon.
£10-15 *COB*

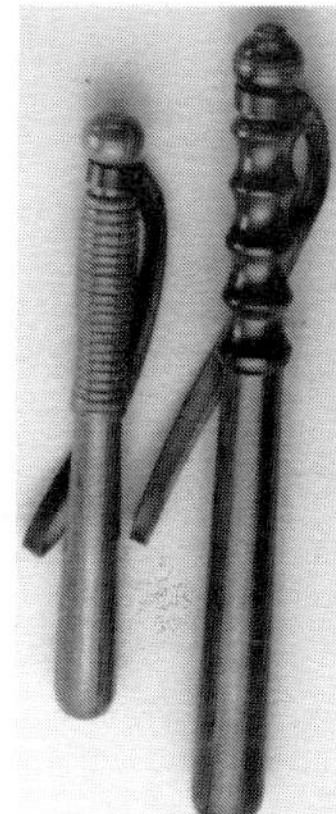

Modern truncheons.
l. Inspectors.
r. C.I.D.
£25-30 each *MIT*

Various styles of tipstaffs.
£350-1,000 each *MIT*

A Day's patent combined truncheon and percussion pistol, Birmingham proof marks, c1823, 16in (40.5cm).
£950-1,000 *CSK*

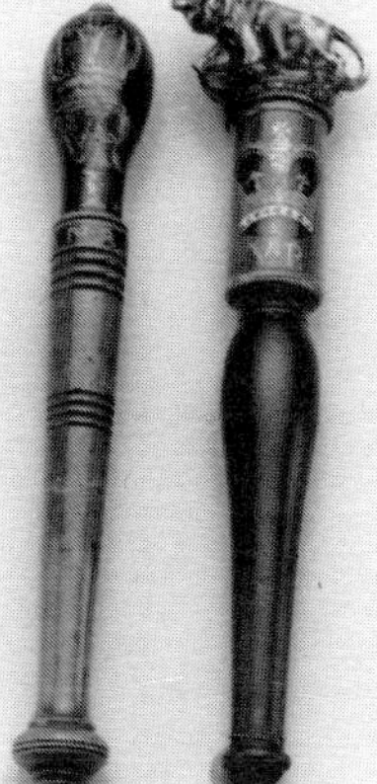

Rare canal truncheons.
£400-500 each *MIT*

A nightwatchman's truncheon, c1835.
£40-50 *SAD*

Portrait Miniatures

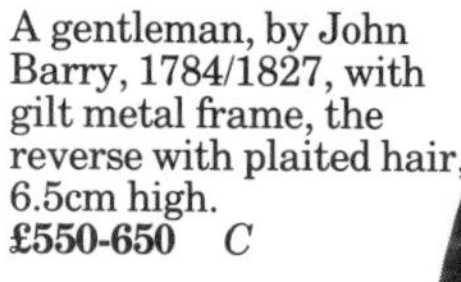

A gentleman, by John Barry, 1784/1827, with gilt metal frame, the reverse with plaited hair, 6.5cm high.
£550-650 *C*

A gentleman, English School, early 18thC, with black wood frame, 7cm high.
£700-750 *C*

An officer, by William John Thomson, c1771-1845, gilt metal frame, 7.5cm high.
£500-550 *C*

A gentleman, by Thomas Frye, 1710-62, signed and indistinctly dated, gilt metal frame, 3cm high.
£500-600 *C*

Viscount Newark, by Edward Miles, 1753-1828, with gold frame, the reverse with plaited hair within gold mount and blue glass border, 7cm high.
£450-550 *C*

A lady, by John Cox Dilman Engleheart, 1782-1826, signed in full on reverse and dated 1821, gilt metal frame, 7.5cm high.
£900-1,000 *C*

An officer, by W. Hay, 1776-97, signed, gilt metal frame, 6.5cm high
£300-350 *C*

An Infantry officer, by John Thomas Barber Beaumont, 1746-1803, signed with monogram, gold frame, the reverse with hair piece, 7cm high.
£400-450 *C*

A gentleman, by John Wright, c1745-1820, signed on the reverse, gold frame, the reverse with hair piece tied with seed pearls and gold wire, 6cm high.
£500-600 *C*

William Sherlock, a self portrait, c1738-1806, gilt metal frame, inscribed on reverse, 7.5cm high.
£600-650 *C*

Thomas A. Shaw, by Andrew Robertson, 1777-1845, signed and dated 10 May, 1816, with ormolu mount, fitted leather case, 8cm high.
£950-1,000 *C*

Postcards

Aviation

Original Pigeon Post, 1905.
£250-350 *N*

Cross Reference
Aeronautica

Australian first Autogiro Flight LE No. 777, 1934, with special Airmail Society cancel, G.
£12-18 *N*

First U.K. Aerial Post, 1911, FR to G.
£15-20 *VS*

Balloon Ascent Yorkshire Gala, published by Arthur, slight scuffing, G to VG.
£20-30 *VS*

Military Aeroplane Competition 1912, Larkhill Aerodrome, VG.
£16-20 *VS*

Preparing for Flight Yorkshire Gala, published by Arthur, slight scuffing, G to VG.
£30-35 *VS*

Commonly used abbreviations — See Miller's Collectables Price Guide, Vol I, page 304.

Balloons, Daily Graphic, VG.
£150-160 *VS*

DID YOU KNOW?
Miller's Collectables Price Guide is designed to build up, year by year, into the most comprehensive reference system available.

Postal history, salvaged mail from aircraft crash, Singapore, 1954.
£15-25 each *N*

Raphael Kirchner

Girl with pig, scarce, published 1902, FR.
£25-30 *VS*

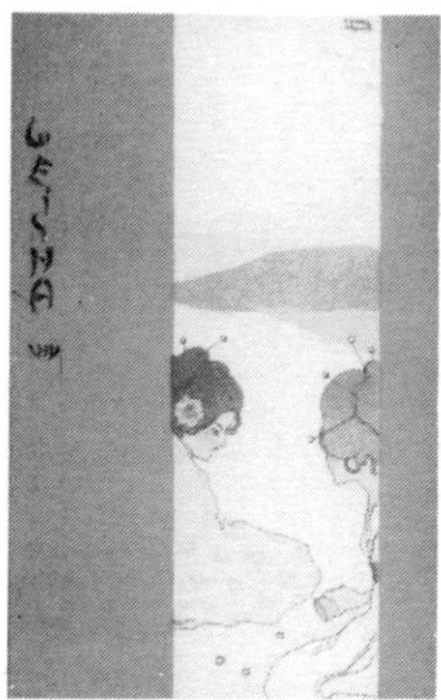

Geisha VIII, G to VG.
£25-30 *VS*

Geisha X, G to VG.
£25-30 *VS*

Mikado III, G to VG.
£25-30 *VS*

Cross Reference
Advertising postcards

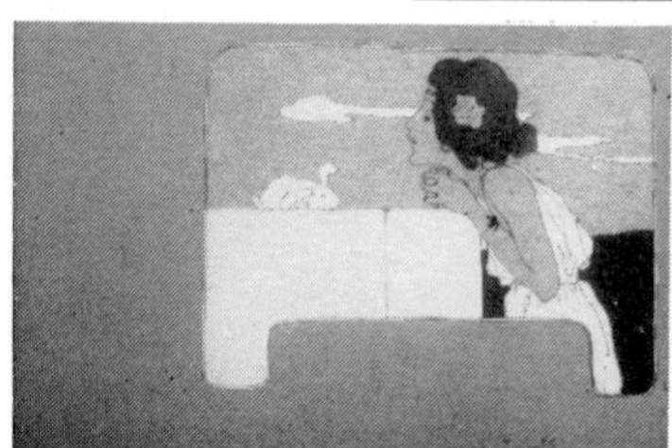

Purple series, rare, EX.
£50-60 *VS*

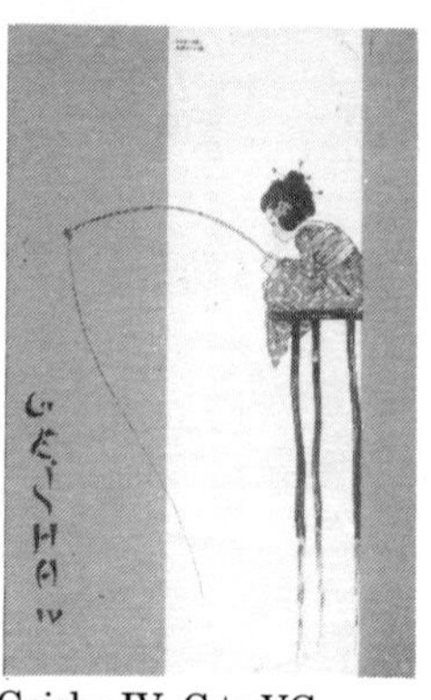

Geisha IV, G to VG.
£25-30 *VS*

Geisha II, G to VG.
£25-30 *VS*

Alphonse Mucha

Design for a postcard, published 1905, G.
£50-60 *VS*

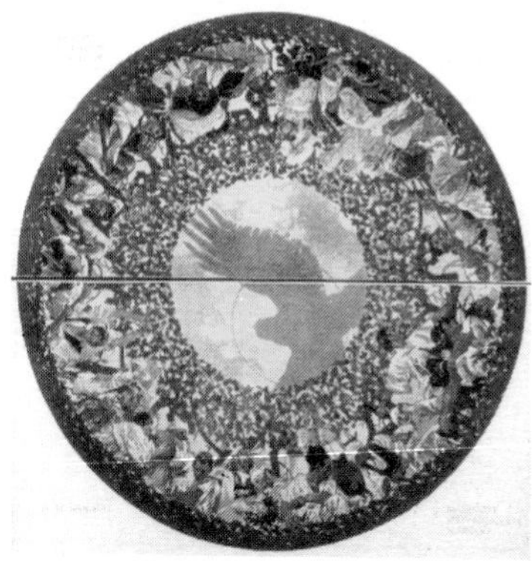

Slav Period, pair of cards, EX.
£70-80 *VS*

Louis Wain

Tucks 6444, complete, EX to MT.
£90-100 *VS*

Disasters

Hamstead Colliery, W. Gothard, 1908, G. **£15-60** *VS*

U.S.A., Tram smash, G to VG. **£15-20** *N*

Tram smash, Egerton, June 6th, 1905, G. **£14-18** *N*

Barrow Colliery, near Barnsley, W. Gothard, G. **£15-60** *VS*

Geographic

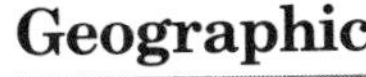

Early coloured views of Scotland, by Valentine, VG. **£1-3 each** *VS*

Natives of the Magallanes, Tierra Del Fuego, published in Chile, VG. **£1-3 each** *VS*

More if postally used.

Exploration

36 Pitcairn Islands, G. **£18-20** *VS*

Far more desirable and valuable if postally used.

Scott's Expedition 1901, Wrenches Links of Empire Series 3 No. 2, not pu, G. **£80-95** *N*

Military

Nazi Germany, Stuttgart, 1938, G.
£10-12 *VS*

8 WWII Russian Generals, Raphael Tuck, G.
£50-55 *VS*

HMS Bruizer.
£2-3 *MS*

12 WWI Belgium Anti-German propaganda, G to VG.
£35-40 *VS*

Crew of HMS Tiger, April 2, 1908.
£18-25 *MS*

Cross Reference
Militaria

5 German Art Caricatures, series 705, G.
£20-25 *VS*

Royalty

Victoria's Jubilee, VG.
£25-30 *VS*

Edward VIII, signed Christmas gift tag, G.
£60-100 *VS*

Royal Visit to Leeds, W. Gothard, FR to G. **£25-30** *VS*

Queen Victoria. **£10-15** *MS*

Social History

London Hyde Park.
£1-2 *MS*

General interest, traction engine, if location known. **£30-50**
If not known. **£18-25** *MS*

London Life, G.
£10-120 *N*

Serial number very important, scarce examples can sell in excess of £100.

Cricket.
£5-8 *MS*

Picture Theatre, Ponders End, pu. 1915, G. **£14-16** *VS*

A Coaching Meet in Hyde Park, VG.
£90-95 *VS*

6 Burwell Turf Industry, G.
£35-40 *VS*

Hereford May Fair, RP.
£15-20 *MS*

Lake District postmen, pu 1904, G.
£14-18 *N*

Gt. Hampton, St. Dairy, G.
£12-15 *VS*

Joan Fry. **£3-8** *MS*

Woven Silks

Patriotic, G.
£30-35 *VS*

Wounded soldier at monument, by Neyret Freres, G to VG.
£18-20 *VS*

Joh Gutenberg, pub. by Krieger, pu. 1900, G.
£55-65 *VS*

Christ, Bertrand & Boiron, G.
£40-50 *VS*

Exposition de Marseille, 1908, by Bodoy Guitton et Cie, G to VG.
£140-160 *VS*

Pius X, French Edition, 1914, G.
£12-18 *VS*

N.D. De La Garde, Bertrand & Boiron, G. **£40-50** *VS*

Happy Christmas, pub. by E. Deffrene, G.
£14-18 *VS*

Bonne Année, G.
£30-40 *VS*

Transport

Early Michelin advert, pu. 1908, G.
£20-25 *VS*

Horse cart, pu. 1910, G.
£12-18 *N*

Leyland lorry, pub. 1913, G.
£10-15 *N*

Horse drawn delivery carts, G to VG.
£20-30 each *N*

Comedy advert for Opel cars, by Daneket, FR to G.
£30-35 *VS*

Two French motor cycling, G.
£20-25 *VS*

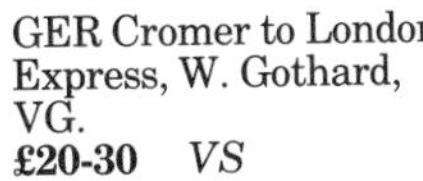

GER Cromer to London Express, W. Gothard, VG.
£20-30 *VS*

Floods, G. **£18-20** *VS*

Cross Reference
Automobilia

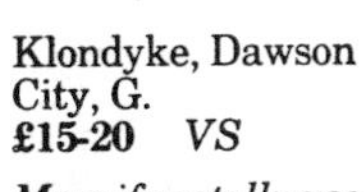

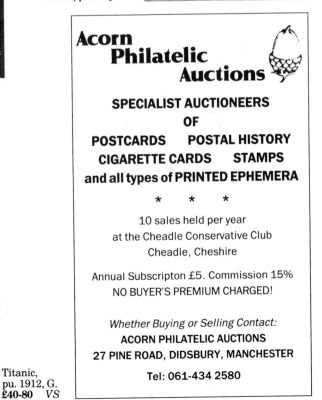

Klondyke, Dawson City, G.
£15-20 *VS*
More if postally used.

Auto Oil, French reverse, VG.
£14-18 *VS*

Lorry with Pratts Petrol adverts, G to VG.
£20-30 *VS*

Titanic, pu. 1912, G.
£40-80 *VS*

General

Is This the Road To Fairyland? **£2-4** *MS*

Wiener Werkstaette, No. 503, by Moriz Jung, G to VG. **£110-120** *VS*

Date, day and month, Portugal, pu. 1916, G. **£15-20** *VS*

A set of 12 glamorous girls by Sydney Carter, FR to G. **£20-30** *P*

Postal history, 1903. **£100-120** *VS*

Russian Art, VG. **£10-15** *VS*

Five Fantasy Mountains, by F. Killinger, Nos 111-115, VG. **£45-50** *VS*

Political, hand coloured, numbered 38 of 75, G. **£18-20** *VS*

4 Exhibitions, Leipzig, 1897, G to VG. **£30-35** *VS*

4 Chiostri, Art Deco, Pierrots, Series 240, published by Ballerini & Fratini, G to VG. **£40-45** *VS*

4 Portugal Exhibition, 1934. **£18-25** *VS*

Postmen of British Empire. **£4-8** *MS*

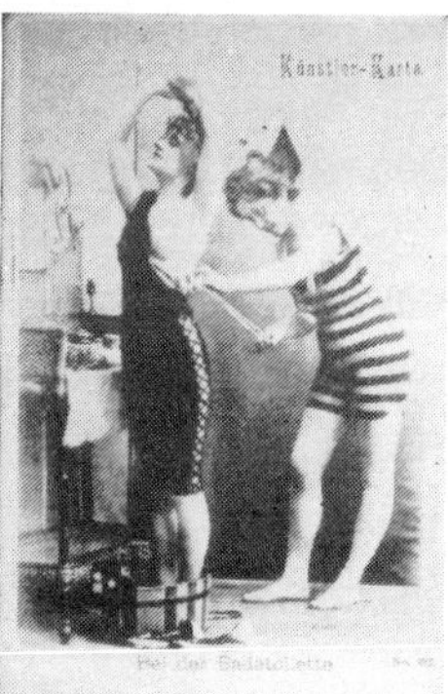

5 Lesbians, VR. **£30-35** *VS*

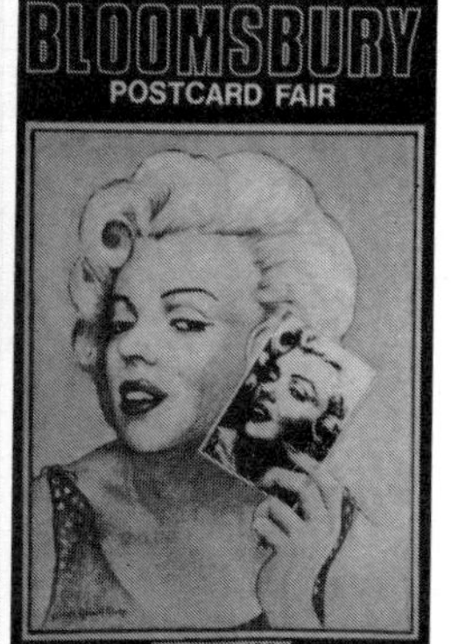

Popular modern cards.
25-50p each *MS*

Cross Reference
Pop, Rock & Film Memorabilia

Edwardian postcards.
10-15p each *MS*

Santa, hold to light, with 52 lights, pu. 1912, G.
£35-40 *VS*

A set of 6 Wagner, by Hoffmann, Series 127, pub. by Fabenphotographischaft, G to VG.
£40-45 *VS*

A collection of boxing postcards in two albums.
£350-400 *P*

Collection des Cents, No. 10, by L. Grégoire, VG.
£45-50 *VS*

6 Colombo, Glamour, Series 954 complete, G.
£30-40 *VS*

Leroy, a set of 10, pub. by Gallais, G to VG.
£35-40 *VS*

18 Dog Carts, Belgium and Holland, G.
50p-£4 each *VS*

Rare – France. Common – Belgium and Holland. The more dogs per card, the greater the value.

2 Chiostri, Art Deco Pierrots, series 256, pub. by Ballerini & Fratini, G to VG.
£20-25 *VS*

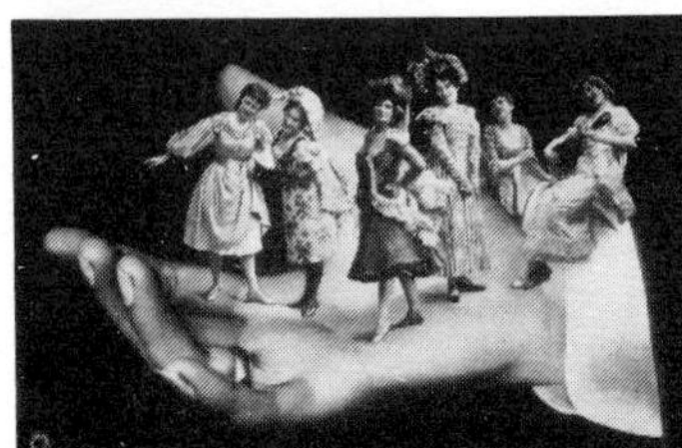

7 Novelty, Portugal, 1909, G.
£20-25 *VS*

Cross Reference
Toys

Scattina, classical Art Deco, Pierrot, G.
£15-20 *VS*

Finland propaganda, c1930-40, G.
£30-35 *VS*

A collection of 44 cards relating to Salvation Army.
£50-60 *VS*

FURTHER READING
Hill, C. W., *Discovering Picture Postcards,* Aylesbury, Bucks, 1978.
Radley, C., *The Woven Silk Postcard,* Barking, 1978.
Smith, J. H. D., *IPM Catalogue of Picture Postcards and Year Book 1989,* Hove, 1989.
White, G., *Collecting Military Postcards,* Bristol, 1987.

Prints

Baxter & Le Blond Prints

George Baxter produced high quality coloured prints in the 1830s and is acknowledged as the pioneer of oil colour prints.

Robert Le Blond was Baxter's pupil and was licensed by Baxter to produce a set of 32 oval shaped prints in 1850. These were printed directly onto the mount, surrounded by an embossed rim with the serial number and title appearing on a small panel in the bottom right hand corner.

Please Remember the Grotto, No. 50.
£80-120
BEE

The Burning Glass, No. 73.
£80-120 *BEE*

The Image Box, No. 49.
£80-120 *BEE*

Pet Rabbits, No. 75.
£80-120 *BEE*

Good News, No. 72. **£80-120** *BEE*

Blowing Bubbles, No. 74.
£80-120 *BEE*

The Blackberry Gatherers, No. 76.
£80-120 *BEE*

The Sailor's Departure, No. 78.
£90-130 *BEE*

The Gleaners, No. 79.
£80-120 *BEE*

The Mill Stream, Towing the Prize, No. 80.
£80-120 *BEE*

The Young Angler, No. 84.
£80-120 *BEE*

May Day, No. 85.
£90-130 *BEE*

The Fifth of November, No. 86.
£90-130 *BEE*

The Pedlar, No. 82.
£80-120 *BEE*

The Cherry Seller, No. 81.
£80-120 *BEE*

The Village Spring, No. 88. **£80-120** *BEE*

The Showman, No. 83.
£90-130 *BEE*

Crossing the Brook, No. 87.
£100-140 *BEE*

The Fisherman's Hut, No. 90.
£90-130 *BEE*

Waiting at the Ferry, No. 91.
£80-120 *BEE*

The Bird's Nest, No. 93.
£80-120 *BEE*

The Swing, No. 92.
£100-140 *BEE*

Grandmother's Snuff Box, No. 100.
£90-130 *BEE*

Grandfather's Pipe, No. 99.
£90-130 *BEE*

Baxter Prints

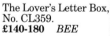

The Lover's Letter Box, No. CL359.
£140-180 *BEE*

The Fruit Girl of the Alps, No. CL333.
£100-130 *BEE*

Radios

An A.J.S. 4-valve battery receiver, by A. J. Stevens & Co., c1923.
£300-350 *MR*

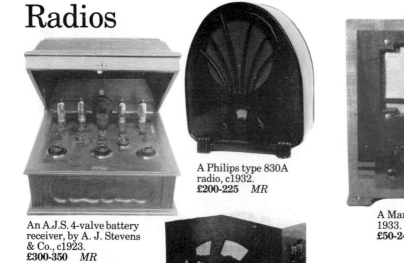

A Philips type 830A radio, c1932.
£200-225 *MR*

A Marconiphone 252, 1933.
£50-240 *RC*

A Marconi type 41 4-valve battery receiver, c1925.
£180-225
Amplion horn speaker, c1923.
£100-125 *MR*

Two radios:
Pye MM model, 1931.
£90-300
r. Philips 834A model, 1933.
£100-350 *RC*

A Bush type AC3 MW/LW T.R.F. radio, c1932.
£150-200 *MR*

A Penthouse radio/drinks cabinet, by R.K. Radio, U.S.A., 1934. **£250-275** *RR*

An Ultra Blue Fox radio, 1932.
£95-225 *RC*

A Zetavox T.R.F. receiver, 1931.
£140-400 *RC*

A Midgetronic EMU 4214 mains valve receiver, in maroon, 1950.
£35-40 *RR*

An Ekco RG25 radiogram, c1932.
£100-150 *MR*

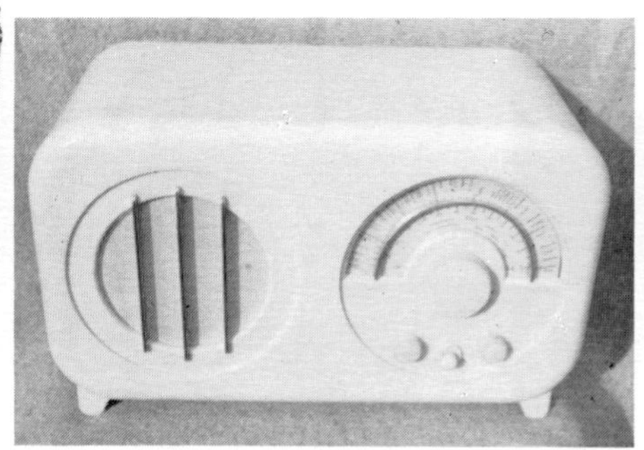

An Ekco AC85 model, c1934.
In white **£250-300** *MR*

Normally cheaper when in standard colours of brown or black.

An Ekco radio.
£130-150 *MGM*

A G.E.C. 3520 Universal Mains Three in brown Bakelite, c1934.
£100-125 *MR*

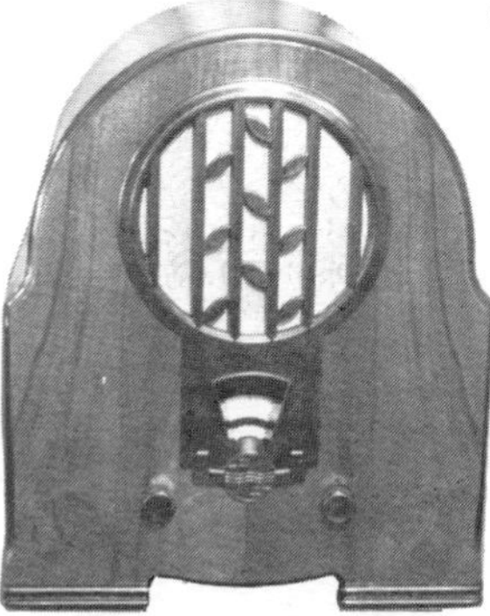

A Philips 634A model, 1933.
£150-500 *RC*

A Philips type 930C D.C. mains radio, c1931.
£200-250 *MR*

An R.G.D. 166 radio, 1939.
£50-280 *RC*

An Emerson 5-valve AC/DC radio, c1934.
£70-80 *MR*

A K.B. valve radio, 1932.
£50-60 *COB*

An Ekco type AD65 in black Bakelite cabinet, c1934.
£300-350 *MR*

H.M.V. 491 model, 1937.
£25-200 *RC*

A Philips 636A MW/LW 8-valve T.R.F. radio, c1933.
£500-600 *MR*

A KB type FB.10 model with cream Bakelite case, c1950.
£65-75 *MR*

A Ferranti 146 radio, 1946.
£35-140 *RC*

A Ferguson 378AC, 1937.
£90-350 *RC*

A Goblin radio and clock.
£75-85 *DH*

A Ferranti model 145, c1945.
£125-150 *MR*

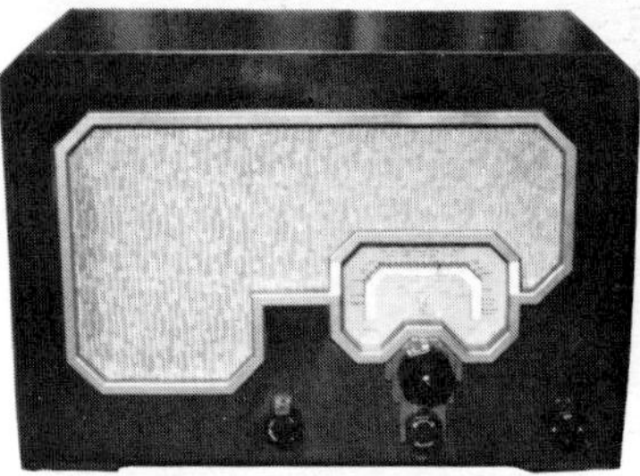

A Cossor 378 model, 1935.
£30-195 *RC*

A Bush type DAC.91 in brown Bakelite, c1946.
£60-70 *MR*

A Philips 462A model in brown Bakelite, c1947.
£40-50 *MR*

A Pye model 123BQ portable, 1957.
£75-100 *RR*

A Bush DAC.10 radio, 1950.
£25-75 *RC*

A Pye model M78F 4-valve battery portable, 1948.
£150-225 *MR*

A De-Luxe transistor radio/spice rack, 1972.
£15-20 *RR*

A panda radio, 1950s.
£10-15 *BEV*

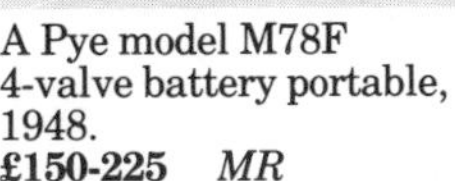

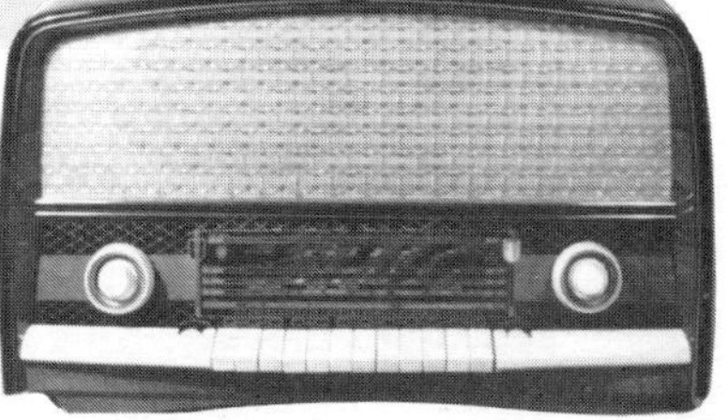

An Orion AR.612 table receiver, 1962.
£40-180 *RC*

A Decca Deccette, c1953.
£75-85 *MR*

An Adam and Eve transistor radio, Hong Kong, 1977.
£25-30 *RR*

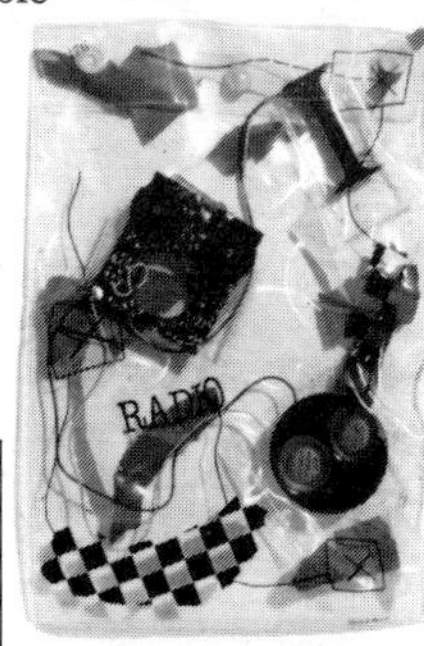

A Modern Art transistor radio, by Daniel Weil, 1981.
£20-30 *RR*

DID YOU KNOW?
The 1924 Bijou Radio card, a working crystal radio in a 5½ by 3½in postcard, predates the Casio and Sony 'credit cards' by 60 years.

Television

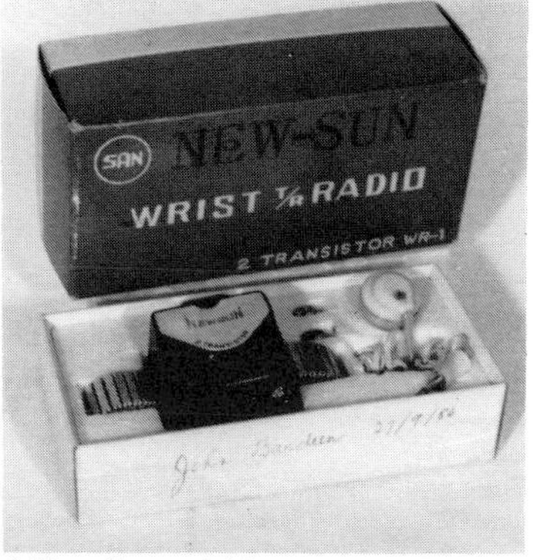

A New Sun wrist-type transistor radio, 1965.
£25-30 without signature *PC*

Box signed by John Bardeen, one of the inventors of the transistor – a unique signature!

A Bush television type TV.22, c1950.
£100-150 *MR*

A Marconiphone 702 television set, 1937.
£350-900 *RC*

Railways

It is now over 20 years since the last steam locomotive was withdrawn from regular service and railway memorabilia continue to increase both in interest and value. Railway posters are now recognised as an established area for art collections, with many famous designers and artists of the 20th century being featured.

Coats-of-Arms

Midland & Great Northern Joint Railway, 14 by 12in (35 by 30cm).
£40-60 *ONS*

Cork, Blackrock & Passage Railway Co, 17 by 15½in (43 by 39cm).
£100-120 *ONS*

South Eastern & Chatham Railway, 20in (50cm) square.
£100-120 *ONS*

South Eastern Railway, 16 by 15in (41 by 38cm).
£35-45 *ONS*

Cutlery & Crockery

Pottery jug and basin.
£250-300 *ONS*

Various earthenware items, and 2 silver plated toast racks.
£50-150 each *ONS*

A salmon dish, Midland Grand Hotel.
£250-300 *ONS*

Ice buckets and dish.
£50-100 *ONS*

DID YOU KNOW?
Miller's Collectables Price Guide is designed to build up, year by year, into the most comprehensive reference system available.

General

Various medallions and passes.
Gold.
£600-700 each *ONS*
Others.
£50-350 each *ONS*

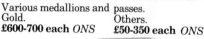

Oil on canvas, West Country class engine Exeter 34001, 20 by 30in (50 by 75cm).
£350-450 *MN*

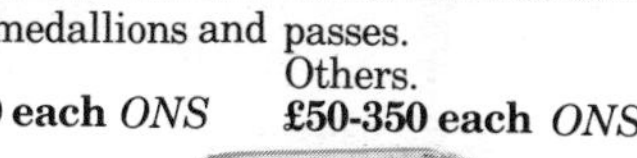

G.W.R. key. **£50-200** *WIN*

L.N.W.R. carpet, 86in (220cm).
£280-300 *ONS*

A timetable, 1911.
£30-35 *COB*

Photographs

A collection of nearly 1,000 glass negatives, 1900-1939. **£1,800-2,000** *ONS*

G.W.R. King Class, James I.
£70-100 *ONS*

Lamps

Three lamps.
£50-100 each *ONS*

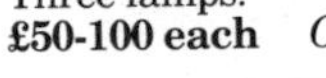

Three lamps.
£50-100 each *ONS*

A collection of lamps.
£30-50 each *WIN*

Signalling Equipment

Signal box block bell instruments.
£80-150 each *WIN*

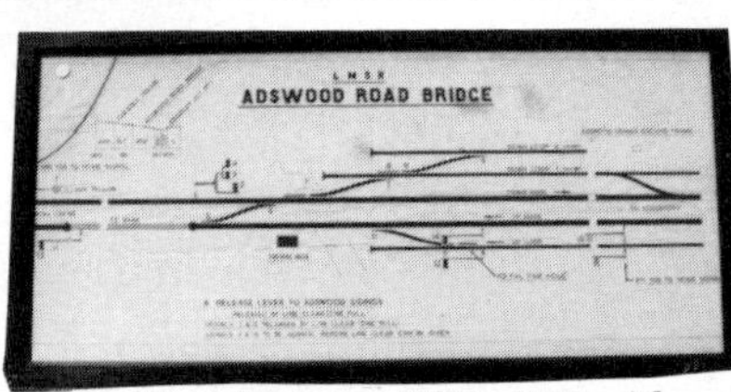

A signal box diagram, 42½in (106cm) long.
£25-100 *WIN*

Signal indicators.
£10-20 each *WIN*

Two block bells.
£50-100 each *WIN*

Plates

Royal train locomotive panel, No. 30119, c1935, 13in (33cm) high.
£600-700 *ONS*

Bonaventura 3342, Great Western Railway, 25½in (63cm) long.
£2,000-3,000 *WIN*

A brass maker's plate, slightly worn, 16in (41cm) wide. **£400-450** *CSK*

G.N. & G.E. bridge plate.
£35-65 *WIN*

Railway bridge plates.
£25-65 each *WIN*

Rhodesian Railways, No. 250.
£250-350 *WIN*

South African Railways, No. 377, Class S.1.
£250-400 *WIN*

Nameplates

Station nameplates, 36in (91cm) long.
£100-600 each *WIN*

Four wagon plates, 11in (29cm) long.
£10-40 each *WIN*

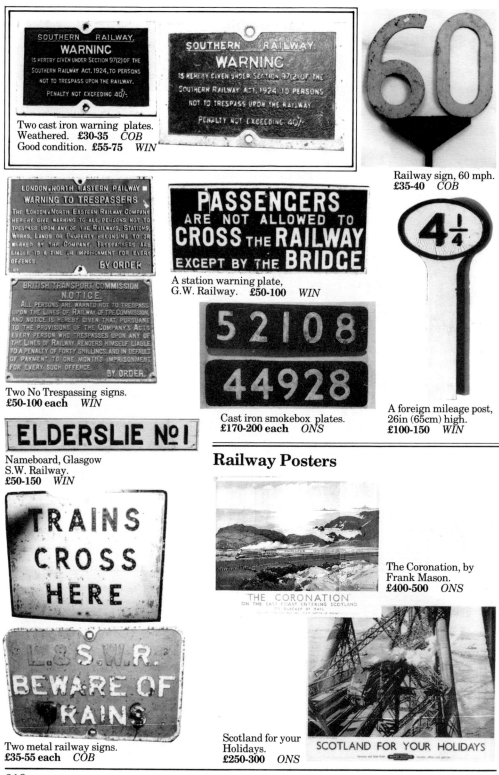

Two cast iron warning plates.
Weathered. **£30-35** *COB*
Good condition. **£55-75** *WIN*

Railway sign, 60 mph.
£35-40 *COB*

Two No Trespassing signs.
£50-100 each *WIN*

A station warning plate,
G.W. Railway. **£50-100** *WIN*

Cast iron smokebox plates.
£170-200 each *ONS*

A foreign mileage post,
26in (65cm) high.
£100-150 *WIN*

Nameboard, Glasgow
S.W. Railway.
£50-150 *WIN*

Two metal railway signs.
£35-55 each *COB*

Railway Posters

The Coronation, by
Frank Mason.
£400-500 *ONS*

Scotland for your
Holidays.
£250-300 *ONS*

Harrogate, Newcastle and Edinburgh.
£65-75 *ONS*

Bridlington. **£500-600** *ONS*

Canadian National Railways, W. Y. Calder.
£55-65 *ONS*

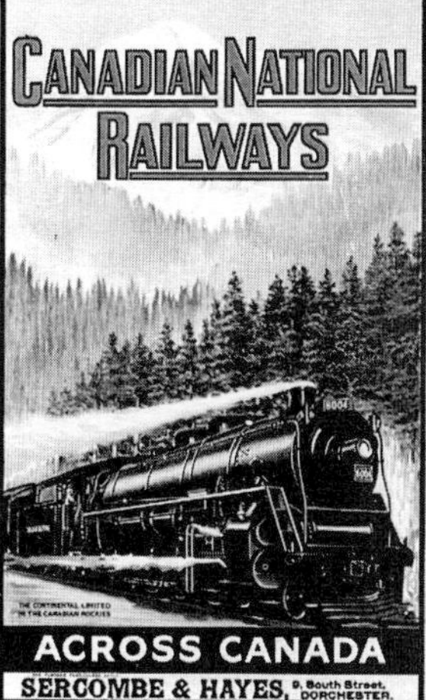

Canadian National Railways, C. Norwich.
£180-200 *ONS*

The Broads, by Spurrier.
£800-900 *ONS*

East Coast by LNER.
£500-600 each *ONS*

Lowestoft.
£400-500 *ONS*

SECR Folkestone.
£1,000-1,200 *ONS*

LNER locomotive, Silver Link, by Frank Newbould.
£200-250 *ONS*

Cruden Bay, H. G. Gawthorn.
£1,300-1,500 *ONS*

The Flying Scotsman's Cocktail Bar.
£1,300-1,500 *ONS*

Scarborough.
£200-250 *ONS*

East Coast Types.
£180-200 *ONS*

East Coast, Frank H. Mason. **£650-750** *ONS*

Getting Ready on the East Coast.
£280-320 *ONS*

Riverside Excursions.
£250-300 *ONS*

Royal Albert Bridge, Saltash.
£250-300 *ONS*

Norfolk Coast, Septimus E. Scott.
£440-450 *ONS*

Rock & Pop Memorabilia

The Beatles

An autographed single, John Lennon.
£2,200-2,500 *CSK*

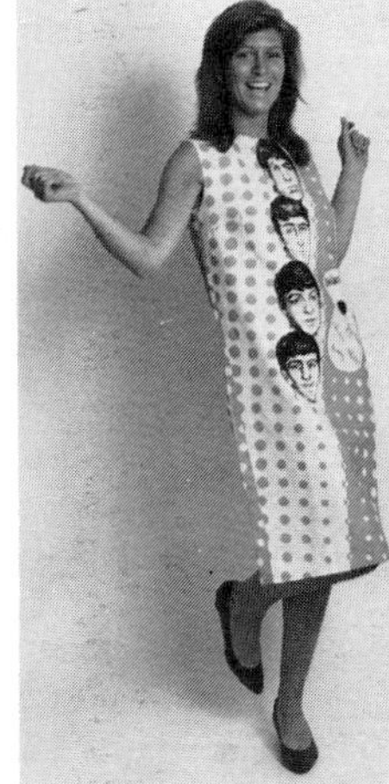

A signed dress, c1964.
£2,800-3,000 *C*

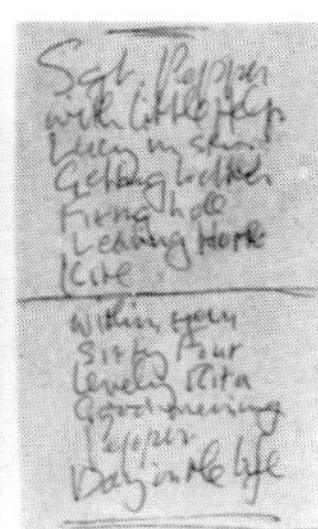

A handwritten song order and print of Sgt. Pepper LP sleeve, John Lennon.
£800-900 *P*

A Star Club flight bag
£200-220 *C*

A presentation Gold disc, The Beatles 1967-1970.
£2,000-2,500 *CSK*

A fan club post card, c1964.
£500-550 *C*

Beatles wallpaper, 1964.
£40-45 *COB*

Autographed programmes.
£150-200 *CSK*

Egg cups, 1960s.
£40-45 *COB*

Photograph and copy of Paul McCartney's marriage certificate, 1969.
£220-250 *CSK*

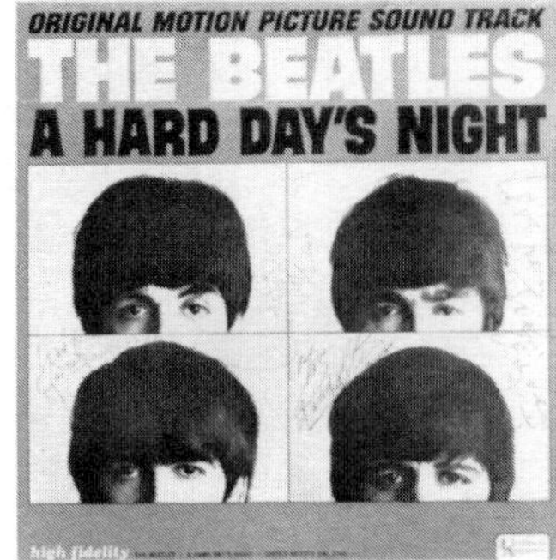

An album cover, signed by each Beatle.
£1,300-1,500 *CSK*

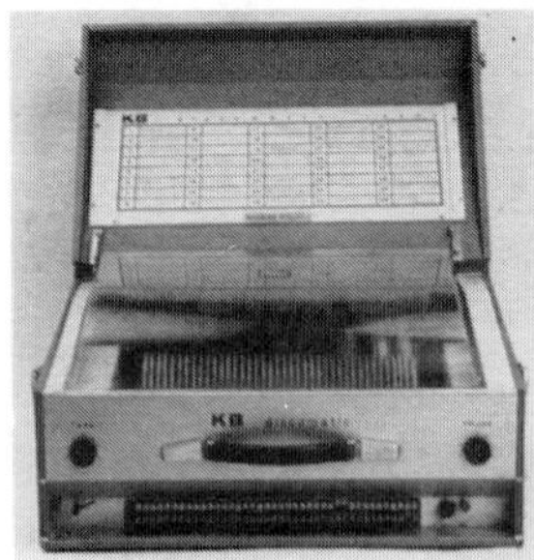

A KB discomatic portable record player/juke box, allegedly owned by John Lennon, 1960s.
£1,000-1,200 *C*

Elvis Presley

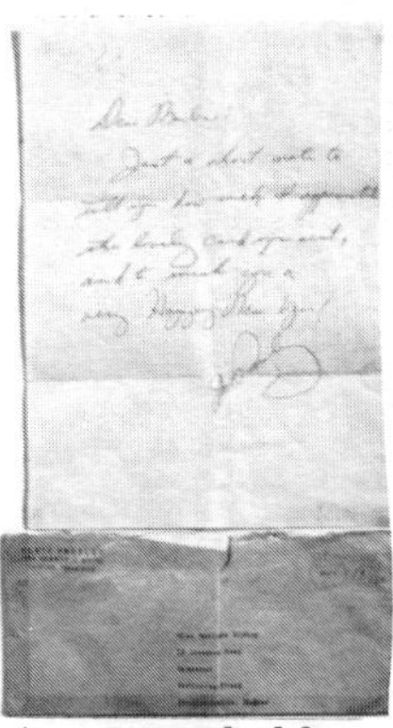

An autographed fan letter, 1961.
£550-600 *C*

A presentation Gold disc, Moody Blue.
£400-450 *C*

A brass belt buckle, 3in (7.5cm) diam.
£150-200 *C*

A signed record cover.
£550-650 *CSK*

Jimi Hendrix

Four previously unpublished photographs of Jimi Hendrix.
£600-650 *C*

A publicity photograph and autograph, 1968.
£350-400 *C*

Photograph and 2 pages from an autograph book.
£500-550 *CSK*

A signed concert programme, 1967.
£800-900 *C*

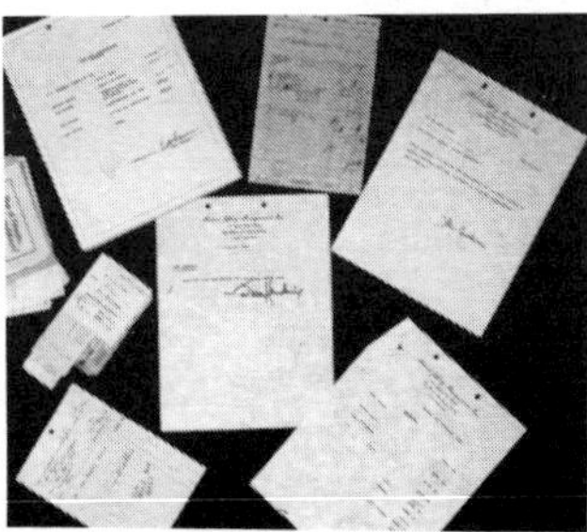

A collection of receipts and invoices, 1968-69.
£700-750 *CSK*

Pop Groups

A signed Rolling Stones concert programme, 1964.
£450-500 *C*

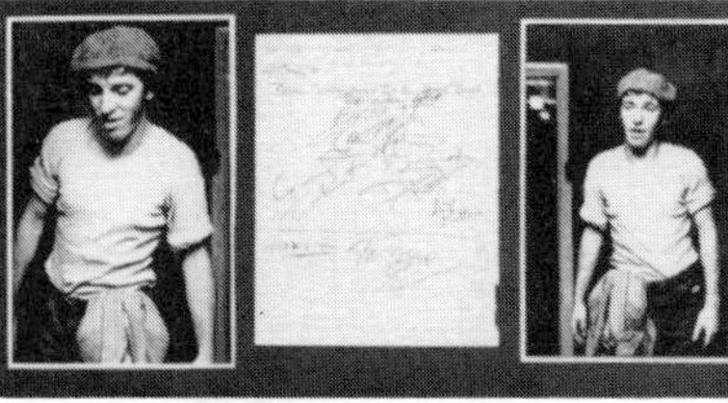

Two photographs and page signed by Bruce Springsteen.
£275-300 *CSK*

A signed album cover, Bob Dylan, with various souvenirs.
£400-450 *C*

Roy Orbison memorabilia.
£150-200 *CSK*

A signed promotional album, The Rolling Stones.
£250-300 *C*

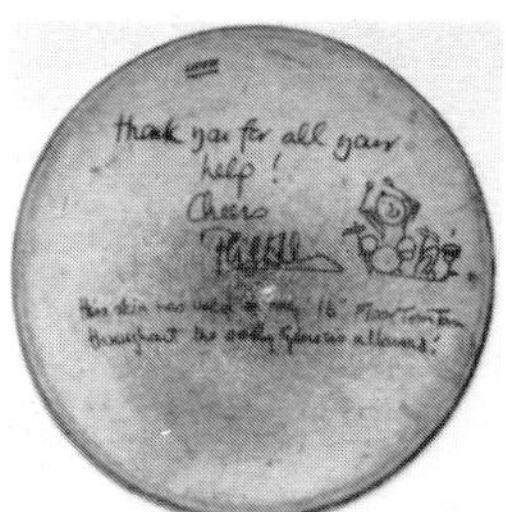

An autographed drum skin, signed by Phil Collins.
£1,800-2,000 *CSK*

An autographed Buddy Holly souvenir concert programme, 1958.
£1,200-1,400 *C*

Souvenir programme, The Jacksons.
£150-200 *CSK*

A photograph and autographed page, Sam Cooke.
£250-300 *C*

A publicity still showing Keith Emerson, c1970.
£50-60 *CSK*

A signed publicity photograph, The Doors.
£550-600 *C*

A photographic silk screen printed, signed Elvis Costello, 1980.
£550-650 *C*

Instruments

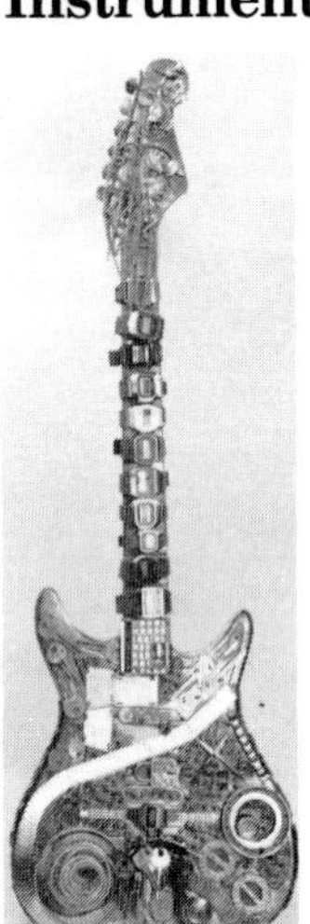

A well decorated guitar, Boy George.
£700-750 *CSK*

A Fender Stratocaster guitar, signed Eric Clapton '89.
£2,200-2,500 *C*

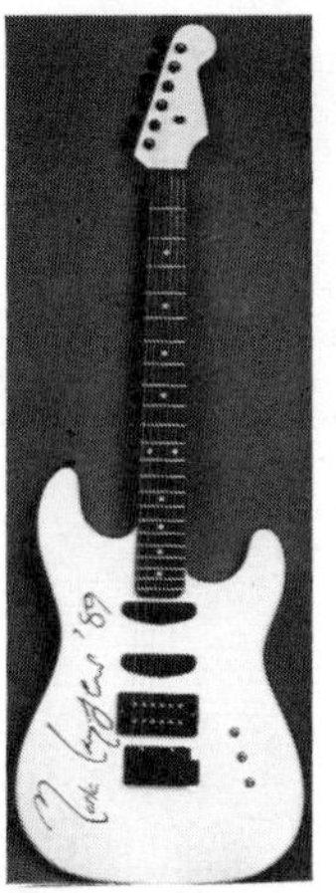

A Stratocaster electric guitar, signed Mark Knopfler, '89.
£1,500-1,800 *C*

A Gibson L6-S electric guitar, Mike Oldfield.
£800-900 *C*

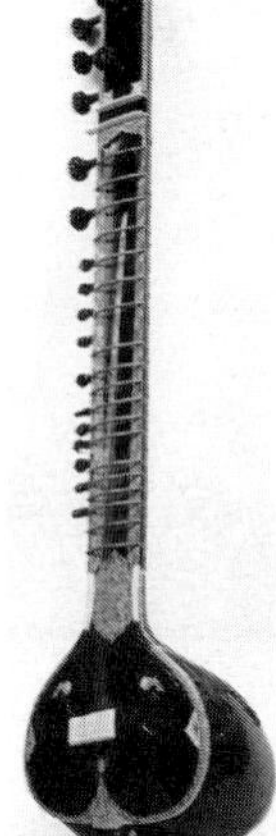

A sitar, signed by Ravi Shankar.
£450-500 *C*

Clothing

A Stars and Stripes stage suit for Elton John, designed by Bob Mackie.
£1,100-1,300 *CSK*

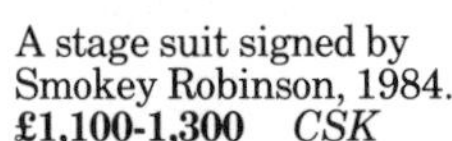

An autographed hat, Keith Moon and Pete Townshend.
£450-500 *CSK*

A pair of platform soled shoes, one signed by Elton John.
£600-650 *C*

A stage suit signed by Smokey Robinson, 1984.
£1,100-1,300 *CSK*

Three David Bowie items, signed.
£500-550 *CSK*

Four well decorated stage costumes, the Osmonds, c1975.
£2,500-3,000 *P*

Presentation Discs

A presentation platinum disc, Wings.
£600-650 *CSK*

A presentation platinum disc, The Police.
£250-350 *CSK*

A presentation multi-platinum disc, Bruce Springsteen.
£900-1,000 *C*

A presentation silver disc, Mike Oldfield.
£400-500 *CSK*

A metal pressing disc for the album Endless Summer, The Beach Boys, 1974.
£300-350 *C*

A presentation platinum disc, Prince.
£650-750 *CSK*

A presentation silver disc, The Clash.
£350-450 *CSK*

A presentation platinum disc, Donna Summer.
£300-400 *C*

A presentation gold disc, The Jacksons.
£900-1,000 *CSK*

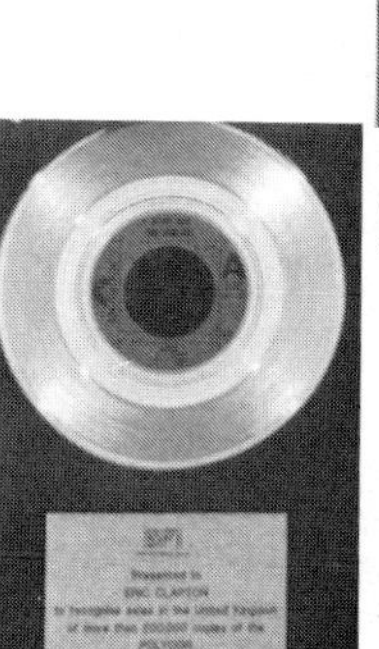

A presentation gold disc, Derek and the Dominoes.
£3,300-3,500 *CSK*

A presentation gold disc, The Beatles.
£3,500-4,000 *CSK*

A presentation gold disc, John Lennon.
£3,000-3,500 *C*

Posters

A polychrome film poster, Help, The Beatles.
£150-200 *CSK*

A polychrome tour poster, Jimi Hendrix.
£300-400 *CSK*

A page from Another Beatles Christmas Show, 1964, and 15 signatures.
£1,300-1,500 *CSK*

An advertising poster, 1964.
£1,200-1,500 *CSK*

Two Rolling Stones tour posters.
£100-150 *C*

Two posters, T. Rex, 1971.
£800-900 *CSK*

A concert advertising poster, Sounds 68.
£50-60 *CSK*

Miscellaneous

A pin-ball machine, once the property of The Who.
£200-250 *CSK*

A flower power wrist watch, in original box.
£250-300 *P*

A self-portrait caricature with Yoko Ono, by John Lennon, 1969.
£3,000-3,500 *C*

Film Memorabilia

A half-length signed still of Mae West.
£150-200 *CSK*

A portrait photograph, Montgomery Clift, with inscription.
£150-200 *CSK*

An oil on canvas portrait of Charlie Chaplin, by Emile T. Mazy, 1917.
£600-700 *CSK*

A publicity photograph of Ronald Reagan.
£250-300 *CSK*

A portrait photograph of Alec Guinness, by Cecil Beaton, c1952.
£200-300 *CSK*

A publicity photograph of Rita Hayworth, signed
£25-30 *CSK*

A portrait photograph, Gary Cooper, secretarial signature.
£300-400 *CSK*

A portrait photograph of Basil Rathbone, signed.
£150-200 *CSK*

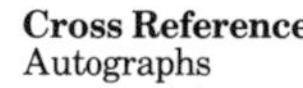

Cross Reference
Autographs

Four polychrome film posters, Hammer Horror.
£400-450 *CSK*

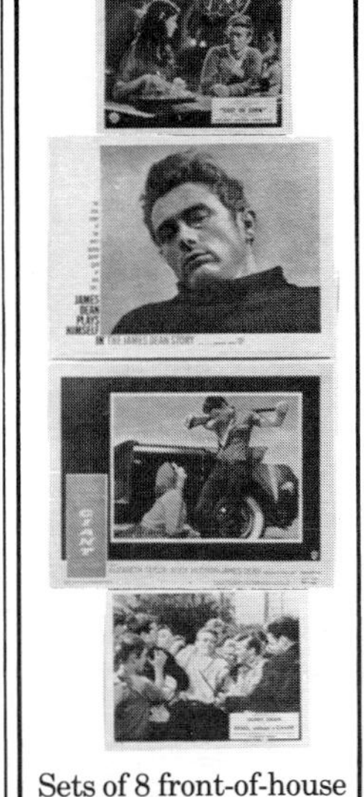

Sets of 8 front-of-house stills, James Dean.
£100-150 each *CSK*

A portrait photograph of Carole Lombard.
£150-200 *CSK*

Film Costume

A model of the head of The Creature from the Black Lagoon, 1954.
£900-1,000 *CSK*

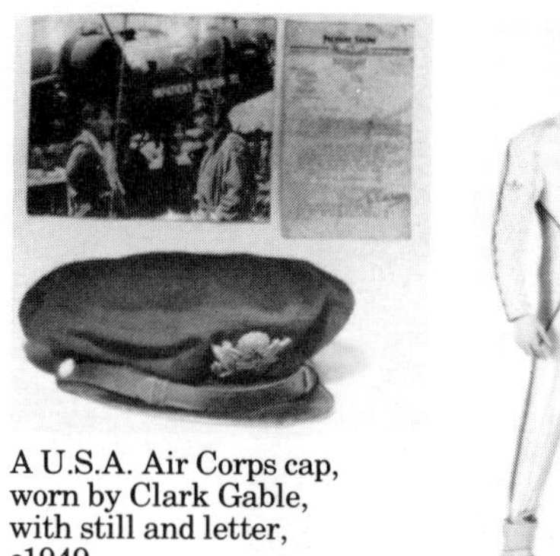

A U.S.A. Air Corps cap, worn by Clark Gable, with still and letter, c1949.
£500-600 *CSK*

A one-piece running suit and accessories, for the film Running Man, Arnold Schwarzenegger, 1987.
£350-400 *CSK*

Two costumes of various materials, made for the film The Wiz, 1978.
£200-250 *CSK*

A tweed jacket worn by Ronald Reagan, together with still, c1946.
£900-1,000 *CSK*

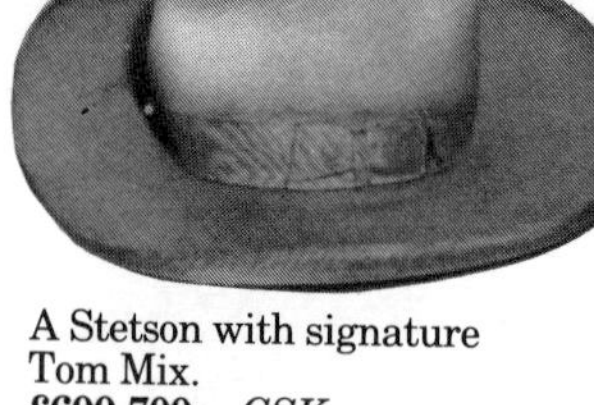

A Stetson with signature Tom Mix.
£600-700 *CSK*

An original Paco Rabanne leather jacket, made for Brigitte Bardot, 1960s.
£1,000-1,500 *CSK*

A stetson belonging to John Wayne.
£2,200-2,500 *CSK*

A stand-in model of Boris Karloff as Frankenstein's monster in the 1935 Universal Pictures film The Bride of Frankenstein.
£16,000+ *CSK*

Marilyn Monroe

A portrait photograph, with inscription.
£650-750 *CSK*

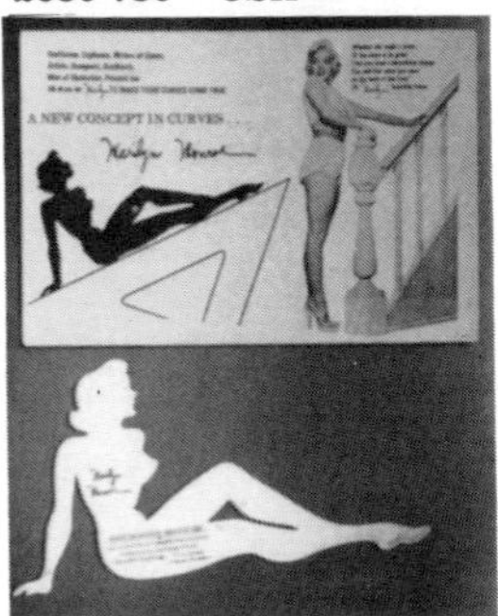

A Marilyn Monroe Drawing Aid.
£600-650 *CSK*

A pink silk blouse, with film still.
£2,000-2,500 *CSK*

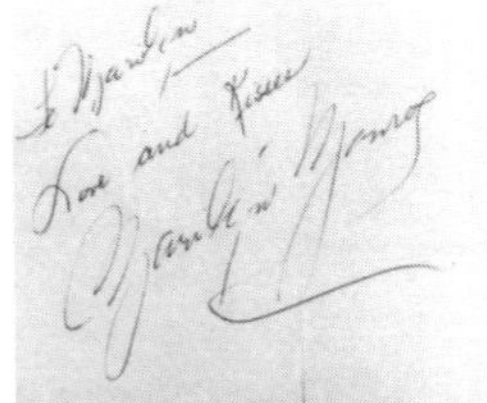

A page from an autograph book with inscription by Marilyn Monroe.
£600-700 *CSK*

A polychrome poster, Bus Stop.
£700-750 *CSK*

A colour print and photographer's contract, 1949.
£2,600-3,000 *CSK*

A theatre programme, signed by Marilyn Monroe and Joe Di Maggio.
£650-750 *CSK*

Two previously unpublished photographs and signed paper, c1956.
£800-900 *CSK*

A 2-piece pant suit of gold lurex, with 13 prints, c1954.
£1,500-2,000 *CSK*

Four early Marilyn Monroe black and white negatives, with photographs, c1947, 4½ by 3½in (11 by 9cm).
£900-1,000 *CNY*

Scales & Balances

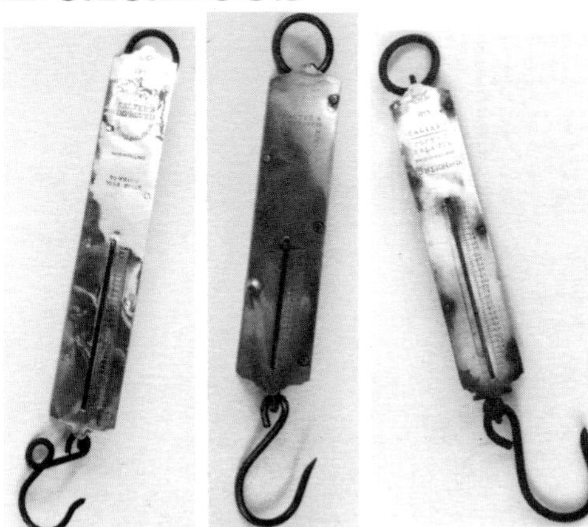

A selection of Salter's spring balances.
£15-25 each *AL*

Harper's kitchen scales, c1950.
£5-6 *DH*

Small hanging scales, 11in (29cm) long.
£45-50 *MCA*

Metal scales, 6½in (16cm) long.
£8-10 *AL*

Kitchen scales, c1930.
£4-5 *DH*

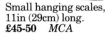

A balance, 17½in (43cm).
£40-45 *MCA*

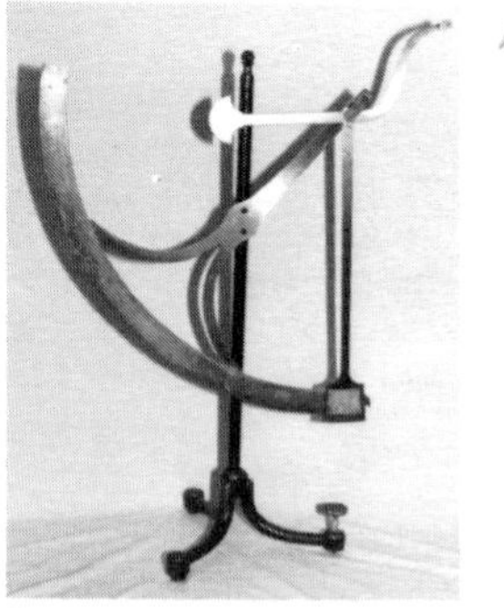

Postal scales, 27in (68cm) high.
£170-180 *PH*

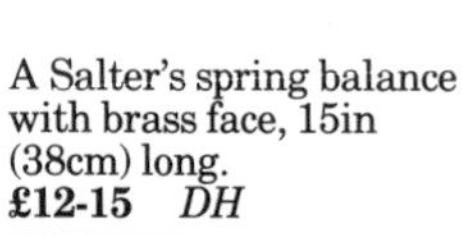

A Salter's spring balance with brass face, 15in (38cm) long.
£12-15 *DH*

Salter postal scales, 7½in (18cm) high.
£25-30 *MCA*

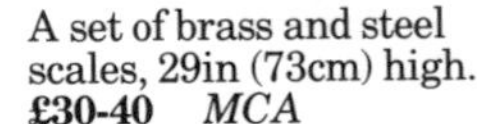

A set of brass and steel scales, 29in (73cm) high.
£30-40 *MCA*

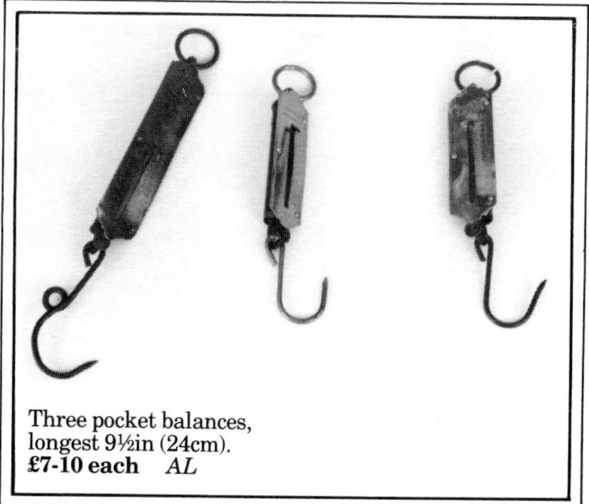

Three pocket balances, longest 9½in (24cm).
£7-10 each *AL*

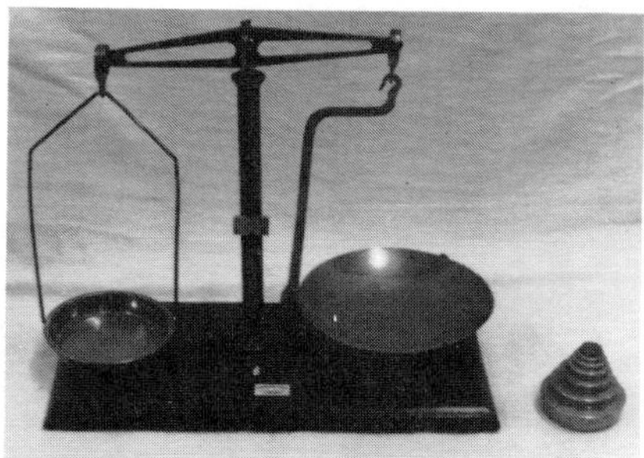

Brass tobacco scales on mahogany base, with weights, early 20thC.
£110-120 *PCh*

A set of scales.
£700-750 *MCA*

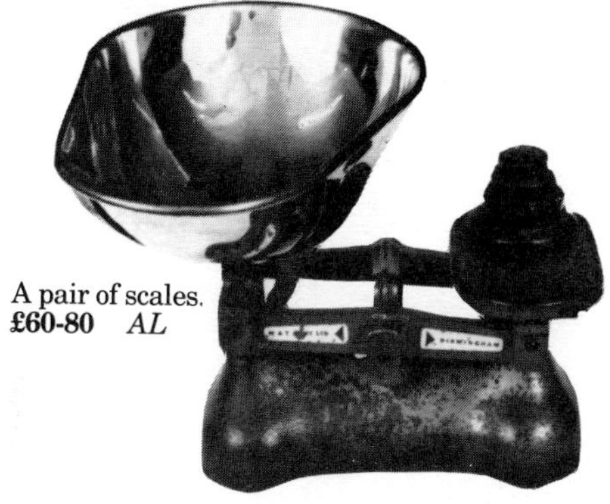

A pair of scales.
£60-80 *AL*

A set of analytical scales, 12½in (33cm) high.
£85-90 *MCA*

Large letter scales.
£100-120 *MAI*

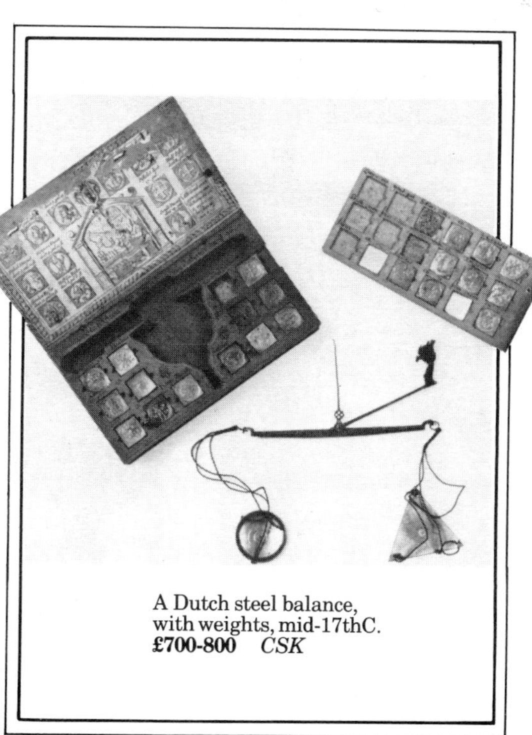

A Dutch steel balance, with weights, mid-17thC.
£700-800 *CSK*

Scientific Instruments

A barograph in oak case, early 20thC, 13½in (34cm) wide.
£125-150 *PCh*

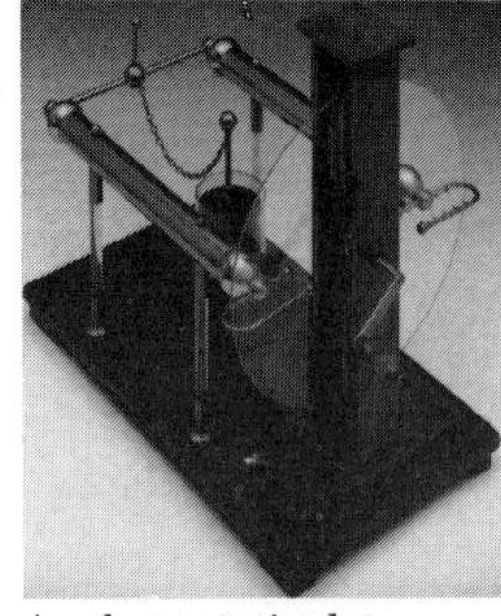

An electrostatic plate machine, unsigned, 19thC, 20in (50cm) wide.
£550-600 *CSK*

A lacquered brass swinging arm protractor, 19thC, 7in (18cm) diam, in mahogany case.
£220-250 *CSK*

A French lacquered graphometer, late 19thC, 9in (24cm) wide, with mahogany and brass tripod.
£200-300 *CSK*

A sundial, 6½in (16.5cm) square.
£70-100 *CAC*

A lacquered brass multi-cellular voltmeter, late 19thC, 14in (35cm) high.
£250-300 *CSK*

A pair of parallel rules, in ebony with brass fittings.
£30-40 *AL*

A boxwood folding rule.
£8-10 *AL*

Globes

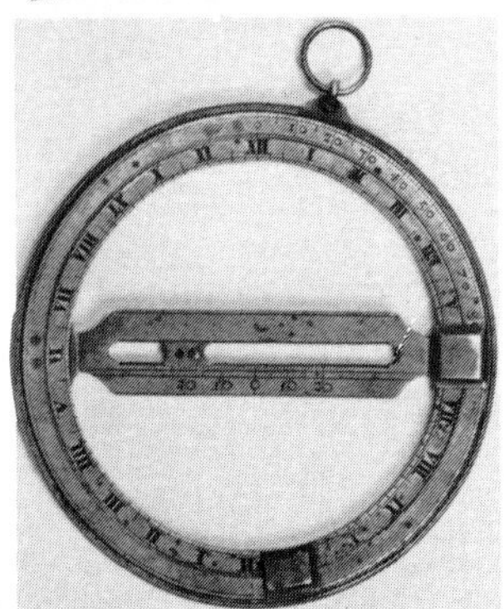

A brass equinoctial ring dial, unsigned, 18thC, 4in (10cm) diam.
£500-550 *CSK*

A Dutch 8½in (22cm) terrestrial globe, late 19thC, 17in (43cm) high.
£300-350 *CSK*

A miniature globe on stand, 18thC.
£300-400 *PC*

A 6in (15cm) celestial globe, early 19thC, 10in (25cm) high.
£850-950 *CSK*

FURTHER READING
Daumas, Maurice, *Scientific Instruments of the 17thC and 18thC and their Makers,* London 1972.
Herbert, Sir Alan P., *Sundials, Old and New,* London 1967.
Wynter, Harriet and Turner, Anthony, *Scientific Instruments,* London 1975.

Hour-Glasses

Hour-glasses, in pine frames, c1800, 7in (17.5cm) high.
£120-130 each *P*

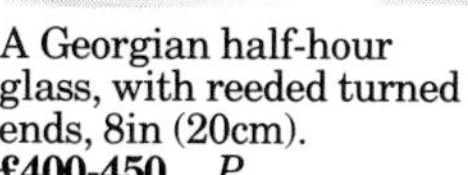

A Georgian half-hour glass, with reeded turned ends, 8in (20cm).
£400-450 *P*

An hour-glass in pine frame, c1800.
£150-200 *P*

A quarter-hour sand glass, each end engraved with flowers and scrolls, 18thC, 7in (17.5cm) high.
£250-300 *P*

Surveying

A black enamelled and nickel plated brass transit theodolite, by E. R. Watts & Son, London, 18in (45cm).
£500-600 *CSK*

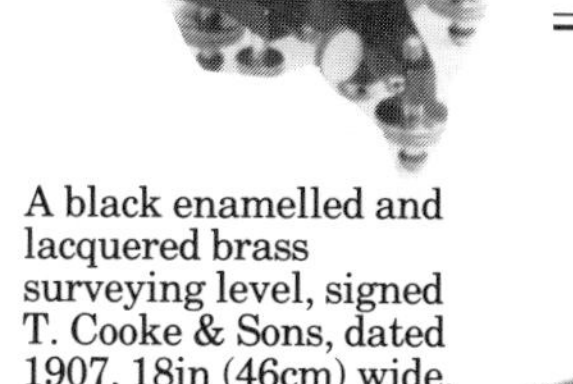

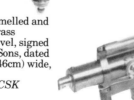

A black enamelled and lacquered brass surveying level, signed T. Cooke & Sons, dated 1907, 18in (46cm) wide, with strap.
£100-150 *CSK*

A lacquered brass surveying level, by Troughton & Simms, 17in (43cm) wide, with case.
£200-250 *CSK*

FURTHER READING
Wilbur, Keith, M.D., *Antique Medical Instruments,* Millbank Books, U.K.

Medical Instruments

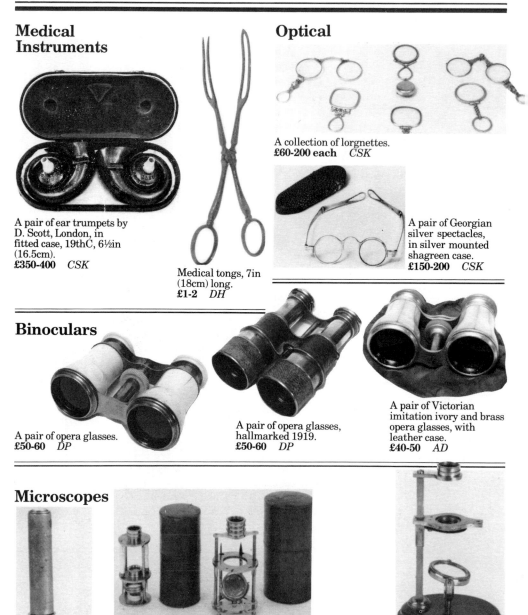

A pair of ear trumpets by D. Scott, London, in fitted case, 19thC, 6½in (16.5cm).
£350-400 *CSK*

Medical tongs, 7in (18cm) long.
£1-2 *DH*

Optical

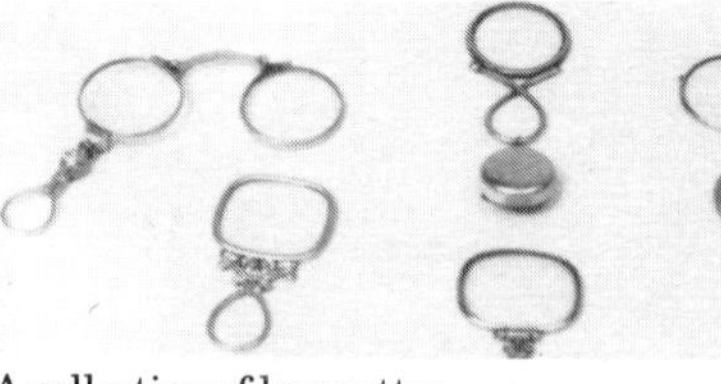

A collection of lorgnettes.
£60-200 each *CSK*

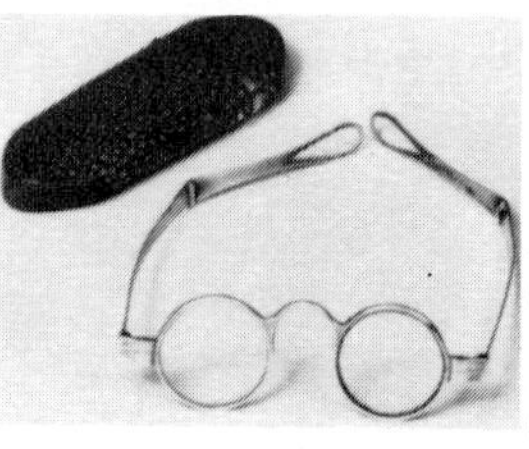

A pair of Georgian silver spectacles, in silver mounted shagreen case.
£150-200 *CSK*

Binoculars

A pair of opera glasses.
£50-60 *DP*

A pair of opera glasses, hallmarked 1919.
£50-60 *DP*

A pair of Victorian imitation ivory and brass opera glasses, with leather case.
£40-50 *AD*

Microscopes

Brass simple botanical microscopes of Withering pattern, mid-19thC.
£350-450 *CSK*

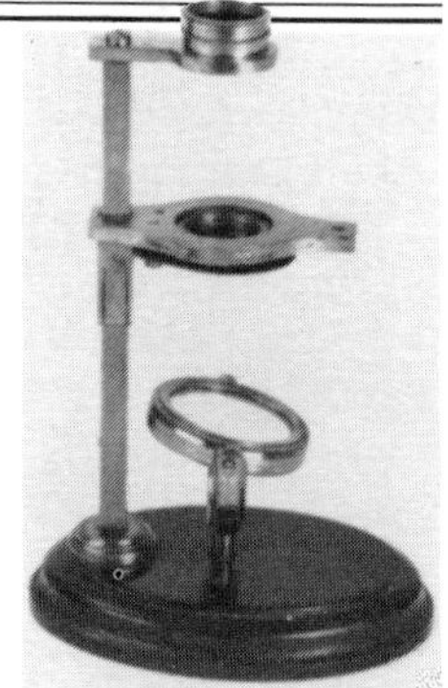

A lacquered brass aquatic microscope, in fitted case, late 18th/ early 19thC.
£200-250 *CSK*

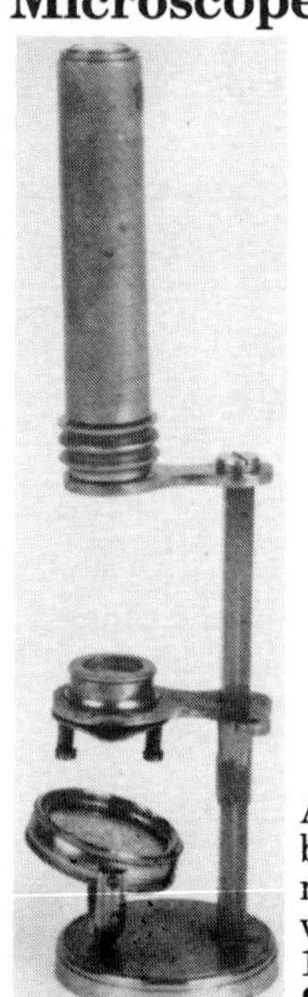

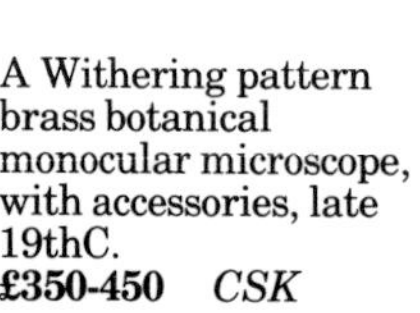

A Withering pattern brass botanical monocular microscope, with accessories, late 19thC.
£350-450 *CSK*

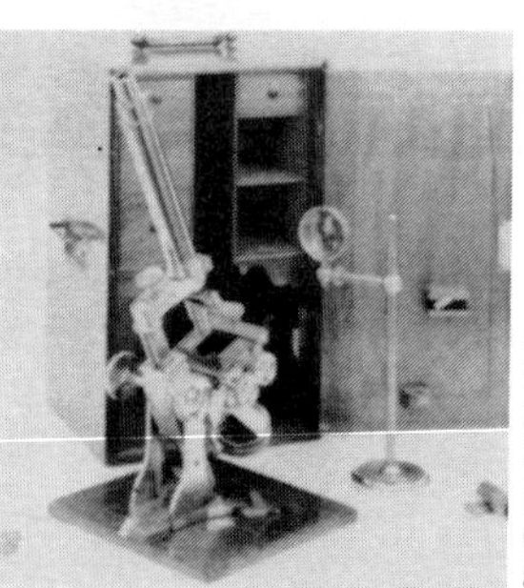

A brass Cary-type compound monocular microscope, signed Thos. Rubergall, with accessories, in mahogany case, early 19thC.
£450-550 *CSK*

Lacquered brass compound binocular microscopes, one by Baker, with accessories and fitted cases.
£450-500 *CSK*

Telescopes

A lacquered brass refracting telescope, 19thC, and associated equatorial mounting.
£550-600 *CSK*

A day or night brass telescope, by G. Willson, London, late 19thC.
£50-80 *PCh*

A refracting telescope, signed John Browning, with accessories and fitted case, late 19thC. **£450-500** *CSK*

A set of 3 Matthew Berge old Sheffield plate naval telescopes, in mahogany case, early 19thC.
£700-1,000 *P*

Sewing

Pin Cushions

An elephant pin cushion, c1925, 8in (20cm) long.
£30-35 *PP*

A pin cushion box, c1925, 5in (13cm) square.
£25-30 *PP*

A dog pin cushion, c1925, 3½in (9cm) square.
£25-30 *PP*

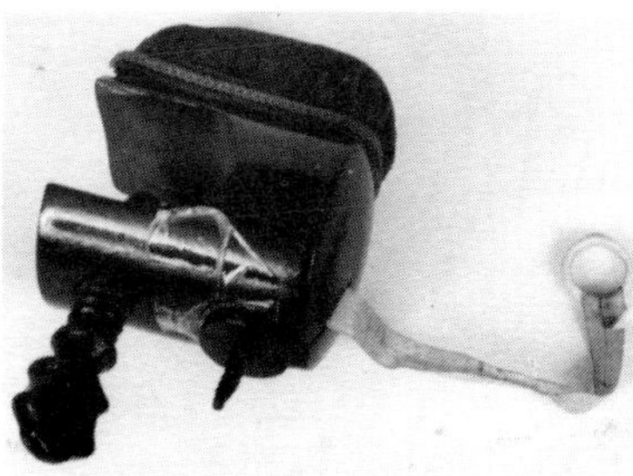

A pin cushion, c1920, 8in (20cm) high.
£12-15 *PP*

A wooden clamp pin cushion and tape, c1850.
£45-50 *PP*

A metal reel stand with pin cushion, c1900, 6½in (16cm) high.
£75-85 *PP*

A Victorian rococo style reel stand, c1850, 16in (40cm) high.
£190-200 *PP*

Three pin cushions.
£10-20 each *PP*

A bone winding clamp and pin cushion clamp, c1830.
l. **£45-50**
r. **£80-85** *PP*

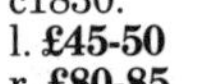

A carved bear pincushion and thimble holder, c1860.
£60-70 *CA*

A selection of silver pin cushions, hallmarked, the swan silver plate, 2 to 3in (5 to 7.5cm). **£80-120** *PC*

Cross Reference
Pin Cushion Dolls

Three pin cushions, c1925.
£15-30 each *PP*

Three pin cushions, c1925.
£20-30 each *PP*

Three pin cushions.
£15-35 each *PP*

A brass elephant pincushion, c1880.
£45-55 *CA*

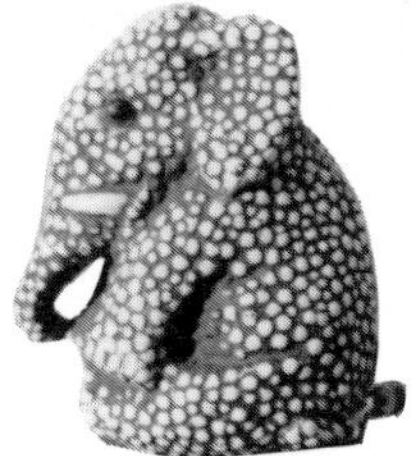

A painted Celluloid elephant tape, c1900.
£40-50 *CA*

Two needlecases, c1860.
£75-85 each *CA*

Sewing Needles

Needle packet holders. **£30-40** *PC*

Two knitting needle sheaths, one dated 1719, the other 1746. **£40-60** *PC*

Three needle packets. **£10-15** *PC*

Georgian bright cut silver bodkin cases.
£25-35 each
PC

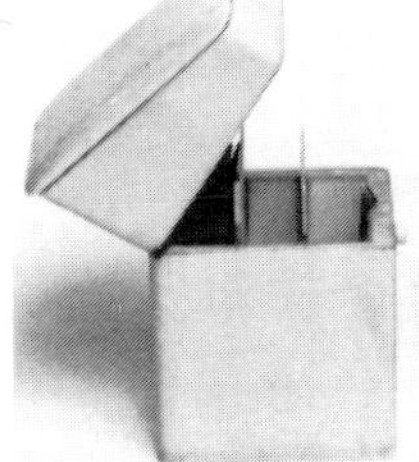

Needle cases, one ivory, the other tortoiseshell and mother-of-pearl.
£300-350 each *PC*

Sewing Machines

An English Bradbury VS hand-driven machine, c1920.
£25-50 *MN*

A Victorian sewing machine, 12½in (33cm) wide.
£100-120 *PAR*

A Wanzer hand-driven sewing machine, English, c1870.
£100-120 *MN*

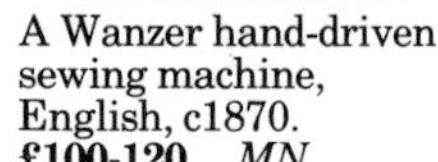

A miniature Singer sewing machine, 10½in (26cm) wide.
£85-95 *PAR*

An Edwardian sewing machine, 12in (31cm) wide.
£35-45 *PAR*

Sewing Boxes

A Georgian sewing box, with mother-of-pearl and shell decoration, 6in (15cm) wide.
£200-250 *PC*

A French amboyna sewing box, with musical movement, 19thC, 8in (20cm) wide.
£400-500 *CSK*

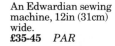

A sewing case with silver items, 5in (13cm) wide.
£80-120 *PC*

A George III satinwood and mahogany sewing box, 15in (38cm) wide.
£400-600 *P*

A miniature Georgian sewing box, 3in (7.5cm) wide.
£200-250 *PC*

A Regency penwork sewing box, 11½in (29cm) wide.
£1,400-1,600 *P*

Shipping

General

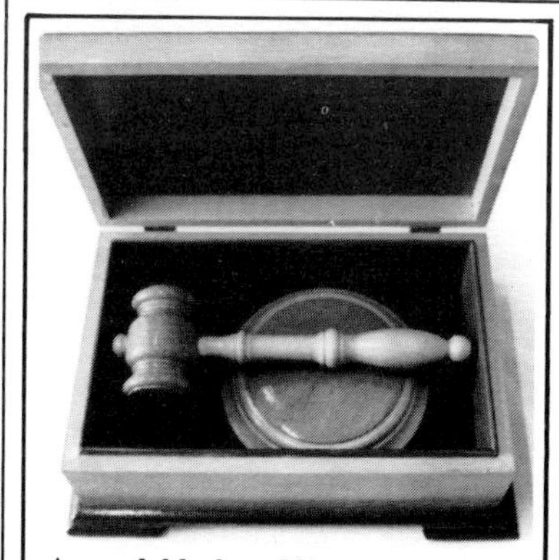

A gavel, block and box made from the timber of the Royal Yacht Victoria and Albert and H.M.S. Victory, 1930s.
£150-160 *COB*

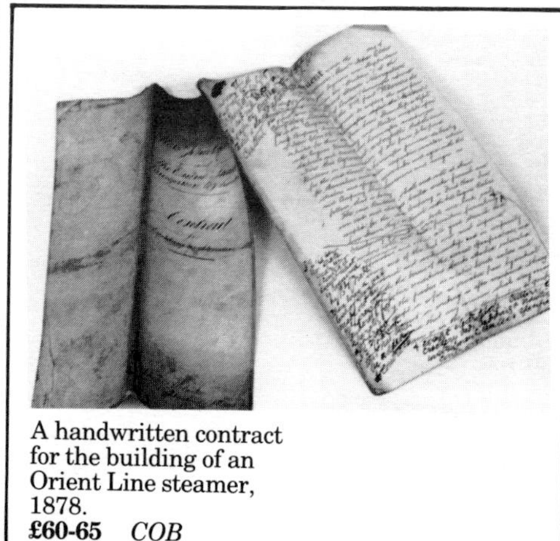

A handwritten contract for the building of an Orient Line steamer, 1878.
£60-65 *COB*

A British & Irish Steam Packet Company plate, made in Dublin, c1840.
£40-60 *PC*

A watercolour by David Brown of The Titanic en route to Cherbourg, c1980.
£130-140 *COB*

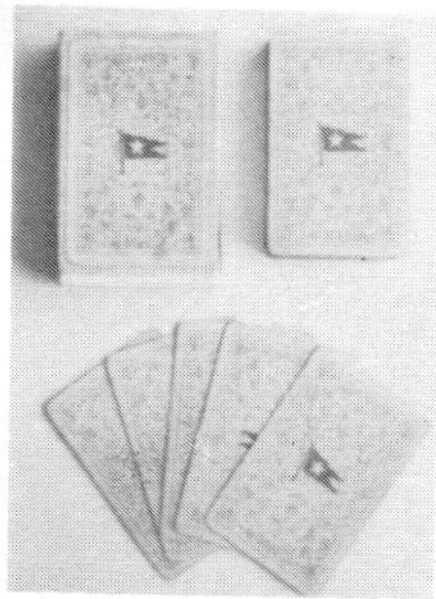

A pack of White Star Line playing cards.
£400-450 *ONS*

Cross Reference
Nelson's Navy

A German ashtray from the Europa, 1930.
£30-50 *PC*

A White Star Line calendar for 1928.
£40-60 *PC*

A plastic yacht radio, c1960.
£35-40 *COB*

A Victorian seaman's knife, dated 1895.
£45-50 *COB*

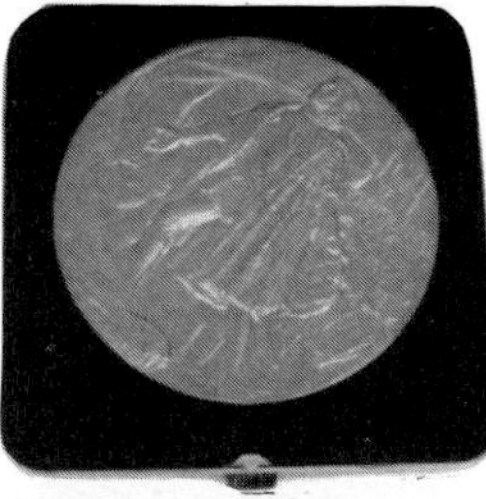

A commemorative plaque presented to William Ault, 1892-93.
£50-100 *ASc*

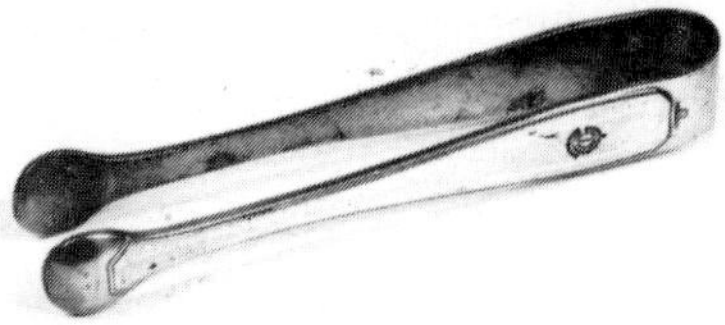

A pair of sugar tongs from the Normandy, c1930. **£30-50** *PC*

A shell and a medallion from the Great Eastern.
£40-60 *PC*

A leather wallet containing bridge score cards, Java-Australia Line.
£7-10 *COB*

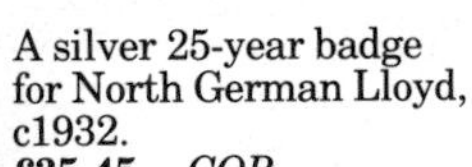

A silver 25-year badge for North German Lloyd, c1932.
£35-45 *COB*

A model of the Lusitania, with the crest of the Borough of Lowestoft Arms.
£75-85 *COB*

A souvenir vase. **£20-30** *PC*

A silver plated tankard presented to the owners of the S.S. Geraldine Mary, sunk by enemy submarines in 1940.
£35-45 *COB*

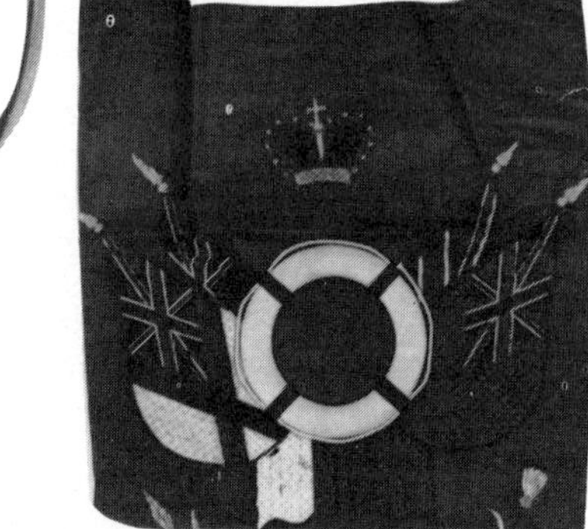

An embroidered silk cushion cover.
£10-15 *COB*

A copper ashtray from H.M. Torpedo Boat, c1917.
£10-15 *COB*

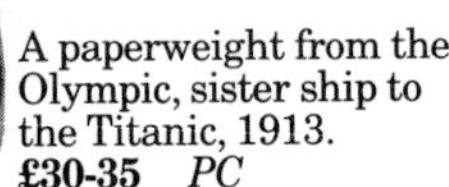

A paperweight from the Olympic, sister ship to the Titanic, 1913.
£30-35 *PC*

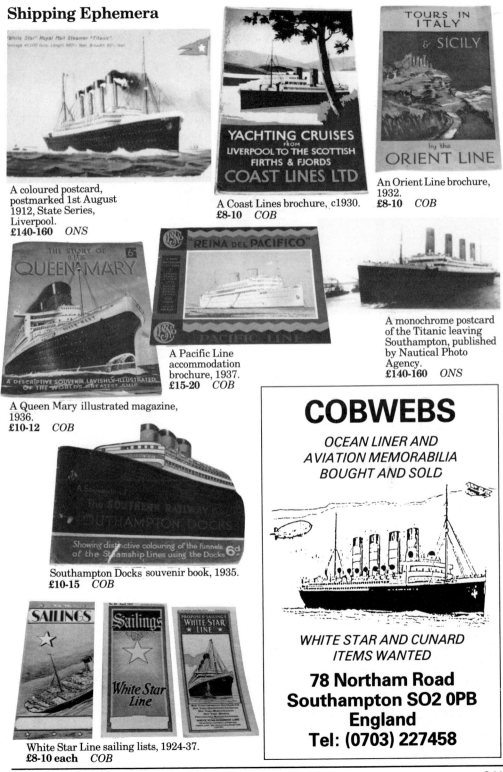

Shipping Ephemera

A coloured postcard, postmarked 1st August 1912, State Series, Liverpool.
£140-160 *ONS*

A Coast Lines brochure, c1930.
£8-10 *COB*

An Orient Line brochure, 1932.
£8-10 *COB*

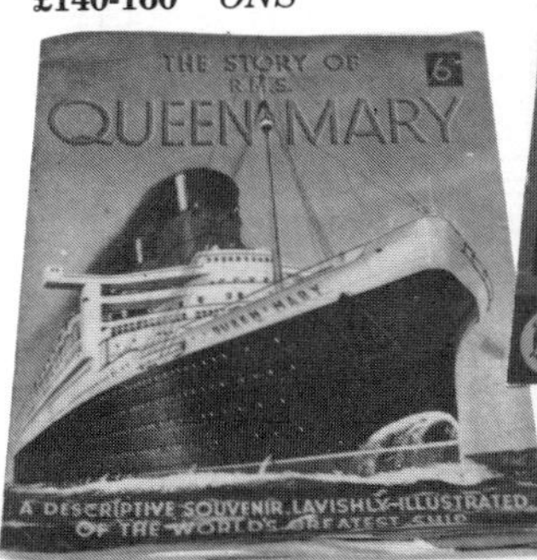

A Queen Mary illustrated magazine, 1936.
£10-12 *COB*

A Pacific Line accommodation brochure, 1937.
£15-20 *COB*

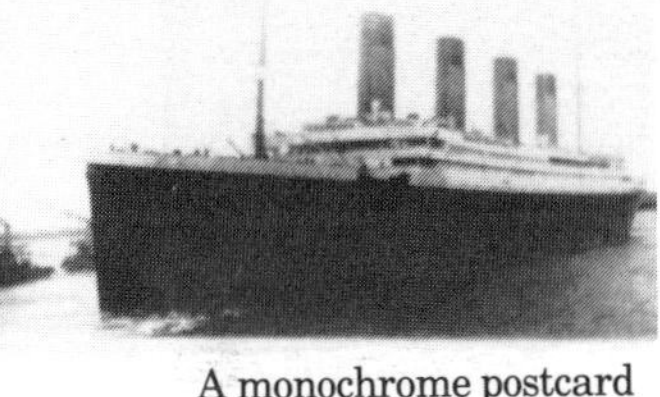

A monochrome postcard of the Titanic leaving Southampton, published by Nautical Photo Agency.
£140-160 *ONS*

Southampton Docks souvenir book, 1935.
£10-15 *COB*

White Star Line sailing lists, 1924-37.
£8-10 each *COB*

Shipping Posters

General

A Cunard Line sailing list, 1911.
£45-50 *COB*

Royal Mail Lines, 1931.
£350-400 each *ONS*

Union Castle poster
£40-80 *ONS*

White Star Line, by Reginald Mills, torn.
£35-45 *ONS*

White Star Line, c1930.
£15-20 *COB*

A P & O brochure, 1925.
£8-10 *COB*

Original artwork for French Line poster, c1950.
£70-80 *COB*

A P & O travel poster, 1958.
£40-50 *COB*

America

American Line via Cherbourg.
£300-350 *ONS*

Holland America Line.
£300-400 *ONS*

Red Star Line, damaged.
£200-220 *ONS*

Australia

P & O.
£200-250 *ONS*

Orient Line.
£200-250 each *ONS*

Canada

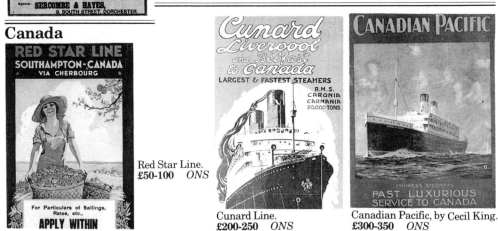

Red Star Line.
£50-100 *ONS*

Cunard Line.
£200-250 *ONS*

Canadian Pacific, by Cecil King.
£300-350 *ONS*

Signs & Advertising

Advertisements

An Edwardian advertisement, in a pine frame. **£12-15** *DH*

A set of 7 glass panels, removed from a public house, mahogany framed.
£1,000-1,500 *GSP*

Public House Advertising

A Carlton Ware pottery lamp base made for Guinness, printed factory mark, 9½in (24cm).
£160-200 *CSK*

Symbol of Good Ale.
£65-75 *REL*

An advertising plaque.
£5-10 *AL*

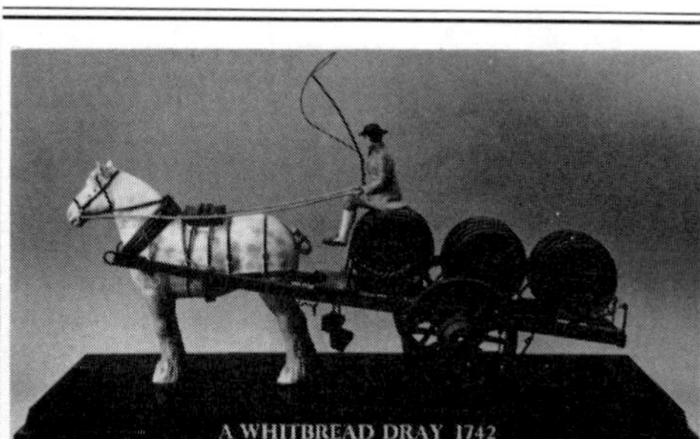

A plastic display item. **£30-40** *K*

A Riley's tin tray.
£15-20 *AL*

A Wm. Younger's tin tray.
£16-20 *AL*

Cross Reference
Drinking
Guinness

A Dragons Blood advertising sign.
£65-75 *REL*

A Whitbread ashtray.
£4-5 *AL*

Worthington's ashtray.
£12-15 *AL*

A Bovril ashtray. **£4-6** *AL*

A pub ashtray.
£6-8 *AL*

Cross Reference
Smoking

An Army Club cigarette holder and ashtray, c1920. **£30-40** *K*

A Double Diamond tin tray.
£4-6 *AL*

A J & B jug.
£10-12 *AL*

An advertising piece.
£30-40 *K*

General Advertising Wares

Two Oxo mugs.
£5-8 *AL*

A Butlin's glass paperweight, 1950s.
£15-20 *COB*

A glass sweet jar.
£25-30 *AL*

An original Zon advertising card, c1930.
£25-50 *NA*

A plastic game marker board, c1910.
£10-15 *K*

Cross Reference
Ephemera

Cross Reference
Glass Paperweights

A plastic coated tin mirror, c1925.
£3-5 *K*

A typical promotional give-away from the 1920s and 1930s.

Cross Reference
Ceramics
— Sylvac

A Shettleston Co- operative Society, Jubilee teapot. **£25-35** *RG*

A Sylvac advertising figure.
£90-100 *SAI*

A Freed's shop window cast and painted metal figure.
£200-250 *K*

Items from small specialist establishments have special interest for collectors.

A Heckmondwike & District Co-Op 70th Anniversary bowl.
£25-30 *RG*

A miniature top hat made for Moss Bross, inscribed inside.
£15-20 *RG*

A Horner's Clotted Cream jar, c1840.
£20-25 *RG*

Cross Reference
Printed Pot Lids

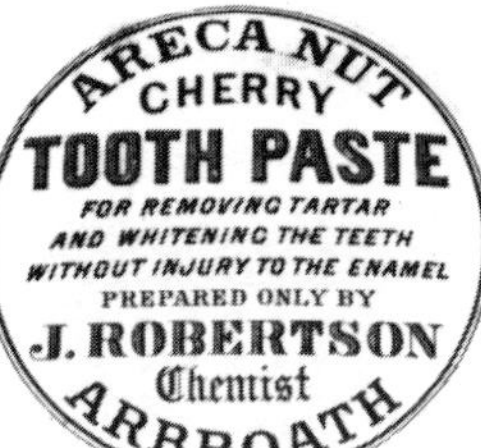

A toothpaste pot, c1885.
£20-25 *DBu*

Small stoneware cream jars.
£6-8 each *RG*

Anchovy paste jars, c1850-60.
£20-30 each *RG*

Stoneware cream jars.
£10-20 each *RG*

Toilet cream jars.
£15-20 each *RG*

A waxed paper cream tub, c1940.
£4-6 *RG*

A dairy pail.
£80-100 *RG*

Enamel Signs

A Style & Wynch brewery sign.
£300-400 *K*

'Cut Out' enamels have a particular charm with collectors.

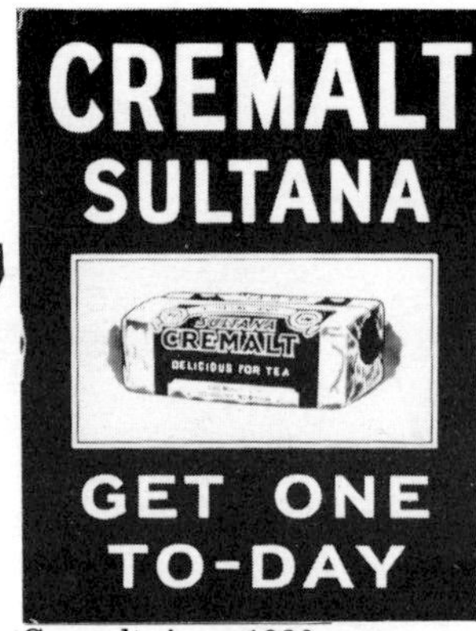

Cremalt sign, c1930.
£70-90 *K*

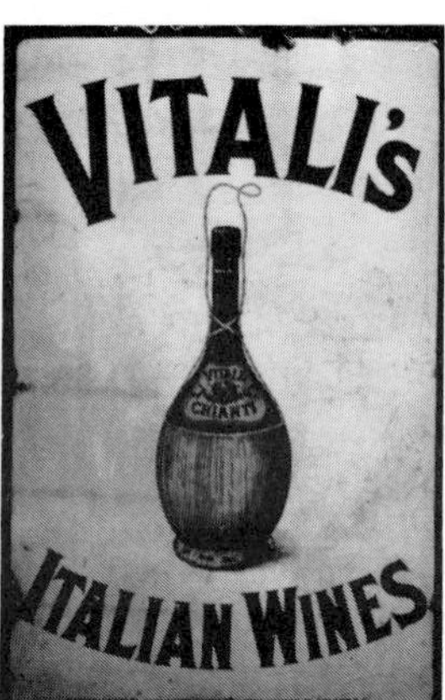

A Vitali's sign, by Patent Enamel Co., Birmingham, c1920.
£150-200 *K*

A very rare metal sign.

An Edwardian enamel sign, by Chrome of Wolverhampton, some damage.
£120-150 *K*

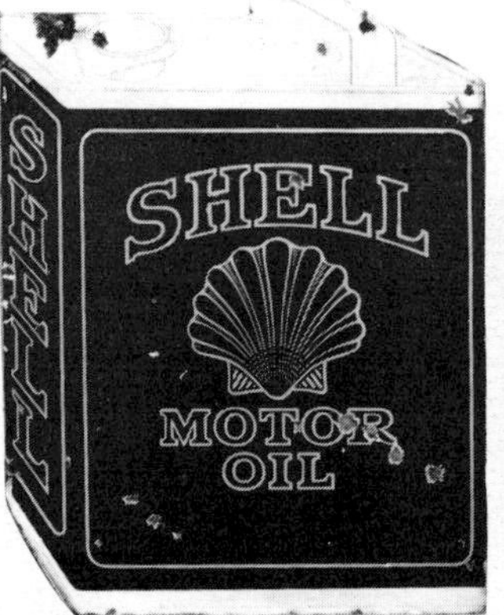

A Shell 'cut-out' double sided sign, c1930.
£100-200 *K*

A Sunlight Soap enamel sign, c1900.
£120-150 *K*

One of the longest running advertising ideas.

A Victorian Dunn's hats sign.
£200-300 *K*

A Craven 'A' enamel finger plate, 1930s.
£90-120 *KG*

A Robertson's Sheep Dips poster-type enamel sign, c1900.
£450-550 *K*

FURTHER READING
Franklin, M. J., *British Biscuit Tins 1868-1939*, Millbank Books, U.K.

A transfer printed tin sign, c1910.
£150-200 *K*

An enamel sign, c1950.
£35-40 *COB*

An enamelled sign, restored.
£200-250 *HP*

A metal door plate, c1930.
£28-30 *COB*

An enamel sign, c1950.
£70-80 *COB*

DID YOU KNOW?
Miller's Collectables Price Guide is designed to build up, year by year, into the most comprehensive reference system available.

A Kodak sign, 1920s.
£40-50 *CSK*

FURTHER READING
Gretton, Keith and Penny, *Advertising Collectables*, BBR Publishing, 1989.

Smoking

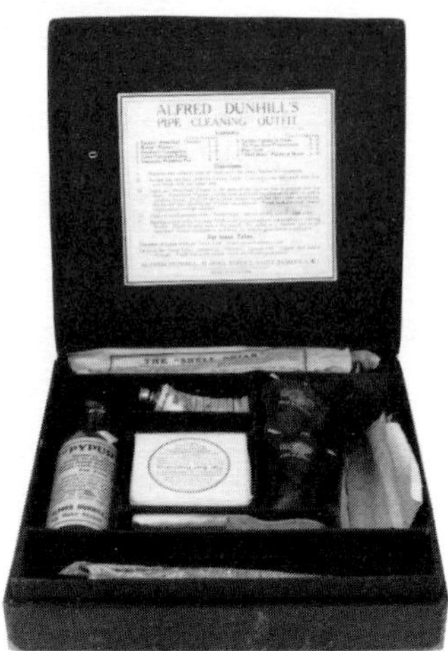

An Alfred Dunhill's pipe cleaning outfit.
£45-50 *P(Ba)*

A silver cigarette case with gold inset, c1935.
£40-50 *AB*

A Continental giltmetal cigarette case.
£550-600 *CSK*

DID YOU KNOW?
Miller's Collectables Price Guide is designed to build up, year by year, into the most comprehensive reference system available.

An Art Nouveau hammered silver cigarette box, Chester hallmarks for 1902, 5in (12.5cm) long.
£300-350 *C*

A Victorian bargeman's pearlware smoking companion.
£220-250 *HSS*

A framed collage of smoker's items.
£40-45 *RG*

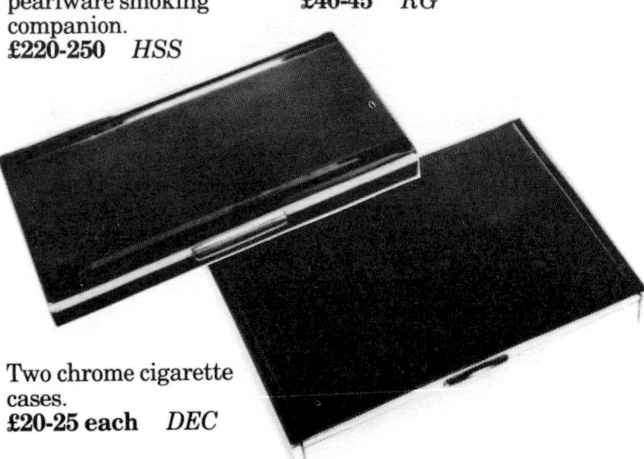

Two chrome cigarette cases.
£20-25 each *DEC*

A chrome and wood cigarette holder, 6in (15cm) wide.
£140-150 *SAI*

Advertising

A Senior Service advertising wall plaque.
£55-60 *PCh*

A St. Bruno change bowl, 7in (17.5cm) square.
£18-20 *RG*

An advertising mirror, 8in (20cm) diam.
£20-25 *AL*

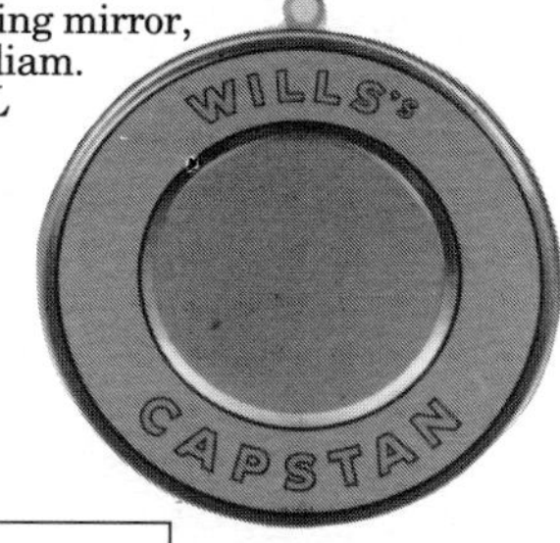

Cross Reference
Signs and Advertising

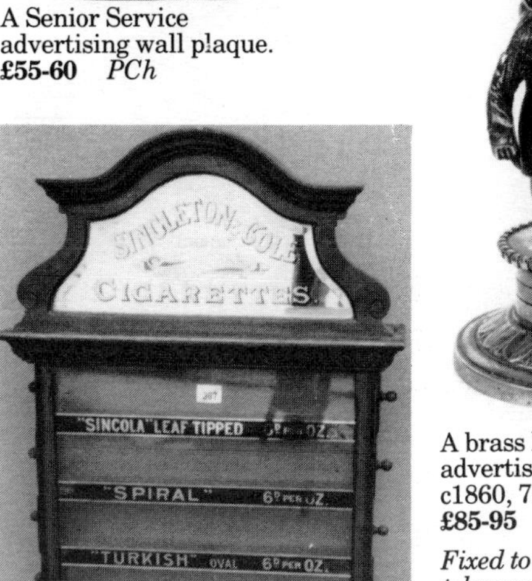

A Victorian mahogany display/dispenser cabinet.
£800-850 *TM*

A brass Punch advertising figure, c1860, 7in (17.5cm) high.
£85-95 *RG*

Fixed to the gas supply of tobacconists' shops for lighting cigars and pipes.

Advertising material by Arrobus for du Maurier cigarettes, c1930.
£150-200 *ONS*

A Nelson tin tray.
£10-12 *AL*

A Victorian vesta case, George Unite, Birmingham 1894, 1½in (4cm).
£160-170 *CSK*

A tin tray, 13in (33cm) diam.
£4-5 *AL*

A pub jug, 5½in (14cm) high.
£7-8 *AL*

Ashtrays & Strikers

A ceramic ashtray, c1930.
£15-30 *K*

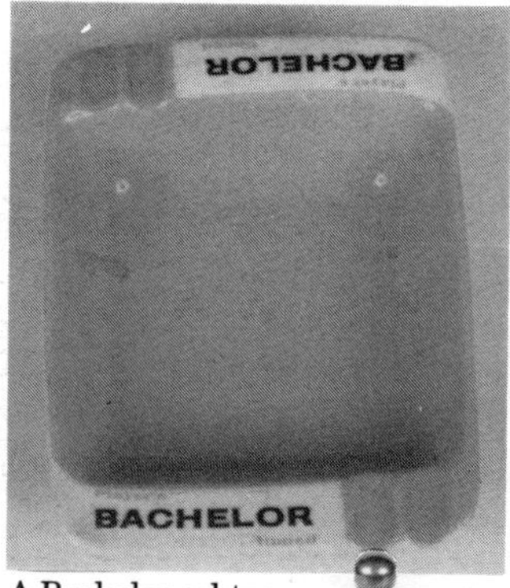

A Bachelor ashtray.
£5-7 *AL*

An Austrian chromium plated ashtray and matchbox holder.
£300-350 *C*

A Schweppes bell ashtray, suitable for a bar, 5½in (14cm) diam.
£25-30 *RG*

A brass cigarette lighter with ashtray.
£5-10 *DH*

A Bryant & May silver plated match striker, 3 by 4½in (7.5 by 11cm).
£18-20 *AL*

A Carlton Ware ashtray, c1960, 9½in (24cm) diam.
£45-50 *STU*

An ashtray and matchbox holder.
£25-28 *AL*

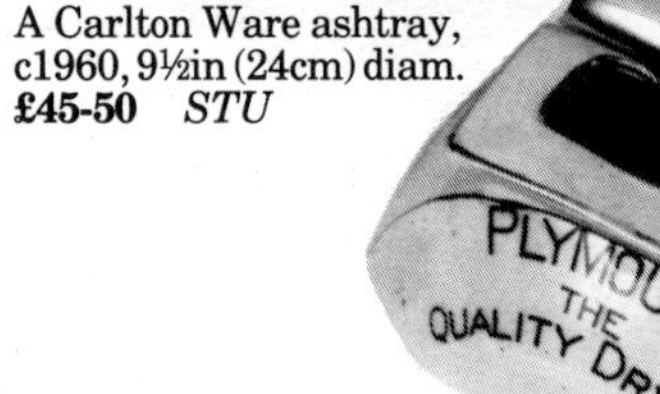

A Plymouth Gin ashtray.
£20-25 *RG*

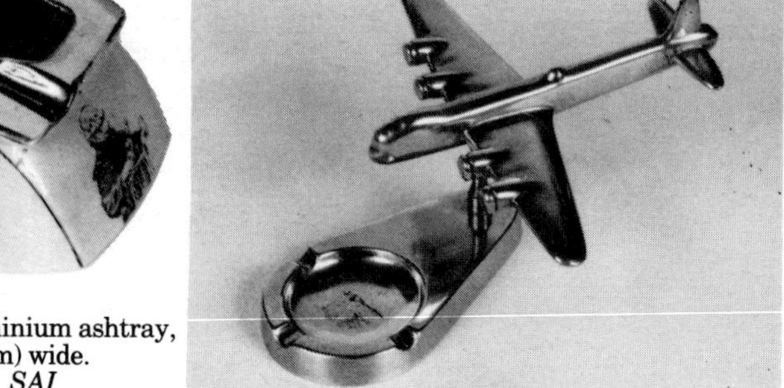

An aluminium ashtray, 8in (20cm) wide.
£35-40 *SAI*

Matchbox Covers

An assortment of labels.
5-10p each *KOL*

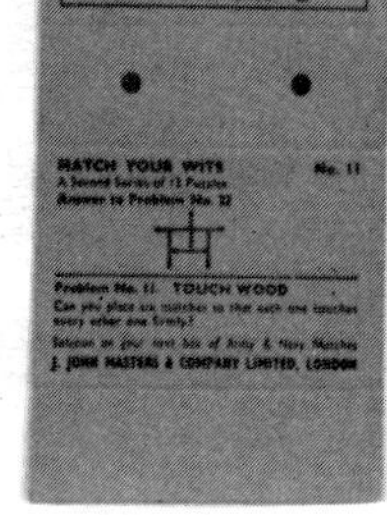

Bryant & May skillets.
5-10p each *KOL*

A matchbox by UPEC, now closed down.
5-10p *KOL*

DID YOU KNOW?
Miller's Collectables Price Guide is designed to build up, year by year, into the most comprehensive reference system available.

Cigarette Packets

A Woodbine metal sleeve to hold packets of cigarettes.
£8-10 *RG*

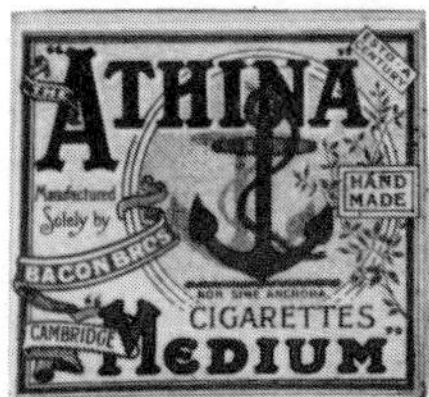

Athina cigarette packet.
50p-£1 *RG*

Oriental labels in different colours.
10-20p each *KOL*

Cigarette Lighters

A chrome and brass cigarette lighter.
£3-5 *DH*

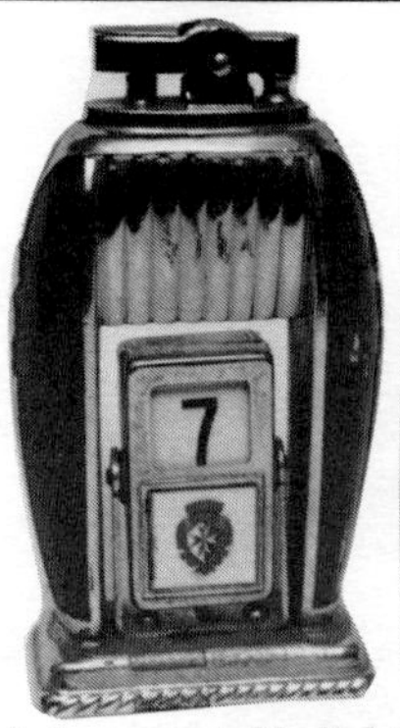

A Japanese table lighter with calendar, c1955.
£20-25 *JLB*

A Mosda silver plated table lighter, c1953.
£25-30 *JLB*

A Polo table lighter, c1953.
£20-25 *JLB*

A chrome plated Ronson Newport lighter, c1955.
£10-15 *JLB*

A table lighter, c1955.
£20-25 *JLB*

A German table lighter, c1950.
£10-15 *JLB*

Zippo petrol lighters, 1960s.
£8-10 each *COB*

Cross Reference
Advertising

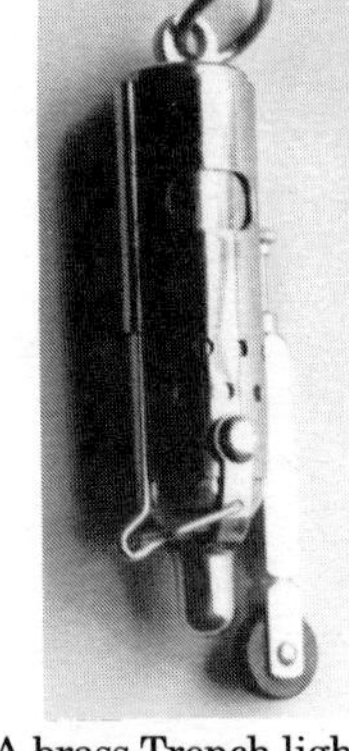

A brass Trench lighter, 1920s.
£8-10 *COB*

A Zippo petrol lighter, 1956.
£10-15 *COB*

A Corona lighter in the form of a pistol, c1950.
£15-20 *JLB*

A Polo lighter, 1930s.
£6-8 *COB*

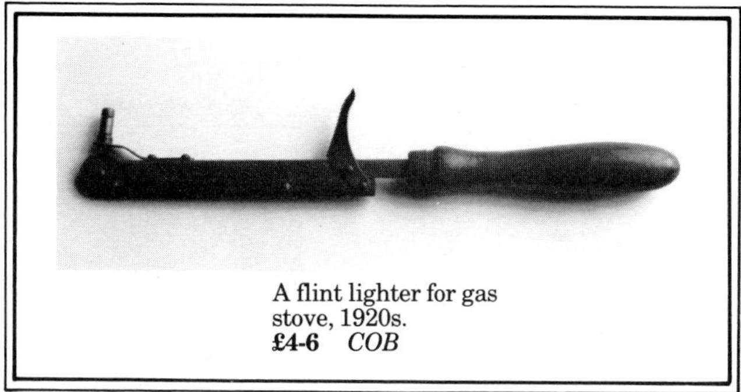

A flint lighter for gas stove, 1920s.
£4-6 *COB*

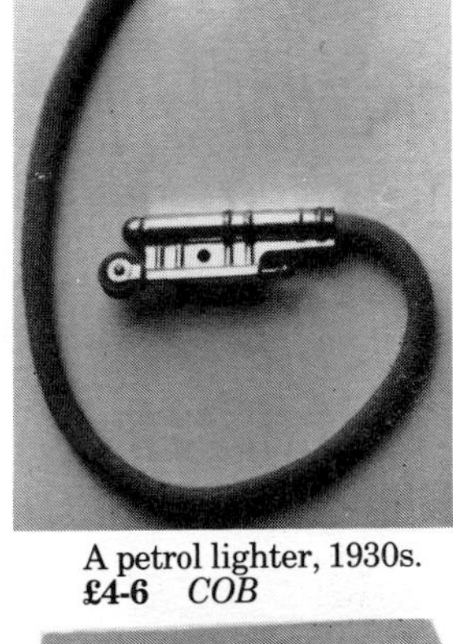

A petrol lighter, 1930s.
£4-6 *COB*

A petrol lighter/paper knife, 1960s.
£8-10 *COB*

A musical pocket lighter, 1955.
£20-25 *JLB*

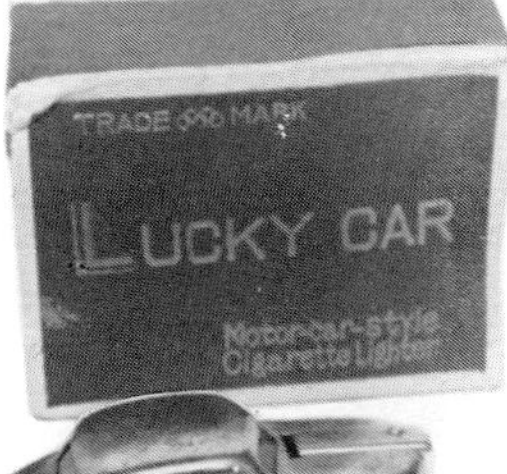

Cross Reference
Automobilia

A table lighter in the form of a small car, boxed and unused, c1950.
£40-50 *JLB*

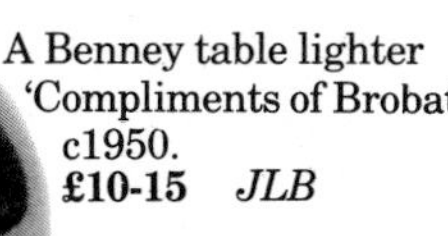

A Benney table lighter 'Compliments of Brobat', c1950.
£10-15 *JLB*

A petrol lighter, 1964.
£8-10 *COB*

A chrome table lighter, 5in (13cm) high.
£10-15 *JLB*

A cast iron table lighter, c1955.
£10-15 *JLB*

A Mosda combined cigarette case and lighter, c1957.
£10-15 *JLB*

A Ronson table lighter, picture signed L. Wood, c1955.
£20-25 *JLB*

A group of 4 McMurdo petrol lighters, c1950.
£30-35 each *JLB*

A brass lighter with watch, by Eclydo, c1953.
£25-30 *JLB*

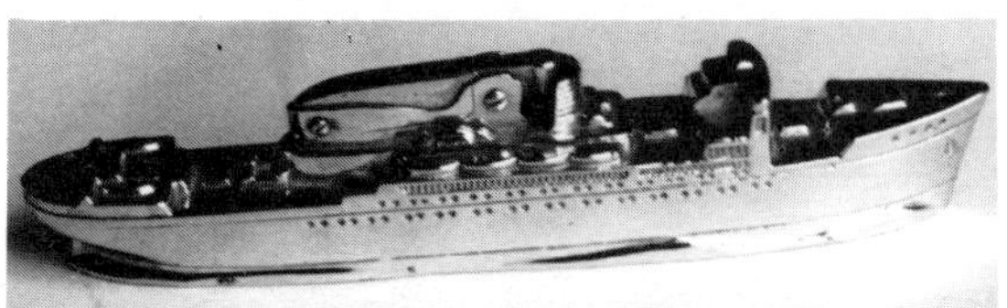

A freighter petrol lighter, 1960s, 8in (20cm) long.
£25-30 *COB*

Cross Reference
Shipping

A petrol lighter, 1930s.
£8-10 *COB*

A Zippo petrol lighter, 1970s.
£6-8 *COB*

A Ronson solid silver pocket lighter, hallmarked, c1955.
£50-60 *JLB*

A Parker table lighter in cast iron, c1950.
£25-30 *JLB*

A Japanese table lighter, 6in (15cm) high.
£35-40 *JLB*

A Japanese musical lighter and cigarette case, c1957.
£30-35 *JLB*

A plastic table lighter, incorporating a musical box, unused, mid-1950s, 8in (20cm) high.
£30-35 *JLB*

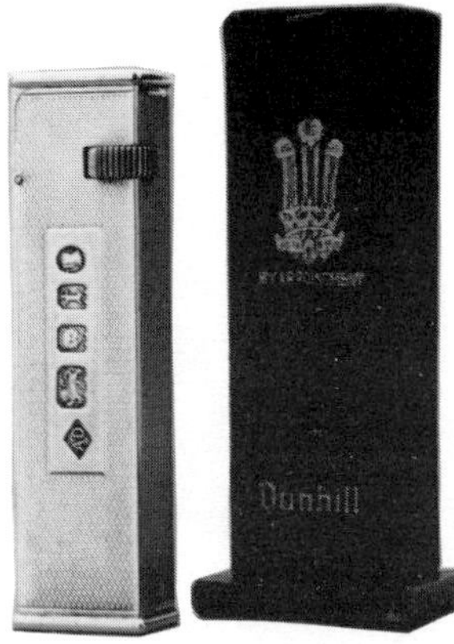

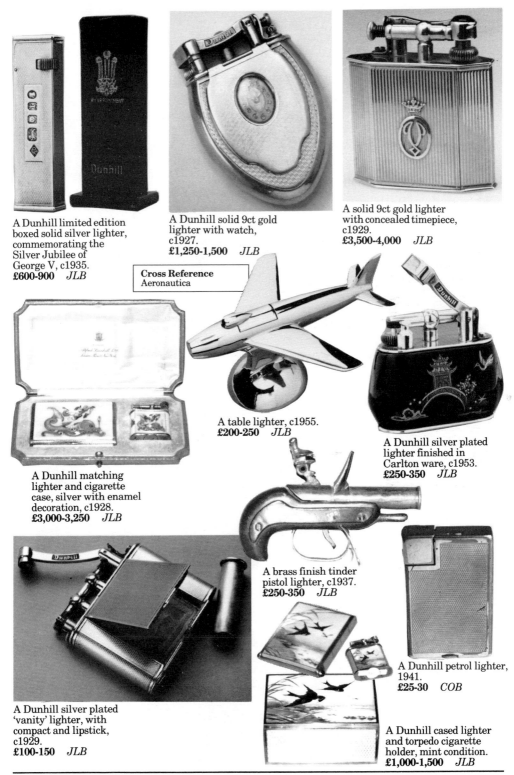

A Dunhill limited edition boxed solid silver lighter, commemorating the Silver Jubilee of George V, c1935.
£600-900 *JLB*

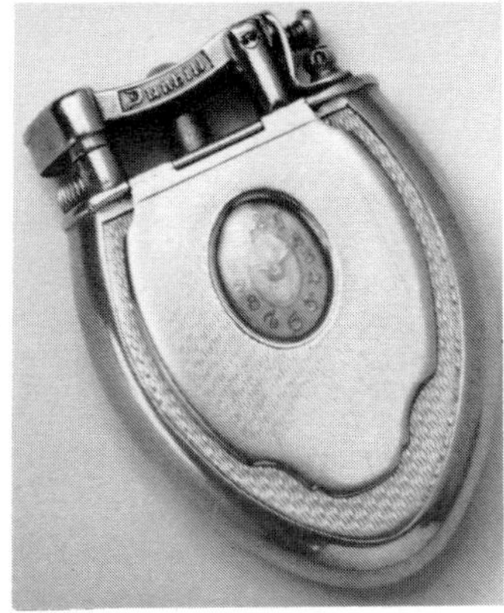

A Dunhill solid 9ct gold lighter with watch, c1927.
£1,250-1,500 *JLB*

A solid 9ct gold lighter with concealed timepiece, c1929.
£3,500-4,000 *JLB*

Cross Reference
Aeronautica

A table lighter, c1955.
£200-250 *JLB*

A Dunhill matching lighter and cigarette case, silver with enamel decoration, c1928.
£3,000-3,250 *JLB*

A Dunhill silver plated lighter finished in Carlton ware, c1953.
£250-350 *JLB*

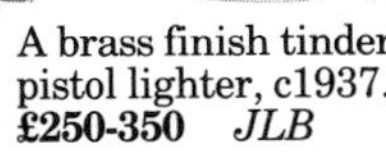

A brass finish tinder pistol lighter, c1937.
£250-350 *JLB*

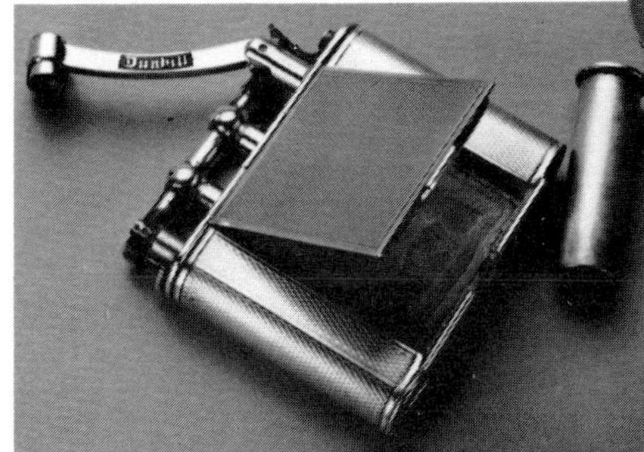

A Dunhill silver plated 'vanity' lighter, with compact and lipstick, c1929.
£100-150 *JLB*

A Dunhill petrol lighter, 1941.
£25-30 *COB*

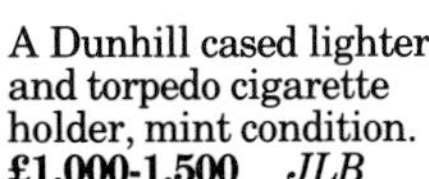

A Dunhill cased lighter and torpedo cigarette holder, mint condition.
£1,000-1,500 *JLB*

Pipes

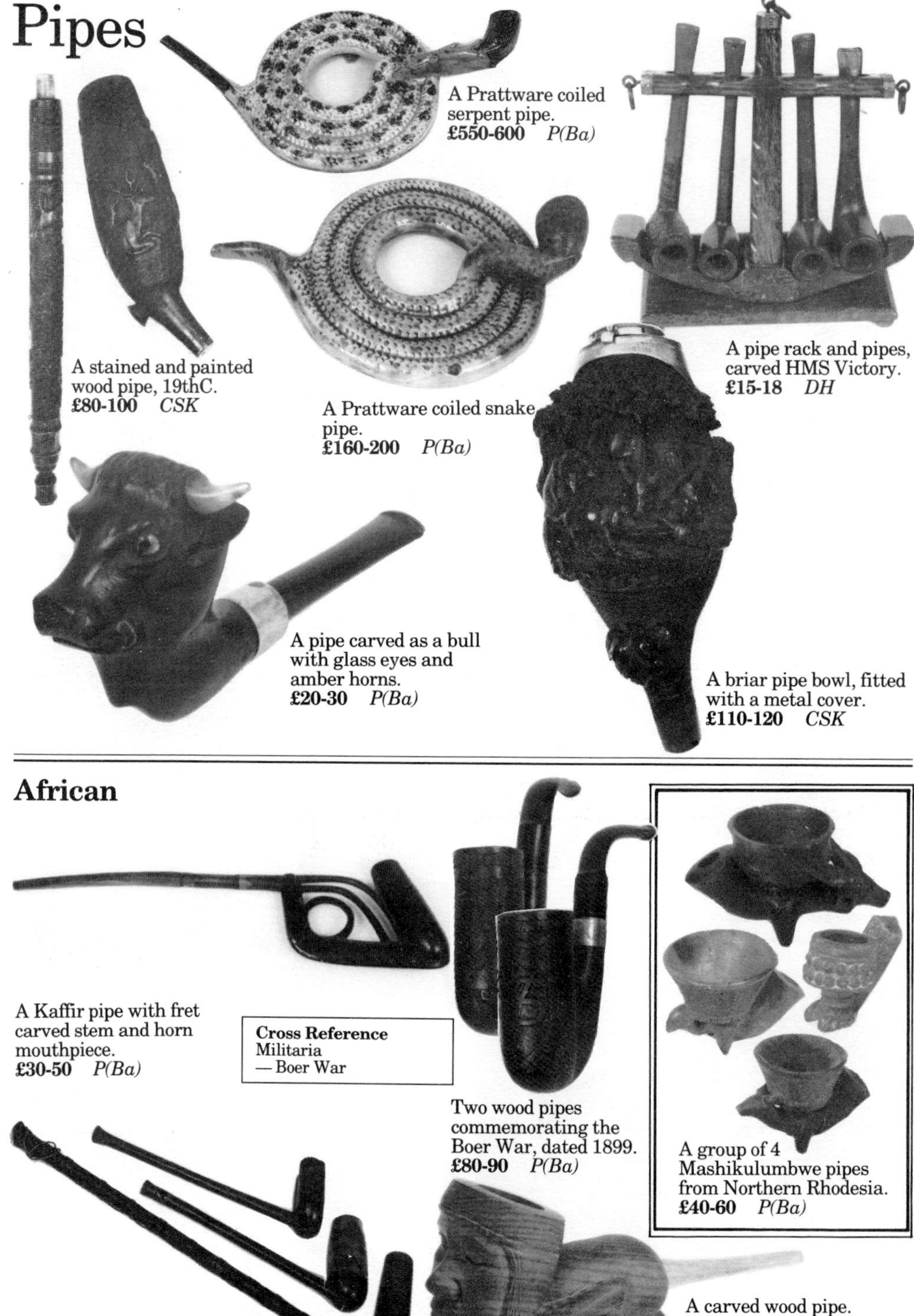

A Prattware coiled serpent pipe.
£550-600 *P(Ba)*

A pipe rack and pipes, carved HMS Victory.
£15-18 *DH*

A stained and painted wood pipe, 19thC.
£80-100 *CSK*

A Prattware coiled snake pipe.
£160-200 *P(Ba)*

A pipe carved as a bull with glass eyes and amber horns.
£20-30 *P(Ba)*

A briar pipe bowl, fitted with a metal cover.
£110-120 *CSK*

African

A Kaffir pipe with fret carved stem and horn mouthpiece.
£30-50 *P(Ba)*

Cross Reference
Militaria
— Boer War

Two wood pipes commemorating the Boer War, dated 1899.
£80-90 *P(Ba)*

A group of 4 Mashikulumbwe pipes from Northern Rhodesia.
£40-60 *P(Ba)*

Three Kaffir pipes.
£130-150 *P(Ba)*

A carved wood pipe.
£10-15 *P(Ba)*

Eastern

A hookah with an enamel glass bowl and inlaid mother-of-pearl stem.
£100-150 *P(Ba)*

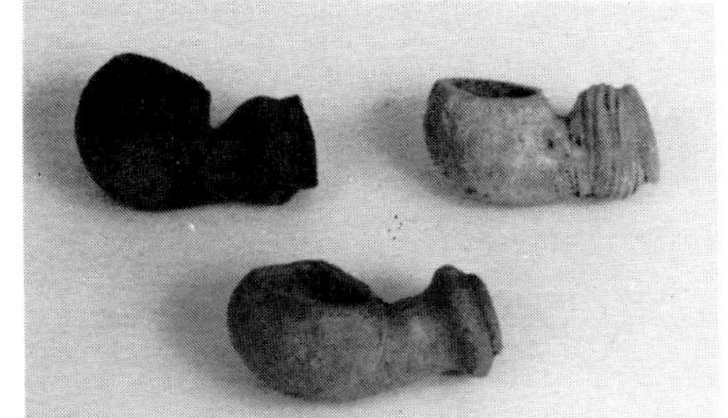

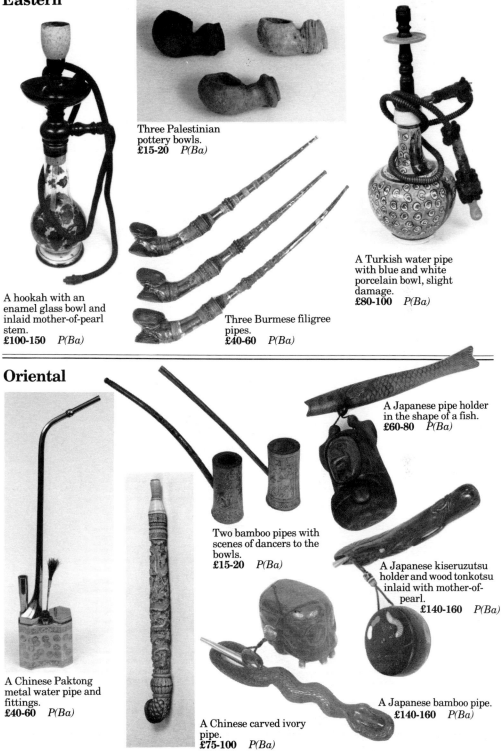

Three Palestinian pottery bowls.
£15-20 *P(Ba)*

Three Burmese filigree pipes.
£40-60 *P(Ba)*

A Turkish water pipe with blue and white porcelain bowl, slight damage.
£80-100 *P(Ba)*

Oriental

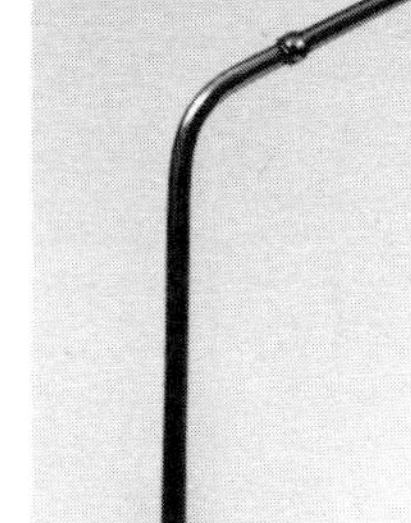

A Chinese Paktong metal water pipe and fittings.
£40-60 *P(Ba)*

Two bamboo pipes with scenes of dancers to the bowls.
£15-20 *P(Ba)*

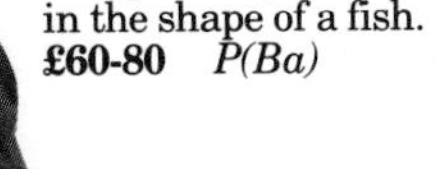

A Japanese pipe holder in the shape of a fish.
£60-80 *P(Ba)*

A Japanese kiseruzutsu holder and wood tonkotsu inlaid with mother-of-pearl.
£140-160 *P(Ba)*

A Japanese bamboo pipe.
£140-160 *P(Ba)*

A Chinese carved ivory pipe.
£75-100 *P(Ba)*

Meerschaum

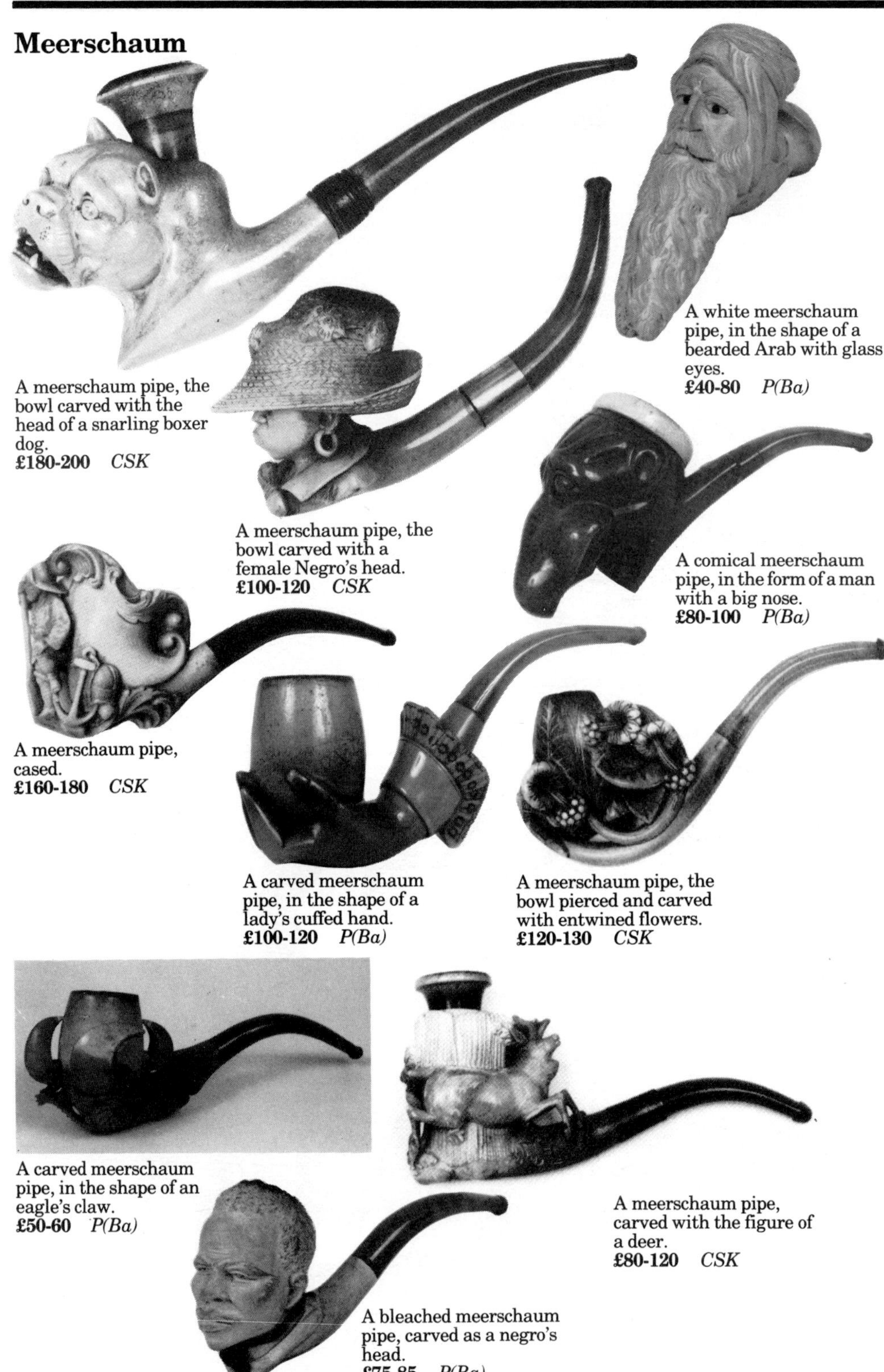

A meerschaum pipe, the bowl carved with the head of a snarling boxer dog.
£180-200 *CSK*

A meerschaum pipe, the bowl carved with a female Negro's head.
£100-120 *CSK*

A white meerschaum pipe, in the shape of a bearded Arab with glass eyes.
£40-80 *P(Ba)*

A comical meerschaum pipe, in the form of a man with a big nose.
£80-100 *P(Ba)*

A meerschaum pipe, cased.
£160-180 *CSK*

A carved meerschaum pipe, in the shape of a lady's cuffed hand.
£100-120 *P(Ba)*

A meerschaum pipe, the bowl pierced and carved with entwined flowers.
£120-130 *CSK*

A carved meerschaum pipe, in the shape of an eagle's claw.
£50-60 *P(Ba)*

A meerschaum pipe, carved with the figure of a deer.
£80-120 *CSK*

A bleached meerschaum pipe, carved as a negro's head.
£75-85 *P(Ba)*

A meerschaum pipe, carved as Dr. Livingstone.
£60-80 *P(Ba)*

A meerschaum pipe, carved as a Moor's head, slight damage.
£100-120 *P(Ba)*

A meerschaum pipe, carved as a snipe's head.
£120-150 *P(Ba)*

A meerschaum pipe, carved as a lady's cuffed hand, in 2 sections.
£40-50 *P(Ba)*

A meerschaum pipe, in the shape of a bull's head.
£80-100 *P(Ba)*

A meerschaum pipe, the bowl carved with a fox.
£30-50 *CSK*

A meerschaum pipe.
£20-30 *P(Ba)*

A meerschaum pipe, carved as a Confederate soldier.
£75-85 *P(Ba)*

A meerschaum pipe, the bowl carved with the figure of a man smoking a pipe, with 2 dogs.
£130-150 *CSK*

A meerschaum pipe, carved as a lady's head with a bonnet, slight damage, and another of a bearded and hatted gentleman.
£30-50 each *P(Ba)*

Tobacco Jars

Tobacco jars, c1920.
£10-15 each *RG*

A High Life tobacco jar, still filled with tobacco, c1850.
£18-20 *RG*

A green glazed tobacco jar, c1840.
£25-35 *RG*

Note the spelling of 'Segars'.

A cigarette jar.
£25-30 *RG*

Cross Reference
Ceramics

An apple wood tobacco jar, c1775.
£320-350 *Cas*

Cross Reference
Treen

A painted tobacco jar, c1850.
£175-200 *Cas*

A French faience tobacco jar, c1890.
£85-90 *MCA*

A tobacco jar, c1860.
£40-50 *RG*

A Doulton tobacco jar, c1890.
£110-120 *RG*

Snuff Boxes

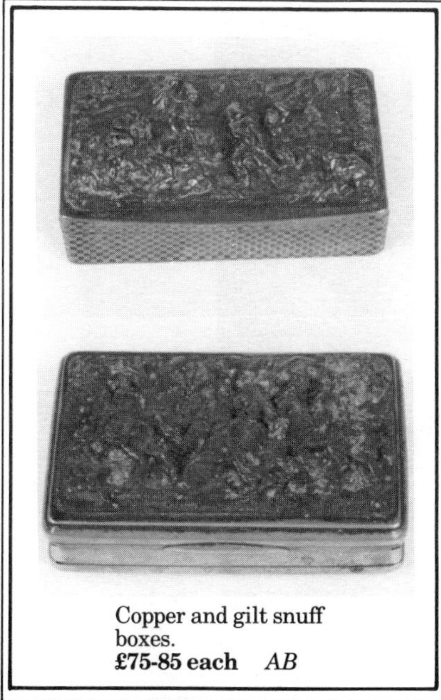

Copper and gilt snuff boxes.
£75-85 each *AB*

Carved wood snuff boxes.
£65-75 each *AB*

A silver plated snuff box.
£55-65 *AB*

DID YOU KNOW?
Miller's Collectables Price Guide is designed to build up, year by year, into the most comprehensive reference system available.

A copper snuff box.
£40-50 *AB*

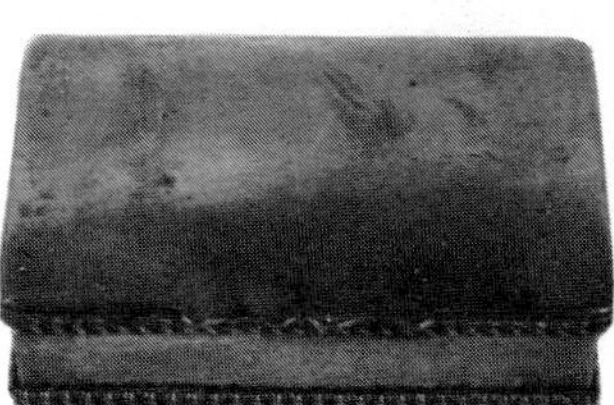

A Sheffield plate snuff box.
£45-55 *AB*

A horn snuff box.
£95-100 *AB*

A horn snuff holder.
£40-50 *AB*

A wooden snuff box, in the shape of a coffin.
£55-65 *AB*

Spoons

Three silver teaspoons, unmarked.
£12-15 each *MAN*

Three silver Apostle spoons.
£8-12 each *MAN*

A Charles II spoon, by Lawrence Coles, marks rubbed, c1680.
£250-300 *P*

A silver teaspoon, 1909.
£5-10 *PC*

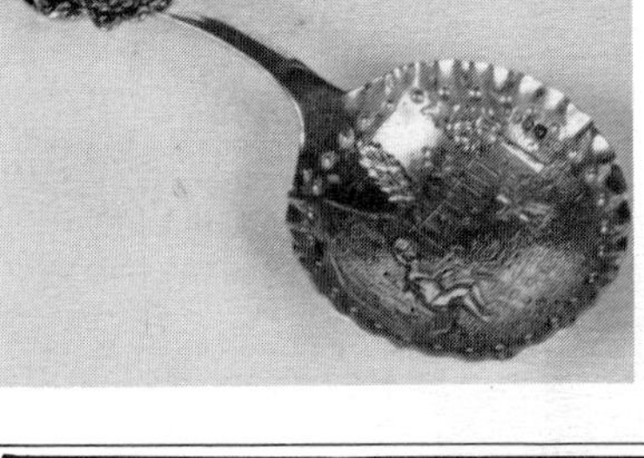

A Danish silver caddy spoon.
£40-50 *AB*

A Danish silver caddy spoon. **£35-40** *AB*

A silver berry spoon.
£30-40 *AB*

Wooden scoops.
£15-20 each *AL*

A collection of horn spoons.
£7-10 each *AL*

The horn is heated and then moulded.

SPORT

Cricket

A hand coloured lithograph of 4 Surrey cricketers, 16th July 1852. **£300-400** *P*

A pair of Royal Doulton vases, 5½in (14.5cm). **£100-200** *Bon*

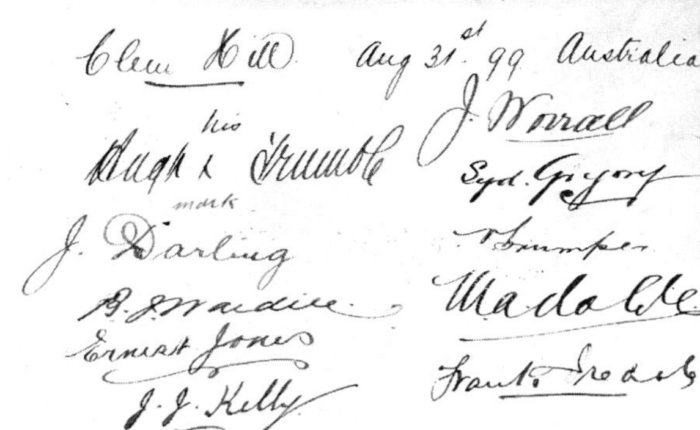

An autograph album dated Aug. 31st 1899, with various Australian and British players' autographs. **£550-650** *CSK*

A signed postcard of the Australian team, 1921. **£130-150** *VS*

A cricket ball with a white metal plaque inscribed 'Surrey v Kent, Blackheath 1923, The Bogey Laid', P. G. H. Fender, Captain of Surrey. **£180-200** *CSK*

A signed photograph of Jack Hobbs. **£25-30** *VS*

A commemorative silk handkerchief of the first England XI to tour Australia in 1861/62. **£2,000-2,500** *CSK*

Golf

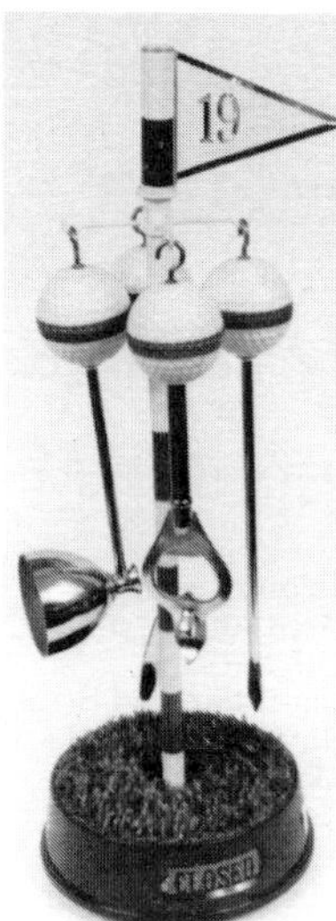

A golf cocktail set.
£75-85 *BEV*

A golfing chrome ashtray.
£40-50 *BEV*

A golf club and ball pen stand.
£40-50 *BEV*

A framed advertising mirror, 60in (152cm) square.
£750-800 *CEd*

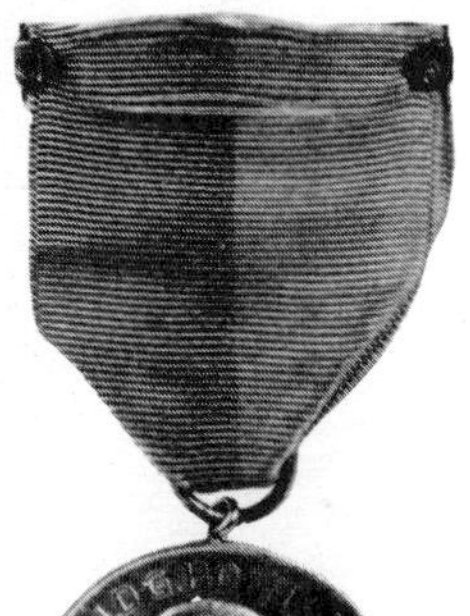

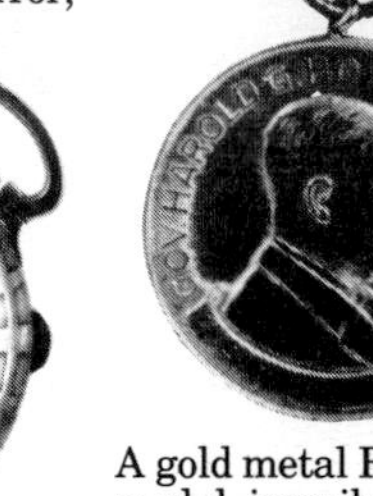

A gold metal Ryder Cup medal, inscribed G.B. Int. Ryder Cup 1935 Team.
£600-650 *CEd*

A silvered metal pocket watch, with white enamel dial.
£300-350 *CEd*

A cardboard cut-out.
£4-5 *SAR*

A ladies gold wrist watch.
£350-400 *CEd*

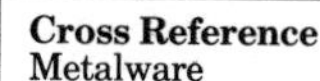

Cross Reference
Metalware

A pair of bronzed spelter book ends, c1930.
£800-850 *GIL*

A gouache caricature of British Golf Professionals of 1932, by Sybil Young, in gilt frame.
£400-500 *CEd*

A blue glass pin tray. **£20-30** *SAR*

A series of 3 chromolithographs, 15 by 10in (38 by 25cm).
£40-60 *CEd*

A green enamel cigarette box, with 'Gutty Ball', c1920.
£120-140 *SAR*

A silver photo frame.
£60-70 *SAR*

Avon after shaves.
£10-15 each *SAR*

A Golfing Union of Ireland, Open Championship Medal for 1936, 19ct gold and enamel, inscribed, in original box.
£1,000-1,200 *CEd*

A Royal Doulton Seriesware plate, painted with a typical golfing scene and inscription.
£140-160 *CEd*

A patinated spelter figure of a golfer, with presentation plaque dated 1941.
£250-300 *CDC*

A silver golf club hat pin, Birmingham, 1910.
£20-25 *VB*

A Royal Doulton Kingsware pottery jug, in the style of Charles Crombie, 9in (23cm) high.
£300-350 *CEd*

A golf game in pine box, stamped F. H. Ayres.
£850-950 *CEd*

A Ferdinand Strauss mechanical tin plate Play Golf game.
£450-500 *CEd*

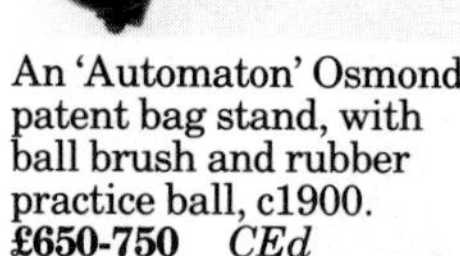

A pine and metal bound golf box, inscribed Mr. Thos. Graham, Union Club, St. Andrews, c1875.
£1,800-2,000 *CEd*

A hand painted plaque by M. Woodhouse.
£150-170 *SAR*

An 'Automaton' Osmond patent bag stand, with ball brush and rubber practice ball, c1900.
£650-750 *CEd*

DID YOU KNOW?
Before the time of golf bags, golf clubs were transported in boxes.

A Snoopy golfing trophy.
£10-15 *SAR*

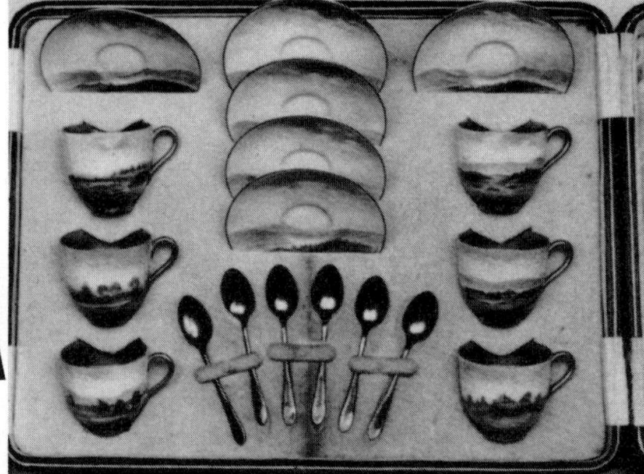

A set of 6 Royal Worcester coffee cups and saucers, and 6 silver gilt spoons, dated 1924, in fitted case.
£1,000-1,500 *CEd*

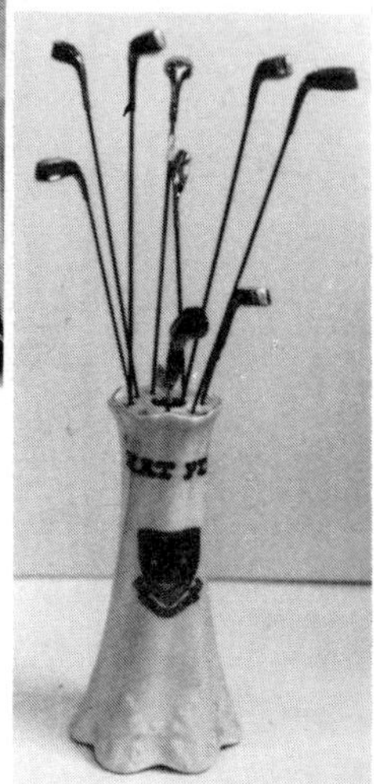

Silver hat pins.
£30-60 each *SAR*

Various golfing books.
£100-800 each *CEd*

Golf Balls

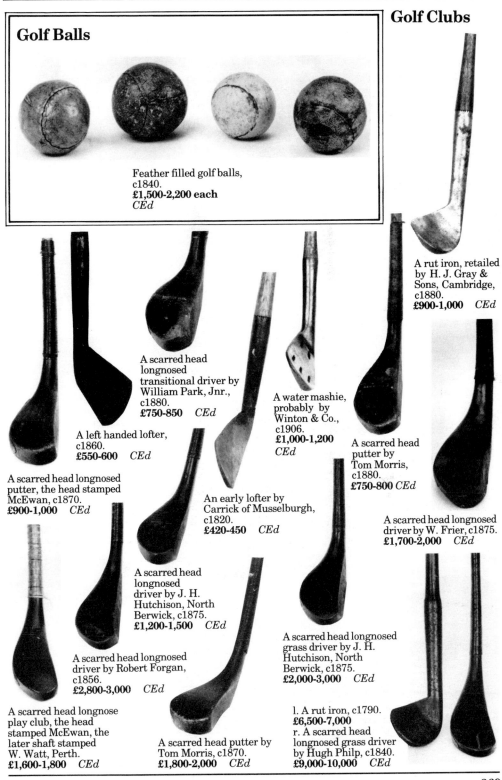

Feather filled golf balls, c1840.
£1,500-2,200 each
CEd

Golf Clubs

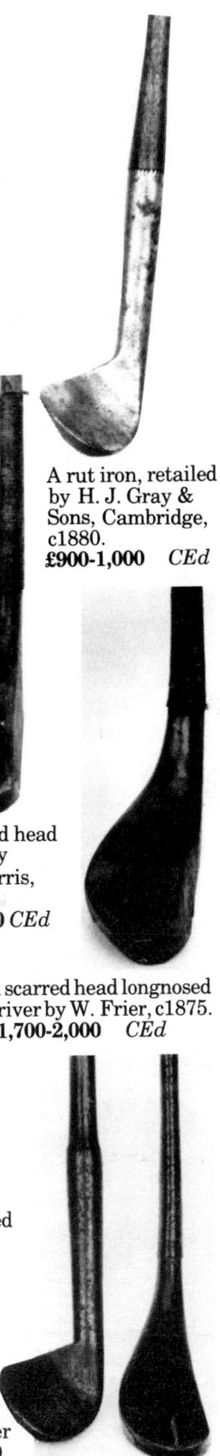

A rut iron, retailed by H. J. Gray & Sons, Cambridge, c1880.
£900-1,000 *CEd*

A scarred head longnosed transitional driver by William Park, Jnr., c1880.
£750-850 *CEd*

A water mashie, probably by Winton & Co., c1906.
£1,000-1,200 *CEd*

A scarred head putter by Tom Morris, c1880.
£750-800 *CEd*

A left handed lofter, c1860.
£550-600 *CEd*

A scarred head longnosed putter, the head stamped McEwan, c1870.
£900-1,000 *CEd*

An early lofter by Carrick of Musselburgh, c1820.
£420-450 *CEd*

A scarred head longnosed driver by W. Frier, c1875.
£1,700-2,000 *CEd*

A scarred head longnosed driver by J. H. Hutchison, North Berwick, c1875.
£1,200-1,500 *CEd*

A scarred head longnosed grass driver by J. H. Hutchison, North Berwick, c1875.
£2,000-3,000 *CEd*

A scarred head longnosed driver by Robert Forgan, c1856.
£2,800-3,000 *CEd*

A scarred head longnose play club, the head stamped McEwan, the later shaft stamped W. Watt, Perth.
£1,600-1,800 *CEd*

A scarred head putter by Tom Morris, c1870.
£1,800-2,000 *CEd*

l. A rut iron, c1790.
£6,500-7,000
r. A scarred head longnosed grass driver by Hugh Philp, c1840.
£9,000-10,000 *CEd*

Football

A photograph album, early 20thC.
£95-120 *FW*

A Continental spelter figure, c1920.
£75-85 *FW*

A metallic match striker with marble base, c1930.
£75-85 *FW*

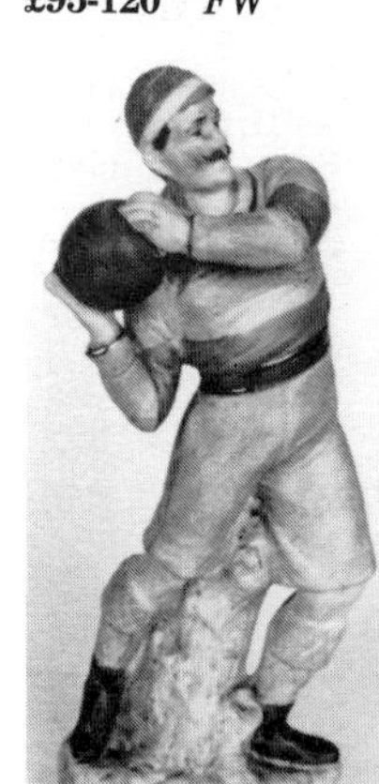

A bisque statue, early 20thC.
£95-120 *FW*

A World Cup Willie money box.
£25-30 *FW*

World Cup Willie's Football, c1966.
£18-20 *FW*

A spelter figure, c1890.
£230-250 *FW*

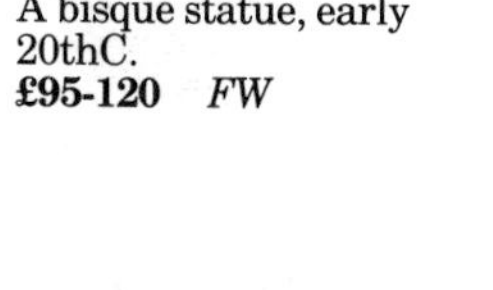

A tobacco tin, early 1900s.
£35-45 *FW*

A Dartmouth blue and white pottery mug, c1940.
£30-40 *FW*

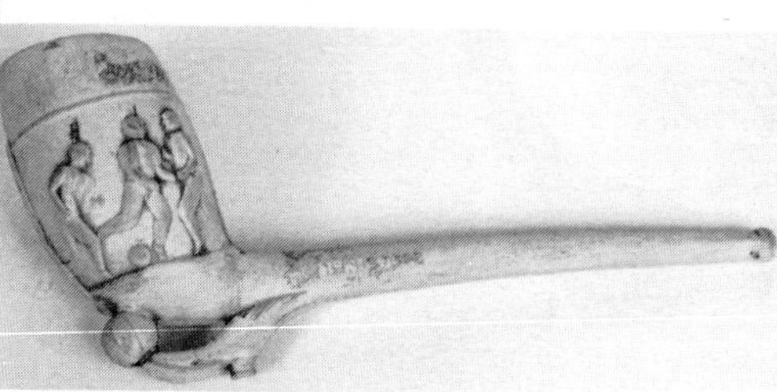

A clay pipe, probably 1880s. **£55-65** *FW*

A Staffordshire mug, c1940.
£35-45 *FW*

A Staffordshire ceramic biscuit barrel, c1940.
£60-80 *FW*

A pewter footballing trophy, c1881.
£50-60 *FW*

A photo album.
£6-8 *FW*

A stick badge and a key ring for Yugoslavia in 1974 World Cup.
£6-8 *FW*

A Football Association blazer badge, c1898.
£55-65 *FW*

A bronze statue of man playing Tsu Chu, 20thC
£95-120 *FW*

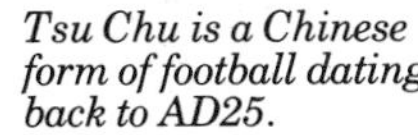

Tsu Chu is a Chinese form of football dating back to AD25.

A ceramic figure of Stanley Matthews, c1940.
£30-40 *FW*

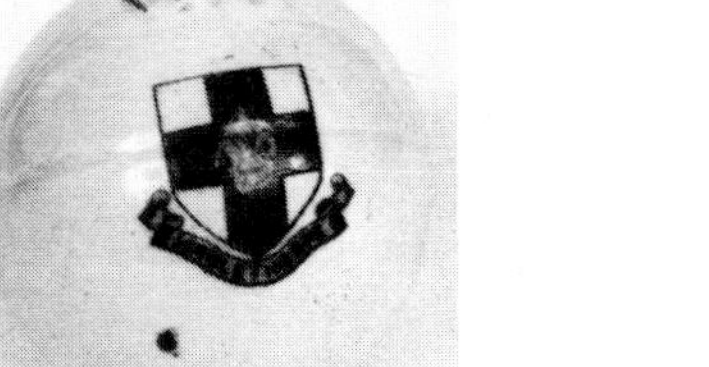

A Goss football.
£14-16 *FW*

A ceramic wall plaque, c1900.
£45-55 *FW*

A clay football ashtray.
£10-12 *FW*

A German bisque style figure, c1930.
£12-15 *FW*

A Staffordshire mug, c1940.
£30-40 *FW*

A clock, made by British United Clock Corporation, Birmingham, c1890.
£285-300 *FW*

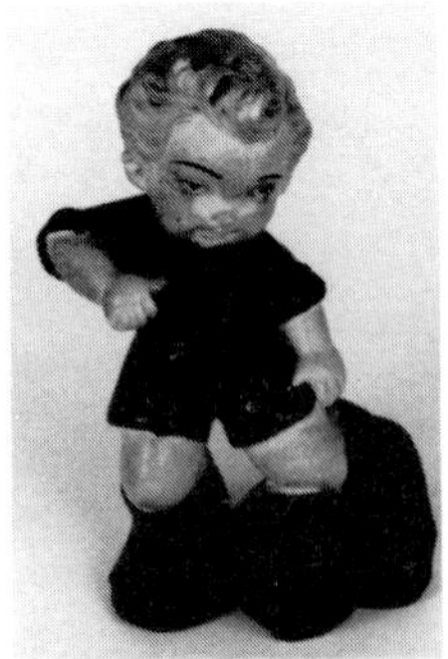

A plaster boy footballer, c1950.
£12-15 *FW*

A glazed ceramic figure, early 1900s.
£40-50 *FW*

A Football print, c1860.
£40-60 *FW*

DID YOU KNOW?
Miller's Collectables Price Guide is designed to build up, year by year, into the most comprehensive reference system available.

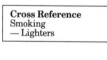

Cross Reference
Smoking
— Lighters

A brass football trophy, c1945.
£30-40 *FW*

Lighters, 1930-70.
£12-150 each *FW*

A Polish vase, for 1982 Spanish World Cup, 6½in (16cm).
£7-10 *FW*

A ceramic match-holder, 1930s.
£14-16 *FW*

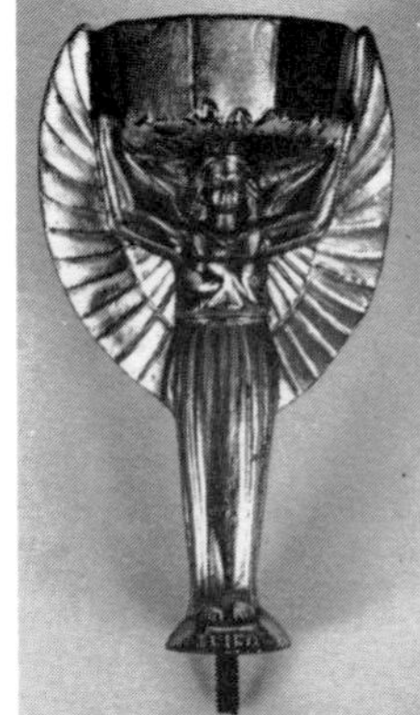
A silvered metalic replica of the World Cup, produced to commemorate England's 1966 victory.
£30-40 *FW*

A Staffordshire figure dedicated to A. Bennet.
£225-250 *FW*

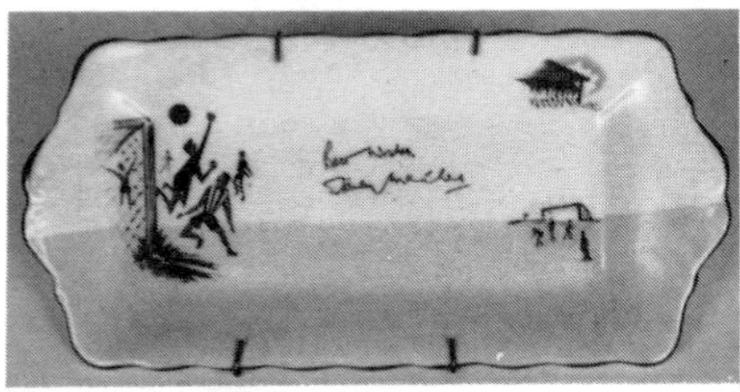
A Stanley Matthews commemorative plate, c1946.
£40-50 *FW*

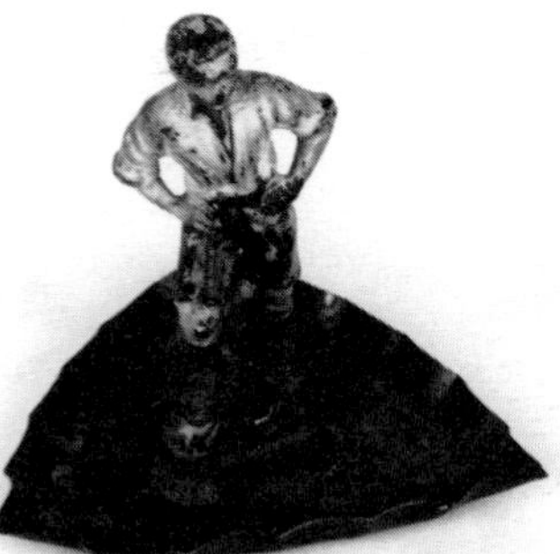
An ashtray, c1920.
£25-35 *FW*

Football Who's Who.
£3-5 *FW*

A cigarette case, 1890.
£35-45 *FW*

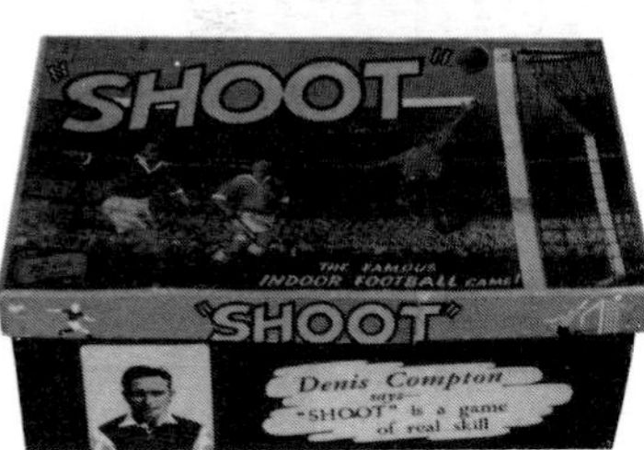

A boxed football game, c1950.
£15-20 *FW*

A Victorian tinplate toy.
£12-15 *FW*

A football game, c1950.
£15-20 *FW*

Charlie George, c1970.
£7-10 *FW*

A wooden picture frame, c1908.
£35-45 *FW*

A silvered metallic statue, c1940.
£85-95 *FW*

'Georgie'.
£10-15 *FW*

A tobacco tin, c1910.
£35-45 *FW*

A cigarette case, c1930.
£25-35 *FW*

An unusual brass car bonnet mascot, c1920.
£65-75 *FW*

General

An American money box, in original carton.
£30-35 *SAR*

A pigeon racing trophy goblet, with inscription, c1929, 18oz.
£45-55 *CSK*

A Tavannes 10ct. gold filled wrist watch, inscribed Ryder Cup Team 1935, from P.G.A. of America, Reginald A. Whitcombe.
£450-500 *CEd*

A selection of signed pieces.
£140-160 *VS*

An oil on canvas, by E. H. Windred.
£200-300 *CSK*

The Bill Tovell boxing belt, Birmingham, 1937, in fitted case.
£480-500 *CSK*

An oil on canvas by Andrew Beer.
£350-400 *CSK*

A selection of horse racing ephemera, including badges and tickets, 1920s.
£50-60 *VS*

A Royal Copenhagen plate, depicting Royal Lytham & St. Annes Golf Club, c1979.
£35-40 *SAR*

A Continental gilt lined rowing trophy cup, with inscriptions, c1948.
£250-300 *CSK*

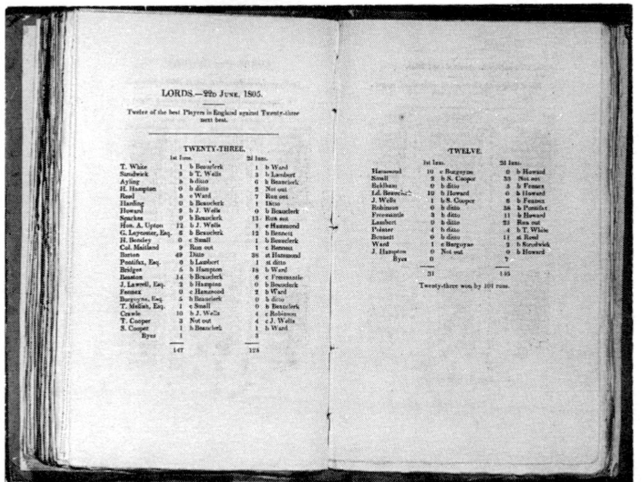

LORDS.—22d June, 1805.

Twelve of the best Players in England against Twenty-three next best.

TWENTY-THREE.

	1st Inns.		2d Inns.	
T. White	1	b Beauclerk	1	b Ward
Sandwick	3	b T. Wells	3	b Lambert
Ayling	5	b ditto	6	b Beauclerk
H. Hampton	0	b ditto	2	Not out
Reed	5	c Ward	7	Run out
Harding	0	b Beauclerk	1	Ditto
Howard	9	b J. Wells	0	b Beauclerk
Sparkes	0	b Beauclerk	13	Run out
Hon. A. Upton	12	b J. Wells	1	c Hammond
G. Leycester, Esq.	8	b Beauclerk	12	b Bennett
H. Bentley	0	c Small	1	b Beauclerk
Col. Maitland	9	Run out	1	c Bennett
Barton	49	Ditto	38	st Hammond
Pontifax, Esq.	6	b Lambert	1	st ditto
Bridger	5	b Hampton	18	b Ward
Beaston	14	b Beauclerk	6	c Freemantle
J. Lawrell, Esq.	2	b Hampton	0	b Beauclerk
Fennex	0	c Hammond	2	b Ward
Burgoyne, Esq.	5	b Beauclerk	0	b ditto
T. Mellish, Esq.	1	c Small	0	b Beauclerk
Crawte	10	b J. Wells	4	c Robinson
T. Cooper	3	Not out	4	c J. Wells
S. Cooper	1	b Beauclerk	1	b Ward
Byes	1		3	
	147		128	

TWELVE.

	1st Inns.		2d Inns.	
Hammond	10	c Burgoyne	0	b Howard
Small	2	b S. Cooper	33	Not out
Beldham	0	b ditto	5	b Fennex
Ld. Beauclerk	10	b Howard	0	b Howard
J. Wells	1	b S. Cooper	8	b Fennex
Robinson	0	b ditto	38	b Pontifax
Freemantle	3	b ditto	11	b Howard
Lambert	0	b ditto	23	Run out
Pointer	4	b ditto	4	b T. White
Bennett	0	b ditto	11	st Reed
Ward	1	c Burgoyne	2	b Sandwick
J. Hampton	0	Not out	0	b Howard
Byes	0		7	
	31		143	

Twenty-three won by 101 runs.

A score book for cricket matches 1786-1822, H. Bentley.
£200-300 *P*

A cricket ball stamped in gilt with inscription, F. C. Cobden, 1870.
£500-550 *CSK*

Taxidermy

A Victorian display of birds.
£135-145 *HCH*

A lion's head.
£170-180 *WD*

A wild boar's head.
£335-350 *SSA*

A fox's head, c1960.
£45-50 *SSA*

A lion, Roland Ward, 166 Piccadilly, London W1, c1900.
£800-1,000 *SSA*

A Victorian display of exotic birds, with glass dome.
£150-200 *WIL*

Chalkey Winchester, c1910.
£65-75 *SSA*

A fur rug made from the skin of a wild cat, on felt backing, patched repair.
£10-15 *WAL*

A tom cat, c1930.
£70-80 *SSA*

Tea Caddies

A Sheraton style tea caddy, with ceramic interior, 5in (13.5cm).
£90-100 *PCh*

A Victorian tea caddy, veneered in diamond shaped mother-of-pearl, some veneer missing.
£200-250 *WIL*

A silver tea canister, the lid with monogram M.S., Birmingham, 1899.
£100-150 *WIL*

A Victorian burr walnut tea caddy with bowl.
£300-350 *MB*

A silver plated tea caddy.
£45-55 *AB*

A Victorian silver plated tea caddy.
£80-100 *AB*

A George III mahogany inlaid tea caddy.
£180-240 *MB*

A Sheffield plated tea caddy, 4in (10cm) high.
£60-80 *AB*

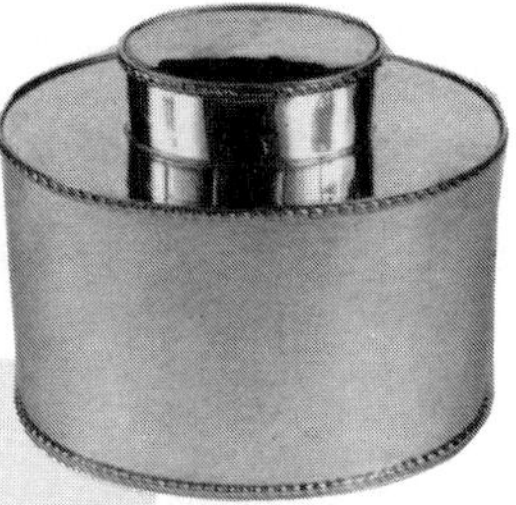

Victorian silver plated tea caddies.
£75-100 each *AB*

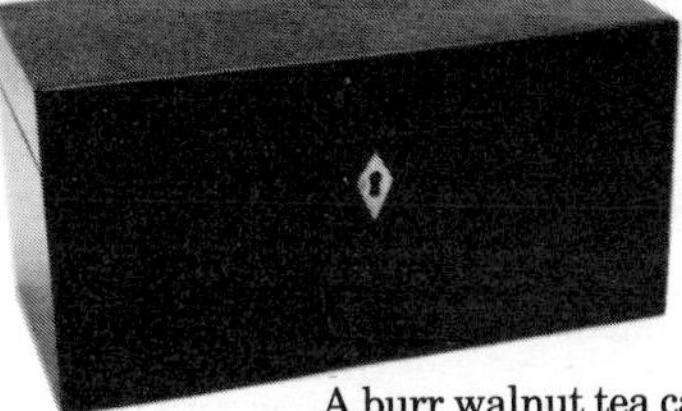

A burr walnut tea caddy with inlaid ivory key plate, early 19thC.
£95-120 *PCh*

Telephones

Although a German, Reis, had displayed a form of telephone in 1861, the invention is credited to Alexander Graham Bell who first transmitted recognisable speech at Boston, Massachusetts, in 1876. In 1878 he demonstrated his invention before Queen Victoria at Osborne House. A year later the first telephone exchange was opened in London at 36 Coleman Street.

Edwardian mahogany cased telephones by Gent.
£110-140 *GIL*

A Post Office candlestick telephone, with Bakelite mouthpiece, early 1930s.
£90-120 *BT*

An Ericsson skeleton magneto telephone.
£275-350 *BT*

In production from 1895 to early 1930s.

A Post Office wall telephone, No. 121, early 1930s.
£90-120 *BT*

A 20-line telephone exchange, Swedish, 1896.
£550-650 *BT*

An Electric and Ordnance Accessories Co., Birmingham, intercom telephone with nickel plated Ericsson style handset, 1900s.
£60-95 *SM*

This style of handset was first introduced in 1892.

A candlestick telephone by Stromberg-Carlson Tel. Man. Co., U.S.A., 1905.
£120-150 *BT*

A Bell-Blake magneto telephone, a standard instrument of the National Telephone Co., when it was formed in 1889.
£150-200 *BT*

A GPO candlestick telephone with Bell receiver and fixed transmitter, 1920-30s.
£95-185 *SM*

An Edwardian Ericsson cradle telephone.
£200-250 *GIL*

A Société des Telephones, Paris, candlestick telephone with monophone handset and Ader receiver, 1920s.
£75-125 *SM*

Listening-in receivers were quite popular on early telephones.

A type 232 black telephone.
£35-45 *BT*

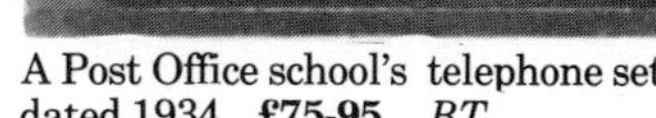

A Post Office school's telephone set, dated 1934. **£75-95** *BT*

An Ericsson 10-line internal office telephone, 1901.
£90-120 *BT*

A Bell Telephone Mfg. Co., Antwerp, desk set, with integral bell and early automatic dial, 1912.
£75-100 *SM*

A Siemens Brothers, London, black Bakelite Neophone desk set with integral bell, 1930s.
£60-85 *SM*

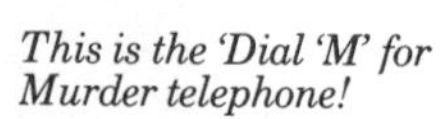

This is the 'Dial 'M' for Murder telephone!

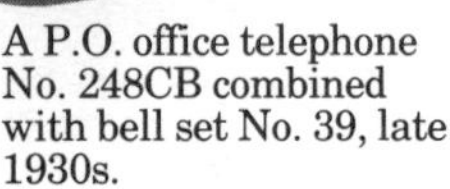

A P.O. office telephone No. 248CB combined with bell set No. 39, late 1930s.
£55-75 *BT*

A Siemens Brothers, London, Neophone desk set in ivory coloured plastic with matching bell set, 1930s.
£75-150 *SM*

The Neophone was advertised as 'The World's Most Efficient Telephone', and was standardised by telephone administrations all over the world.

A Standard Telephones & Cables, London, black Bakelite desk set with integral bell, 1930s.
Black **£50-65**
Coloured
£100-150 *SM*

This set was produced for STC by the Bell Telephone Mfg. Co., Antwerp, in various colours including red, green, cream, white, as well as imitation wood.

A GPO hand microphone, introduced to replace the candlestick telephone in the 1930s.
Black **£50-80**
Coloured
£150-200 *SM*

Produced in various colours including Chinese red, jade green and ivory. Earlier versions do not have the pull-out directory tray.

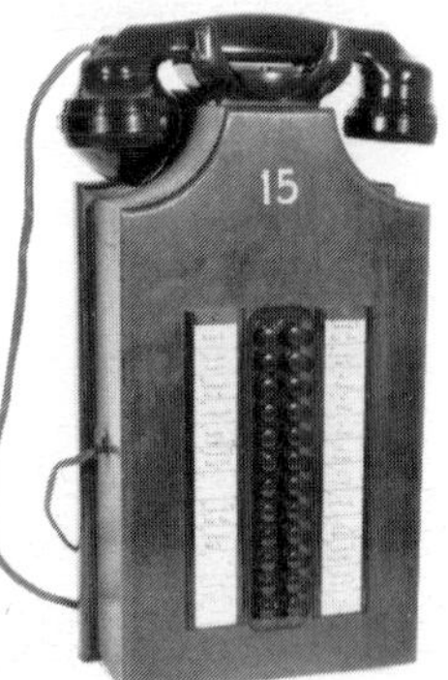

A 24-line internal telephone, installed at Pinewood Film Studios in 1936.
£45-55 *BT*

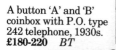

A button 'A' and 'B' coinbox with P.O. type 242 telephone, 1930s.
£180-220 *BT*

An Automatic Telephone Mfg. Co., Liverpool, black Bakelite Strowgerphone with circular base, 1930s.
£75-95 *SM*

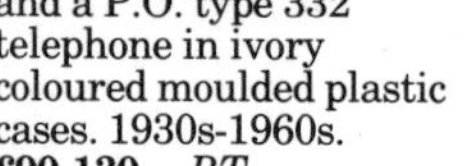

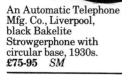

A P.O. type 232 telephone and a P.O. type 332 telephone in ivory coloured moulded plastic cases. 1930s-1960s.
£90-130 *BT*

A P.O. call office sign, No. 5, in blue and white enamelled iron, c1930.
£75-95 *BT*

FURTHER READING

Goss, M., *Britains Public Payphones,* British Telecom, 1984.

Jolley, E. J., *Introduction to Telephony & Telegraphy,* Pitman, 1968.

TEXTILES
Beadwork

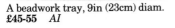

A beadwork tray, 9in (23cm) diam.
£45-55 *AI*

A Victorian floral stool, 12in (30.5cm) diam.
£85-95 *AI*

A Belgian bugle bead and diamanté bag, c1930.
£15-20 *EAS*

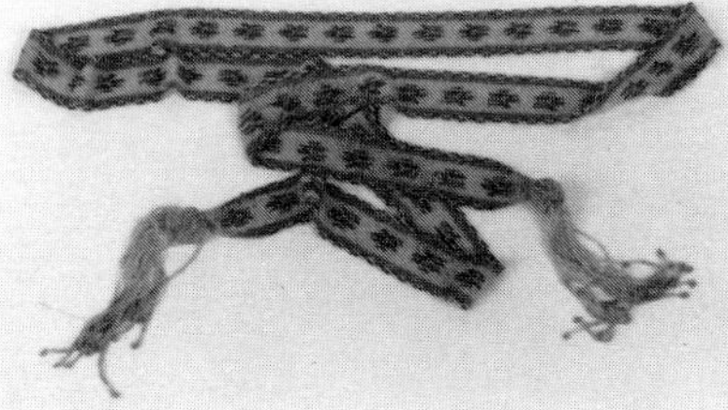

A beaded belt, c1930. **£45-50** *EAS*

Beadwork on woven silk.
£25-30 *AI*

A beaded tea cosy and matching stand.
Tea Cosy **£125-135**
Stand **£95-105** *PP*

A beaded bag and purse, dated 1927. **£40-50** *PAR*

Beadwork on woven wool. **£20-25 each** *AI*

A silk cushion with beadwork decoration, 15in (38cm) diam.
£75-85 *AI*

A cut steel evening bag, c1920. **£40-50** *PAR*

A peach bugle bead and pearl on crêpe-de-chine purse, foreign.
£25-30 *EAS*

A sampler style beaded bag, c1930.
£40-50 *EAS*

A Victorian beaded purse with silk lining.
£45-55 *EAS*

A royal blue bugle beaded bag, c1930.
£45-55 *EAS*

A beaded bag with gilt clasp.
£30-40 *CBA*

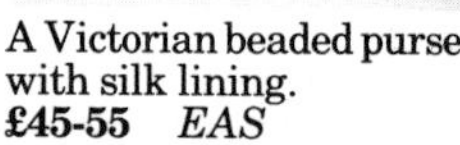

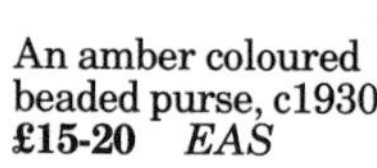

An amber coloured beaded purse, c1930.
£15-20 *EAS*

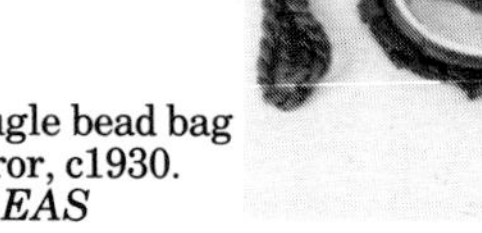

A blue bugle bead bag with mirror, c1930.
£35-45 *EAS*

Cushions

A patchwork cushion, 15in (38cm) square. **£35-45** *AI*

A tapestry cushion with velvet back.
£35-45 *AI*

A cushion.
£30-40 *CBA*

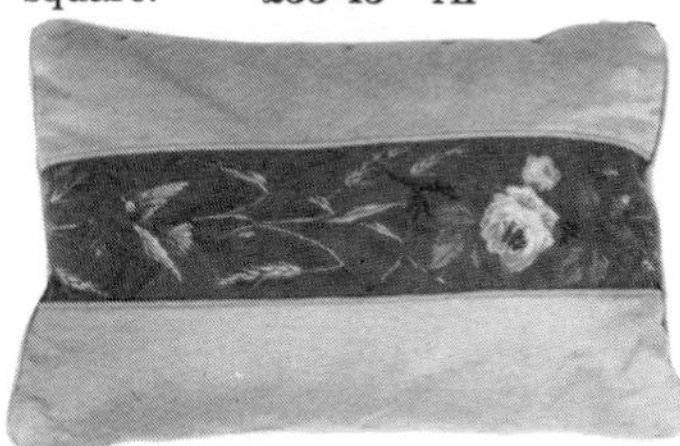

A cushion with wool embroidery strip.
£35-45 *AI*

A wool tapestry cushion with hessian backing.
£40-45 *AI*

A Paisley wool cushion.
£40-50 *AI*

A beaded cushion, 7½in (19cm) square.
£30-35 *AI*

An Edwardian nightdress case, now made into a cushion.
£30-35 *LB*

A gold silk beadwork cushion, 18in (45.5cm) diam.
£90-100 *AI*

A tapestry cushion, the tapestry 17thC.
£400-500 *CSK*

Costume

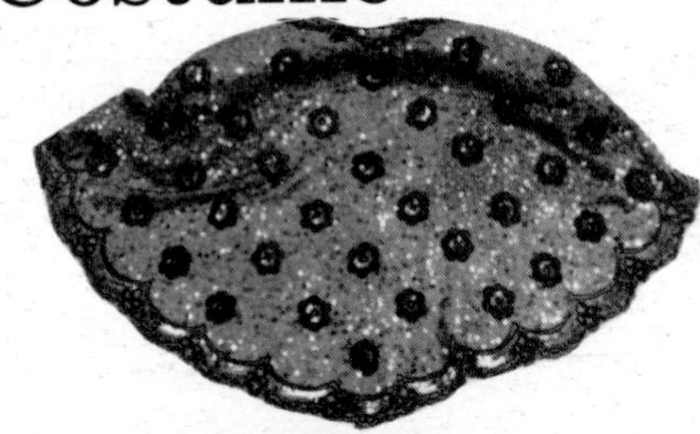

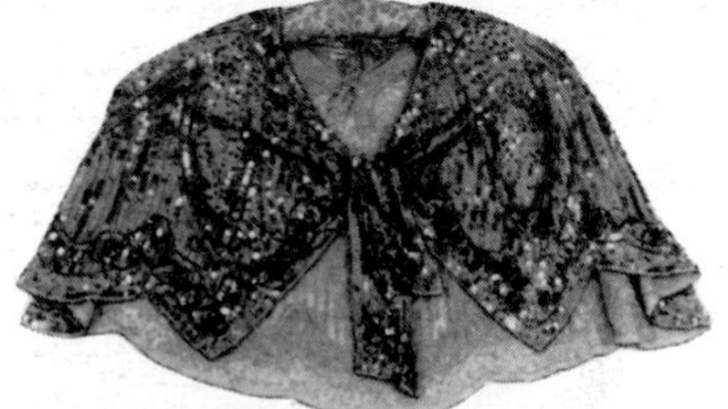

Two sequined boleros, 1920s. **£70-100** *LB*

A Victorian hand made Christening gown, in linen, lace and white embroidery.
£70-90 *OBS*

A pair of late Victorian cotton drawers.
£30-40 *OBS*

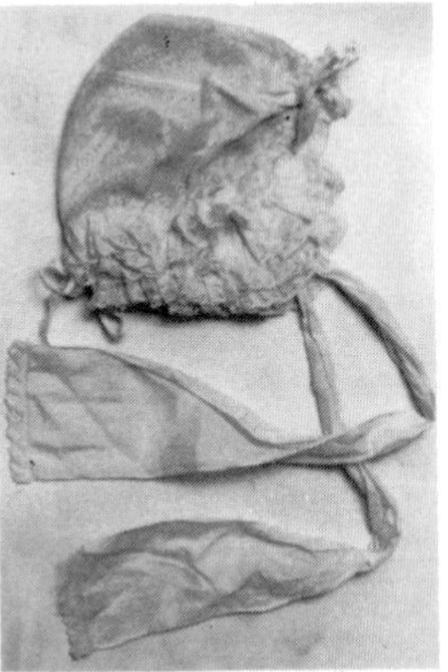

A Victorian linen and lace bonnet, with needlepoint crown.
£45-50 *OBS*

A farmworker's white linen smock, 19thC.
£60-80 *P*

A Dorset bonnet, hand stitched on linen, c1890.
£45-50 *OBS*

A Victorian Dorset bonnet.
£45-55 *OBS*

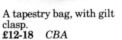

A tapestry bag, with gilt clasp.
£12-18 *CBA*

A pair of late Victorian cotton drawers.
£30-40 *OBS*

A Victorian blue cotton bonnet, with cane inserts to the brim.
£45-50 *OBS*

A cotton voile baby gown with lace inserts.
£40-50 *MAN*

A Victorian gentleman's silk embroidered smoking cap.
£60-90 *LB*

A cotton voile Christening gown, with pin tucks and Ayrshire work.
£85-95 *MAN*

An Edwardian cotton and lace nightgown.
£65-75 *LB*

Cross Reference
Smoking

Tapestry

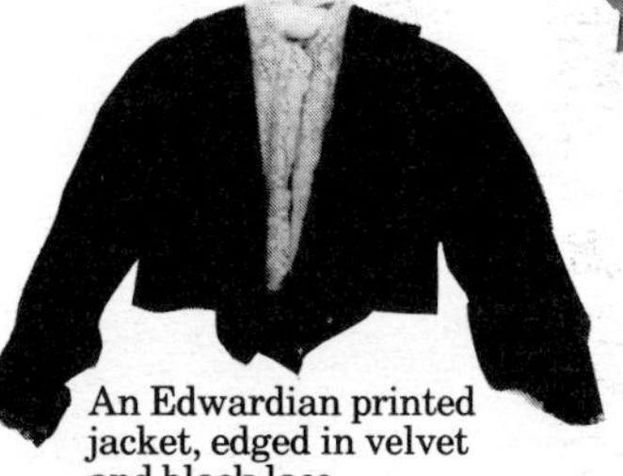

An Edwardian printed jacket, edged in velvet and black lace.
£60-80 *LB*

A wool tapestry on maroon felt.
£65-75 *AI*

A wool tapestry with silk braiding.
£75-85 *AI*

Household

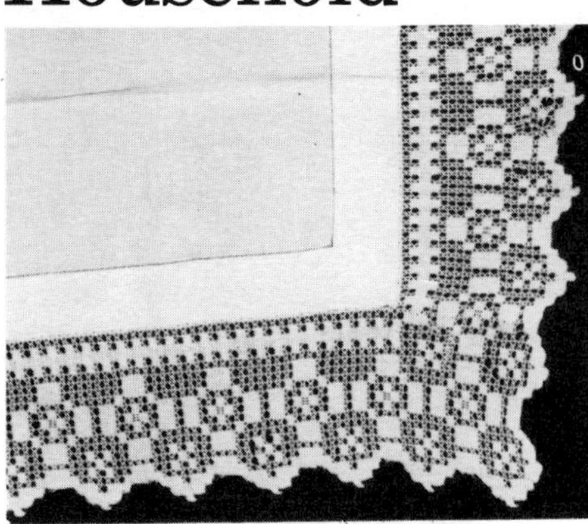

A crocheted tablecloth, 50in (127cm) square.
£35-45 *MAN*

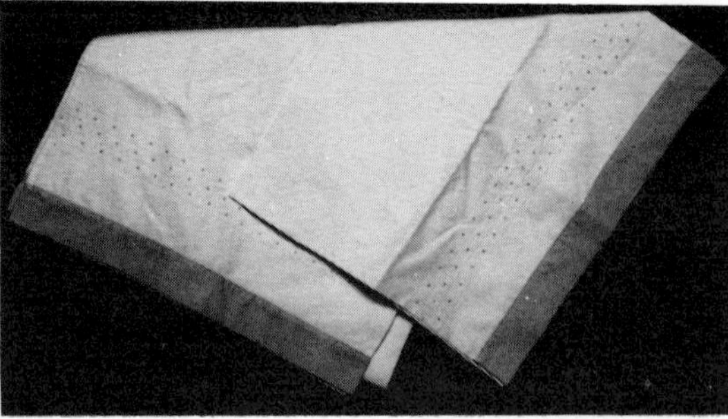

A linen bolster case and 2 pillow cases, with blue trim.
£25-35 *LAM*

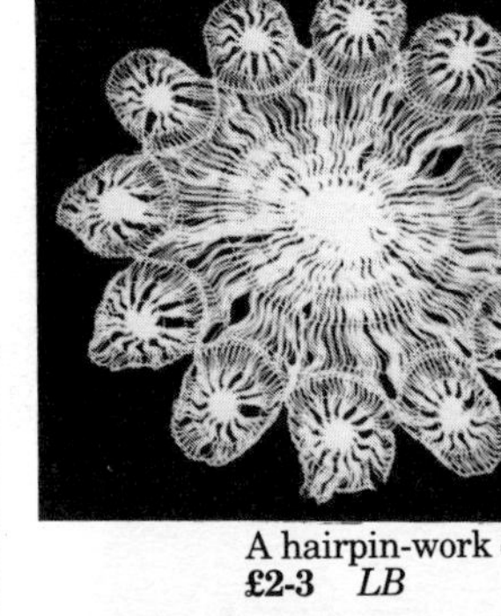

A hairpin-work doily.
£2-3 *LB*

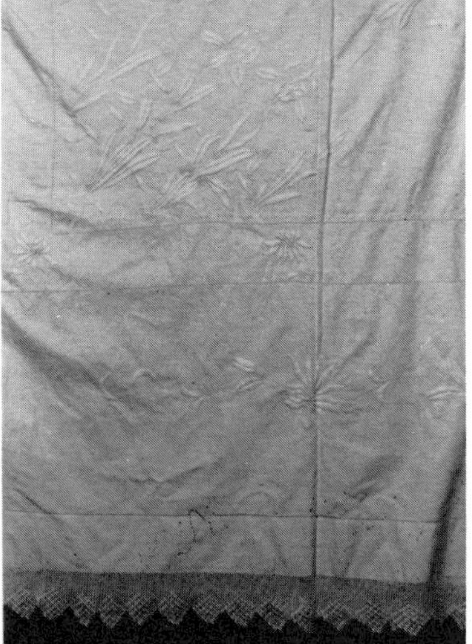

A large Edwardian white linen bedspread, hand embroidered with crochet edge.
£150-200 *LB*

MAKE THE MOST OF MILLERS
Condition is absolutely vital when assessing the value of any item. Damaged pieces appreciate much less than perfect examples. However, a rare, desirable piece may command a high price even when damaged.

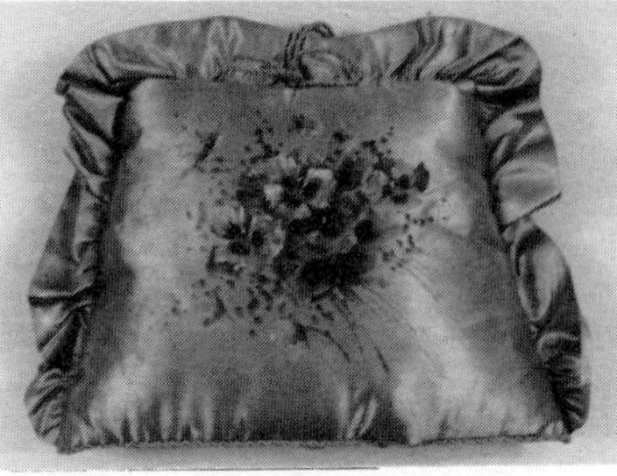

A hand painted satin tea cosy.
£15-20 *LB*

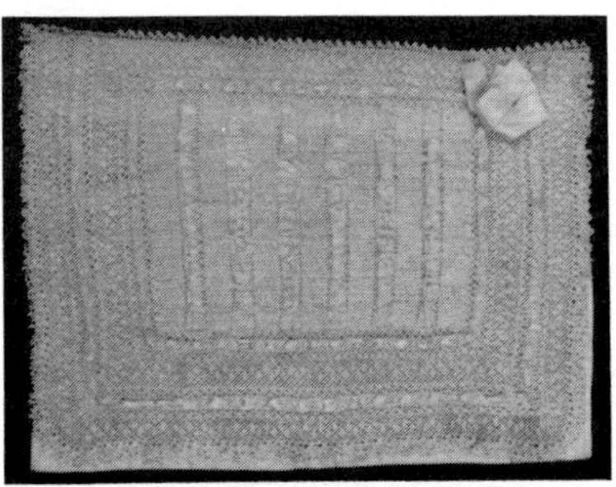

An Edwardian nightdress case.
£30-35 *LB*

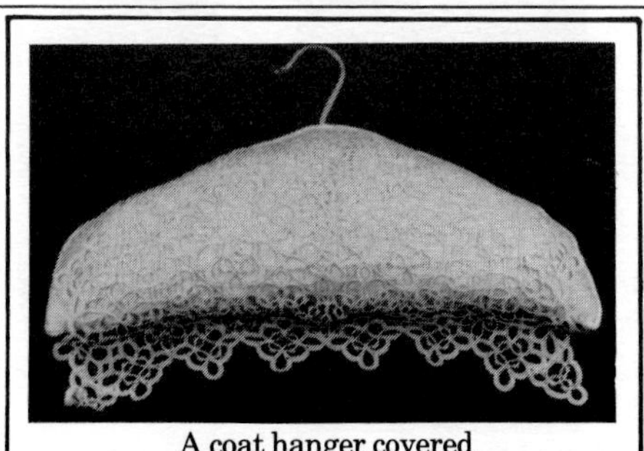

A coat hanger covered with old lace.
£10-15 *LB*

DID YOU KNOW?
Hairpin work is done on a very tiny needle in the shape of a hairpin with a small hook on it.

Lace

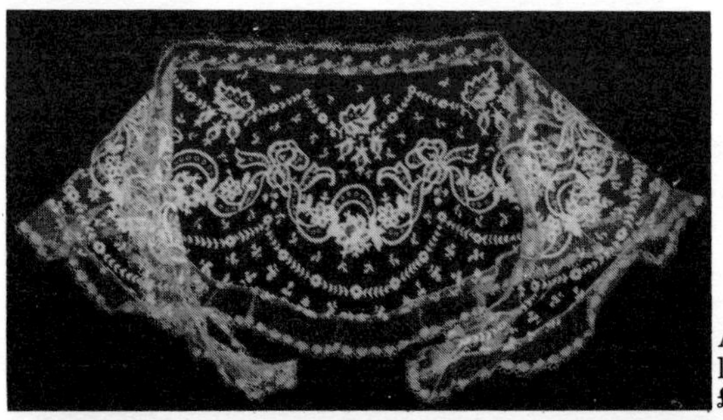

A Victorian lace fichu.
£65-85 *LB*

An Edwardian tape lace collar with needlepoint filling.
£30-40 *LB*

An Edwardian collar of Maltese lace.
£20-30 *LB*

An Edwardian chemical lace collar.
£25-35 *LB*

An Alençon lace fichu.
£50-70 *LB*

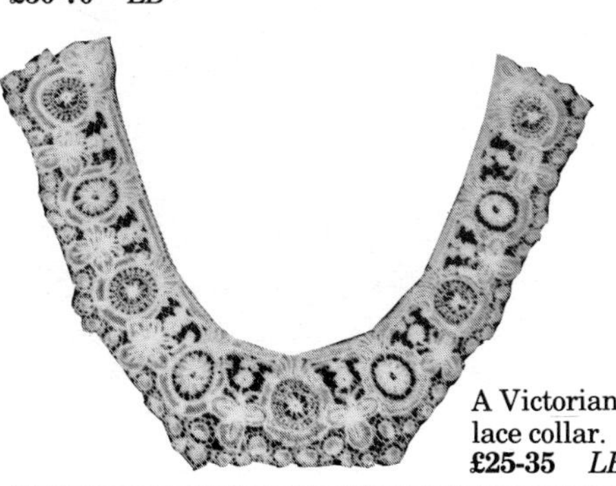

A Victorian lace collar.
£25-35 *LB*

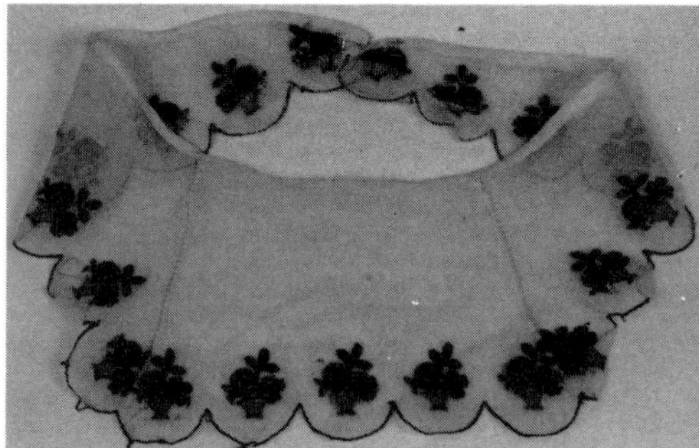
A lawn collar with silk embroidery. **£5-10** *CAC*

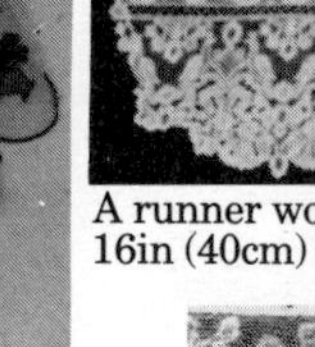
A runner worked with borders of point de Paris, 16in (40cm) wide. **£130-150** *P*

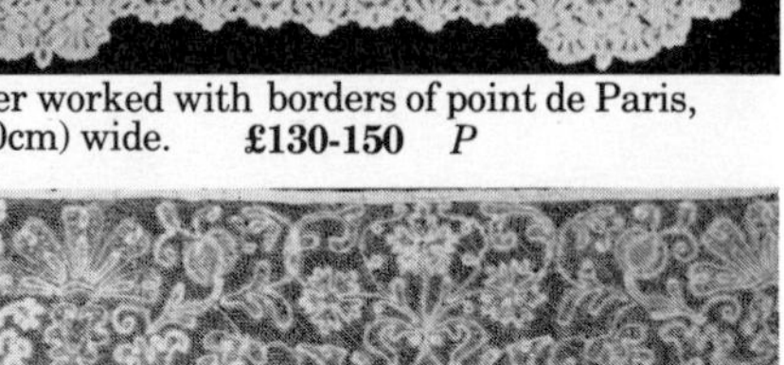
A Milanese lace flounce, early 18thC. **£50-70** *P*

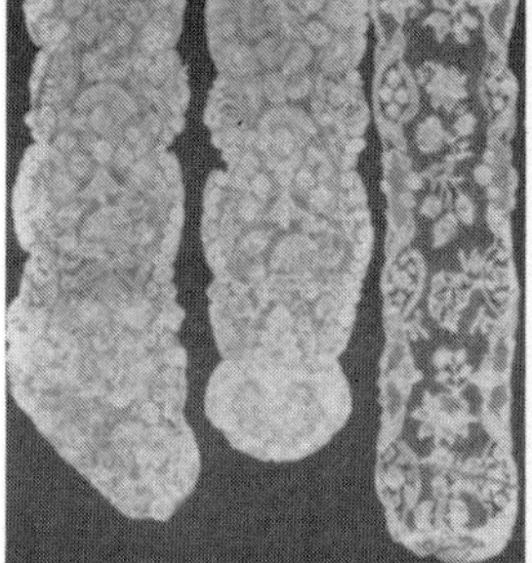
A pair of Brussels bobbin lace lappets and a border, 18thC. **£300-350** *CSK*

An Edwardian chemical lace collar, c1860. **£10-25** *LB*

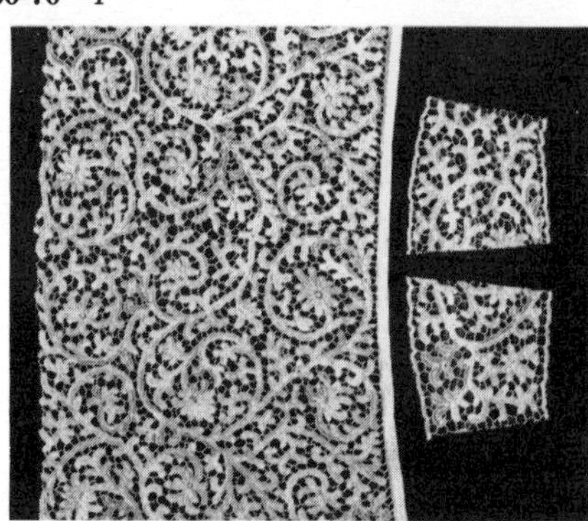
A lace collar and cuffs, late 19thC. **£100-120** *P*

A Buckinghamshire lace scarf, early 19thC, with 18thC Brussels lace border. **£100-120** *P*

Costume

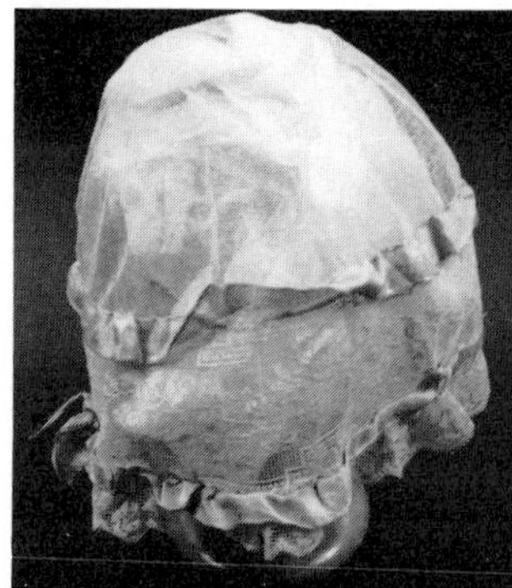
A Victorian lace boudoir cap. **£25-30** *LB*

A Honiton lace handkerchief. **£40-60** *LB*

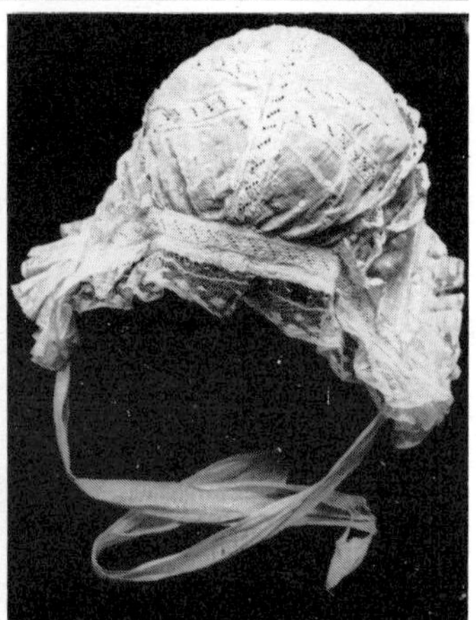
An early Victorian ecru lace bonnet, damaged. **£40-50** *LB*

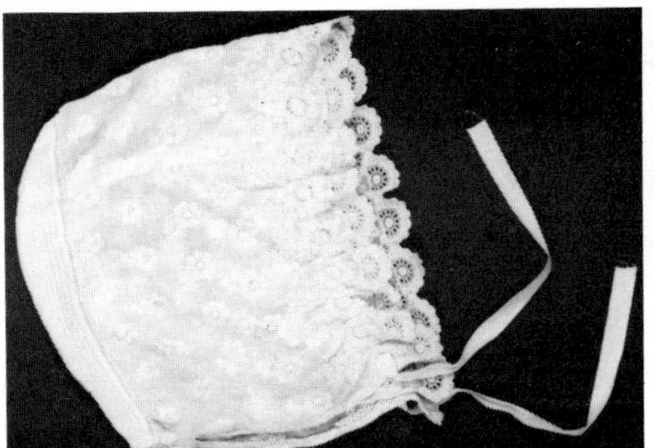

A Victorian child's bonnet in Ayrshire work.
£35-45 *LB*

A Victorian high neck collar.
£25-35 *LB*

A baby's bonnet.
£30-60 *LB*

A fine lawn handkerchief edged in Bedfordshire lace.
£3-10 *LB*

An Edwardian child's dress.
£60-75 *LB*

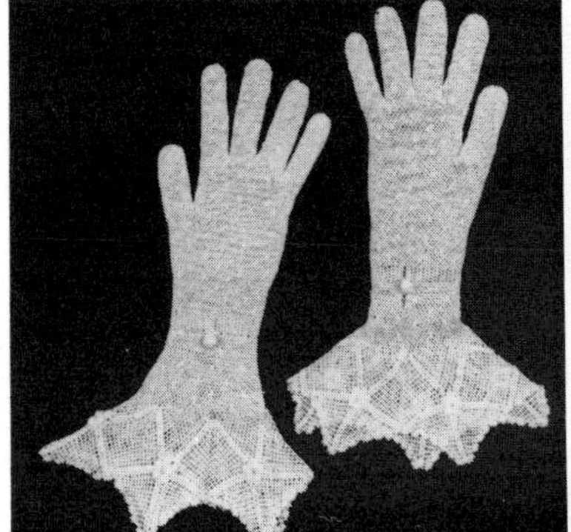

A pair of Edwardian lace gloves.
£18-25 *LB*

Two lace tea cosies.
£10-20 each *LB*

A Victorian Honiton lace veil.
£150-200 *LB*

A cream lace dress, 1940s.
£55-60 *LB*

A coat hanger covered with old lace, 17in (43cm) wide. **£12-15** *LB*

Two lace tea cosies.
£15-20 each *LB*

Lace Making

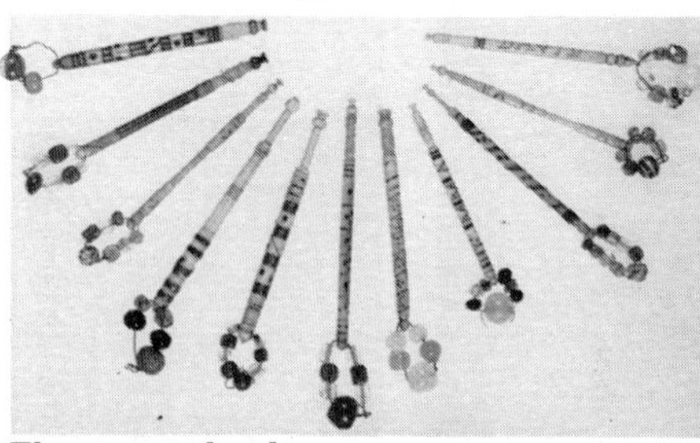

Eleven carved and stained turned bone bobbins, c1870.
£10-12 each *P*

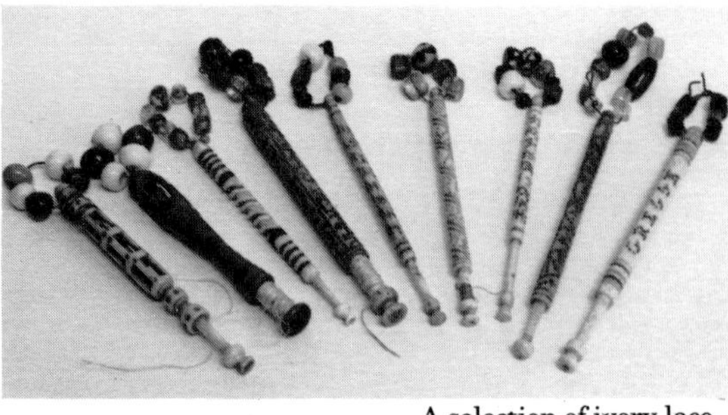

A selection of ivory lace bobbins, some named.
£50-60 *PC*

Named or in ivory, more expensive.

Ten Honiton wood bobbins, with dates from 1835-80.
£120-140 *P*

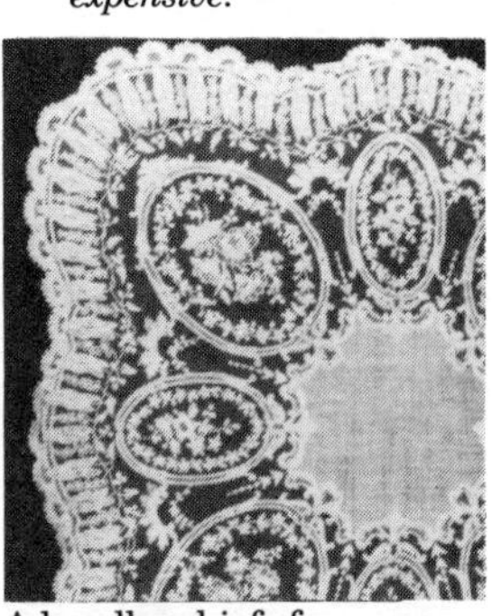

A handkerchief of applied Brussels bobbin lace, with border of ivy leaves, 15in (38cm) square.
£100-150 *CSK*

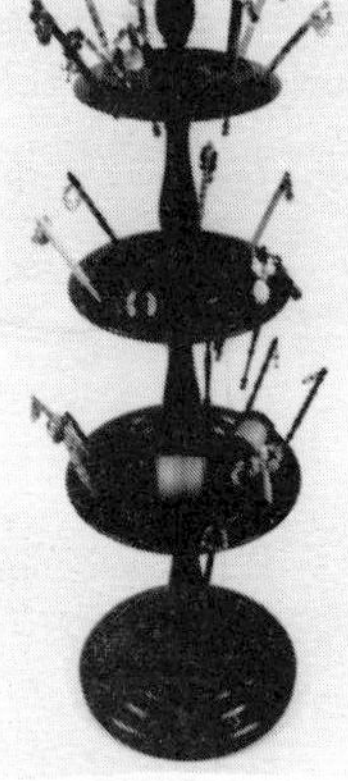

A mahogany bobbin stand, with lace bobbins, 29in (73cm) high.
Stand **£40-60**
Bobbins
£5-15 each *LB*

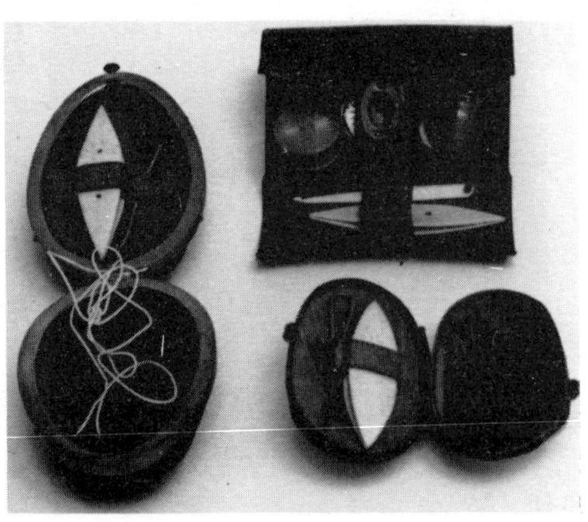

Three mid-Victorian tatting sets.
£25-35 *PC*

A flounce of Venetian raised needlelace, 17thC, later edging, 104in (264cm) long.
£350-400 *CSK*

Patchwork

An American Edwardian patchwork.
£250-300 *LB*

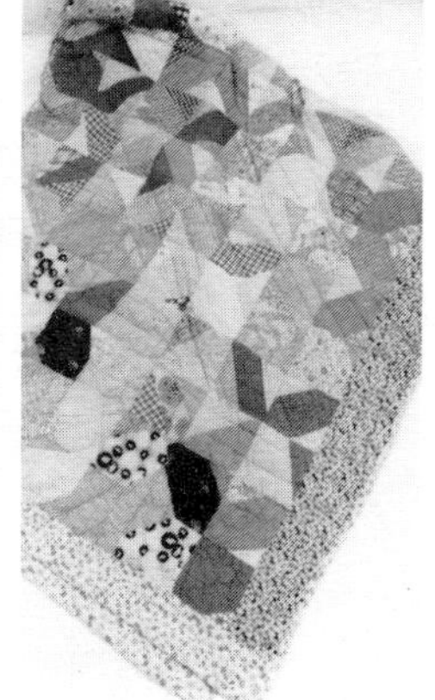

An Edwardian patchwork quilt.
£150-200 *LB*

Patchwork quilts.
£185-375 each *AI*

Pictorial

A Pavot tapestry panel, 19thC.
£500-550 *CSK*

A woolwork-on-silk picture of Bonnie Prince Charlie and Flora MacDonald.
£250-300 *OSc*

A pair of embroidered pictures, worked in coloured wools, framed and glazed, mid-19thC.
£175-185 *C*

Samplers

A sampler by Emma Morle, 1828, framed and glazed.
£550-600 *CSK*

A sampler by Rosa Robinson, framed and glazed, mid-19thC. **£300-400** *CSK*

A sampler by Jane Williams, 1864.
£325-350 *PAR*

A sampler by Ann Diggle, 1820, framed and glazed.
£350-400 *CSK*

A sampler by Elizabeth Stephens, 1839, framed and glazed.
£170-200 *GD*

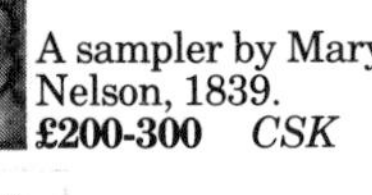

A sampler by Mary Nelson, 1839.
£200-300 *CSK*

A sampler by Mary Kins, framed and glazed.
£150-200 *CSK*

A darning sampler, late 18thC.
£350-450 *CSK*

Shawls

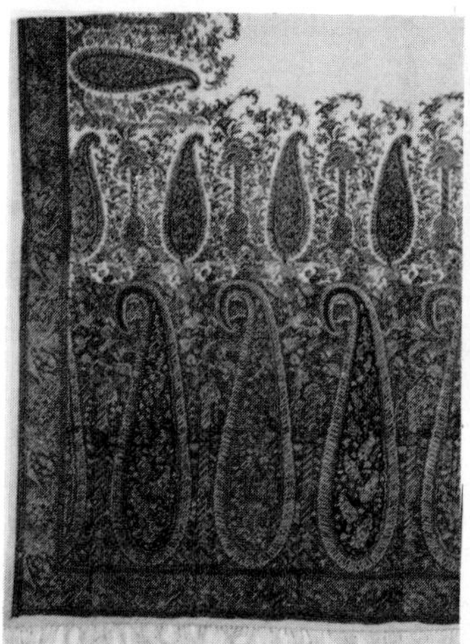

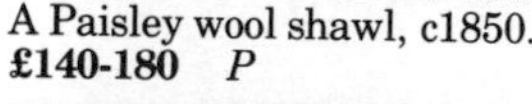

A Paisley wool shawl, c1850.
£140-180 *P*

A printed paisley shawl in fine wool, c1890.
£150-200 *LB*

Printed designs are always cheaper than woven ones.

A printed Paisley shawl, c1840.
£140-160 *P*

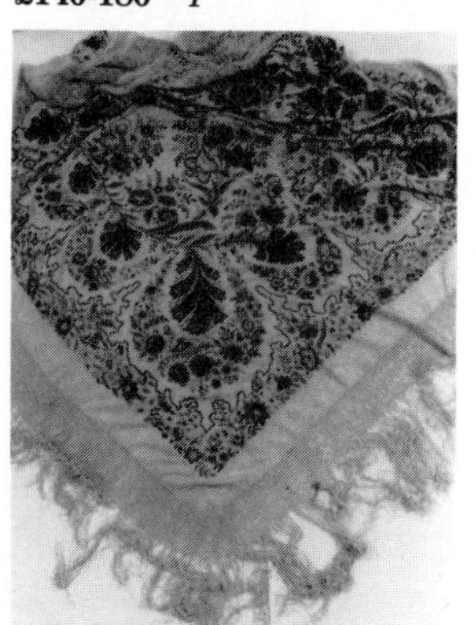

A Victorian Chinese silk embroidered shawl.
£250-350 *LB*

A small Cashmere Paisley shawl, c1860.
£200-300 *LB*

Very Collectable.

A selection of early 19thC shawls.
£50-80 each *P*

General

A wooden fabric printing block.
£8-18 *CAC*

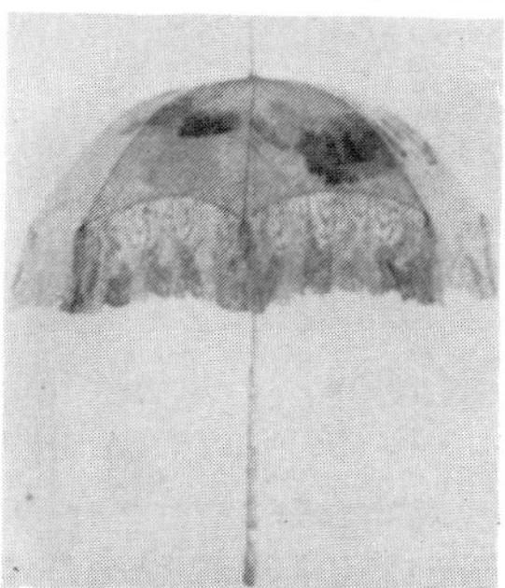

An ivory silk covered parasol, with mother-of-pearl handle, in lined box by Falize, Paris, c1900.
£300-400 *CSK*

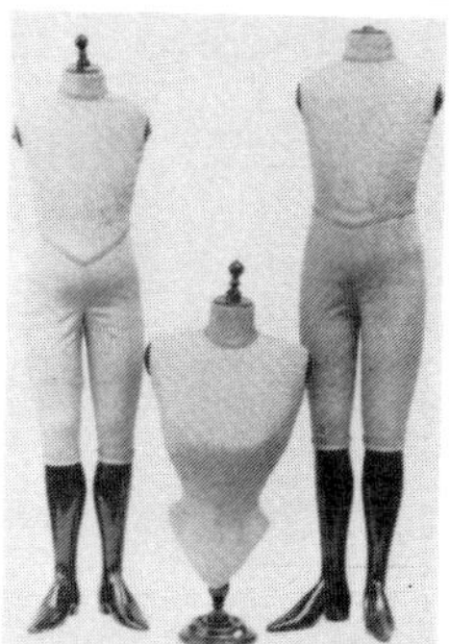

Two gentlemen's mannequins and a lady's bust, recovered, c1905.
£550-600 *C*

Tiles

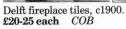

Delft fireplace tiles, c1900.
£20-25 each *COB*

A mountainous scene, 3in (8cm) wide.
£65-75 *RG*

Minton Shakespeare series, designed by Moyr Smith.
£25-35 *VF*

A Lambeth tile, Pilot washing his hands, c1730.
£55-60 *BRE*

Delft blue and white tiles, c1750.
£45-55 each *BRE*

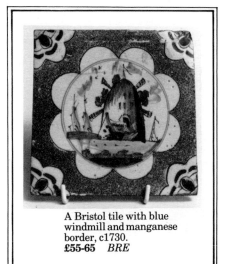

A Bristol tile with blue windmill and manganese border, c1730.
£55-65 *BRE*

Four tiles depicting Longfellow, Tennyson, Milton and Byron.
£120-150 *WRe*

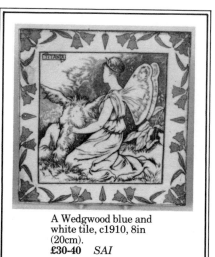

A Wedgwood blue and white tile, c1910, 8in (20cm).
£30-40 *SAI*

A framed manganese tile, possibly Lambeth, c1740.
£70-80 *BRE*

A set of French tiles, signed F. Vogler, Montereau, L.M. & Cie.
£200-250 *OMH*

A black transfer set, Minton, Hollins.
£25-30 *VF*

Usually 10 or 12 in a set.

A Bristol blue and white tile, c1730.
£60-70 *BRE*

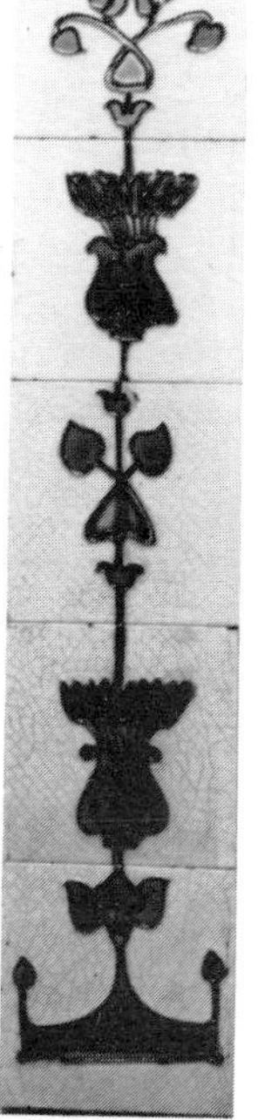

A five-tile fireplace run, Corn Bros.
£22-55 *VF*

Tins

Biscuit Tins

A Macfarlane & Lang sample tin.
£4-6 *AL*

A Huntley & Palmers biscuit tin, 12in (31cm) wide.
£6-8 *AL*

A Macfarlane & Co. tin as a writing slope.
£12-15 *AL*

A Carr & Co. Carlisle tin, c1890.
£50-75 *K*

DID YOU KNOW?
Stagecoach travellers passing Thomas Huntley's shop in Reading, purchased biscuits packed in airtight tins, hand-made by his brother Joseph, who ran an ironmonger's shop.

Medicine

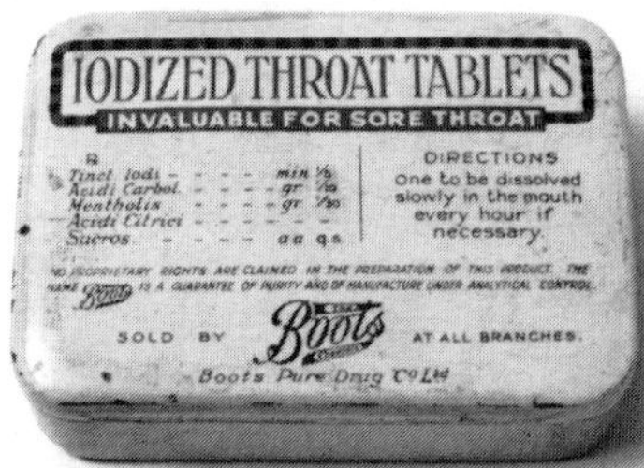

Throat tablet tin from Boots, 1940s.
£4-6 *OBS*

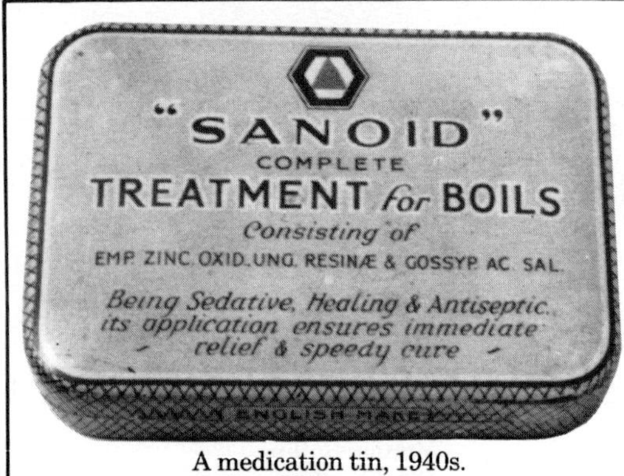

A medication tin, 1940s.
£4-6 *OBS*

Tobacco Tins

A tobacco tin, c1900.
£8-10 *OBS*

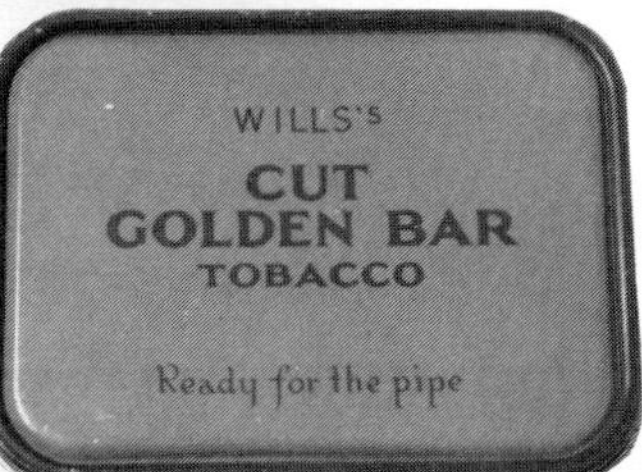

Tobacco tins, early 20thC.
£6-8 each *OBS*

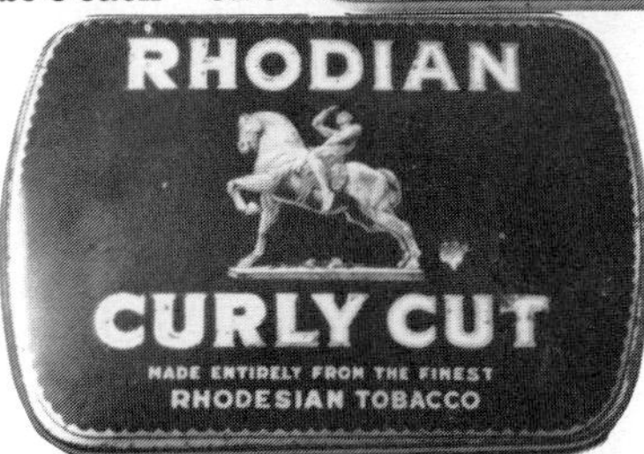

A tobacco tin, c1900. **£8-10** *OBS*

A tobacco tin, c1900.
£8-10 *OBS*

Tea

A Ridgway's Tea tin.
£5-8 *BC*

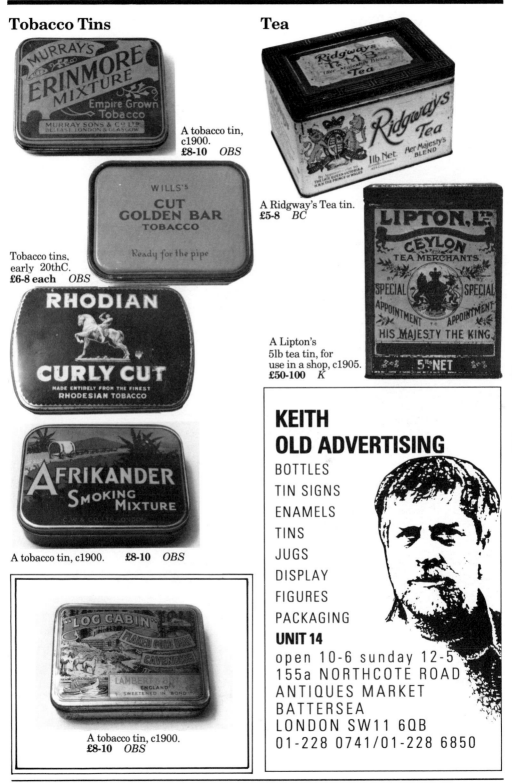

A Lipton's 5lb tea tin, for use in a shop, c1905.
£50-100 *K*

Toffee & Sweet Tins

A Macintosh's toffee tin, 10in (25cm) diam.
£10-15 *BC*

ROYAL
assorted
SUPER-KREEM
TOFFEE
ROYAL
assorted super-kreem
TOFFEE

A Sharp's toffee tin, 9½ by 7in (24 by 17.5cm).
£10-12 *AL*

A Clarnico tin, 7lb size, c1930. **£10-15** *K*

A Horner's fluorescent painted toffee tin.
£8-10 *AL*

A Thorne's Premier Toffee tin, late 1950s.
£20-30 *DIM*

A Cadbury's tin from the Bourneville factory.
50p-£1 *DH*

Sharp's toffee tins.
£4-10 each *AL*

General Tins

An Australian Olympic tin, c1956.
£8-10 *AL*

A tin decorated with strawberries, 4 by 5in (10 by 12.5cm).
£10-15 *AL*

A pair of string tins.
£30-40 each *K*

Before the days of Sellotape and plastic bags, string and brown paper ruled the retail counter and a string dispenser was essential.

A tin suitcase holding Victory V Lozenges.
£15-20 *DH*

An Edward VIII commemorative tin. **£10-15** *BC*

A Colman's mustard tin.
£22-25 *AL*

A Coronation tin, 6in (15cm) wide.
£8-10 *BC*

Various tins in the form of books.
£50-200 each *P*

DID YOU KNOW?
Queen Victoria's son-in-law, Prince Henry of Battenberg, who died in the tropics, was pickled in a tank made from biscuit tins for shipping back to England.

Tools

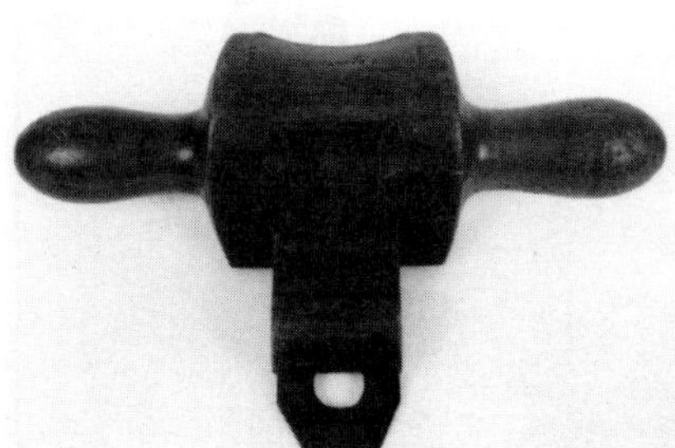

A wheelwright's jarvis, by Nurse of Maidstone, 12in (31cm) wide.
£55-65 *WO*

A millwright's fid, 19½in (49cm) long.
£80-85 *WO*

A wheelwright's auger, by Marples, 19in (48cm) long.
£25-30 *WO*

A yoke, 35in (88cm).
£55-60 *WO*

Two wheelwrights bros, 16 to 18in (40 to 45cm) long.
£15-20 each *WO*

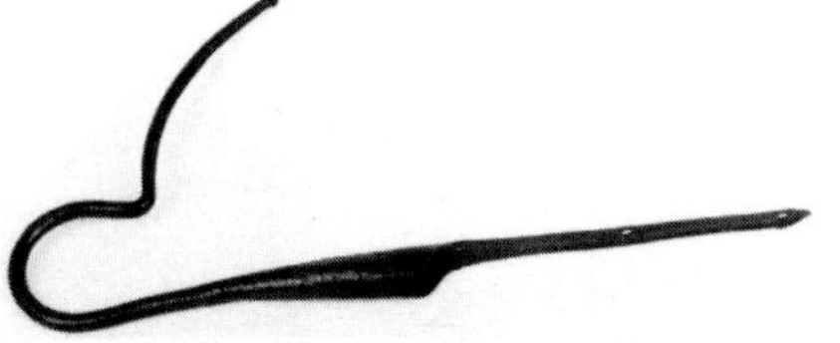

A shepherd's crook, 19in (48cm) long.
£45-50 *WO*

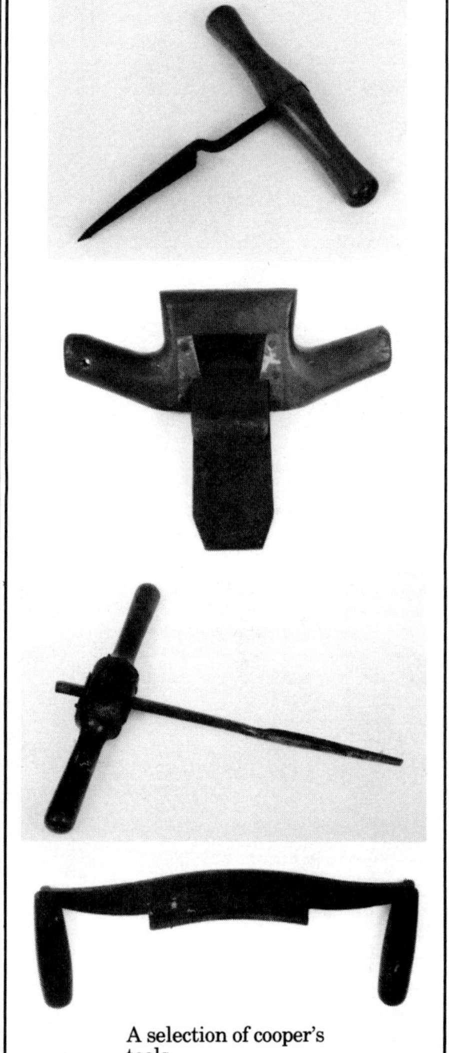

A selection of cooper's tools.
£15-35 each *WO*

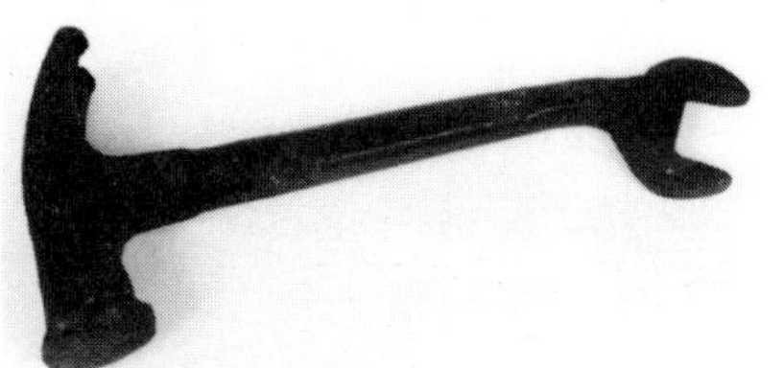

A plough hammer, 10in (25cm) long.
£15-20 *WO*

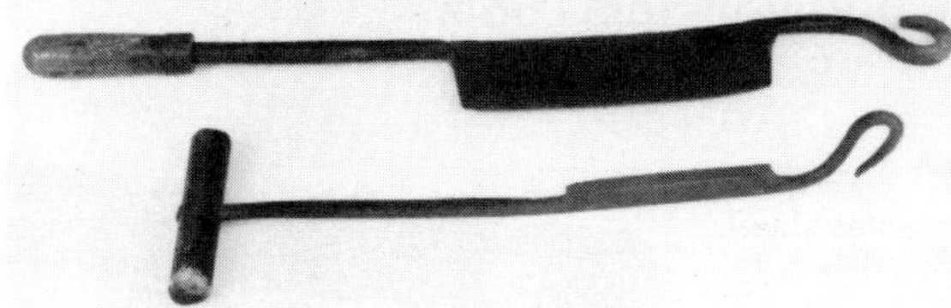

Clog-maker's bench knives, 20 to 28in (50 to 70cm) long.
£40-45 each *WO*

Ladder rounders, 9 to 10½in (23.5 to 26cm).
£20-25 each *WO*

A farmer's stook whimple.
£15-45 *WO*

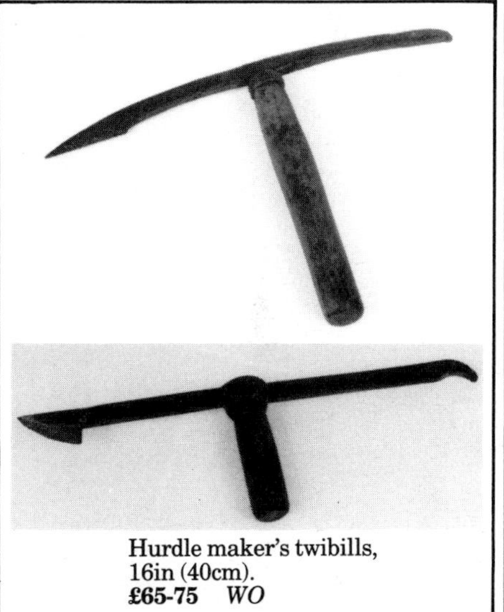

Hurdle maker's twibills, 16in (40cm).
£65-75 *WO*

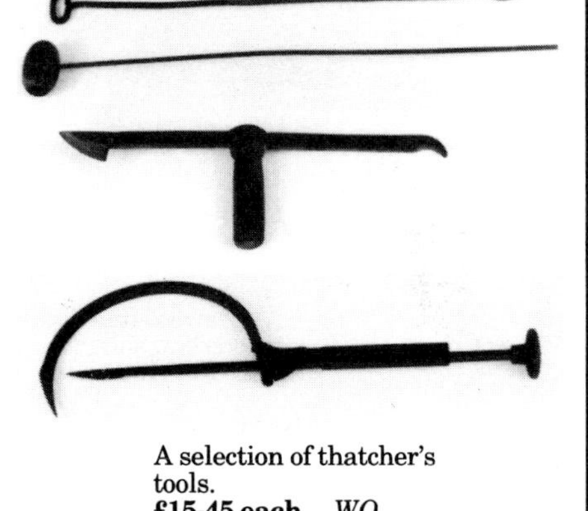

A selection of thatcher's tools.
£15-45 each *WO*

An ebony parallel rule, 15in (38cm) long.
£15-20 *WO*

A wheelwright's rounding plane, 13½in (34cm).
£25-30 *WO*

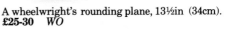

A waffle iron, 32in (80cm).
£65-70 *WO*

Woodworking Tools

A boxwood handled chisel, by I. & H. Sorby, 18in (45cm) long.
£25-30 *WO*

An early Dutch spike borer, 11in (28cm) long.
£25-30 *WO*

A bricklayer's level and plumb, 60in (150cm).
£22-25 *WO*

A pair of winced dividers, 18thC, 16in (40cm) long.
£25-30 *WO*

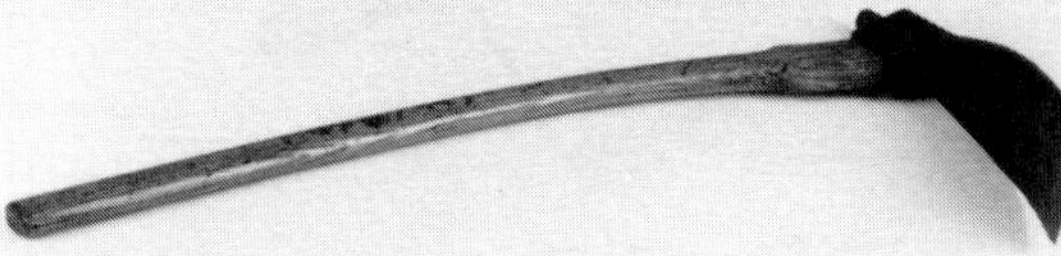

A shipwright's adze, by Gilpin, 32in (80cm) long.
£50-65 *WO*

Two early hand adze, 6½ to 10in (16 to 25cm).
£60-80 each *WO*

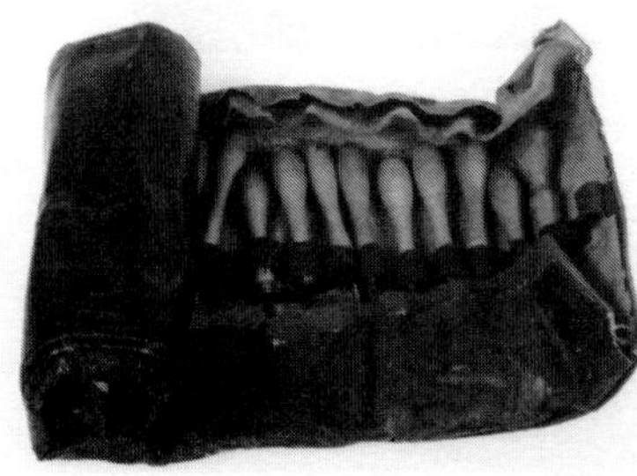

A set of 22 boxwood handled carving chisels, by C. Hill.
£220-250 *WO*

A boxwood handled beech bow saw.
£12-15 *WO*

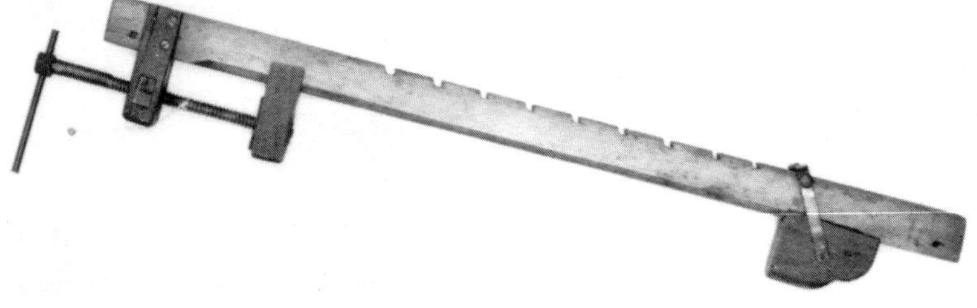

A sash cramp, in pine and oak, 19thC, 40in (100cm).
£20-25 *WO*

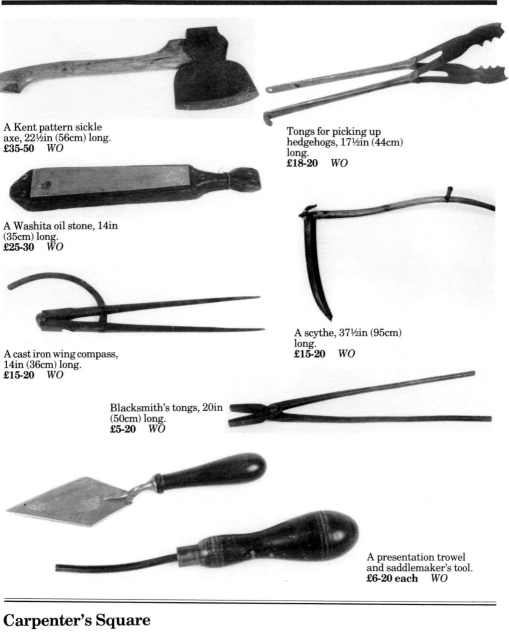

A Kent pattern sickle axe, 22½in (56cm) long.
£35-50 *WO*

Tongs for picking up hedgehogs, 17½in (44cm) long.
£18-20 *WO*

A Washita oil stone, 14in (35cm) long.
£25-30 *WO*

A scythe, 37½in (95cm) long.
£15-20 *WO*

A cast iron wing compass, 14in (36cm) long.
£15-20 *WO*

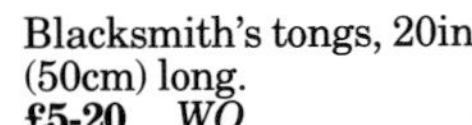

Blacksmith's tongs, 20in (50cm) long.
£5-20 *WO*

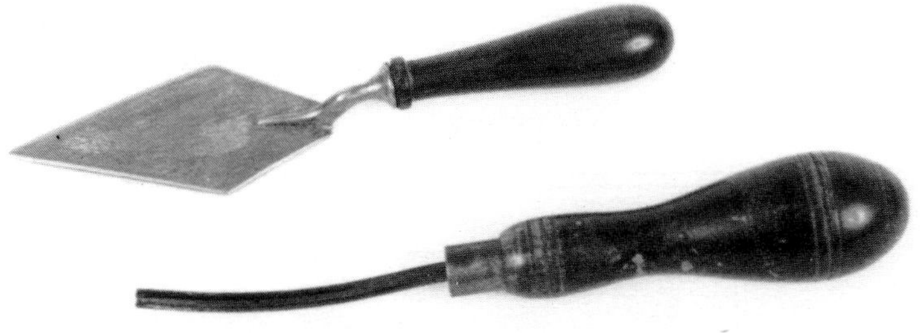

A presentation trowel and saddlemaker's tool.
£6-20 each *WO*

Carpenter's Square

A joiner's bevel in rosewood, 13½in (34cm).
£20-25 *WO*

An oval mortice gauge, 6½in (16cm) long.
£35-40 *WO*

Woodworking Planes

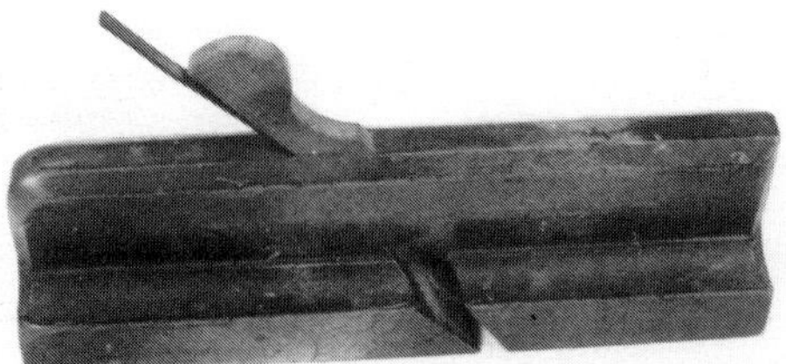

A moulding plane by Michael Saxby of Biddenden, 10in (25cm). **£350-450** *WO*

Unnamed panel raising planes, 18thC, 12in (31cm) long.
£150-200 each *WO*

A selection of English smoothing and panel planes, by Spiers & Norris, Slater, Preston.
£50-220 each *WO*

A jointing plane, early 19thC, 30in (75cm) long.
£35-45 *WO*

A 3in (8cm) complex moulding plane, by Gleave, 9½in (24cm).
£35-40 *WO*

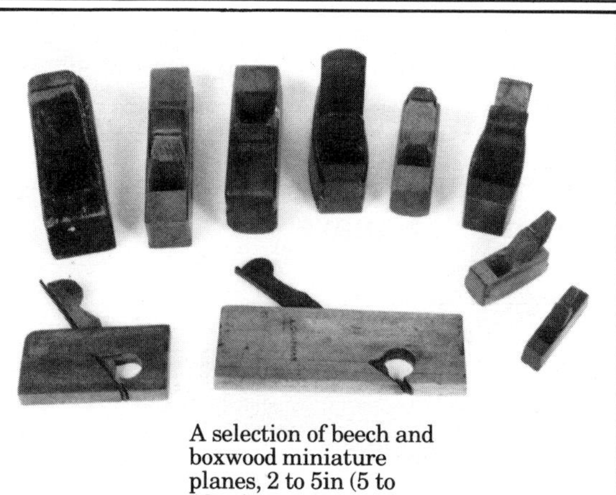

A selection of beech and boxwood miniature planes, 2 to 5in (5 to 13cm).
£20-80 each *WO*

A plough plane, 19thC, 11in (28cm) wide.
£22-32 *WO*

A bullnose plane, marked W. Haigh, 4in (10cm) wide.
£40-50 *WO*

A stop chamber plane by Nurse of Maidstone, 6in (15cm).
£80-85 *WO*

A shipwright's spar plane.
£30-35 *WO*

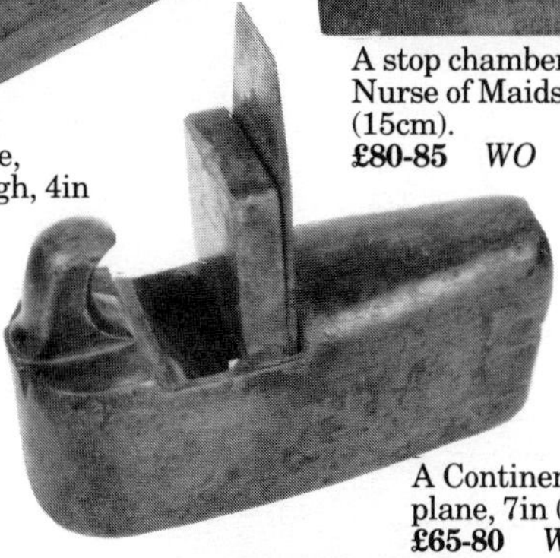

A Continental veneer plane, 7in (17cm) wide.
£65-80 *WO*

A gunmetal bullnose plane, 5in (14cm) wide.
£45-60 *WO*

A side rebate plane in mahogany, brass and steel, 7in (17cm) wide.
£60-75 *WO*

A boxwood bullnose plane, 6in (15cm) wide.
£70-80 *WO*

A gunmetal chariot plane, 8in (20cm).
£70-80 *WO*

A gunmetal ebony shoulder plane.
£75-100 *WO*

TOYS

Diecast Aircraft

A Dinky pre-war No. 60 Aeroplanes, 2nd Issue, damage.
£550-600 *CSK*

A French Dinky 60 Aeroplane gift set.
£375-425 *MIN*

Cross Reference
Aeronautica

A Dinky 61 RAF aircraft display set.
£1,500-1,650 *MIN*

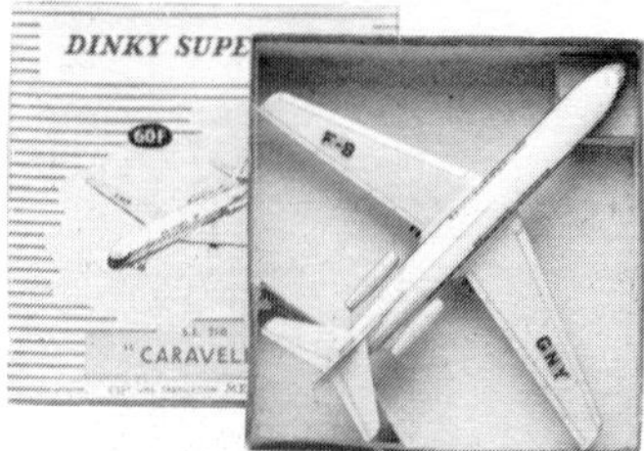

A French Dinky 60F, Caravelle Air France airliner.
£125-175 *MIN*

A French Dinky 60C Super Constellation airliner.
£125-175 *MIN*

A Dinky 704 Avro York airliner.
£125-175 *MIN*

A Dinky 998, Bristol Britannia airliner.
£125-175 *MIN*

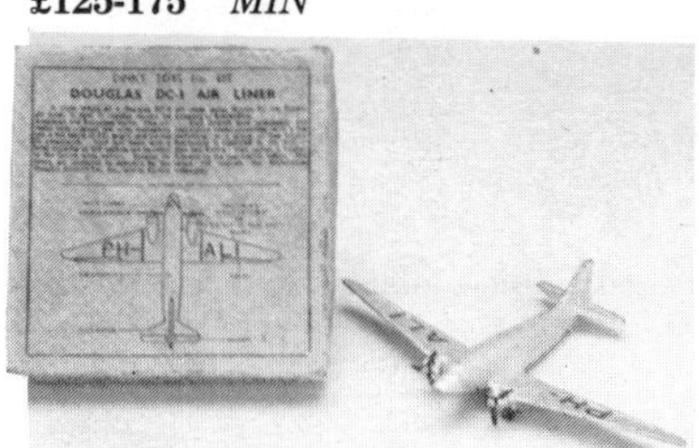

A Dinky 60T Douglas DC3 airliner.
£250-300 *MIN*

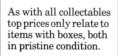

As with all collectables top prices only relate to items with boxes, both in pristine condition.

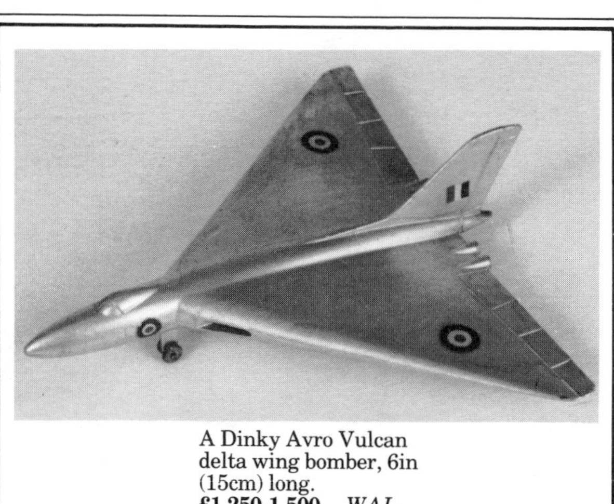

A Dinky Avro Vulcan delta wing bomber, 6in (15cm) long.
£1,250-1,500 *WAL*

Diecast Automobiles

General

Three Western models, Bluebird, Golden Arrow and 1000 H.P. Sunbeam.
£100-120 *CSK*

An Aoshin Porsche 911S.
£150-175 *MIN*

An SKK Porsche Turbo Racer.
£40-60 *MIN*

A Norev 154 Breakdown Land Rover.
£50-65 *MIN*

Two Tekno fire engines, in original boxes, damaged.
£100-120 *CSK*

Britain's Royal Artillery Mobile Howitzer unit, No. 1727, boxed.
£250-300 *SWO*

Century 21 Thunderbird 2.
£100-125 *MIN*

Mebetoys 31 Mini Cooper Rallye.
£50-65 *MIN*

Century 21 Lady Penelope's FAB 1.
£75-95 *MIN*

A Tekno 814 Jeep and Bren Gun.
£100-115 *MIN*

Corgi Toys

A Corgi 1144 Chipperfield's Circus crane truck.
£125-135 *MIN*

A Corgi 200 Ford Consul.
£50-70 *MIN*

A Corgi 234 Ford Consul Classic.
£35-45 *MIN*

A Corgi 441 VW Toblerone Van.
£75-115 *MIN*

A Corgi 201M Austin Cambridge.
£50-75 *MIN*

A Corgi 1123 Chipperfield's Circus animal cage.
£45-65 *MIN*

A Corgi 216M Austin A40.
£45-75 *MIN*

A Corgi Lotus gift set No. 37, original box, c1960s.
£60-70 *CSK*

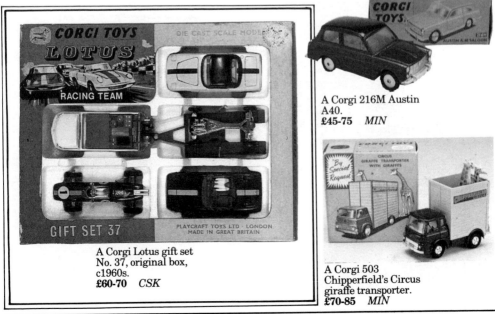

A Corgi 503 Chipperfield's Circus giraffe transporter.
£70-85 *MIN*

A Corgi 344 Ferrari Dino 206 Sport.
£25-45 *MIN*

A Corgi 256 VW 1200 East African Safari.
£75-95 *MIN*

A Corgi 474 Musical Wall's Ice Cream van.
£55-115 *MIN*

A Corgi 472 Public Address Land Rover.
£45-95 *MIN*

A Corgi GS18 Tractor and Plough.
£60-75 *MIN*

A Corgi 358 Oldsmobile H.Q. Staff Car.
£70-85 *MIN*

A Corgi 408 Bedford A.A. van.
£80-115 *MIN*

A Corgi 1118 International 6 x 6 military truck.
£80-125 *MIN*

FURTHER READING
Van Cleemput, Marcel R., *The Great Book of Corgi,* New Cavendish Books, 1989.

Dinky Toys

Three motor buses, pre-war, F-G.
£250-300 *CSK*

Gift set No. 699, Military Vehicles, E.
£250-300 *CSK*

Set No. 796 Healey Sports Boat on Trailer.
£25-35 *MIN*

Supertoys No. 930 Bedford Pallet Jekta Van, E.
£175-200 *CSK*

Set No. 291 London Bus.
£150-175 *MIN*

Supertoys No. 923 Bedford Van, G.
£600-650 *CSK*

Set No. 975 Ruston Bucyrus Excavator.
£150-175 *MIN*

A French Dinky set No. 50 Salev Crane.
£65-95 *MIN*

Set No. 308 Leyland Tractor.
£35-45 *MIN*

Set No. 292 Leyland Bus. **£75-110** *MIN*

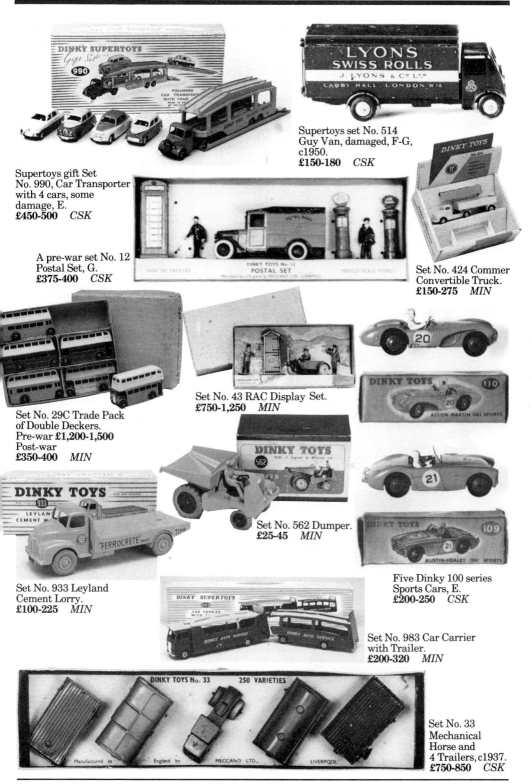

Supertoys gift Set No. 990, Car Transporter with 4 cars, some damage, E.
£450-500 *CSK*

Supertoys set No. 514 Guy Van, damaged, F-G, c1950.
£150-180 *CSK*

A pre-war set No. 12 Postal Set, G.
£375-400 *CSK*

Set No. 424 Commer Convertible Truck.
£150-275 *MIN*

Set No. 29C Trade Pack of Double Deckers.
Pre-war **£1,200-1,500**
Post-war
£350-400 *MIN*

Set No. 43 RAC Display Set.
£750-1,250 *MIN*

Set No. 562 Dumper.
£25-45 *MIN*

Five Dinky 100 series Sports Cars, E.
£200-250 *CSK*

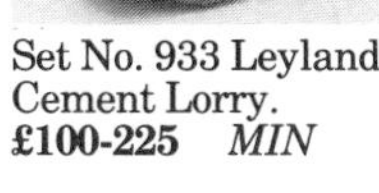

Set No. 933 Leyland Cement Lorry.
£100-225 *MIN*

Set No. 983 Car Carrier with Trailer.
£200-320 *MIN*

Set No. 33 Mechanical Horse and 4 Trailers, c1937.
£750-850 *CSK*

Set No. 651 Centurion Tank.
£35-75 *MIN*

Set No. 341 Land Rover Trailer.
£15-30 *MIN*

Pre-war series No. 33 Mechanical Horse and Trailers, G.
£220-250 *CSK*

Set No. 666 Missile Erector Vehicle.
£150-325 *MIN*

Set No. 240 Cooper Racing Car.
£20-40 *MIN*

Set No. 152 Rolls Royce Phantom V.
£35-80 *MIN*

A French Dinky set No. 899 Turntable Fire Escape.
£150-275 *MIN*

Set No. 073 Land Rover and Horse Trailer.
£45-65 *MIN*

Set No. 231 Maserati Racing Car.
£50-75 *MIN*

Set No. 076 Station Porter's Tractor and Trailer.
£40-65 *MIN*

Pre-war series No. 28/3 Fry's Van, damaged, G.
£100-120 *CSK*

Pre-war series No. 28/3 Ovaltine Van, F-G.
£150-180 *CSK*

Set No. 49 Petrol Pump Set.
£100-250 *MIN*

Set No. 785 Service Station.
£100-175 *MIN*

Set No. 323 Triple Gang Mower.
£30-45 *MIN*

Set No. 756 Double Lamp Standard.
£15-30 *MIN*

Set No. 755 Single Lamp Standard. **£12-20** *MIN*

Set No. 294 Police Vehicles.
£100-125 *MIN*

A Field Marshall Tractor.
£65-75 *MIN*

A Dinky Way set for export only, and Dinky Builda Blazing Inferno, late 1970s, E, boxes G.
£25-30 *CSK*

Matchbox Toys

Series No. 43 Shovel Dozer.
£10-15 *MIN*

Series No. 6 Quarry Trucks.
£12-40 each *MIN*

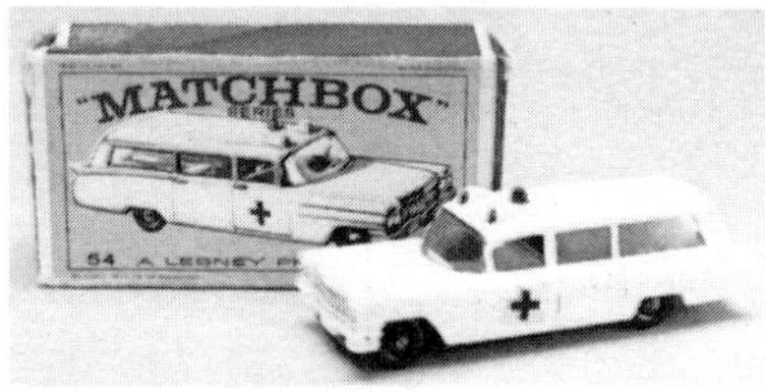

Series No. 54 Cadillac Ambulance.
£10-15 *MIN*

Series No. 15 VW Beetle Rallye.
£8-15 *MIN*

Series No. 13 BP Wrecker Truck.
£12-15 *MIN*

Series No. 8 Caterpillar Tractor.
£22-40 *MIN*

Series No. 61 BP Stalwart.
£12-15 *MIN*

Series No. 16 Trailer.
£10-15 *MIN*

Series No. 16 Shovel Dozer.
£12-15 *MIN*

A Series No. 74 Daimler Bus.
£20-25 *MIN*

Lesney Matchbox 1-75 series, various items, G-E.
£3-4 each *CSK*

Series No. 46 Pickfords Lorry.
£35-55 *MIN*

Lesney Models of Yesteryear, 1st and 2nd Issue.
£50-60 each *CSK*

Series No. 30 German Crane Truck.
£25-45 *MIN*

Series No. 51 Trailer.
£8-15 *MIN*

Series No. 57 Fire Tender.
£20-30 *MIN*

Spot-On Models

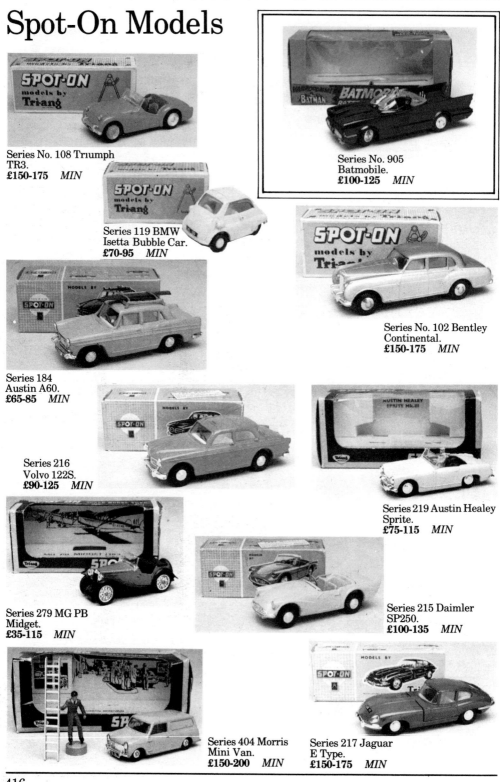

Series No. 108 Triumph TR3.
£150-175 *MIN*

Series No. 905 Batmobile.
£100-125 *MIN*

Series 119 BMW Isetta Bubble Car.
£70-95 *MIN*

Series No. 102 Bentley Continental.
£150-175 *MIN*

Series 184 Austin A60.
£65-85 *MIN*

Series 216 Volvo 122S.
£90-125 *MIN*

Series 219 Austin Healey Sprite.
£75-115 *MIN*

Series 279 MG PB Midget.
£35-115 *MIN*

Series 215 Daimler SP250.
£100-135 *MIN*

Series 404 Morris Mini Van.
£150-200 *MIN*

Series 217 Jaguar E Type.
£150-175 *MIN*

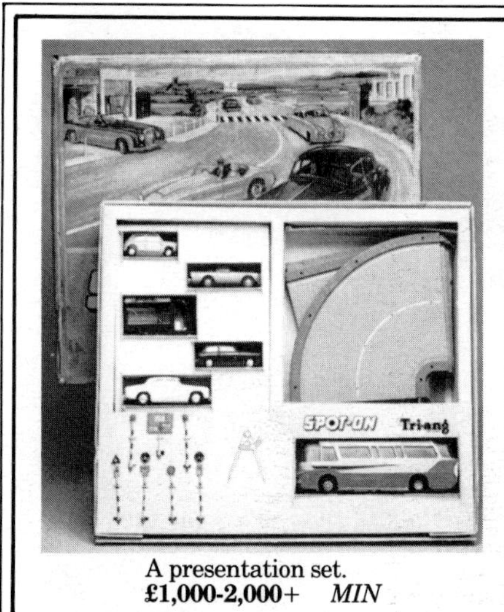

A presentation set.
£1,000-2,000+ *MIN*

Series 264 Tourist Caravan.
£50-80 *MIN*

Series 137 Massey-Ferguson tractor.
£500-775 *MIN*

Series 229 Lambretta scooter.
£100-150 *MIN*

Series 199 Meadows Frisky.
£70-95 *MIN*

Series 271 Express Dairy milk float.
£100-150 *MIN*

Series 262, Morris 1100.
£50-85 *MIN*

Series 191/1 Sunbeam Alpine.
£90-135 *MIN*

Series 193, NSU Prinz.
£70-75 *MIN*

Series 260 Royal Rolls Royce Phantom V.
£400-500 *MIN*

Miscellaneous

A Husky Mercedes 220.
£12-20 *MIN*

A Tri-ang Minic London bus, 7½in (19cm).
£35-70 *GWT*

A Tri-ang Minic 3125 P.O. telephone van.
£100-125 *MIN*

A Husky Volvo 400 tractor.
£12-25 *MIN*

A Tri-ang Minic Ford delivery van.
£300-375 *MIN*

A Tri-ang Minic tractor.
£100-120 *MIN*

A Husky Aston Martin DB6.
£15-30 *MIN*

A Tri-ang Minic 3133 Riley Police car.
£75-95 *MIN*

A Crescent 1290 Maserati racer.
£75-95 *MIN*

A Solido 167 Ferrari F1.
£25-35 *MIN*

A Crescent 1289 Gordini racer.
£65-75 *MIN*

A Solido Vanwall racer.
£75-95 *MIN*

A Crescent 1292 Jaguar D Type racer.
£65-75 *MIN*

Disney

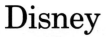

A Japanese Mickey Mouse.
£10-15 *CT*

Magnets.
£1-4 each *COB*

A back scratcher, 1970s.
£5-8 *COB*

A biscuit tin, 1936.
£20-25 *COB*

A Mickey Mouse, 1960s.
£10-15 *COB*

A plastic Donald Duck, 1930s.
£15-18 *COB*

A Mickey Mouse telephone, 1970s. **£40-45** *COB*

Goofy.
£3-4 *CT*

A Mickey Mouse puppet.
£10-15 *CT*

Cross Reference
Telephones

A pair of toothbrush holders, c1965.
£2-3 *CT*

Minnie Mouse.
£8-10 *CT*

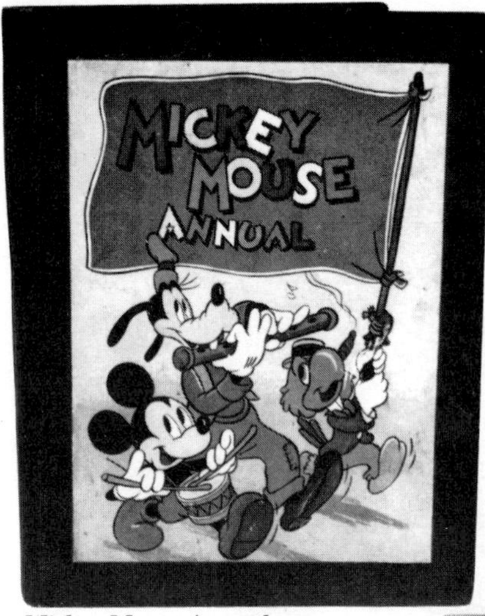

Mickey Mouse Annual, 1947.
£15-18 *COB*

A Pluto candle, 1960s.
£5-8 *COB*

A Mickey Mouse Annual, 1936.
£40-45 *COB*

A polychrome woollen rug, c1930s.
£350-400 *CSK*

A Mickey Mouse toy.
£5-6 *CT*

An Art Deco style Mickey Mouse cast iron figure, finished in gilt.
£350-400 *CSK*

Cross Reference
Children's Books

Sleeping Beauty gouache on celluloid, 1959.
£240-260 *CSK*

Snow White and the 7 Dwarfs, gouache on full celluloid applied to a wood veneer background, framed and glazed, 1937.
£1,500-2,000 *CSK*

Mickey Mouse in a Police car.
£15-20 *CT*

Mechanical Toys

A Japanese battery operated toy, The Bartender, late 1950s.
£60-80 *DOW*

A wind-up monkey.
£50-75 *PC*

A wind-up tap dancer.
£100-150 *PC*

An eating bear, 1958.
£80-130 *PC*

A knitting bear, 1958.
£80-130 *PC*

A jolly pianist.
£100-150 *PC*

A wind-up monkey organ grinder, 1965.
£60-90 *PC*

A Hobo with accordian.
£150-200 *PC*

A Wild West Rodeo, blows bubbles.
£80-130 *PC*

A wind-up papier mâché monkey, with banana.
£150-200 *PC*

Very rare.

A French wind-up drummer and a mouse, c1948.
£150-200 *PC*

A battery operated American bomber.
£80-140 *PC*

A Shoe-Shine Bear, 9in (23cm).
£100-150 *PC*

The Sneezing Bear, 9in (23cm).
£125-175 *PC*

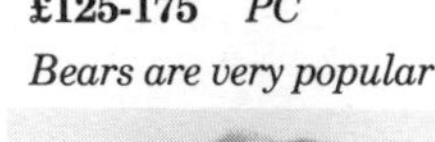

Bears are very popular.

A remote control smoking Papa bear.
£80-125 *PC*

A tin balloon blowing teddy, 11in (28cm).
£125-175 *PC*

Busy housekeeper, 9½in (24cm).
£80-100 *PC*

A drinking panda bear, 1955, 10in (25.5cm).
£130-175 *PC*

The Telephone Boss, clockwork, 10in (25.5cm).
£125-175 *PC*

A wind-up telephoning bear, 1967, 6½in (17cm).
£75-90 *PC*

A tin girl with baby carriage, 8½in (22.5cm).
£80-130 *PC*

A wind-up bear violinist, 7½in (19cm).
£80-125 *PC*

A Japanese wind-up ironing rabbit and an ice cream eating monkey, 1950s.
£50-70 each *PC*

A Japanese battery operated Pete The Parrot, by Marx, 1962.
£300-400 *PC*

A Japanese tin friction operated fire engine, c1958, 13in (33cm) long.
£75-100 *PC*

DID YOU KNOW?
Toys made of tin only are most valuable and hard to find.

A Father Christmas money bank, 11½in (29cm).
£175-250 *PC*

A wind-up trumpeter, 11in (28cm).
£80-125 *PC*

Japanese tin cowboy and Indian horse riders, by Daiya, 1967, 5½in (14cm).
£55-75 each *PC*

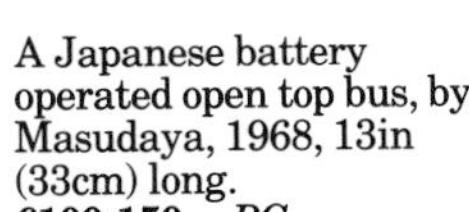

A Japanese battery operated open top bus, by Masudaya, 1968, 13in (33cm) long.
£100-150 *PC*

A Japanese tin battery operated novelty veteran car, 1960s, 9in (23cm) long.
£100-150 *PC*

The Piano Pooch, a Japanese tin wind-up toy, 7in (18cm).
£150-225 *PC*

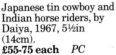

A Japanese battery operated tug boat, 1965, 13in (33cm).
£50-80 *PC*

A Japanese tin battery operated aircraft carrier with aircraft, 1960, 3in (7.5cm).
£120-150 *PC*

A Japanese battery operated army jeep, with telephone operator, 1950s, 11in (28cm).
£150-200 *PC*

A tin battery operated sniper, 14in (35.5cm) long.
£100-125 *PC*

A tin mechanical hula-hoop girl, 1960, 9in (23cm).
£75-100 *PC*

A Japanese battery operated combat jeep, by TN, 1963, 11in (28cm).
£65-95 *PC*

A Japanese tin battery operated U.S. Army tank, 11in (28cm).
£75-100 *PC*

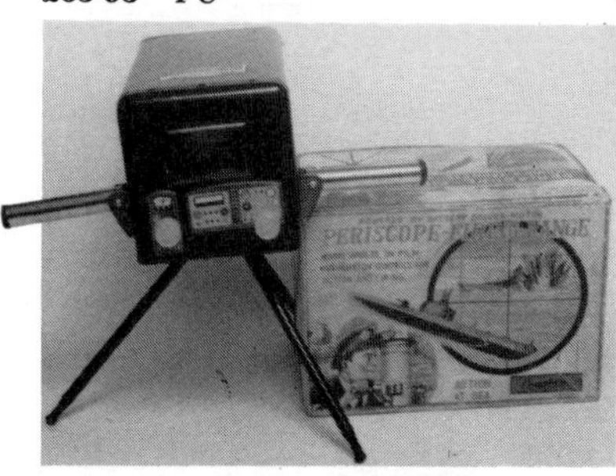

A Japanese battery operated Periscope-Firing Range, 11in (28cm) high.
£100-150 *PC*

A Japanese battery operated remote control roller skating monkey, 1960s, 9in (23cm).
£100-150 *PC*

Original colours and markings are important.

A Japanese wind-up Little Miss Hula Dancer, 1960s, 9in (23cm).
£50-75 *PC*

A Japanese battery operated police jeep, by TN, 1963, 11in (28cm).
£50-70 *PC*

Meccano

Dealer's display model, double Ferris wheel fairground ride, with electric motor, late 1970s.
£300-400 *CSK*

Display model of a roundabout, in blue and yellow, with electric motor and speaker for music, 1980s, 38in (98cm) diam.
£1,500-1,800 *CSK*

Dealer's display model with electric motor, c1960.
£400-500 *CSK*

Dealer's display model, Blackpool Tower, with electric motor operating lifts and lights, c1950.
£700-800 *CSK*

Dealer's display model, Rolling Cavalcade, with electric motor, c1950, in original packing case.
£600-700 *CSK*

Display model dockyard crane, with 4 electric motors, 1970s, 75in (190cm).
£1,500-2,000 *CSK*

An aeroplane constructor outfit No. 1, 2nd series, Monoplane Racer, c1936.
£500-600 *CSK*

A two-seater sports car, c1935, some parts missing.
£550-650 *CSK*

A No. 1 motor car constructor outfit, with motor, c1934.
£200-300 *CSK*

A Primus Engineering Motor Chassis outfit, 1920s.
£200-300 *CSK*

An aeroplane constructor outfit No. 2, 2nd series, Single Seater Fighter, No. 2 aero motor, c1932.
£400-500 *CSK*

A blue and gold Bluebird, land speed record car, c1934.
£300-400 *CSK*

An early nickel-plated 'B' type omnibus with clockwork motor, 1916 parts.
£300-400 *CSK*

Dealer's display model, Mississippi Showboat, with electric motor, late 1970s, 36in (92cm) long.
£350-450 *CSK*

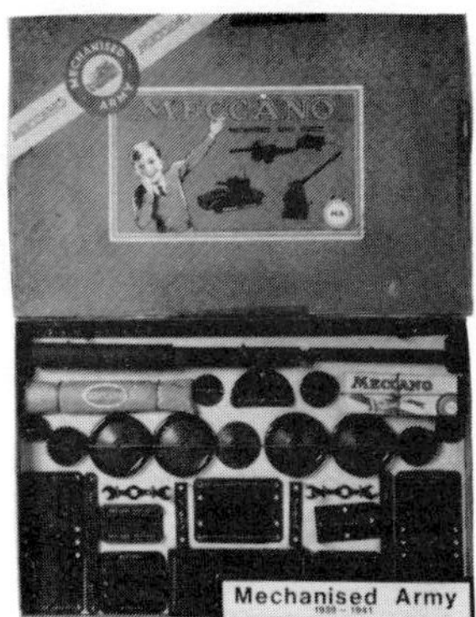

A Mechanised Army Outfit No. MA, c1939.
£1,000-1,200 *CSK*

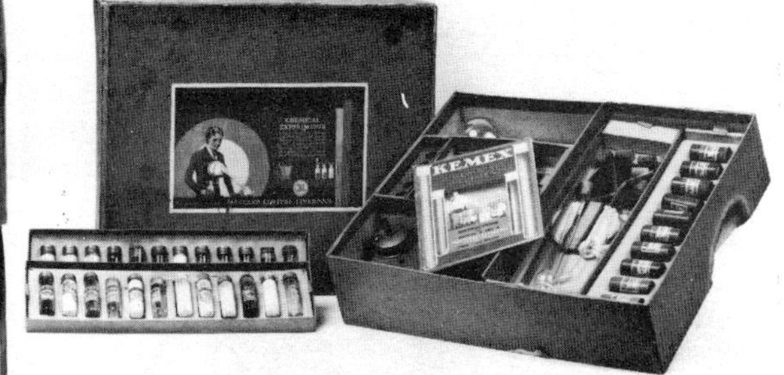

A Kemex Chemical Experiment set No. 3L, c1933, in original box.
£350-450 *CSK*

A radio crystal receiving set No. 1, c1921.
£400-500 *CSK*

A steam engine with electric motor, c1928.
£100-150 *CSK*

An Elektron Electrical Experiments Outfit, with motors, c1936.
£200-300 *CSK*

A wooden cabinet with Meccano items and instruction manuals, c1973.
£1,200-1,500 *CSK*

A live steam spirit fired vertical steam engine, c1929, in original box.
£700-800 *CSK*

Model Figures & Animals

A Dinky shepherd set.
£100-125 *MIN*

Britain's lead models.
£50-60 *WIL*

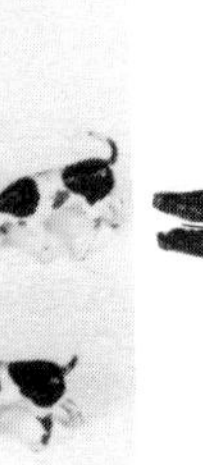

Lead animals.
£8-10 each *PW*

Huntsmen and hounds.
£40-50 *PW*

Lead animals.
£6-10 each *PW*

Lead animals.
£6-12 *PW*

Lead animals.
£3-4 each *PW*

Lead animals.
£5-6 each *PW*

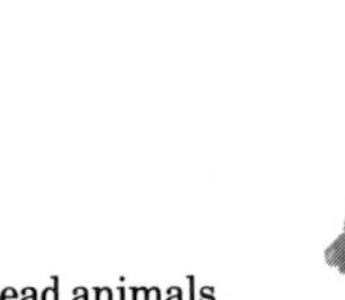

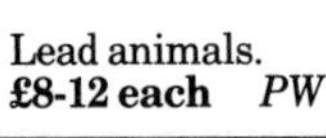

Lead animals.
£8-12 each *PW*

Britains Floral Miniature Garden.
£18-20 *GWT*

Unopened boxes are most valuable.

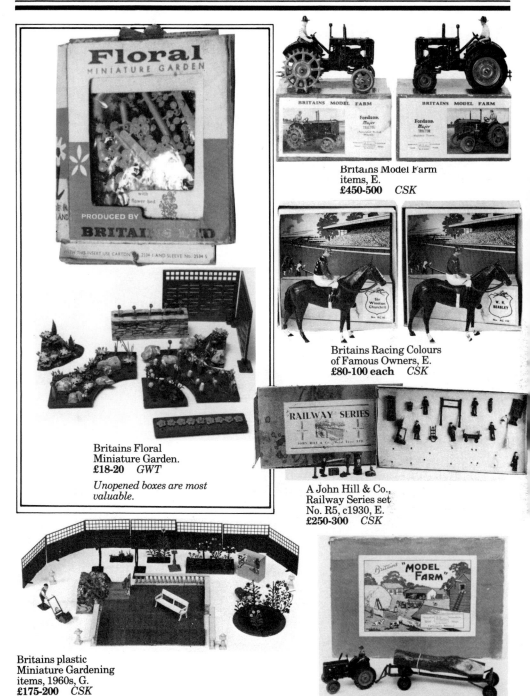

Britains Model Farm items, E.
£450-500 *CSK*

Britains Racing Colours of Famous Owners, E.
£80-100 each *CSK*

A John Hill & Co., Railway Series set No. R5, c1930, E.
£250-300 *CSK*

Britains plastic Miniature Gardening items, 1960s, G.
£175-200 *CSK*

A Britains Model Farm Set No. 146F, tractor and implements set, parts missing and replacements.
£160-180 *CSK*

A collection of hand painted carved wood and composition farm items, Bavarian, some slight damage, c1920.
£120-140 *CSK*

Model Soldiers

A gun team.
£12-15 *PW*

A hand made gun team.
£50-60 *PW*

A set of 7 German grenadiers. **£30-40** *PW*

A set of Indians.
£14-18 *PW*

Great Retreat.
£10-15 *PW*

Royal Artillery, c1759.
£15-20 *PW*

Robin Hood Series.
£2-3 each *GWT*

GLOSSARY
- M = Mint toys apparently never taken out of mint original boxes.
- E = Excellent toys with no apparent paint chipping or defects.
- G = Good toys with a minimum of scratches to the paint.
- F = Fair toys with an acceptable amount of paint damage.
- P = Poor toys probably suitable for repainting or restoration.

Seven horse guards.
£30-35 *PW*

Britains 'Swoppets', Wars of the Roses knights, plastic, 1960s.
£8-10 *GWT*

Britains for Gamages Set No. 1462 covered lorry with gun and limber, G.
£120-150 *CSK*

Courtenay No. M3 mounted figure of Thomas, Earl of Warwick, Constable of England, G.
£150-200 *CSK*

Britains Set No. 203 Royal Engineers Pontoon Section, c1924, in original Whisstock box, G.
£250-300 *CSK*

Courtney & Doran for Azitis Robin Hood boxed set, G.
£150-180 *CSK*

Fifteen Elastolin 70mm scale S.A. figures, c1933, G-E.
£300-350 *CSK*

A Courtenay No. 8A foot figure of the Duke of Athens, signed, G-E.
£200-300 *CSK*

A Courtenay No. 6A figure of the Earl of Sancerre, signed, G-E.
£400-500 *CSK*

Lineol 70mm scale Spanish Infantry soldiers, c1938, G.
£150-200 *CSK*

A Heyde 52mm scale set of figures, The Triumph of Germanicus, c1910, G-E, box damaged.
£150-200 *CSK*

Two Elastolin 70mm scale German Kriegsmarine figures, damaged, c1938, G.
£50-80 *CSK*

Britains set No. 12, 11th Hussars, c1930.
£200-300 *P*

Britains set No. 315, 10th Hussars.
£150-250 *CSK*

A selection of Elastolin soldiers. **£350-400** *CSK*

Model Ships

A Hess lithographed tinplate battleship, with clockwork mechanism and 4 submarines, parts missing, c1912.
£90-100 *CSK*

A Hornby speedboat No. 2, c1936.
£90-100 *CSK*

A Sutcliffe's live steam spirit fired battleship, c1928, 16½in (42cm) long.
£200-250 *CSK*

A Japanese boxed set of composition battleships.
£200-250 *P*

An early Japanese composition and painted model of Dreadnought, c1905, 5in (13cm) long.
£160-180 *CSK*

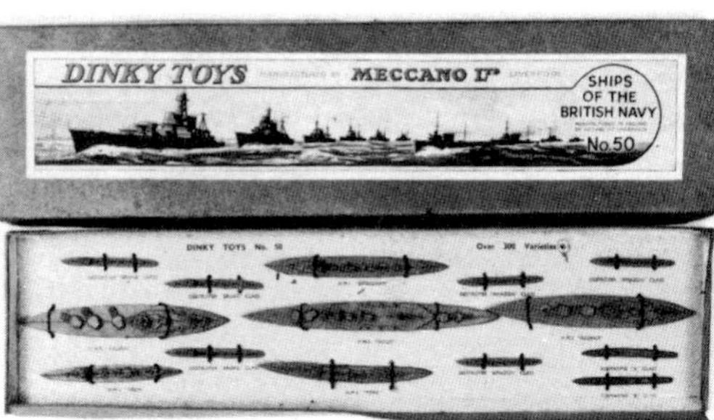

A Dinky pre-war set No. 50, Ships of the British Navy, damaged, c1937, F-G.
£100-120 *CSK*

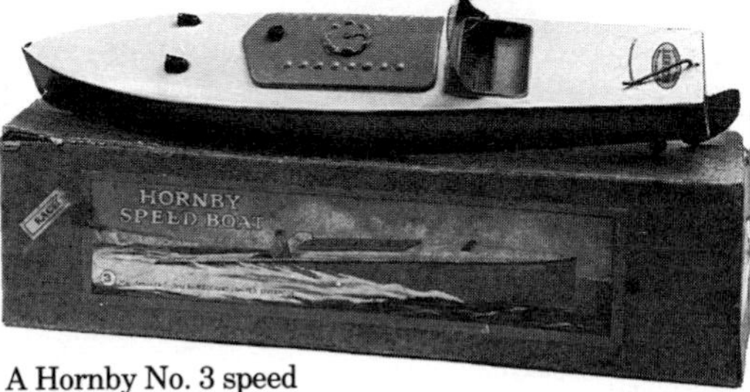

A Hornby No. 3 speed boat, c1938.
£350-400 *CSK*

Model Trains

A cast iron painted floor train, comprising a 4–4–0 locomotive and tender, King Edward, by Wallwork, c1892.
£100-150 *CSK*

An export 3-rail gauge 0 electric model of the S.A.R. 4–4–2 No. E.320 locomotive and tender No. 4472, Flying Scotsman, lacking bulb.
£400-500 *CSK*

A 3-rail gauge 0 electric model of the S.R. 4–4–2 No. E.320 locomotive and tender No. 850, Lord Nelson, lacking bulb.
£350-450 *CSK*

An export 3-rail gauge 0 electric model of the S.A.S. 4–4–2 No. E.320 locomotive and tender No. 6100, Royal Scot.
£300-400 *CSK*

Five gauge 0 S.A.R. and S.A.S. vans.
£350-400 *CSK*

An export gauge 0 S.A.S. clockwork model of the 4–4–2 No. 2 special tank locomotive and a S.A.S. No. 2 special tender, rear panel missing.
£350-450 *CSK*

A gauge 0 clockwork model of the L.N.E.R. 4–4–0 No. 2 special locomotive No. 234 Yorkshire and No. 2 special tender, in original box.
£600-700 *CSK*

A rare 3-rail gauge 0 electric model of the 0–4–0 No. LE.220 locomotive No. 10655, finished in green livery, c1934, bulb missing.
£1,500-1,750 *CSK*

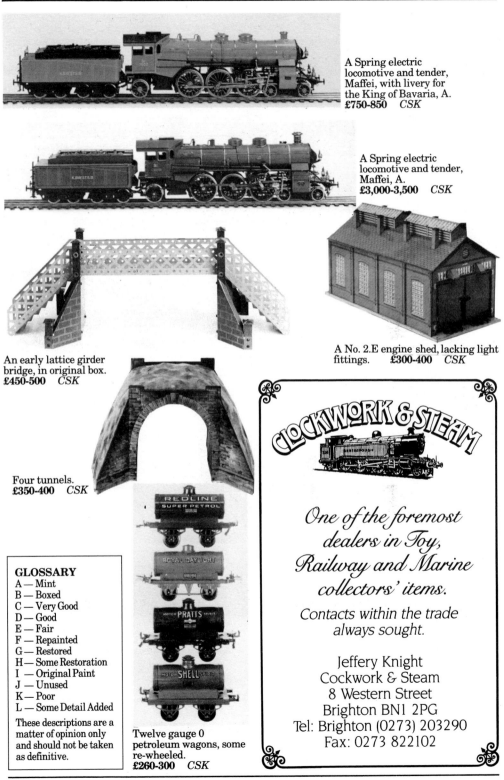

A Spring electric locomotive and tender, Maffei, with livery for the King of Bavaria, A.
£750-850 *CSK*

A Spring electric locomotive and tender, Maffei, A.
£3,000-3,500 *CSK*

An early lattice girder bridge, in original box.
£450-500 *CSK*

A No. 2.E engine shed, lacking light fittings. **£300-400** *CSK*

Four tunnels.
£350-400 *CSK*

Twelve gauge 0 petroleum wagons, some re-wheeled.
£260-300 *CSK*

GLOSSARY
A — Mint
B — Boxed
C — Very Good
D — Good
E — Fair
F — Repainted
G — Restored
H — Some Restoration
I — Original Paint
J — Unused
K — Poor
L — Some Detail Added

These descriptions are a matter of opinion only and should not be taken as definitive.

A Lionel electric standard gauge locomotive, tender and lumber wagon, c1927, D, I.
£350-450 *CSK*

A BLZ French electric train, c1948, D, I.
£350-450 *CSK*

Japanese battery- operated toys, A. **£250-300** *CSK*

A Spring electric DB shunter, A.
£500-600 *CSK*

A Carette gauge 1 steam locomotive and tender, c1905, C, G.
£2,000-2,500 *CSK*

A Lionel electric standard gauge locomotive and box cars, c1926, D, I.
£650-750 *CSK*

Three Japanese toys, 2 battery operated and one push-and-go, A to C.
£150-200 *CSK*

Two Japanese K.T.M. passenger cars, A.
£200-250 *CSK*

A Rossignol, Paris, tram engine clockwork carpet toy, copper plated tinplate, mechanism missing, c1890, E.
£500-600 *CSK*

Two freight cards, one by Darstead, A.
£100-150 *CSK*

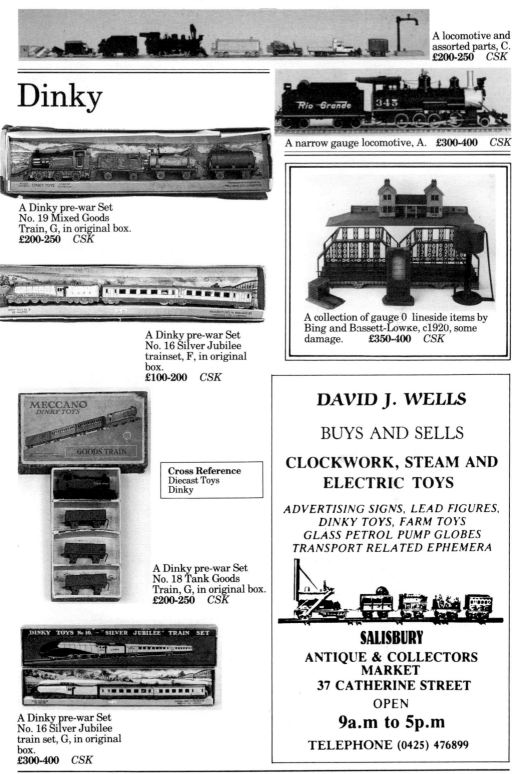

A locomotive and assorted parts, C.
£200-250 *CSK*

Dinky

A Dinky pre-war Set No. 19 Mixed Goods Train, G, in original box.
£200-250 *CSK*

A narrow gauge locomotive, A. **£300-400** *CSK*

A collection of gauge 0 lineside items by Bing and Bassett-Lowke, c1920, some damage. **£350-400** *CSK*

A Dinky pre-war Set No. 16 Silver Jubilee trainset, F, in original box.
£100-200 *CSK*

Cross Reference
Diecast Toys
Dinky

A Dinky pre-war Set No. 18 Tank Goods Train, G, in original box.
£200-250 *CSK*

A Dinky pre-war Set No. 16 Silver Jubilee train set, G, in original box.
£300-400 *CSK*

Bassett-Lowke

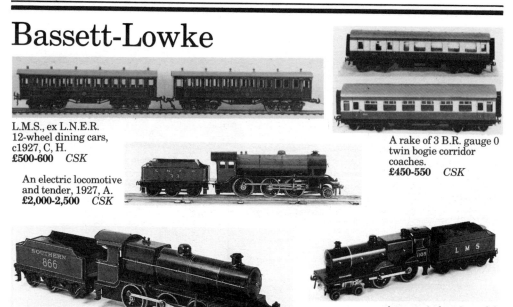

L.M.S., ex L.N.E.R. 12-wheel dining cars, c1927, C, H.
£500-600 *CSK*

An electric locomotive and tender, 1927, A.
£2,000-2,500 *CSK*

A rake of 3 B.R. gauge 0 twin bogie corridor coaches.
£450-550 *CSK*

A clockwork gauge 0 model of the S.R. 2–6–0 locomotive and tender No. 866, c1931, with box of Mogul 2–6–0 track.
£400-500 *CSK*

A gauge 0 electric model of the L.M.S. 4–4–0 locomotive and tender No. 1180, c1930.
£350-400 *CSK*

Gauge 0 railway accessories, c1935, E, I.
£400-500 *CSK*

A clockwork gauge 0 model of the L.N.E.R. 2–6–0 Mogul locomotive and tender No. 33, original box.
£300-350 *CSK*

A live steam spirit fired L.M.S. Mogul locomotive construction set, with 1954 catalogue.
£400-500 *CSK*

Two gauge 0 S.R. twin bogie coaches, in original paintwork.
£250-350 *CSK*

A 3-rail gauge 0 electric model of the L.M.S. 4–6–2 locomotive No. 6201, Princess Elizabeth, c1937, rusted.
£600-700 *CSK*

A gauge 0 live steam spirit fired model of the G.W.R. 2–6–0 locomotive and tender No. 4331, lacking front wheels.
£200-300 *CSK*

A gauge 0 live steam spirit fired model of the B.R. 4–4–0 Enterprise locomotive and tender No. 62759, slight damage.
£450-550 *CSK*

Three Carette for Bassett-Lowke G.W.R. coaches, c1912, E, H.
£700-800 *CSK*

Two gauge 2 lithographed and painted L.N.W.R. refrigerator vans, slight damage.
£120-150 *CSK*

A Euston-Watford electric 3-car set with extra coach, D to E, I.
£1,000-1,200 *CSK*

A gauge 1 live steam spirit fired model of the M.R. 4–4–0 locomotive and tender No. 1000, restored.
£600-700 *CSK*

Three S.R. coaches, C, H.
£800-900 *CSK*

Carette/Bassett-Lowke L.N.W.R. and L.M.S. 12-wheel dining cars, c1933, D, H.
£250-350 *CSK*

Bing

The Bing Company was founded in Nuremberg in 1863 by Adolf and Ignaz Bing. Bing were keen competitors of Märklin but by the 1930s, had virtually been overtaken by other manufacturers. Bing enjoyed a close relationship with the British company Bassett-Lowke making toys to order.

A gauge 1 clockwork model of the M.R. 4–4–0 locomotive and 6 wheel tender No. 2631, repainted and damaged, c1902.
£350-450 *CSK*

An observation car, c1902, D, I.
£1,750-2,000 *CSK*

A gauge 1 live steam spirit fired model of the L.N.W.R. 0–4–0 locomotive and tender No. 1902, damaged and repaired, c1912.
£250-350 *CSK*

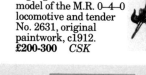

One special order passenger car and a dining car, c1924 and 1904, C, I.
£550-650 *CSK*

A gauge 1 clockwork model of the M.R. 0–4–0 locomotive and tender No. 2631, original paintwork, c1912.
£200-300 *CSK*

Six wagons, C, H.
£600-700 *CSK*

A Bing for Bassett-Lowke gauge 2 clockwork model of the G.W.R. 4–4–0 locomotive and tender No. 3410, Sydney, damaged, c1912.
£1,300-1,500 *CSK*

A steam locomotive and tender, 1912, C, I.
£1,800-2,000 *CSK*

A passenger car, c1905, C, I.
£700-800 *CSK*

A steam locomotive, C, H.
£350-450 *CSK*

Two 1921 series teak coaches, and a Bassett-Lowke coach, c1926, C, I.
£450-550 *CSK*

A hand painted gauge 1 3-rail electric model of the Canadian Pacific 4–4–4 locomotive, some chipping, c1926.
£400-500 *CSK*

A Bing for Bassett-Lowke gauge 1 clockwork model of the L. & N.W.R. 4–4–2 Precursor tank locomotive No. 44, some damage, c1912.
£500-600 *CSK*

A gauge 0 lithographed clockwork G.W.R. trainset of 0–4–0 locomotive and tender, with 3 coaches and track, slight damage, c1908.
£180-200 *CSK*

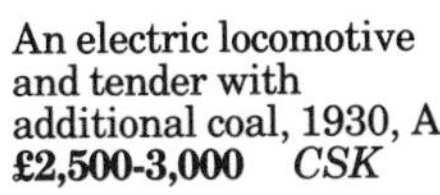

An electric locomotive and tender with additional coal, 1930, A.
£2,500-3,000 *CSK*

A Bing for Bassett-Lowke 3-rail gauge 1 electric model of the G.C.R. 4–6–0 locomotive and 6 wheel tender, No. 423, Sir Sam Fay, in original paintwork, c1914.
£2,000-2,500 *CSK*

Hornby

The Hornby Company, manufacturers of Meccano and other toys, produced their first clockwork trainset in 1920. Hornby trainsets are rapidly appreciating and proving to be a very good investment at the moment.

A Hornby Dublo pre-war 3-rail EDL7 S.R. 0–6–2 tank locomotive No. 2594, in original box, c1938.
£600-650 *CSK*

A Hornby gauge 0 clockwork 4–4–2 locomotive and tender, boxed.
£400-500 *Bon*

A collection of Hornby-Dublo catalogues, leaflets and advertising signs.
£600-650 *CSK*

Nine Hornby Books of Trains, some incomplete.
£800-900 *CSK*

A gauge 0 clockwork No. E310 No. 3 Flying Scotsman trainset, in original box.
£450-500 *CSK*

A gauge 0 early clockwork LNER No. 2 goods set, in original box, c1926.
£550-650 *CSK*

Three lineside items, original boxes.
£180-200 *CSK*

A gauge 0 clockwork model of the S.A.R. 0–4–0 No. 1 tank locomotive, No. 7206, in original box, c1926.
£300-350 *CSK*

A Hornby gauge 0 clockwork model of the S.R. 4–4–2 No. 2 special tank locomotive No. E492, worn.
£200-250 *CSK*

A Hornby lattice girder bridge, c1925.
£400-450 *CSK*

Six early Hornby gauge 0 wagons, including a LNER snow plough, c1923.
£600-650 *CSK*

A rake of 3 Hornby gauge 0 twin bogie No. 2 Pullman coaches, c1922.
£350-400 *CSK*

A rake of 3 gauge 0 L.N.E.R. No. 2 corridor coaches, in original boxes.
£600-650 *CSK*

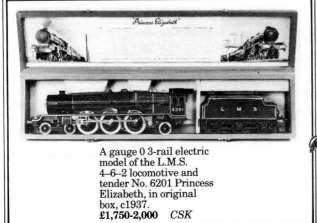

A gauge 0 3-rail electric model of the L.M.S. 4–6–2 locomotive and tender No. 6201 Princess Elizabeth, in original box, c1937.
£1,750-2,000 *CSK*

Nine Hornby gauge 0 rolling stock items, in original boxes.
£900-1,000 *CSK*

Märklin

Theodore Märklin started making toys in 1859 and when he died in 1866, his widow and sons continued the business. They did not make toy trains until about 1891. The company then went from strength to strength and is still renowned for products of extremely high quality and great variety, especially the range of track-side items available, some of which are shown on page 447.

A Märklin gauge 1 clockwork model of the MR. 2–4–4 'flatiron' tank locomotive, slight wear and rust, c1913. **£1,000-1,200** *CSK*

A Märklin gauge 0 hand painted twin bogie hospital coach, No. 1828, c1908.
£1,800-2,000 *CSK*

An early Märklin repair wagon No. 1827, c1906.
£400-450 *CSK*

A Mendosa for Märklin, gauge 0 twin bogie restaurant car, slightly chipped, c1933.
£300-350 *CSK*

A Märklin steam L.N.E.R./G.N.R., Pacific locomotive, The Great Bear, No. 4021, C, I.
£2,500-3,000 *CSK*

A Märklin steam locomotive and tender No. 4021, 1929, A, F, G.
£1,750-2,000 *CSK*

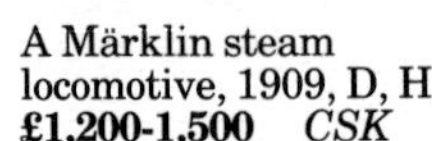

A Märklin steam locomotive, c1913, A, I, J, and tender G, J.
£800-900 *CSK*

A Märklin steam locomotive, 1909, D, H.
£1,200-1,500 *CSK*

A Märklin gauge 1 clockwork model of the L.B.S.C. 4–4–2 tank locomotive, No. 21, repainted, c1921.
£500-550 *CSK*

A Märklin steam Flying Scotsman, restored by Horst Reichert, C, F.
£2,000-2,500 *CSK*

A Märklin electric locomotive and tender, D, I.
£250-300 *CSK*

A Märklin steam locomotive and tender, c1930, G, F.
£4,000-4,500 *CSK*

A Märklin steam locomotive, c1910, A, J, tender by Bub, A.
£650-700 *CSK*

A Märklin clockwork locomotive and tender, c1930, E, H.
£200-250 *CSK*

A Märklin 00/H0 gauge electric Commodore Vanderbilt, part c1937, A to C, I.
£3,000-3,500 *CSK*

A Märklin Kaiser's saloon, c1909, C, I.
£3,000-3,500 *CSK*

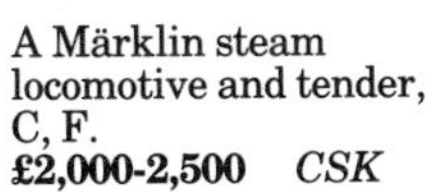

A Märklin electric locomotive and tender, c1904, D, I.
£2,000-2,500 *CSK*

One of the first Märklin electric locomotives.

A Märklin steam locomotive and tender, C, F.
£2,000-2,500 *CSK*

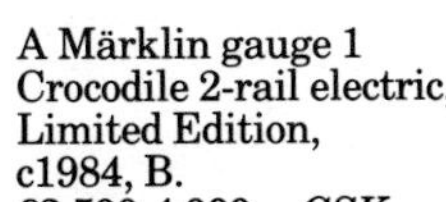

A Märklin gauge 1 Crocodile 2-rail electric, Limited Edition, c1984, B.
£3,500-4,000 *CSK*

Two Märklin rack railway passenger cars, C, I.
£1,200-1,500 *CSK*

A Märklin gauge 1 3-rail electric model of the Paris-Orleans Railway, E, I, electric locomotive, lacking bulbs, 1920s. **£400-450** *CSK*

A rake of 3 Märklin gauge 1 twin bogie coaches, Mitropa No. 789 Speisewagon and a Schlafwagen, 1920s.
£250-300 *CSK*

A Märklin gauge 1 live steam spirit fired model of the G.W.R. 4–6–2 Pacific locomotive and bogie tender No. 11, The Great Bear, repainted and worn, c1909.
£850-1,000 *CSK*

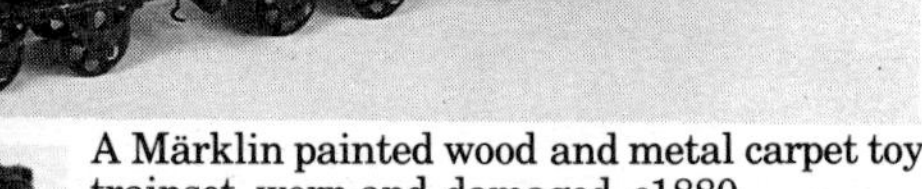

A Märklin painted wood and metal carpet toy trainset, worn and damaged, c1880.
£400-450 *CSK*

A Märklin electric locomotive and tender, c1937, C, H.
£350-400 *CSK*

Three Märklin wagons, 1904-09, C, I.
£550-600 *CSK*

Carette/Märklin assorted wagons, c1912, D, I, H.
£350-400 *CSK*

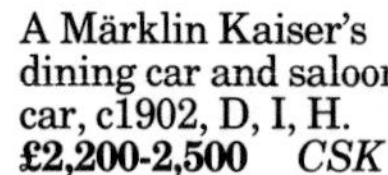

A Märklin Kaiser's dining car and saloon car, c1902, D, I, H.
£2,200-2,500 *CSK*

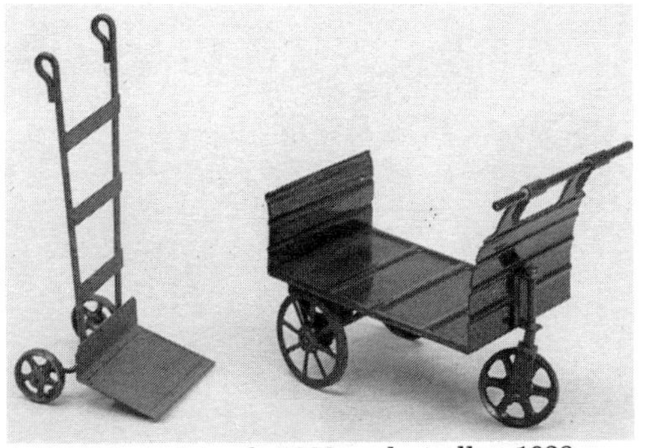

A Märklin sack truck, 1909, and a trolley, 1928, A to C, I. **£200-250** *CSK*

A Märklin automatic level crossing with electric lighting, c1935, C, I.
£500-550 *CSK*

A Märklin gauge 1 bridge, c1925, C, H, I.
£350-400 *CSK*

A Märklin signal box, c1920-30, C, I.
£400-450 *CSK*

Heyde for Märklin hand painted cast lead German sailors, c1912, D.
£1,400-1,600 *CSK*

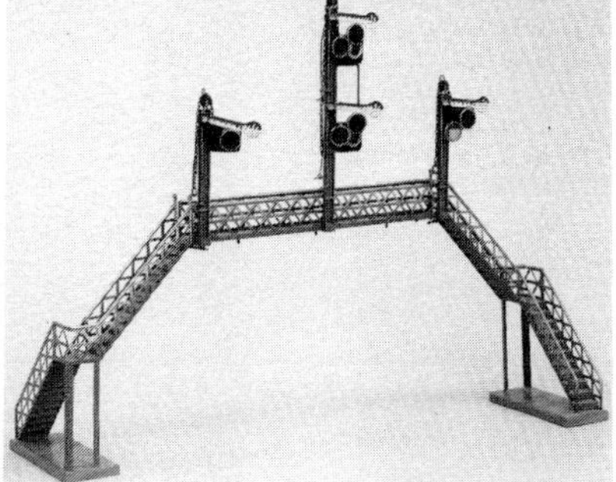

A Märklin bridge with signals, c1905, C, I.
£550-600 *CSK*

A Märklin automatic barrier, c1920, C, I.
£250-300 *CSK*

Robots

A printed and painted tinplate battery operated Mr Patrol, by Horikawa, 1960s, G.
£230-250 *CAm*

A printed and painted tinplate battery operated Fighting Spaceman, by Horikawa, 1960s, G.
£230-250 *CAm*

A printed and painted tinplate Husler, by Horikawa, 1960s, G.
£150-180 *CAm*

A printed and painted tinplate battery operated Dino Robot, by Horikawa, 1960s, E.
£550-650 *CAm*

A printed and painted tinplate and plastic battery operated Space Explorer, by Horikawa, 1960s, E.
£200-250 *CAm*

A printed and painted tinplate battery operated Super Robot, Japanese, 1960s, E.
£300-400 *CAm*

A printed and painted tinplate and plastic battery operated Television Spaceman, by Alps, Japanese, 1950s, G.
£600-700 *CAm*

A polychrome moulded plastic battery operated Mike Robot, by Tomy, Japanese, 1960s, F.
£150-200 *CAm*

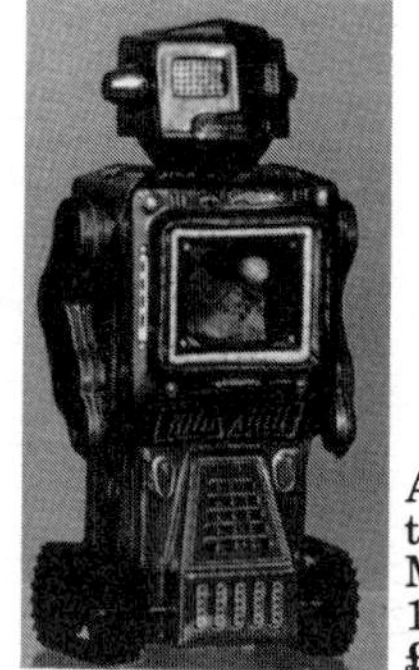

A printed and painted tinplate battery operated Mars King, by Horikawa, 1960s, E.
£200-250 *CAm*

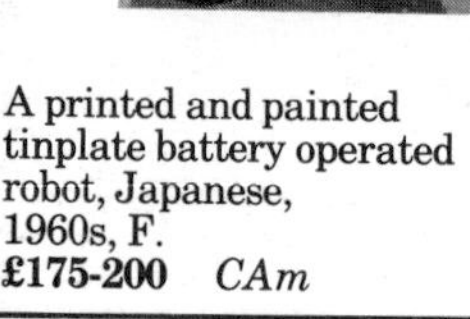

A printed and painted tinplate battery operated robot, Japanese, 1960s, F.
£175-200 *CAm*

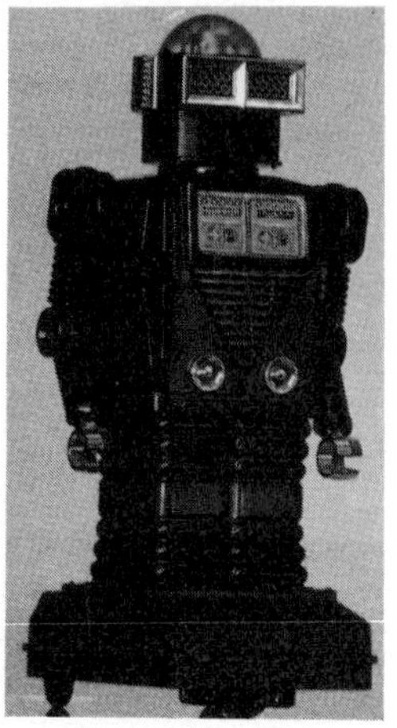

A Japanese coloured plastic battery operated Laughing Robot, by Waco, 1960s, E.
£225-250 *CAm*

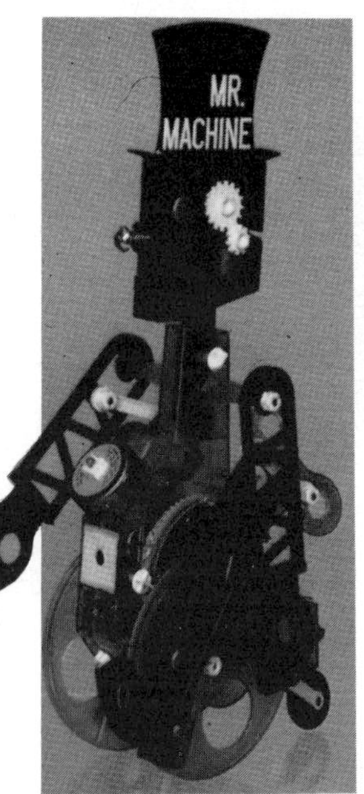

A moulded plastic clockwork mechanism, Mr Machine, by Ideal Toy Corporation, America, 1960s, mechanism faulty.
£400-500 *CAm*

A polychrome coloured plastic battery operated Laughing Clown, Japanese, late 1960s, G.
£300-400 *CAm*

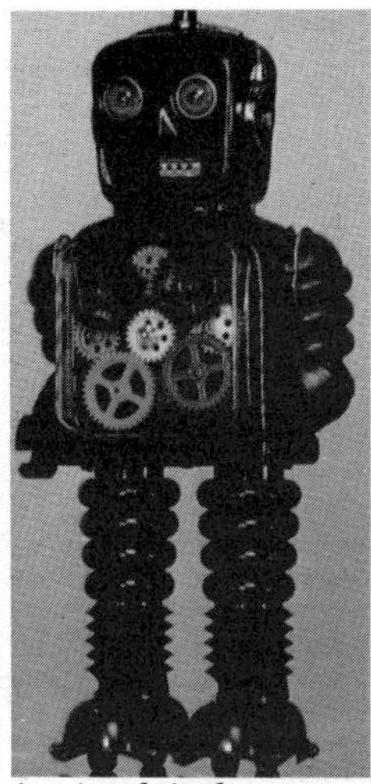

A painted tinplate battery operated Blink-A-Gear, by Taiyo, 1960s, E.
£300-400 *CAm*

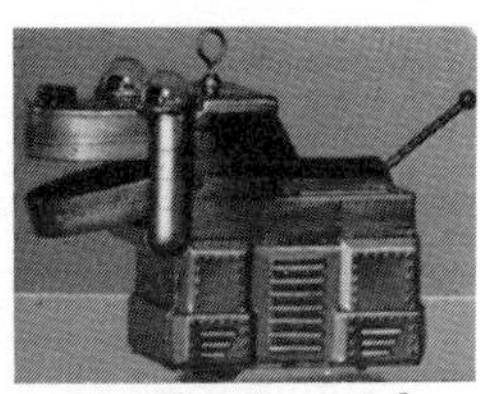

A printed and painted tinplate clockwork Space Dog, by Yoshiya, 1960s, G.
£700-800 *CAm*

A moulded coloured plastic battery operated Robot Jefe, by J. S. Aludes, Spanish, 1970s, E.
£500-600 *CAm*

A printed tinplate and plastic battery operated Space Robot, by Nomura, Japanese, 1960s, G.
£500-600 *CAm*

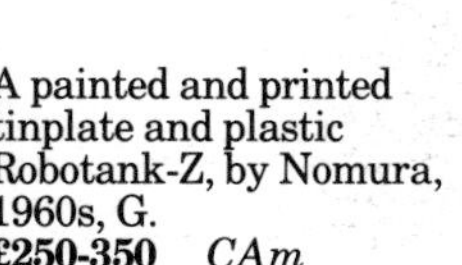

A printed and painted tinplate battery operated Space Explorer, by Yonezawa, 1960s, E.
£400-500 *CAm*

A printed and painted

operated Super Space Giant, by Horikawa, 1960s, E.
£300-400 *CAm*

A painted and printed tinplate and plastic Robotank-Z, by Nomura, 1960s, G.
£250-350 *CAm*

A painted tinplate battery operated Planet Robot, by Yoshiya, 1950s, E.
£350-450 *CAm*

Rocking Horses

Toy horses have always been popular, from basic hobby horses and horses on wheels to sophisticated mechanical toys. Rocking horses vary from beautifully carved replicas, sometimes even covered in horsehair furnished in leather, to simply shaped wooden toys. Rocking horses became fashionable from the late 18th century and are invariably called Dobbin!

A painted rocking horse, 19thC, 38in (97cm) wide.
£450-550 *BH*

A rare Lancashire pine rocking horse, late 18thC, 49in (123cm) wide.
£500-600 *BH*

A Victorian child's rocking horse of iron and wood, replacement stand, 31in (77cm) high.
£550-600 *MCA*

Still valuable in spite of the lost mane and eye.

A Victorian wooden rocking horse.
£1,000-1,200 *MCA*

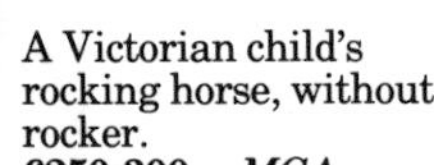

A Victorian child's rocking horse, without rocker.
£250-300 *MCA*

A Victorian horse on wheels, with separate rocker, 30in (75cm) high.
£340-380 *MCA*

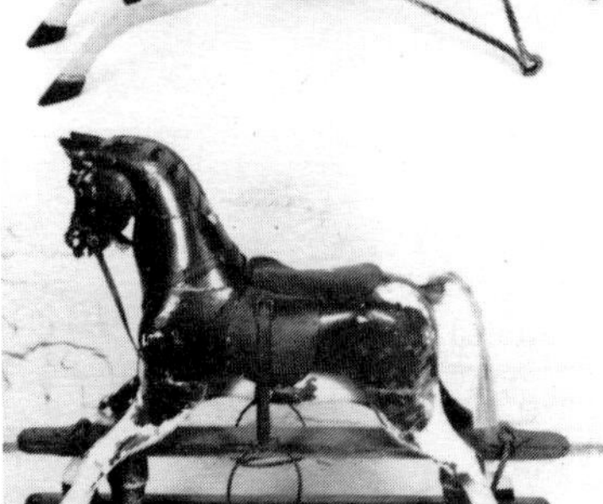

A pine rocking horse, 19thC, 45in (113cm) wide.
£400-500 *BH*

A rocking horse with original paint, 35in (88cm) wide.
£400-450 *BH*

A toy horse, 19thC, 11½in (29cm) wide.
£150-200 *AP*

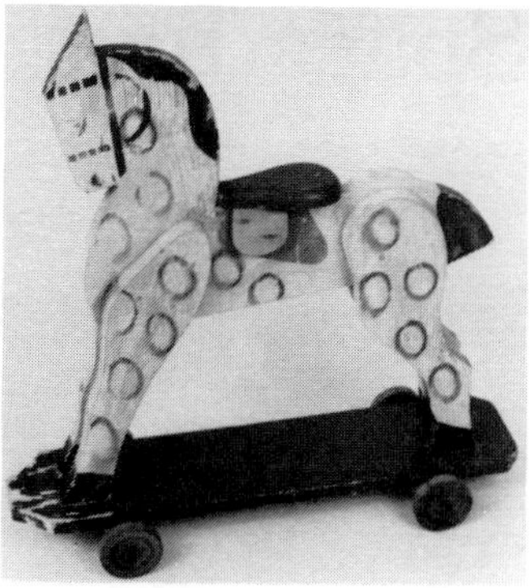

A child's painted wooden horse on wheels, 22in (55cm) high.
£65-75 *MCA*

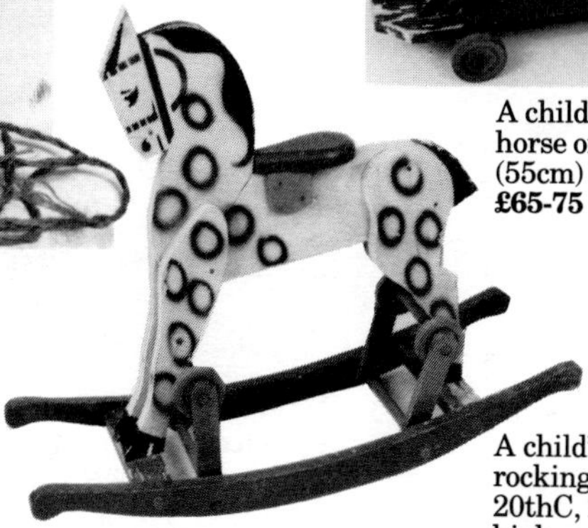

A child's wooden painted rocking horse, early 20thC, 28½in (72cm) high.
£125-150 *MCA*

A pony skin covered pull-along horse, with papier mâché head, German, c1910, 36in (92cm).
£225-250 *CSK*

A child's wooden toy horse, the base with trade label, re-painted, 20in (50cm) high.
£70-90 *WW*

Space Toys

A printed and painted tinplate battery operated Apollo Spacecraft, Japanese, late 1960s, F.
£200-250 *CAm*

A printed and painted tinplate battery operated NASA Apollo, Japanese, 1960s, E.
£200-250 *CAm*

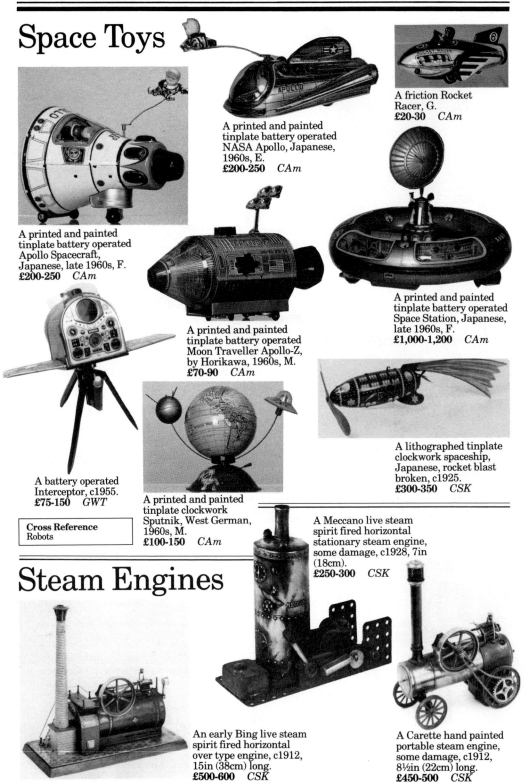

A friction Rocket Racer, G.
£20-30 *CAm*

A printed and painted tinplate battery operated Space Station, Japanese, late 1960s, F.
£1,000-1,200 *CAm*

A printed and painted tinplate battery operated Moon Traveller Apollo-Z, by Horikawa, 1960s, M.
£70-90 *CAm*

A battery operated Interceptor, c1955.
£75-150 *GWT*

A printed and painted tinplate clockwork Sputnik, West German, 1960s, M.
£100-150 *CAm*

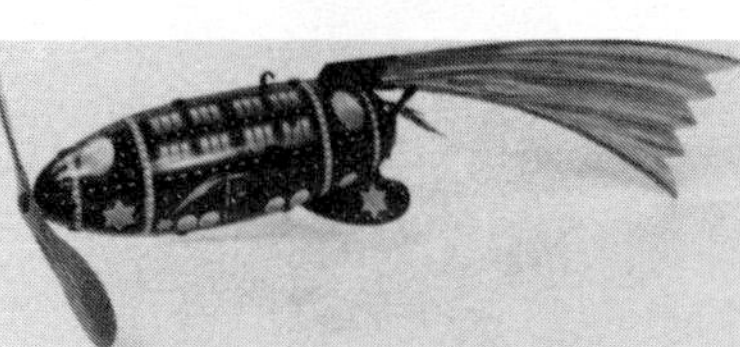

A lithographed tinplate clockwork spaceship, Japanese, rocket blast broken, c1925.
£300-350 *CSK*

Cross Reference
Robots

Steam Engines

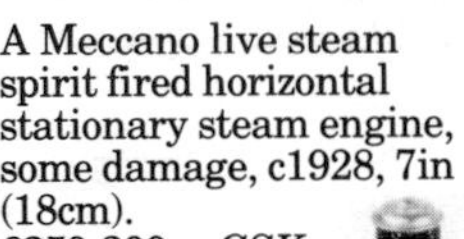

A Meccano live steam spirit fired horizontal stationary steam engine, some damage, c1928, 7in (18cm).
£250-300 *CSK*

An early Bing live steam spirit fired horizontal over type engine, c1912, 15in (38cm) long.
£500-600 *CSK*

A Carette hand painted portable steam engine, some damage, c1912, 8½in (22cm) long.
£450-500 *CSK*

A Falk live steam spirit over type engine, c1907, 15½in (39cm).
£500-600 *CSK*

A Märklin for Gamages live steam spirit fired vertical donkey engine, c1912.
£200-250 *CSK*

A Radiguet live steam spirit fired model steam ship, French, some damage, c1880, 20in (51cm) long.
£1,500-2,000 *CSK*

A Bing gauge 1 live steam spirit fired model of a L&NWR 0–4–0 tank engine, paintwork scorched and chipped, c1902.
£350-400 *CSK*

A Märklin portable live steam spirit fired engine, c1920.
£700-800 *CSK*

A Märklin live steam spirit fired semi-portable over type engine, slight damage, c1911.
£150-200 *CSK*

A Doll live steam spirit fired vertical engine, c1925, 12½in (32cm).
£400-450 *CSK*

A Carette live steam spirit fired over type engine, c1907.
£400-500 *CSK*

Stuffed Toys

A Japanese Pekinese dog, by Herman Becker, c1930. **£10-20** *DOW*

A Merrythought Thumper, c1955, 15in (38cm) high. **£75-85** *SA*

A lion with glass eyes, c1945, 23in (58cm) long. **£50-60** *SA*

Eeyore, c1960, 13in (33cm). **£35-45** *SA*

A terrier, c1950, 12in (30.5cm) long. **£35-45** *SA*

A monkey with glass eyes, c1940, 9in (23cm) high. **£25-30** *SA*

A Nora Wellings monkey. **£40-50** *PAR*

A Chiltern Hygienic toy, c1940, 11in (28cm). **£18-20** *SA*

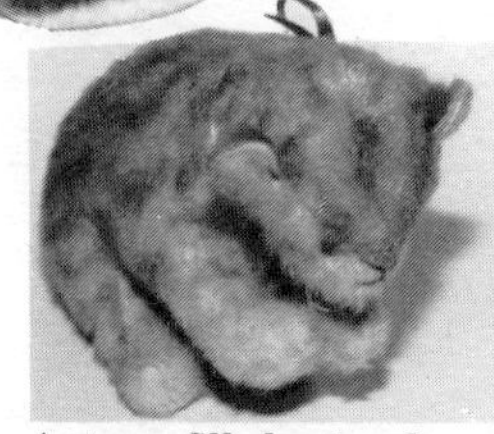

A turtle with Steiff button and original labels, 1950s, 11in (28cm). **£60-70** *DOW*

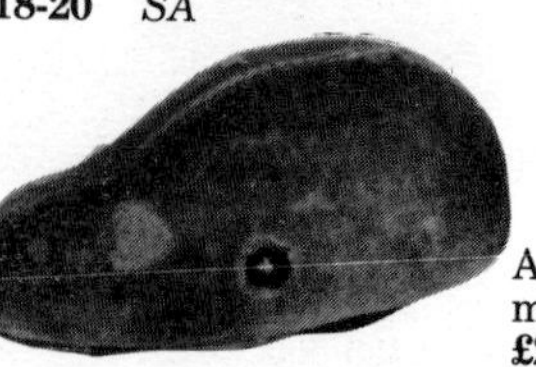

A Schuco wind-up mouse, poor condition. **£25-35** *CT*

A straw filled cat and a dog, with glass eyes and squeakers, c1930. **£20-30** *DOW*

A Merrythought poodle, with blue glass eyes, 1950s, 11in (28cm).
£20-30 *DOW*

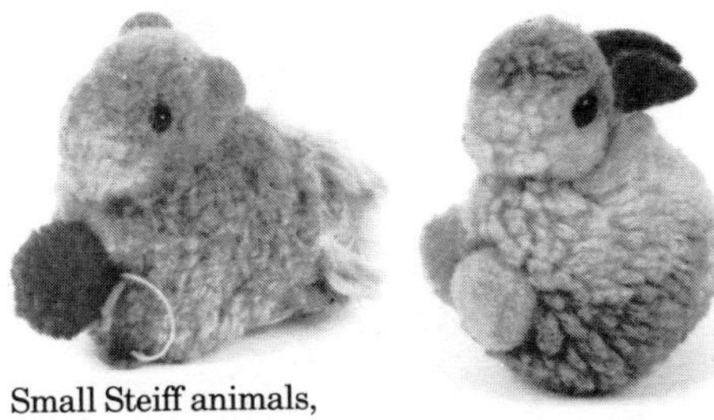

Small Steiff animals, c1930.
£3-4 each *CT*

Gollies

A Pedigree gollywog, c1955, 25in (63.5cm).
£70-80 *SA*

A gollywog mascot.
Priceless *MCA*

Teddy Bears

A clockwork yellow flock covered bear, with tinplate head, possibly by F. Martin, damaged, c1905, 5in (12.5cm).
£80-100 *Bon*

A selection of teddies and a panda.
£80-300 each *CSK*

A clockwork yellow plush covered nursing bear, holding a blonde plush baby bear, with rocking movement, possibly by F. Martin, c1905, 7in (17.5cm).
£130-150 *Bon*

A German pale blonde plush covered teddy bear, probably Steiff, 6in (15cm).
£100-150 *Bon*

A teddy bear on a deckchair, by Lefray Hygienic Toys, c1930, 22½in (56cm).
£160-180 *DOW*

A German hump-backed bear, with replacement pads on paws and feet, c1910.
£300-350 *PAR*

A teddy bear in helmet and goggles as worn by early motorists, c1920, 32in (80cm).
Priceless *PC*

A golden plush covered teddy bear, Bertram, with boot button eyes, hump and growler, some wear, c1904, 22in (55cm).
£450-500 *CSK*

Rupert Bear Bendy toys in sponge rubber, c1955, 11in (29cm).
£18-25 each *SA*

A Steiff dark brown plush covered bear on wheels, with pull string growler, 19in (48cm).
£200-250 *CSK*

An English bear, c1950, 20in (50cm).
£35-45 *SA*

An English bear, c1950, 20in (50cm) high.
£35-45 *PAR*

An English bear, c1940, 30in (75cm).
£65-85 *SA*

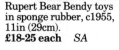

An early German teddy bear, with shoe button eyes and reinforced feet, paws and ears, 19in (48cm).
£300-350 *PAR*

An English panda, c1945, 35in (60cm).
£80-100 *SA*

A pair of small German bears, William and Mary, c1914, 9½in (24cm).
£250-300 each *PAR*

A Merrythought teddy bear, c1925, 20in (50cm).
£250-300 *PAR*

Two Pedigree straw-filled pandas with glass eyes, 17 and 14in (43 and 35cm) high.
£45-60 *DOW*

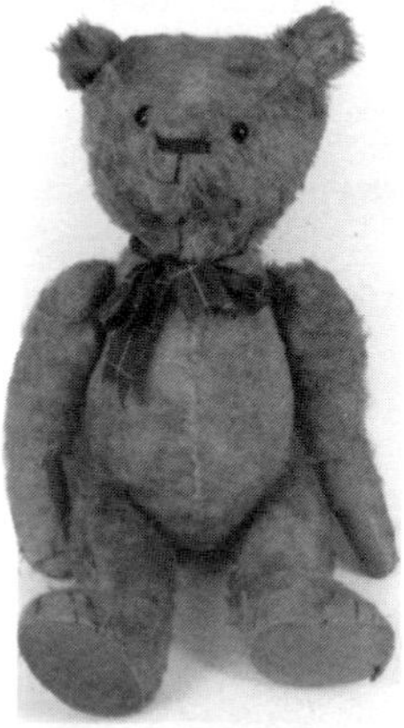

A German teddy bear, Albert, c1920, 26in (65cm).
£450-500 *PAR*

An English teddy bear with a musical bell, c1930, 18in (48cm).
£250-300 *PAR*

A golden plush covered fox, with Steiff button, 20in (50cm).
£150-200 *CSK*

A cotton plush covered teddy bear, c1917, 13½in (34cm).
£300-350 *CSK*

A small bear with velvet tie, 12in (31cm) high.
£100-200 *PC*

Tinplate Toys

A West German Gama Cadillac Convertible, lithographed and painted, some damage, c1954, 12in (30.5cm) long.
£250-350 *CSK*

An early German painted tinplate horse-drawn bus, original paintwork, slightly chipped, c1900, 11in (29cm) long.
£350-450 *CSK*

A Lehmann Autobus, EPL No. 590, a printed and painted tinplate open 'Berlin' type double decker bus, with clockwork mechanism, damaged, c1912, 8in (20cm) long.
£600-700 *CSK*

A Japanese tinplate bus with friction drive, 1960s. **£40-45** *COB*

An early Japanese lithographed tinplate travelling boy, with clockwork mechanism, 1930s, 8in (20cm) high, in original box.
£450-550 *CSK*

A Lehmann Berolina, EPL No. 686, a lithographed and painted tinplate open tourer with clockwork mechanism, lacking flag, c1925, 7in (17cm) long.
£750-850 *CSK*

A painted tinplate model of Henry Segrave's land speed record car Golden Arrow, with clockwork mechanism, slight rust, c1933, 19½in (49cm).
£120-150 *CSK*

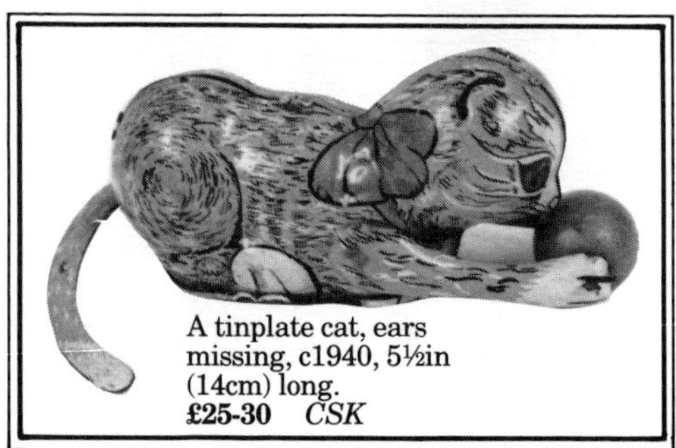

A tinplate cat, ears missing, c1940, 5½in (14cm) long.
£25-30 *CSK*

An early German painted tinplate carousel, worn, 11in (28cm) high.
£220-250 *CSK*

Various lithographed tinplate toys.
£50-80 each *CSK*

A Lehmann Anxious Bride Nanni, EPL No. 470, original hand painted tinplate, c1912, 9in (23cm) long.
£1,400-1,600 *CSK*

A Distler man with trolley, No. 573/1, lithographed and painted tinplate, with clockwork mechanism, original box, 7½in (19cm).
£300-400 *CSK*

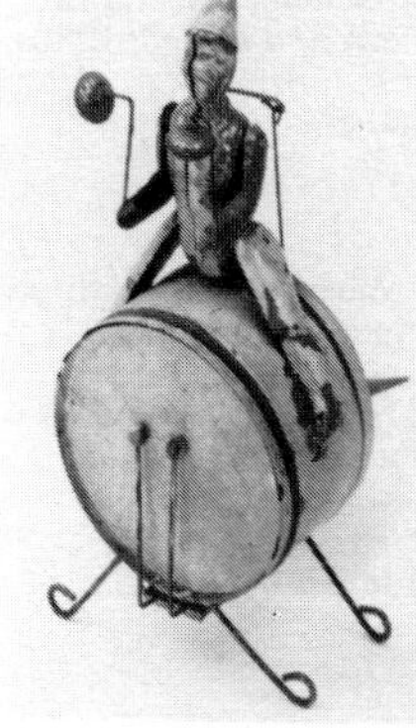

A hand painted tinplate clown percussionist, with clockwork mechanism, probably by Günthermann, worn, c1910, 7in (18cm).
£180-200 *CSK*

A Günthermann lithographed and painted tinplate gig, with clockwork mechanism, German, c1910, 8in (20cm) long.
£250-300 *CSK*

An early Carette lithographed and painted tinplate brewery No. 122/1, c1912, loose supports, 13in (33cm) wide.
£1,750-2,000 *CSK*

Two limousines, c1905.
£750-800 each *CSK*

A lithographed and painted tinplate taxi, with clockwork mechanism, probably by Fischer, c1907, 7in (18cm) long.
£700-800 *CSK*

A Carette lithographed and painted tinplate joinery shop, No. 626/22, with string pulley mechanism, c1912.
£1,500-2,000 *CSK*

A Lehmann Bucking Broncho, EPL No. 625, painted tinplate with clockwork mechanism, slight chipping, c1920.
£300-400 *CSK*

A Yonezawa Starfire aeroplane.
£20-30 *MIN*

A Bing painted tinplate pull-along fire engine, worn and rusted, 1930s, 23in (58cm) long.
£60-80 *CSK*

A Wells painted tinplate saloon car, with clockwork mechanism, c1938, 14in (35.5cm) long.
£160-180 *CSK*

A Märklin hand painted tinplate Blériot monoplane, Ref No. 5415/0, with clockwork mechanism, pilot damaged, c1912, 9in (23cm) wingspan.
£4,000-4,500 *CSK*

A German Nifty Steam Shovel, printed and painted tinplate with clockwork mechanism, some rust, 1920s.
£100-150 *CSK*

Assorted clockwork tinplate toys. **£20-30 each** *CSK*

A Mettoy printed and painted tinplate commercial vehicle, c1950.
£40-60 *CSK*

The Gyroplane, a printed tinplate monoplane with rubber band mechanism, in original box, slight rust, c1933. **£100-120** *CSK*

A Lehmann Performing Seal, EPL No. 445, painted tinplate with clockwork mechanism, c1910, in original box, 7½in (19cm).
£200-250 *CSK*

An Arnold painted triplate police car, with friction drive mechanism, battery operated siren and flashing light, in original box, c1955, 10in (25.5cm) long.
£130-150 *CSK*

A Distler Packard printed and painted tinplate car, with clockwork mechanism, in original box, 1950s, 10in (25cm).
£175-200 *CSK*

Bluebird, a printed and painted tinplate model, c1930, 16in (40.5cm) long.
£400-500 *CSK*

A Lehmann motorcycle and rider, Halloh, EPL No. 683, with clockwork mechanism, damaged, c1914, 9in (23cm) long.
£1,800-2,000 *CSK*

A Tipp printed and painted tinplate limousine, with clockwork mechanism, rusted, c1932, 14½in (37cm) long.
£180-200 *CSK*

A Marx clockwork racing car, 1930s.
£100-125 *DOW*

Wooden Toys

A child's wheelbarrow, early 20thC.
£65-75 *PCh*

An early Victorian wooden toy, 6in (15cm) high.
£100-200 *PC*

The position of the hair can be altered by a clip in the back of the doll.

Edwardian children's toys on composition wheels, 11in (29cm).
£25-30 each *MCA*

A wooden fort, c1940, 10in (25cm) high.
£30-50 *DOW*

A wooden dog, 1930s, 13in (33cm) long.
£45-50 *MCA*

A Victorian child's wheelbarrow, 34in (85cm).
£75-100 *MCA*

A new carved wooden rabbit, for use as a box, 6½in (16cm).
£30-35 *MCA*

Although new, this is beautifully made and therefore collectable — an antique of tomorrow?

A wooden doll, c1930, 15in (38cm) long.
£28-35 *MCA*

A Victorian child's dog-cart, 22in (55cm) high.
£750-800 *MCA*

A painted horse and cart, 13½in (33cm). **£40-50** *MCA*

A wooden penguin, 10½in (26cm) high.
£40-45 *MCA*

A miniature pine chest of drawers, 7½in (17.5cm) high.
£48-50 *MCA*

A cage for a hamster or other small mammal, c1900, 17in (43cm) high.
£350-400 *MCA*

MAKE THE MOST OF MILLER'S
Price ranges in this book reflect what one should expect to *pay* for a similar example. When selling, however, one should expect to receive a lower figure. This will fluctuate according to a dealer's stock, saleability at a particular time, etc. It is always advisable, when selling, to approach a reputable specialist dealer or an auction house which has specialist sales.

A set of 15 soldiers and sailors.
£115-125 *MCA*

A small wooden car, 17½in (44cm) long.
£30-35 *MCA*

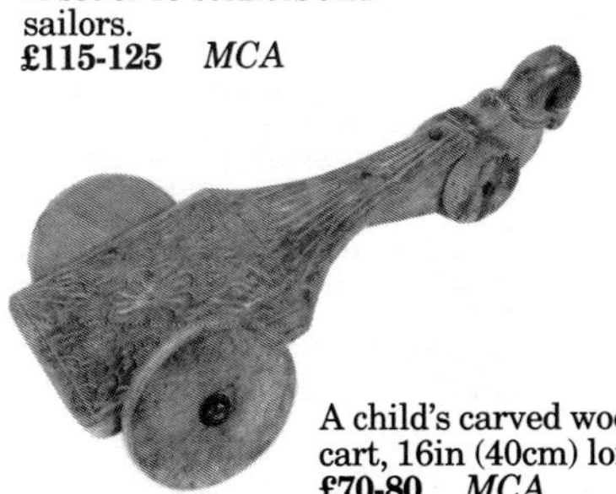

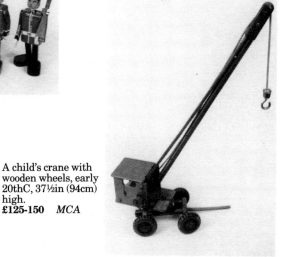

A child's carved wooden cart, 16in (40cm) long.
£70-80 *MCA*

A child's crane with wooden wheels, early 20thC, 37½in (94cm) high.
£125-150 *MCA*

Toys & Games

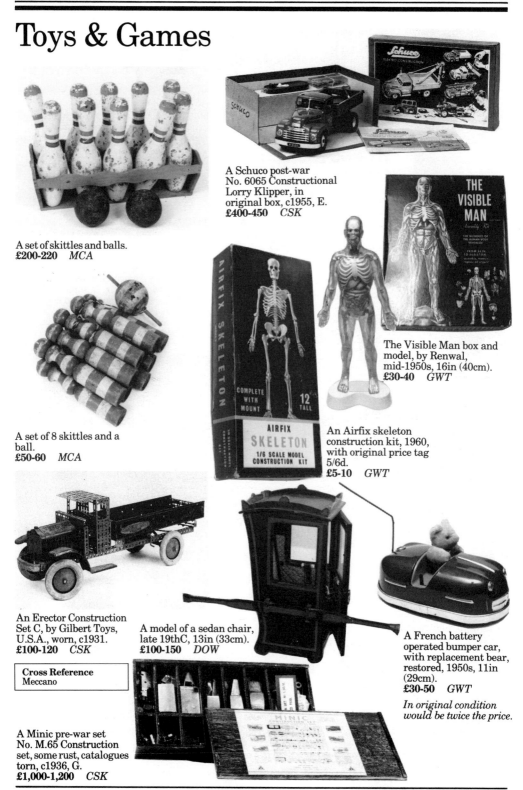

A set of skittles and balls.
£200-220 *MCA*

A Schuco post-war No. 6065 Constructional Lorry Klipper, in original box, c1955, E.
£400-450 *CSK*

The Visible Man box and model, by Renwal, mid-1950s, 16in (40cm).
£30-40 *GWT*

A set of 8 skittles and a ball.
£50-60 *MCA*

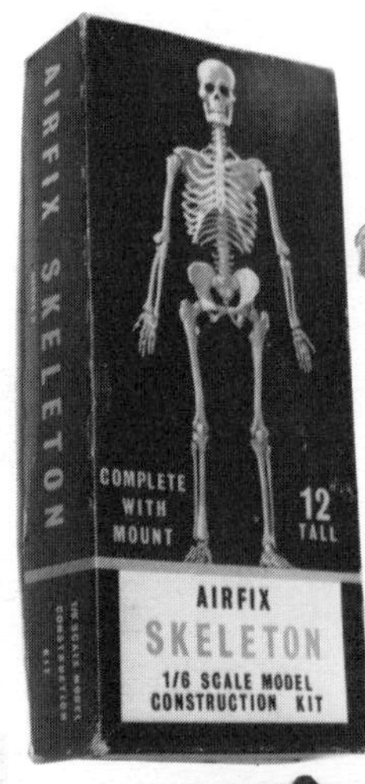

An Airfix skeleton construction kit, 1960, with original price tag 5/6d.
£5-10 *GWT*

An Erector Construction Set C, by Gilbert Toys, U.S.A., worn, c1931.
£100-120 *CSK*

A model of a sedan chair, late 19thC, 13in (33cm).
£100-150 *DOW*

A French battery operated bumper car, with replacement bear, restored, 1950s, 11in (29cm).
£30-50 *GWT*

In original condition would be twice the price.

Cross Reference
Meccano

A Minic pre-war set No. M.65 Construction set, some rust, catalogues torn, c1936, G.
£1,000-1,200 *CSK*

A German Technofix cable car, c1955, 19in (48cm).
£100-120 *GWT*

A green German pram, 1920s, 36in (91cm) wide with handle.
£70-80 *LB*

A framed jig-saw puzzle, c1930, 9½ by 15in (23 by 38cm).
£35-45 *PAR*

The Electro, an early German tinplate magic lantern, with lens, burner and slides, in original box, c1895, 8½in (21cm) high.
£100-120 *CSK*

Gollywog on a plastic box, 4in (10cm) high.
£10-12 *CT*

A German child's sewing machine, with instructions and box, c1905, 8in (20cm) high.
£40-50 *Bon*

A 'Fums Up' character, c1920, 2.5cm high.
£5-6 *CT*

Made in all sizes.

A rare early Carette hand painted Frog Fountain, No. 658/3, original paintwork, c1912, 14½in (36cm) diam.
£700-800 *CSK*

FURTHER READING
White, Gwen, *Antique Toys,* Chancellor Press, 1971.
Miller, Judith and Martin, *Understanding Antiques,* Mitchell Beazley, 1989.

Kermit in a car, 4in (10cm) wide.
£3-4 *CT*

Treen

An oak ladle, 18thC.
£20-25 *PC*

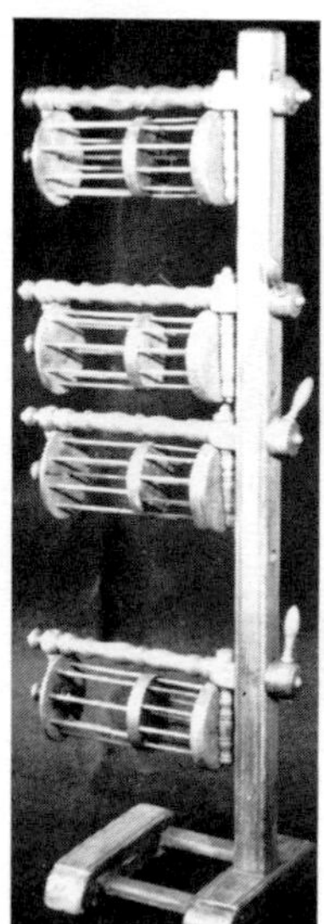

A wool winder with individual spindles for different coloured wools, c1800, 60in (150cm) high.
£160-180 *UP*

A large cheese mould, late 17thC.
£150-200 *PC*

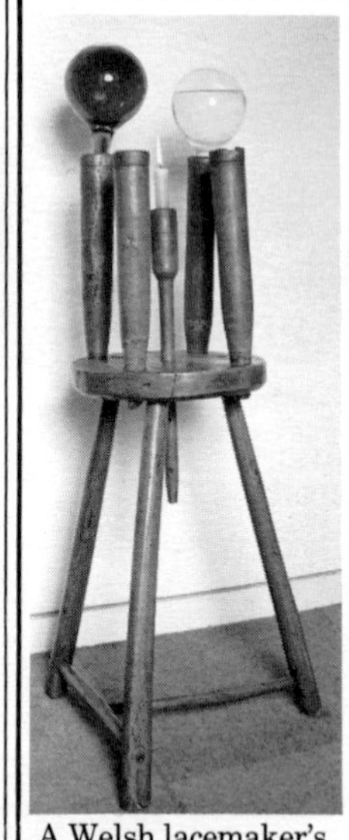

A Welsh lacemaker's 'flash', c1800.
£550-600 *CCA*

A French spice box on wheels.
£55-60 *MCA*

A rosewood mortar, 19thC.
£60-80 *PC*

A gavel, 19thC.
£30-40 *PC*

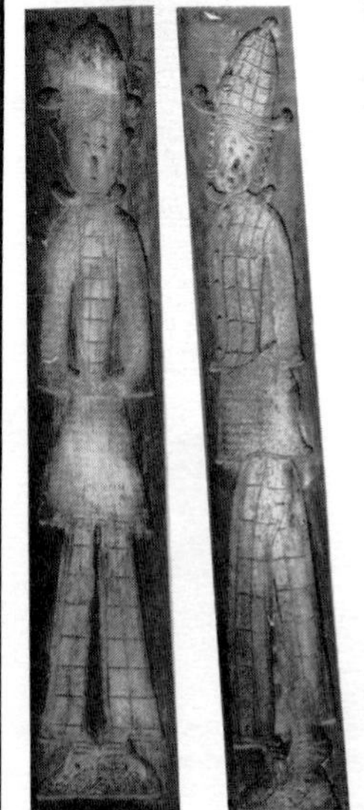

Large Austrian gingerbread moulds.
£120-130 each *MCA*

A spoon rack, 18in (45cm) high.
£75-85 *MCA*
A ladle, 15in (38cm) long.
£35-40 *MCA*

A fruitwood candlestick, 10in (25cm).
£55-65 *SAD*

A small leaf pattern printing block.
£55-60 *PC*

A pill board.
£200-250 *PC*

Two fruitwood wall brackets.
£80-100 each *CSK*

A hand carved oak plaque, early 19thC, 10in (25cm) high.
£120-140 *SAD*

An ebony bottle, probably Dutch Colonial, late 18thC, 6½in (16cm) high.
£180-200 *P*

Two turned wood ladles, c1820, 12in (30cm) long.
£75-100 *Cas*

A fruitwood ladle, 19thC.
£50-60 *PC*

A turned oak spice pot, c1800, 7in (18cm) high.
£160-180 *Cas*

A pair of turned beech salts, c1800.
£380-400 *Cas*

A turned fruitwood chalice, 17thC.
£300-400 *PC*

A Continental boxwood lever action nutcracker, bearing the date 1687 and inscribed W. A. Fecit, 8½in (21cm) long.
£500-600 *CSK*

A French spice rack, c1900, 17½in (44cm) high.
£250-300 *MCA*

A barge tray used for carrying linen, 27½in (69cm).
£110-120 *MCA*

A cider costrel, c1800, 6in (15cm) long.
£100-120 *Cas*

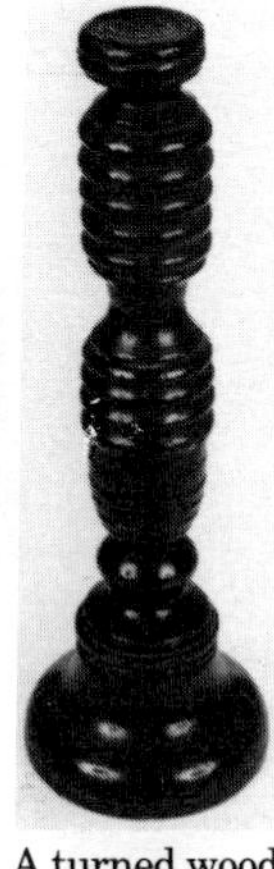

A turned wood stand, 18thC.
£140-160 *PC*

Two weaver's shuttles, 18in (45cm) long.
£5-25 each *SAD*

Measures

A selection of measures.
£60-80 each *PC*

A selection of love tokens, 19thC. **£30-50 each** *PC*

A measure, early 19thC.
£20-30 *PC*

A selection of grain measures, early 19thC.
£60-80 each *PC*

Animals

A newly painted decorative bird, Indian.
£85-95 *MCA*

A new long-billed curlew, used for decoy purposes.
£50-55 *MCA*

A pair of walnut turtle foot stools, c1860.
£400-500 *MCA*

Ethnic Treen

A treen pot, 8in (20cm) diam.
£35-40 *MCA*

A small leaf-shaped spice box, 6in (15cm) wide.
£45-50 *MCA*

A wooden stand, 8in (20cm) diam.
£30-35 *MCA*

A treen drinking vessel, 8½in (21cm) high.
£65-70 *MCA*

A small turned bowl, 9in (23.5cm) diam.
£20-25 *MCA*

A turned wood bottle, 9in (23.5cm) high.
£40-45 *MCA*

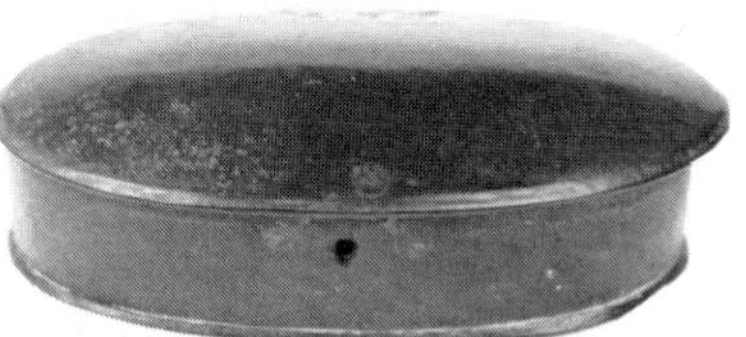

An oval box with inner compartment, 9in (23.5cm) wide. **£75-80** *MCA*

A carved wooden spice box, 7in (17.5cm) wide. **£45-50** *MCA*

Mauchline Ware

A letter rack, with Aberdeen scenes, 8in (20.5cm).
£30-35 *EA*

A money box with Littlehampton scene, 4in (10cm) high.
£45-50 *EA*

A Mauchline ware box, Shakespeare's House, 3½in (9cm) wide. **£25-30** *EA*

A money box, Caister Castle, 2in (5cm). **£30-35** *EA*

A bookmark, Dunblane Cathedral, 5in (12.5cm) long. **£15-20** *EA*

Part of the great tree of Kippenross.

A cauldron, Burns Monument, Kilmarnock, 2in (5cm) high.
£35-40 *EA*

A box with Ann Hathaway's cottage, 2 by 3in (5 by 8cm).
£20-25 *EA*

A serviette ring,
£6-10 *EA*

A wool holder, Ilfracombe, 4in (10cm).
£25-30 *HOW*

A box, The Cross, Troon, 4 by 5in (10 by 14cm).
£20-25 *EA*

Mauchline ware boxes, 3in (7.5cm) high.
£15-20 each *EA*

Tartan Ware

A selection of tartan ware.
£50-150 each *EUR*

Tartan ware boxes. **£55-65 each** *EUR*

A needle case.
£40-50 *EUR*

A selection of tartan ware items.
£35-250 each *EUR*

Tunbridge Ware

A photo frame.
£40-60 *AL*

A Tunbridge ware bookmark, stylo and pen.
£10-20 each *VB*

A thermometer in the shape of an obelisk, 8in (20cm).
£90-100 *VB*

A Tunbridge ware counter box.
£40-60 *PC*

A Tunbridge ware stamp box with Queen Victoria on the lid, 1½in (4cm) wide.
£80-100 *VB*

Tribal Art

North American Indian

A pair of late Victorian moose skin beaded moccasins.
£65-95 *CAS*

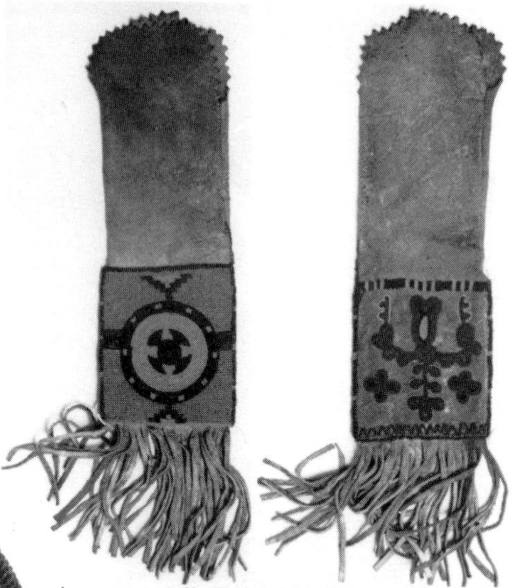

A tourist beaded bag, c1905-15.
£15-55 *CAS*

Unusual with American flags depicted.

A commercially tanned leather woodland pipe bag, 1940s. **£90-160** *CAS*

A pair of gauntlets, 1940s, 11½in (29cm).
£45-65 *CAS*

A Papago basket, South Western U.S., c1900, 11½in (29cm) diam.
£60-125 *CAS*

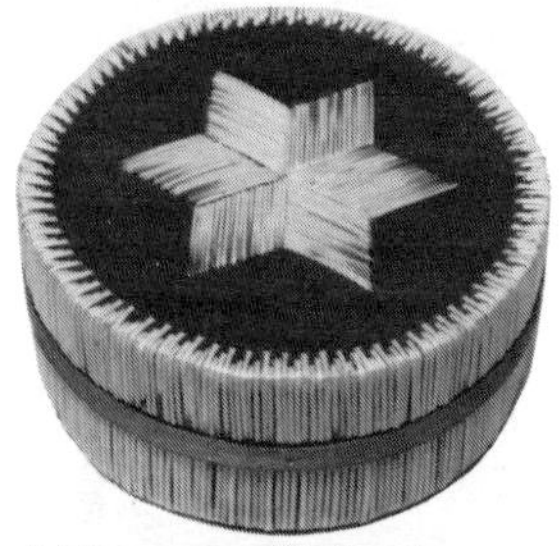

A Mic-mac quilled and birch box, Canadian or Maine, 1940s, 4in (10cm) diam.
£10-35 *CAS*

Condition, size and complexity of pattern are very important and the price will consequently go up accordingly.

A Northwest coast totem pole, made for tourists, c1900, 34in (86cm).
£150-250 *CAS*

A Sioux pipe bag, beaded and quilled, c1880, 25in (63.5cm). **£550-850** *CAS*

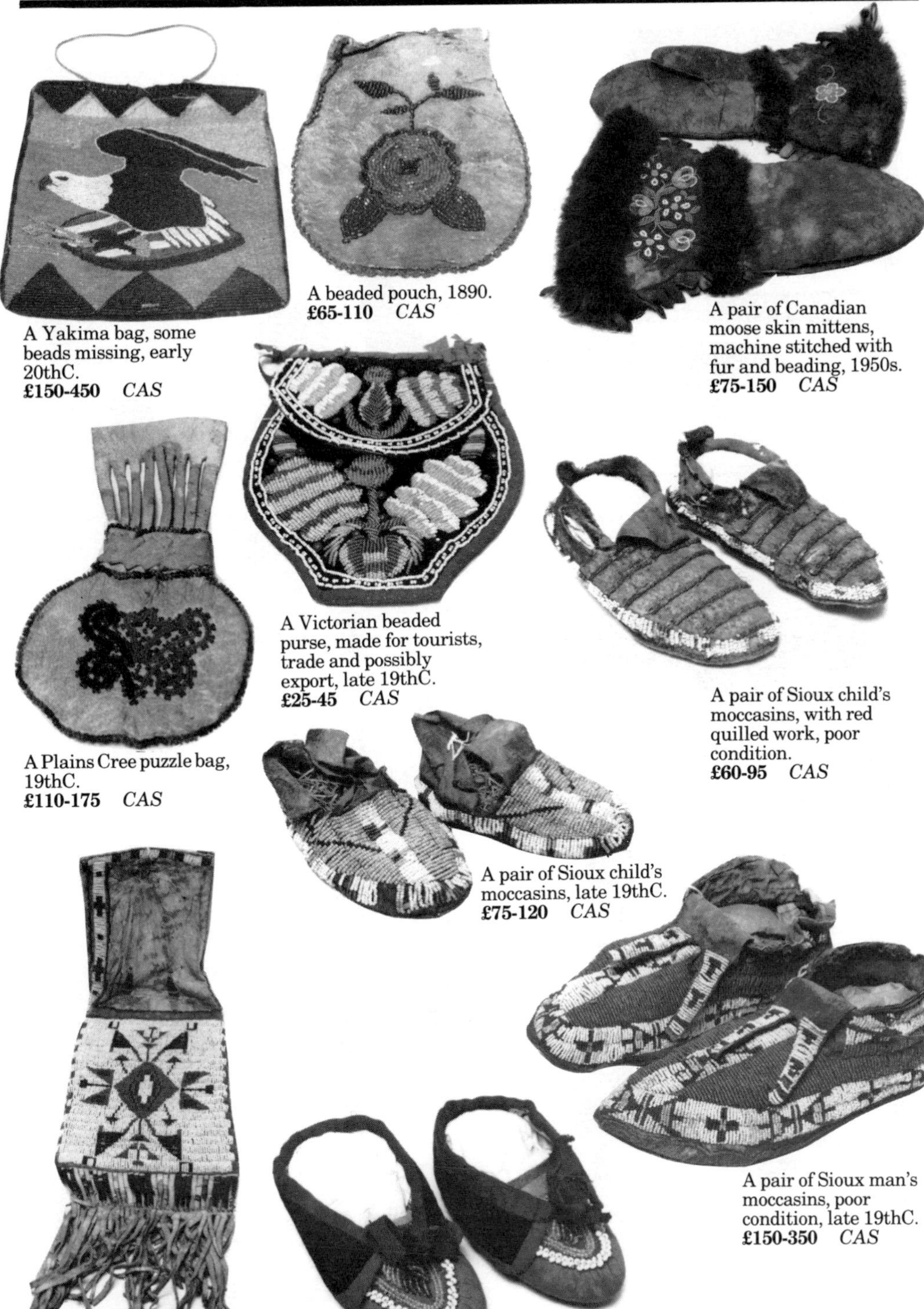

A Yakima bag, some beads missing, early 20thC.
£150-450 *CAS*

A beaded pouch, 1890.
£65-110 *CAS*

A pair of Canadian moose skin mittens, machine stitched with fur and beading, 1950s.
£75-150 *CAS*

A Plains Cree puzzle bag, 19thC.
£110-175 *CAS*

A Victorian beaded purse, made for tourists, trade and possibly export, late 19thC.
£25-45 *CAS*

A pair of Sioux child's moccasins, with red quilled work, poor condition.
£60-95 *CAS*

A pair of Sioux child's moccasins, late 19thC.
£75-120 *CAS*

A pair of Sioux man's moccasins, poor condition, late 19thC.
£150-350 *CAS*

A Sioux pipe bag, beaded and quilled, c1880.
£450-850 *CAS*

A pair of child's moccasins, made for tourists, c1940. **£10-25** *CAS*

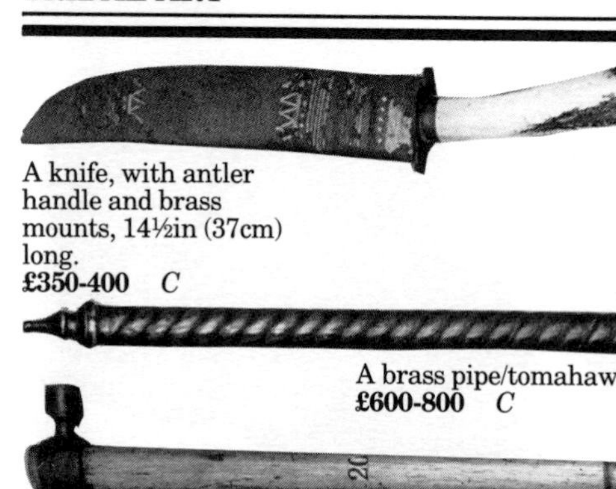

A knife, with antler handle and brass mounts, 14½in (37cm) long.
£350-400 *C*

An American Indian pipe/tomahawk, 20in (51cm) long.
£2,500-3,000 *C*

A brass pipe/tomahawk.
£600-800 *C*

A Huron knife and sheath and a tomahawk.
£400-450 *C*

African

A pair of female ibeji, by Eshubiyi, late 19thC, 8½in (21.5cm) high.
£750-800 *C*

An old carved Zulu porcupine and a Cameroons quadruped.
£80-100 each *DBP*

A Yoruba wood ibeji figure, 12in (30.5cm) high.
£250-300 *DBP*

A Yoruba twin figure, 10in (25.5cm) high.
£300-350 *C*

A Songye janiform staff finial, 15in (38cm) high.
£550-600 *C*

Two ibeji figures, 9½ and 10½in (24 and 26.5cm) high.
£275-300 *C*

A stool, 11½in (30cm) high.
£200-250 *C*

A Yoruba presentation bowl, 16½in (42cm) wide.
£330-350 *C*

A Teke fetish figure, 11in (26cm) high.
£600-700 *C*

A Yaka slit drum, 13in (33cm) high.
£500-550 *C*

An Idoma headdress, carved as a head, chips to mouth, 14in (36cm) high.
£250-300 *C*

A Poto stool, 11½in (27cm) high.
£1,000-1,500 *C*

A Yoruba staff for Shango, carved as a kneeling female figure, 12½in (31.5cm) high.
£260-280 *C*

A Yoruba staff for Shango, 11in (27.5cm) high.
£200-250 *C*

An Akan figure from a chair, 14½in (36cm) high.
£800-900 *C*

Originally a complete chair, and all but this finial was destroyed in a warehouse fire.

A Pende circular split-cane mask, gitenga, 13in (33cm) diam.
£250-300 *C*

An African raffia basket and cover, 9½in (24cm) high.
£80-100 *C*

Rest of the World

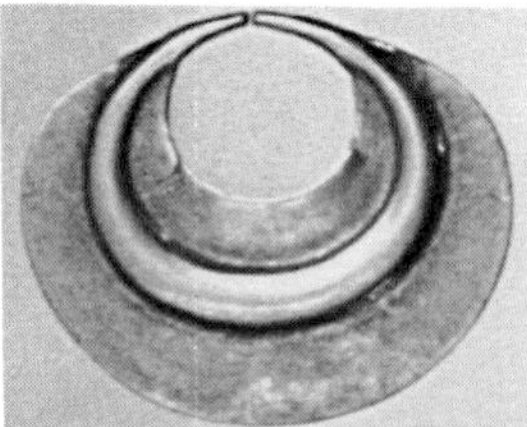

Two Quimbaya gold nose ornaments, 3.5 and 7cm wide. **£500-600** *C*

A Samoa Kava bowl, 15in (38cm) diam. **£150-200** *C*

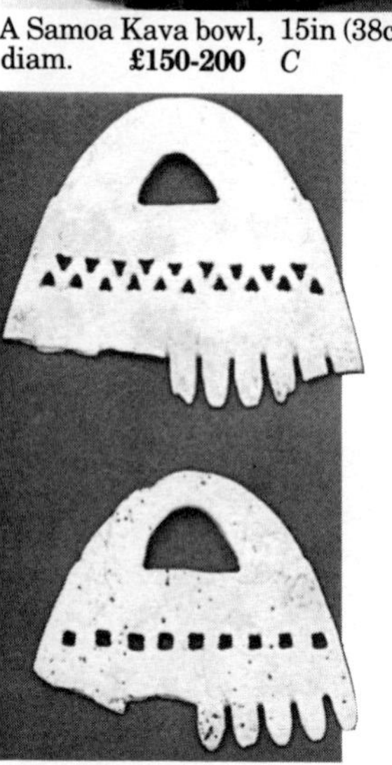

Four Solomon Islands shell ornaments, barava, from Roviana Lagoon, New Georgia, 3½in (9cm). **£850-900** *C*

Three Sinu bird head ornaments, of beaten gold, 3cm long. **£600-650** *C*

A Fiji Kava bowl, 18½in (46.5cm) diam. **£400-450** *C*

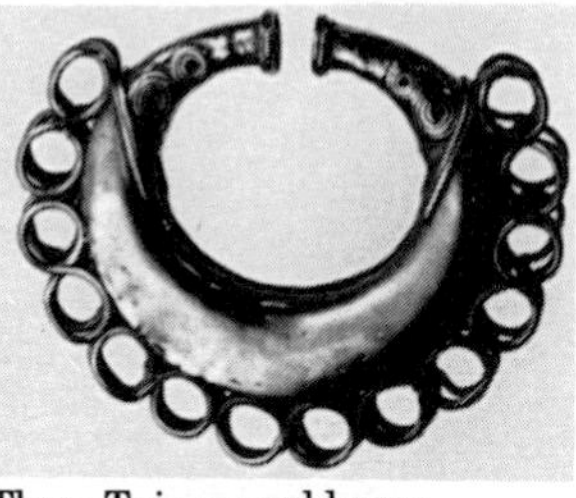

Three Tairona gold nose ornaments, 2 to 6cm wide. **£900-1,000** *C*

A Solomon Islands shell ring, bokolo, 6in (15cm) high. **£450-500** *C*

A Quimbaya rod-like ornament, the shaft of hollow gold with crown boss below the finial, 5½in (14.5cm). **£800-900** *C*

A Tairona figure and 2 bells. **£500-550** *C*

Volkswagens

This collection featuring the ubiquitous Volkswagen is a marvellous illustration of the sheer variety of items that can be amassed within a single theme, in this case, the cult status beetle.

A Beetle wristwatch, Taiwan, c1980.
£15-20 *PC*

An Avon after shave bottle, c1970, 5½in (14cm).
£10-12 *PC*

Cross Reference
Toys Diecast

A Japanese tinplate Beetle in blue, 5in (13.5cm) long.
£10-15 *PC*

A Beetle Husky model diecast police car, c1968, 2½in (6cm) long.
£5-8 *PC*

A wooden model with green and red wheels, 3½in (9cm).
£3-4 *PC*

A Lesney diecast Beetle in blue, late 1950s.
£5-8 *PC*

A battery powered yellow plastic Beetle, Hong Kong, 3in (7.5cm) long.
£1-2 *PC*

A red ceramic foreign Beetle, 2in (5cm) long.
£1-2 *PC*

A modern hand-made hand-painted pottery Beetle, foreign.
£3-4 *PC*

A Corgi Motor School diecast model, with realistic steering mechanism, c1970, 3½in (9cm) long.
£8-10 *PC*

A novelty pencil sharpener, and a yellow friction powered diecast model, 2in (5cm) long.
£1-2 each *PC*

A blue Beetle, hand-made in Cornwall, c1980, 3in (7cm) long.
£5-7 *PC*

Walking Sticks & Canes

A coromandel cane, the hinged cover concealing a timepiece, late 19thC.
£600-700 *CSK*

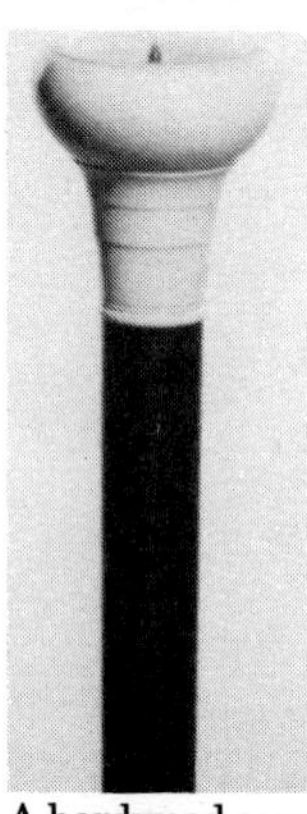

A hardwood cane, the ivory knop fitted with a dice game.
£150-200 *CSK*

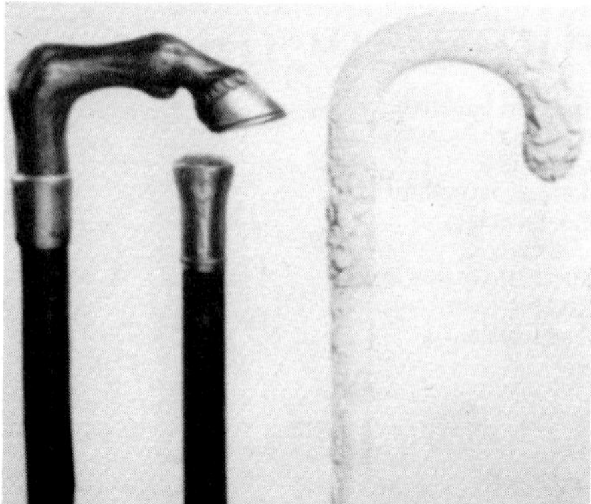

Two walking sticks and a cane.
£150-180 each *CSK*

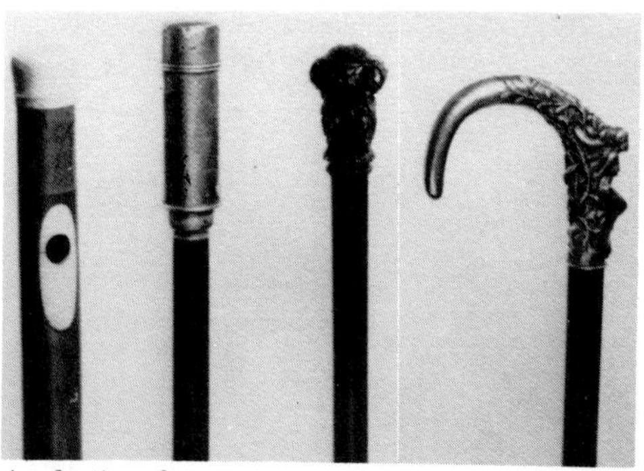

A selection of canes.
£150-200 each *CSK*

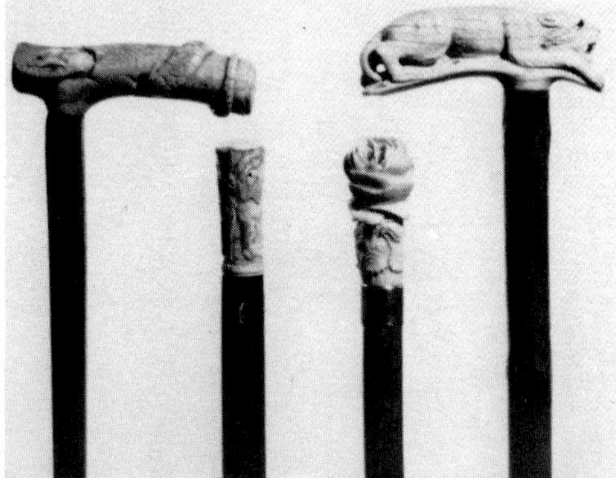

A collection of Japanese canes with ivory decoration.
£125-150 each *CSK*

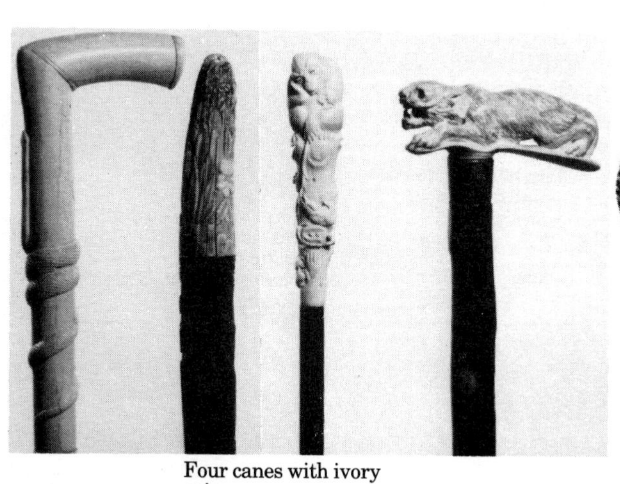

Four canes with ivory grips.
£100-150 each *CSK*

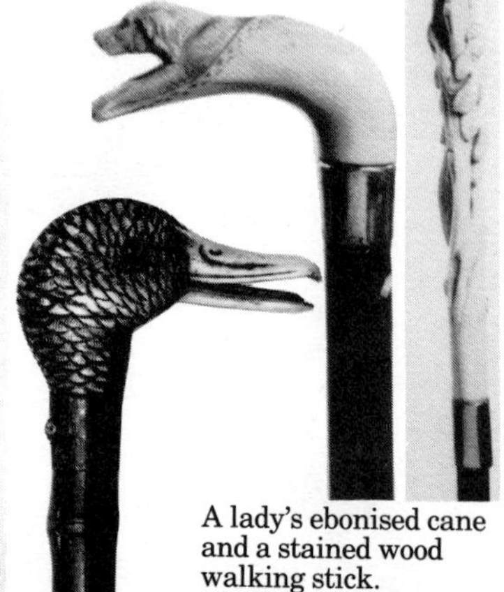

A lady's ebonised cane and a stained wood walking stick.
£330-350 *CSK*

A Victorian umbrella with carved ivory duck's head handle.
£500-550 *GIL*

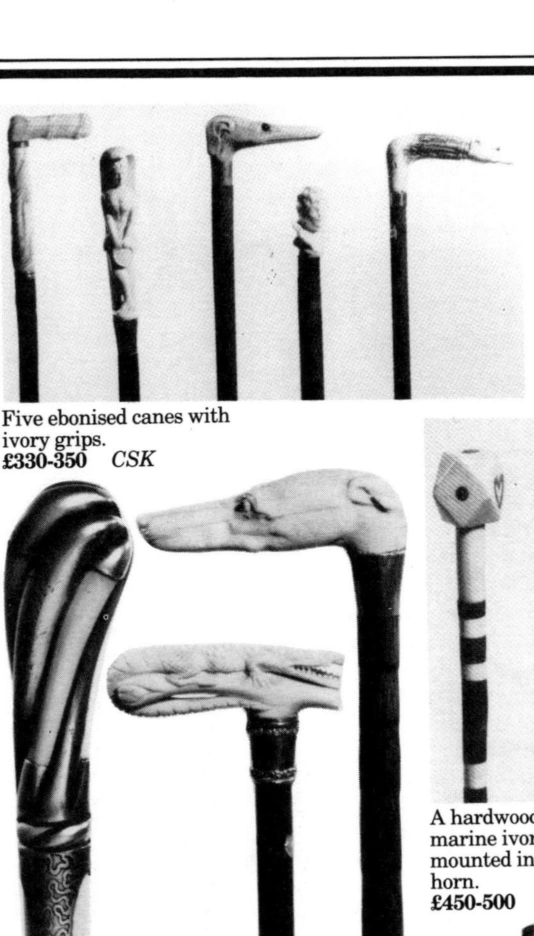

Five ebonised canes with ivory grips.
£330-350 *CSK*

An ivory handled walking stick, c1860.
£270-300 *MG*

A hare's head handled cane, c1880.
£120-140 *MG*

An ebonised cane, the ivory grip carved with a dog's head.
£450-500 *CSK*

A hardwood cane and a marine ivory cane mounted in wood and horn.
£450-500 *CSK*

A bamboo walking stick and a hardwood walking stick.
£375-400 *CSK*

An Art Deco stained wood cane, inscribed with the owner's name A. L. Hall.
£250-270 *CSK*

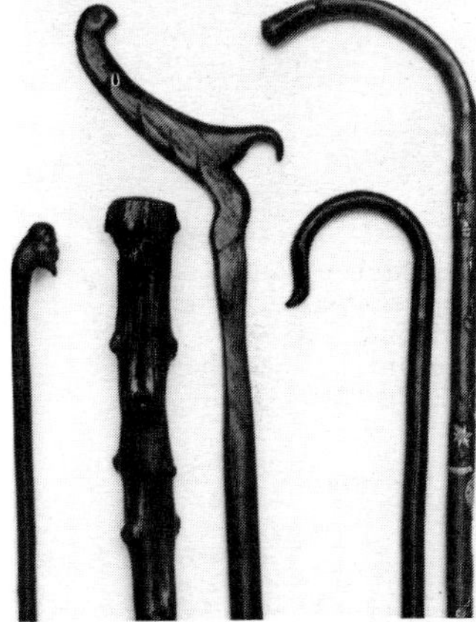

A collection of walking sticks.
£8-40 each *AL*

A parasol handle, bearing maker's mark, late 19thC.
£120-150 *CSK*

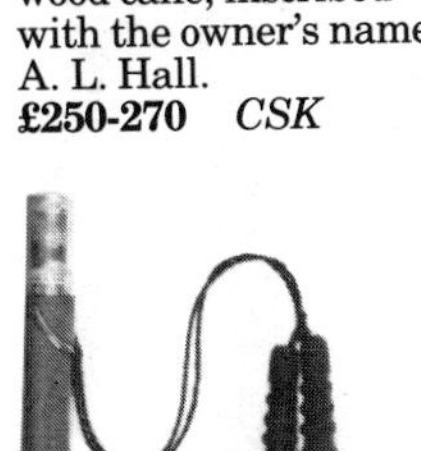

Two wood canes mounted with dogs' heads.
£380-400 *CSK*

A Spanish gold inlaid Toledo handled cane, c1880.
£150-180 *MG*

A two-coloured gold handled malacca cane, hallmarked 1780. **£850-950** *MG*

Watches

A quadruple cased verge pocket watch, for the Turkish market, inscribed George Prior, London, signed Maxn. Borrell, London.
£400-450 *CSK*

A Continental silver open faced quarter repeating verge pocket watch, signed J. P. Radzinski et Fils a Breslau, 5.6cm diam.
£650-700 *CSK*

A Continental open faced calendar verge pocket watch, signed Blainville, Rouen.
£400-450 *CSK*

An 18ct. gold pair cased watch, signed Rt. Roskell, Liverpool No. 1946, with gilt cap, the cases marked Chester 1801, 5.6cm diam.
£500-600 *P*

A gold open faced quarter repeating musical pocket watch, defective movement, 5.9cm diam.
£1,400-1,600 *CSK*

A Swiss gold hunter cased keyless lever watch, the steel bar movement signed Henry Hoffman, Locle, the signed cuvette numbered 36431, signed enamel dial, 5.4cm diam.
£600-800 *P*

A silver pair cased verge doctor's watch, signed Chas. Hewson, London, 5.6cm diam.
£220-250 *CSK*

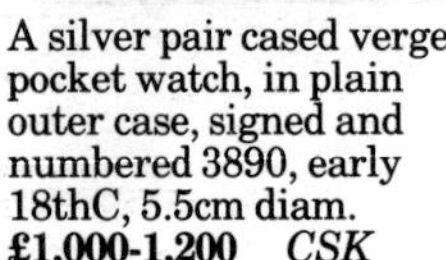

A silver pair cased verge pocket watch, in plain outer case, signed and numbered 3890, early 18thC, 5.5cm diam.
£1,000-1,200 *CSK*

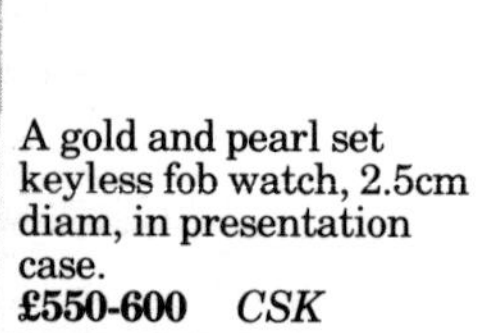

A gold and pearl set keyless fob watch, 2.5cm diam, in presentation case.
£550-600 *CSK*

Wristwatches

A Rolex gold and steel wristwatch.
£650-750 *CSK*

A Rolex Precision gold wristwatch.
£800-850 *CSK*

A Swiss Rolex two-colour gold lady's wristwatch, with presentation case.
£250-300 *P*

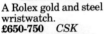

A Rolex gold and steel wristwatch.
£550-600 *CSK*

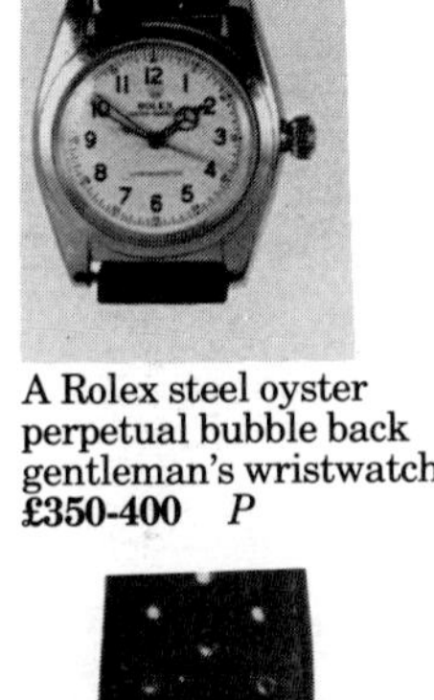

A Rolex steel oyster perpetual bubble back gentleman's wristwatch.
£350-400 *P*

MAKE THE MOST OF MILLERS
Price ranges in this book reflect what one should expect to *pay* for a similar example. When selling, however, one should expect to receive a lower figure. This will fluctuate according to a dealer's stock, saleability at a particular time, etc. It is always advisable, when selling, to approach a reputable specialist dealer or an auction house which has specialist sales.

A Breitling Navitimer stainless steel Chronomatic wristwatch.
£300-350 *CSK*

A Patek Phillipe, Genève, lady's yellow gold wristwatch.
£1,000-1,200 *CSK*

An Omega Flightmaster stainless steel wristwatch.
£200-250 *CSK*

A Swiss Rolex gentleman's gold oyster perpetual wristwatch, with flexible gold bracelet.
£550-650 *P*

Writing Accessories

Pens

A Parker Lucky Curve Duofold Special pen with button filler.
£130-150 *Bon*

A Waterman pen with No. 8 nib, damaged.
£15-20 *Bon*

A Parker Big Red Lucky Curve pen, with gold nib.
£100-120 *Bon*

A black Parker Duofold with 14ct gold nib.
£10-15 *Bon*

A Swan self-filling fountain pen.
£5-10 *DH*

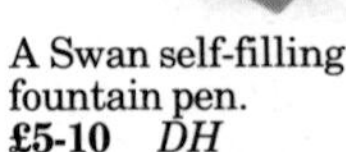

A Swan fountain pen, c1938.
£85-95 *JAS*

A Mentmore fountain pen, c1930, 5in (13cm).
£5-10 *DH*

A Ford's Patent fountain pen, with 14ct gold nib.
£100-110 *Bon*

A Parker Duofold, c1932.
£140-160 *JAS*

A Nova green marbled fountain pen, c1930, 5in (13cm).
£5-10 *DH*

A Waterman safety pen, 3½in (9cm) long.
£100-110 *Bon*

An Onoto black herringbone design fountain pen, 4½in (11cm).
£10-15 *DH*

A Waterman's Ideal fountain pen, with 9ct gold cap band.
£70-80 *Bon*

A green marbled Conklin Endura Symetrik pen.
£70-75 *Bon*

A Parker Lucky Curve pen with gold nib.
£400-450 *Bon*

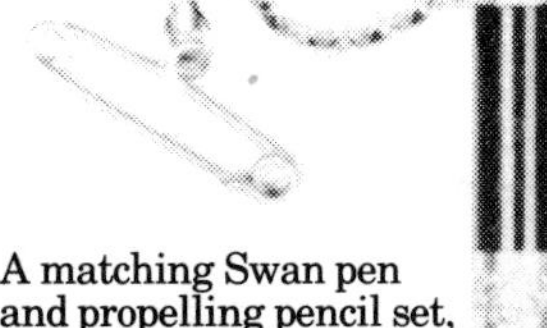

A matching Swan pen and propelling pencil set, in green leather presentation box.
£75-85 *Bon*

A Sheaffer Lifetime pen, c1920.
£120-130 *Bon*

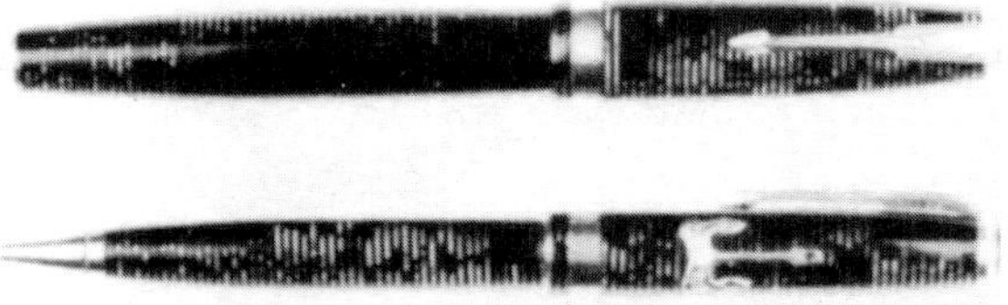

A special order Parker vacuumatic pen and pencil presentation set.
£100-150 *Bon*

These pens were made for Byers Shipmakers of Sunderland.

A matching Namiki pen and propelling pencil set, the pen with Namiki 14ct gold nib, signed Mitsu, the pencil by Masa.
£850-900 *Bon*

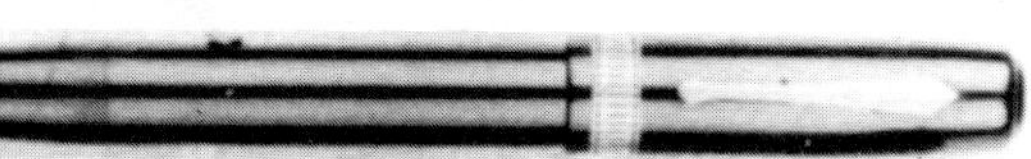

A Waterman's Patrician fountain pen, with gold plated band, lever and clip.
£250-300 *Bon*

A Dunhill-Namiki fountain pen, with 14ct gold nib.
£250-280 *Bon*

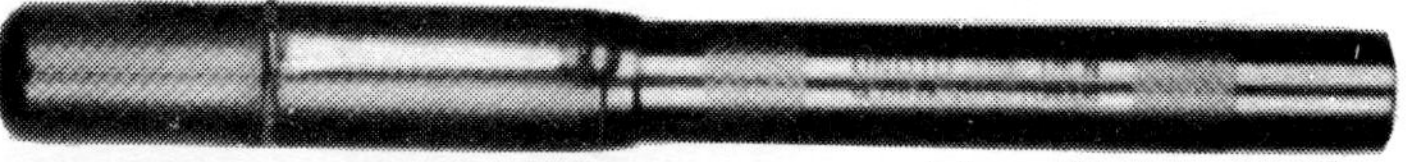

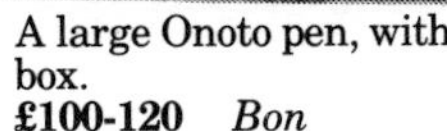

A large Onoto pen, with box.
£100-120 *Bon*

A 'Teddy' fountain pen, with gold nib, by O & G, 2½in (6cm).
£45-55 *Bon*

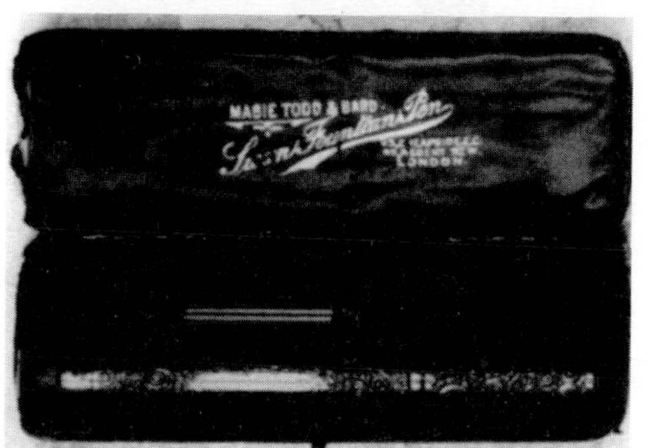

A rolled gold Swan eye-drop pen, in purple velvet lined box.
£150-160 *Bon*

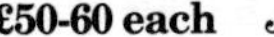

Three dip pens, c1887. **£50-60 each** *JAS*

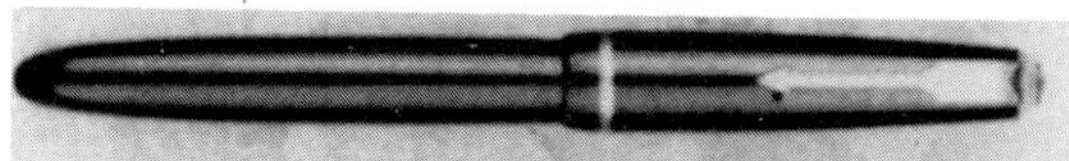

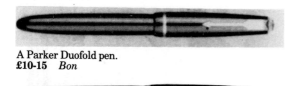

A Parker Duofold pen.
£10-15 *Bon*

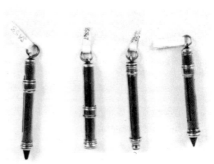

A Waterman Ideal safety pen.
£20-30 *Bon*

A Parker Senior Duofold, with 14ct gold nib, in original packaging.
£20-30 *Bon*

A Waterman's Ideal fountain pen, with box.
£60-70 *Bon*

Pencil Holders

Silver pencil holders.
£10-15 each *VB*

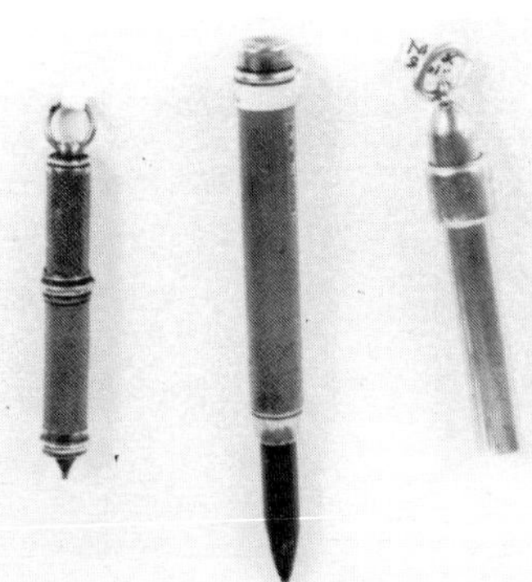

Silver pencil holders, 2½ to 3in (6.5 to 7.5cm).
£15-20 each *VB*

Silver pencil holders, 2in (5cm).
£15-20 each *VB*

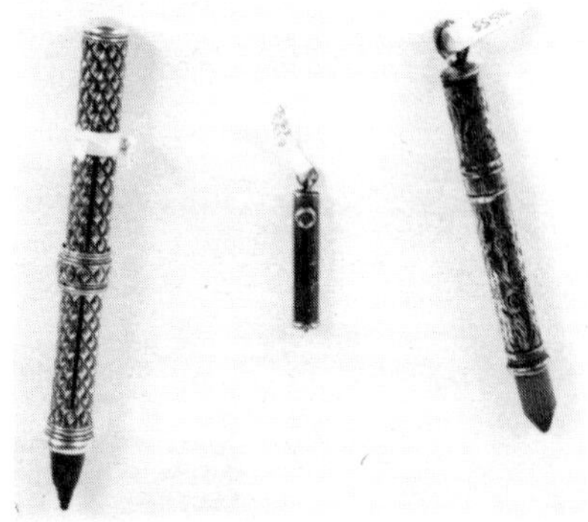

Silver pencil holders, 1½ to 3½in (4 to 7.5cm).
£8-18 each *VB*

Seals

A mother-of-pearl seal and a glass seal.
£10-25 each *VB*

A mother-of-pearl seal.
£25-35 *VB*

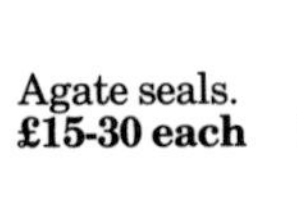

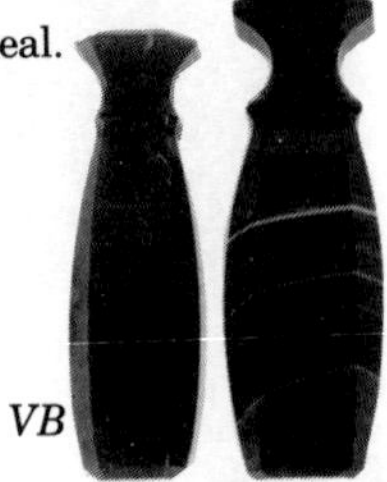

Agate seals.
£15-30 each *VB*

Propelling Pencils

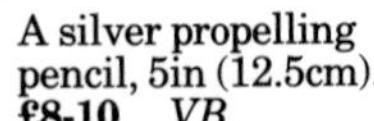

A silver propelling pencil, 5in (12.5cm).
£8-10 *VB*

A chrome travelling inkwell, 2in (5cm) high.
£12-15 *VB*

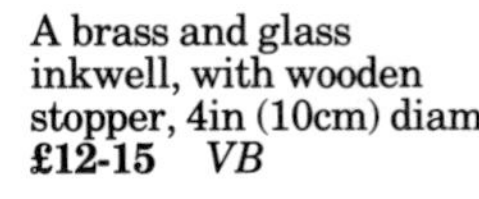

A brass and glass inkwell, with wooden stopper, 4in (10cm) diam.
£12-15 *VB*

Cross Reference
Inkwells

A propelling pencil and a miniature penknife.
£15-18 each *VB*

A late Victorian oak desk stand, 18in (45cm) wide.
£400-450 *CSK*

Desk Stands

A Victorian brass desk stand, 11½in (29cm) wide.
£140-160 *MB*

A chrome and glass pen and inkstand, c1940, 6½in (16cm) wide.
£25-35 *SAI*

A lizard skin writing set, with pad.
£75-100 *BEV*

A Sowerby glass diamond shaped inkstand, marked and dated 1878.
£100-120 *GH*

Cross Reference
Glass

Pen Trays

A Victorian inlaid tortoiseshell and brass desk tray, with painting on the reverse, 13 by 9in (33 by 23cm).
£200-250 *MB*

A Rockingham pen tray, c1820.
£55-65 *JAS*

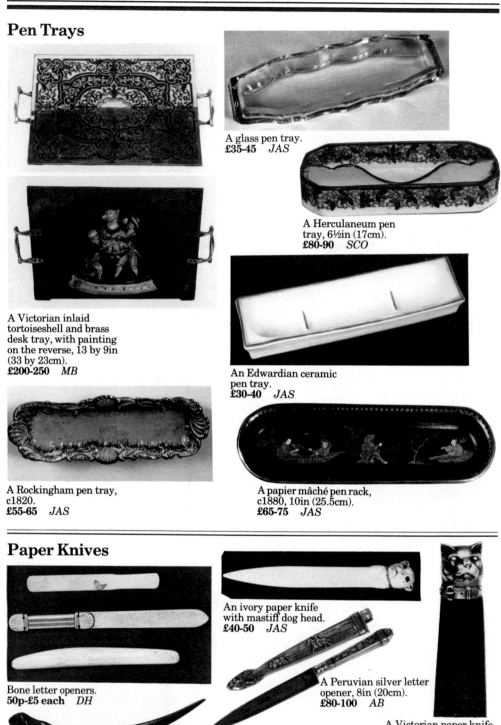

A glass pen tray.
£35-45 *JAS*

A Herculaneum pen tray, 6½in (17cm).
£80-90 *SCO*

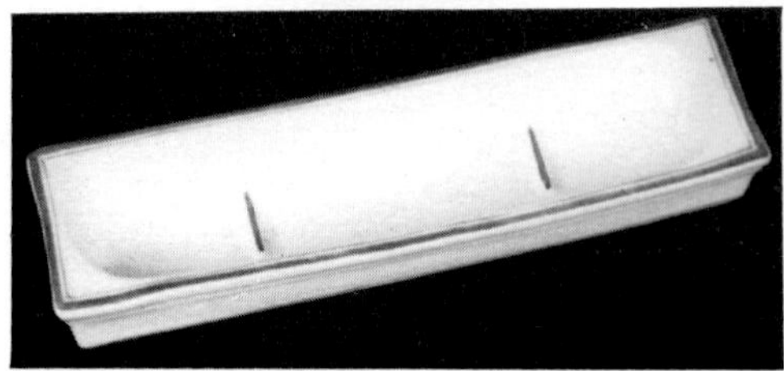

An Edwardian ceramic pen tray.
£30-40 *JAS*

A papier mâché pen rack, c1880, 10in (25.5cm).
£65-75 *JAS*

Paper Knives

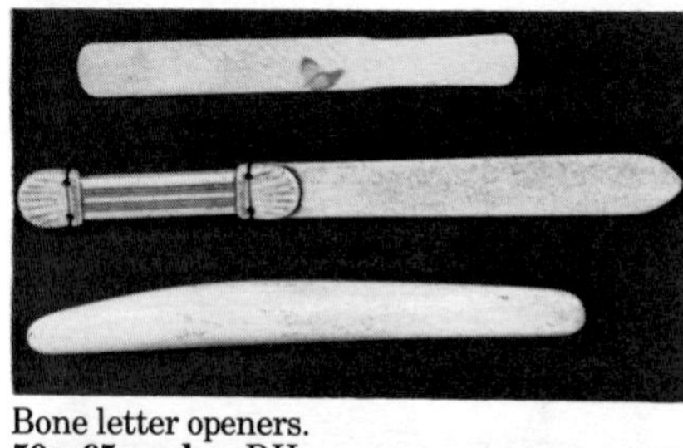

Bone letter openers.
50p-£5 each *DH*

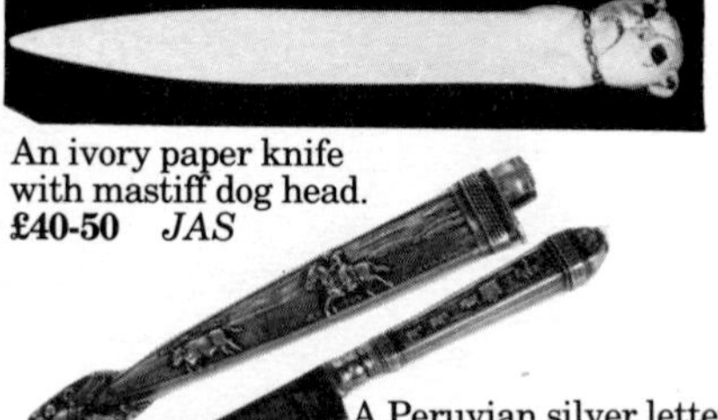

An ivory paper knife with mastiff dog head.
£40-50 *JAS*

A Peruvian silver letter opener, 8in (20cm).
£80-100 *AB*

A selection of paper knives.
£4-10 *VB*

A Victorian paper knife, with tortoiseshell blade, probably Thomas Spencer, London, 1880, 12½in (32cm).
£400-450 *CSK*

General

A writing slope.
£90-110 *DH*

A selection of writing accessories.
£2-12 each *VB*

A Victorian burr walnut writing slope, decorated with brass strapping, c1850.
£450-500 *DAN*

Letter holders, 4in (10cm).
£75-100 each *PC*

An early Victorian lacquer pencil case.
£75-85 *JAS*

Cross Reference
Smoking

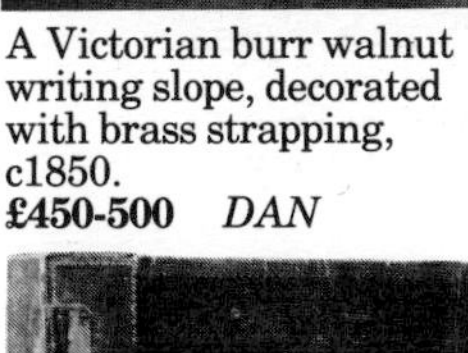

A French scarlet and parcel gilt leather writing case, 18thC, 17in (43cm) wide.
£350-400 *C*

A Persian pencil box, c1780.
£120-140 *JAS*

A red and gold painted tin blotter/cigarette box, advertising Craven A, 6½in (17cm).
£10-15 *DH*

An embosser.
£15-20 *MB*

Vesta Cases

A silver plated vesta case, 2in (5cm) high.
£16-20 *VB*

Cross Reference
Silver
Smoking

Three vesta cases.
£15-25 each *VB*

Three silver vesta cases.
£35-40 each *VB*

DIRECTORY OF SPECIALISTS

This directory is in no way complete. If you wish to be included in next year's directory or if you have a change of address or telephone number, please could you inform us by December 31st 1990. Entries will be repeated in subsequent editions unless we are requested otherwise. Finally we would advise readers to make contact by telephone before a visit, therefore avoiding a wasted journey, which nowadays is both time consuming and expensive.

DEALERS SPECIALISING IN COLLECTABLES

AERONAUTICA

London

Alfie's Antique Market,
13-25 Church Street, London, NW8
Tel: 01-723 6066

Hampshire

Cobwebs,
78 Northam Road, Southampton
Tel: (0703) 227458

AUTOMOBILIA

London

Grays Antique Market,
AAA Stand 121, 58 Davies Street, London, W1
Tel: 01-629 7034

Sarah Baddiel,
S.12 Grays Mews, London, W1
Tel: 01-408 1239/01-452 7243

Brian R. Verrall & Co,
20 Tooting Bec Road, London, SW17
Tel: 01-672 1144

Kent

Falstaff Antiques Motor Museum,
63-67 High Street, Rolvenden, Nr Cranbrook
Tel: (0580) 241234

Hampshire

Cobwebs,
78 Northam Road, Southampton
Tel: (0703) 227458

Lincolnshire

The Complete Automobilist
Dept 1, The Old Rectory, Greatford, Nr Stamford
Tel: (077 836) 312

West Midlands

Walton & Hipkiss,
194A Worcester Road, Hagley, Stourbridge
Tel: (0562) 885555/883426

Cotswold Motor Museum,
The Old Mill, Bourton on the Water, Gloucestershire
Tel: (0451) 21255

South Yorkshire

Bardwell Antiques,
919 Abbeydale Road, Sheffield
Tel: (0742) 584669

BAROMETERS

London

Patrick Capon,
350 Upper Street, Islington, N1
Tel: 01-354 0487/01-467 5722

Barometer Fair, at Cartographia Ltd,
Pied Bull Yard, Bury Place, Bloomsbury, WC1
Tel: 01-404 4521/4050

Avon

Barometer Shop,
3 Lower Park Row, Bristol
Tel: (0272) 272565

Cheshire

Derek Rayment Antiques,
Orchard House, Barton Road, Barton, Nr Malpas
Tel: (0829) 270429

Essex

It's About Time,
863 London Road, Westcliff-on-Sea
Tel: (0702) 72574

Hereford & Worcs

Barometer Shop,
New Street, Leominster
Tel: (0568) 3652

Somerset

Bernard G. House
(Mitre Antiques),
Market Place, Wells
Tel: (0749) 72607

BOTTLES

London

Rob Gee,
Flea Market, Camden Passage, London, N1
Tel: 01-226 6627

Georgian Village – 1st Floor, Islington Green, London, N1
Tel: 01-226 1571/5393

Isle of Wight

Kollectarama,
Old Railway Station, Horringford, Arreton
Tel: (0983) 865306

BOXES

London

Barham Antiques,
83 Portobello Road, London, W11
Tel: 01-727 3845

Berkshire

Boxes From Derek McIntosh,
10 Wickham Road, Stockcross, Newbury
Tel: (0488) 38295

Mostly Boxes,
92 & 52B High Street, Eton, Windsor
Tel: (0753) 858470

Yorkshire

Danby Antiques,
65 Heworth Road, York
Tel: (0904) 415280

BUCKLES

London

Moderne,
Stand 5, Georgian Village, Camden Passage, N1

Monica Jaertelius, The Mall, Camden Passage, N1
Tel: 01-546 2807

Ziggurat,
Stand J.22, Grays Mews, 1-7 Davies Mews, W1
Tel: 01-630 7943

Avon

Jessie's Button Box,
Great Western Antique Centre, Bartlett Street, Bath
Tel: (0272) 299065

BUTTONS

London

The Button Queen,
19 Marylebone Lane, W1
Tel: 01-935 1505

Avon

Jessie's Button Box,
Great Western Antique Centre, Bartlett Street, Bath
Tel: (0272) 299065

Dorset

The Old Button Shop,
Lytchett Minster
Tel: (0202) 622169

BUTTON HOOKS

London

David Hogg,
S.141 Grays Antique Market, 58 Davies Street, W1
Tel: 01-493 0208

Noelle Antiques,
S.26 Chelsea Antiques Market, 253 Kings Road, SW3
Tel: 01-352 5581

Kent

The Variety Box,
16 Chapel Place, Tunbridge Wells
Tel: (0892) 31868/21589

North Wales

Paul Gibbs,
25 Castle Street, Conwy
Tel: (0492) 593429

CAMERAS

London

Jessops,
65 Great Russell Street, WC1
Tel: 01-831 3640

Vintage Cameras Ltd,
254 & 256 Kirkdale, Sydenham, SE26
Tel: 01-778 5416/5841

London & Essex

Cliff Latford Photography,
G006, Aflie's Antique Market, 13-25 Church Street, London, NW8
and Colchester, Essex
Tel: 01-724 5650/(0206) 564474

Hertfordshire

P. Coombs,
87 Gills Hill Lane, Radlett
Tel: (0923) 856949

Warwickshire

Fred Topping,
Warwick Antique Centre, 20 High Street, Warwick
Tel: (0926) 499078

West Yorkshire

The Camera House,
Oakworth Hall, Colne Road, Oakworth
Tel: (0535) 42333

CARD CASES

London

Eureka Antiques,
105 Portobello Road, W11
(Saturdays)

Grays Antique Market,
58 Davies Street, W1
Tel: 01-629 7034

Avon

Carr Linford,
10-11 Walcot Buildings, London Road, Bath
Tel: (0225) 317516

Cheshire

Eureka Antiques,
18 Northenden Road, Sale
Tel: (061 962) 5629

Shropshire

F. C. Manser & Son Ltd,
53 Wyle Cop, Shrewsbury
Tel: (0743) 51120

CERAMICS

ART DECO

London

Beverley,
30 Church Street, Marylebone, NW8
Tel: 01-262 1576

Dimech,
248 Camden High Street, London, NW1
Tel: 01-485 8072

Jag
248 Camden High Street, London, NW1
Tel: 01-485 8072

Monty & Anita,
Stand V14-V15 Antiquarius,
135-141 Kings Road, SW3
Tel: 01-351 5382

A.J. Partners (Shelley),
M12 Antiquarius,
135-141 Kings Road, SW3
Tel: 01-376 3772

Past & Present,
York Arcade, Unit 5, Camden Passage, N1
Tel: 01-833 2640

Patrician Antiques,
1st Floor Georgian Village,
Camden Passage, N1
Tel: 01-359 4560/01-435 3159

Rotation Antiques,
Pierrepont Row Fleamarket,
Camden Passage, London, N1
Tel: 01-226 8211

Sailor Ceramics,
Camden Lock Antique Centre,
248 Camden High Street, London, NW1
Tel: 01-981 1180

Van Den Bosch,
1st Floor Georgian Village,
Camden Passage, N1
Tel: 01-359 4560/01-398 5410

Berkshire

Lupin Antiques,
134 Peascod Street, Windsor
Tel: (0753) 856244

Essex

A. Waine,
Tweedale, Rye Mill Lane,
Feering, Colchester

Hampshire

The Art Deco China Centre,
62 Murray Road, Horndean
Tel: (0705) 597440

Kent

Manor Antiques (Radford Ware)
2A High Street, Westerham
Tel: (0959) 64810

Lancashire

A.S. Antiques,
26 Broad Street, Pendleton, Salford
Tel: 061-737 5938

Shropshire

Antiques on the Square,
2 Sandford Court, Church Stretton
Tel: (0694) 724111

Expressions,
17 Princess Street, Shrewsbury
Tel: (0743) 51731

Somerset

Decoration,
Taunton Antique Centre, Silver Street, Taunton
Tel: (0460) 40958

East Sussex

Cirdeco,
24 North Street, St. Leonards-on-Sea
Tel: (0424) 421187/436996

Le Jazz Hot,
14 Prince Albert Street, Brighton
Tel: (0273) 206091

Tyne & Wear

Ian Sharp Antiques (Maling Ware),
23 Front Street, Tynemouth
Tel: 091-296 0656

Wales

Paul Gibbs Antiques,
25 Castle Street, Conwy
Tel: (0492) 593429

Warkwickshire

Biarritz,
Antique Arcade, 4 Sheep Street, Stratford-on-Avon
Tel: (0789) 297249

Castle Antiques,
1 Mill Street, Warwick
Tel: (0926) 498068

Jazz,
Civic Hall, Rother Street, Stratford-on-Avon
Tel: (0789) 298362

East Yorkshire

Tim Barnett,
Carlton Gallery, 60A Middle Street, Driffield
Tel: (0482) 443954

West Yorkshire

Muir Hewitt,
Halifax Antiques Centre,
Queens Road/Gibbet Street, Halifax
Tel: (0442) 66657/366657

DOULTON

London

Britannia,
Stand 101, Grays Antique Market, 58 Davies Street, W1
Tel: 01-629 6772

The Collector,
Alfie's Antique Market,
13-25 Church Street, NW8
Tel: 01-883 0024/01-706 4586

Doug Pinchin,
Dixons Antique Centre,
471 Upper Richmond Road West, East Sheen, SW14
Tel: 01-878 6788/01-948 1029

Leicester

Janice Williamson,
9 Coverdale Road, Meadows Wiston, Leicester
Tel: (0533) 812926

COMMEMORATIVE

London

Britannia,
Stand 101, Grays Antique Market, 58 Davies Street, W1
Tel: 01-629 6772

British Commemoratives,
1st Floor, Georgian Village,
Camden Passage, N1
Tel: 01-359 4560

East Sussex

Leonard Russell,
21 Kings Avenue, Mount Pleasant, Newhaven
Tel: (0273) 515153

GOSS & CRESTED CHINA

London

British Commemoratives,
1st Floor, Georgian Village,
Camden Passage, N1
Tel: 01-359 4560

Hampshire

Goss & Crested China Ltd,
62 Murray Road, Horndean
Tel: (0705) 597440

Kent

The Variety Box,
16 Chapel Place, Tunbridge Wells
Tel: (0892) 31868/21589

Warwickshire

Midlands Goss & Commemoratives,
Warwick Antique Centre,
22 High Street, Warwick
Tel: (0926) 495704

East Yorkshire

The Crested China Company,
Station House, Driffield
Tel: (0377) 47042

STAFFORDSHIRE

London

Gerald Clark Antiques,
1 High Street, Mill Hill Village, NW7
Tel: 01-906 0342

Jacqueline Oosthuizen,
1st Floor, Georgian Village,
Camden Passage, N1
Tel: 01-226 5393/01-359 4560
and
Chelsea Antique Market,
Unit 30, 253 Kings Road, SW3
Tel: 01-352 6071/5581

Jonathan Horne,
66B & C Kensington Church Street, W8
Tel: 01-221 5658

Kent

Dunsdale Lodge Antiques,
Westerham
Tel: (0959) 62160

Suffolk

Crafers Antiques,
The Hill, Wickham Market
Tel: (0728) 747347

West Midlands

Ray & Diane Ginns,
39 Norman Road, Northfield, Birmingham
Tel: 021-476 8319

Wiltshire

Bratton Antiques,
Market Place, Westbury
Tel: (0373) 823021

TORQUAY POTTERY

London

Jacqueline Oosthuizen,
1st Floor, Georgian Village,
Camden Passage, N1
Tel: 01-226 5393/01-359 4560
and
Chelsea Antique Market,
Unit 30, 253 Kings Road, SW3
Tel: 01-352 6071/5581

POT LIDS

London

Rob Gee,
Flea Market, Camden Passage, N1
Tel: 01-226 6627

East Sussex
Ron Beech,
150 Portland Road, Hove
Tel: (0273) 724477

Warwickshire
Burman Antiques,
5A Chapel Street, Stratford-on-Avon
Tel: (0789) 293917

POTTERY

London
Robert Young Antiques,
68 Battersea Bridge Road, SW11
Tel: 01-228 7847

Valerie Howard,
131E Kensington Church Street, London, W8
Tel: 01-792 9702

Avon
Robert Pugh,
13 Walcot Buildings, London Road, Bath
Tel: (0554) 772613

Hampshire
Millers of Chelsea Ltd,
Netherbrook House,
Christchurch Road, Ringwood
Tel: (0425) 472062

Kent
Angela Page Antiques,
Tunbridge Wells
Tel: (0892) 22217

Shropshire
Howard's Antiques,
73 Wyle Cop, Shrewsbury
Tel: (0743) 60737

Wales
Powys,
Islwyn Watkins, 1 High Street/
29 Market Street, Knighton
Tel: (0547) 520145/528940

Howards Antiques,
10 Alexandra Road,
Aberystwyth, Dyfed
Tel: (0970) 624973

Warwickshire
Janice Paull,
Warwick Antique Centre, 20-22 High Street, Warwick
Tel: (0926) 495704

Yorkshire
In Retrospect,
2 Pavement, Pocklinton, York
Tel: (0759) 304894

VICTORIAN CERAMICS

London
Sue Norman,
Stand L4 Antiquarius,
135 Kings Road, London, SW3
Tel: 01-352 7217

Avon
Scott's,
Stand 24, Great Western Antique Centre, Bartlett Street, Bath
Tel: (0225) 310388

Gloucestershire
Acorn Antiques,
Sheep Street, Stow-on-the-Wold
Tel: (0451) 31519

Nottinghamshire
Breck Antiques,
726 Mansfield Road,
Nottingham
Tel: (0602) 605263

Tyne & Wear
Ian Sharp Antiques (Sunderland Lustre),
23 Front Street, Tynemouth
Tel: 091-296 0656

Warwickshire
Fan Attic,
Stratford Antique Centre, Ely Street, Stratford-on-Avon
Tel: (0789) 297496

Bow Cottage Antiques,
Stratford Antique Arcade,
Sheep Street, Stratford-on-Avon
Tel: (0789) 297249

CORKSCREWS

London
David,
141 Grays Antique Market,
Davies Street, W1
Tel: 01-493 0208

Bedfordshire
Christopher Sykes Antiques,
The Old Parsonage, Woburn
Tel: (0525) 290259

Cumbria
Bacchus Antiques,
Longlands at Cartmel
Tel: (044 854) 475

East Sussex
Chateaubriand Antiques Centre,
High Street, Burwash
Tel: (0435) 882535

DOLLS

London
Antique Dolls,
Stand L14 Grays Mews,
1-7 Davies Mews, W1
Tel: 01-499 6600

Brenda Gerwat-Clark,
Alfie's Antique Market, 13-25 Church Street, London, NW8
Tel: 01-706 4699

Chelsea Lion Dolls,
Chenil Galleries, 181-183 Kings Road, London, SW3
Tel: 01-351 9338

Childhood Memories,
Teapot Arcade, Portobello, London, W11

The Doll Cupboard,
Portwine Galleries, Unit No. 17, 175 Portobello Road, London, W11
Tel: 01-727 4681/(0378) 76848

Dollyland,
864 Green Lanes, Winchmore Hill, London, N21
Tel: 01-360 1053

Pat Walker,
Georgian Village, Camden Passage, N1
Tel: 01-359 4560/01-435 3159

Yesterday Child,
24 The Mall, Camden Passage, N1
Tel: 01-354 1601/(0908) 583403

Cheshire
Dollectable,
53 Lower Bridge Street, Chester
Tel: (0244) 44888/679195

Gloucestershire
Lillian Middleton's Antique Dolls Shop,
Days Stable, Sheep Street,
Stow-on-the-Wold
Tel: (0451) 31542

Hampshire
Toys Through Time,
Fareham
Tel: (0329) 288678

Hertfordshire
Carrousel,
59 High Street, Hemel Hempstead
Tel: (0442) 219772/42518

Kent
Hadlow Antiques,
No. 1 The Pantiles, Tunbridge Wells
Tel: (0892) 29858

Surrey
Dorking Dolls House Gallery,
23 West Street, Dorking
Tel: (0306) 885785

Victoriana Dolls,
Reigate
Tel: (0737) 249525

East Sussex
Dolls Hospital,
17 George Street, Hastings
Tel: (0424) 444117/422758

Sue Pearson,
13½ Prince Albert Street,
Brighton
Tel: (0273) 29247

West Sussex
Amelia Dolls,
Copthorne Group Antiques,
Copthorne Bank, Nr. Crawley
Tel: (0342) 712802/(0342) 713223

DOLLS HOUSE FURNITURE

Essex
Blackwells of Hawkwell,
733 London Road,
Westcliff-on-Sea
Tel: (0702) 72248

TEDDY BEARS

London
Heather's Teddys,
World Famous Arcade,
177 Portobello Road, London, W11
Tel: 01-204 0106

Past and Present Toys,
862 Green Lanes, Winchmore Hill, London N21
Tel: 01-364 1370

Berkshire
Asquiths of Windsor,
10 George V Place, Thames Avenue, Windsor
Tel: (0753) 854954/831200

Gloucestershire
Park House Antiques,
Park Street, Stow-on-the-Wold
Tel: (0451) 30159

Oxfordshire
Teddy Bears,
99 High Street, Witney
Tel: (0993) 702616

East Sussex
Sue Pearson,
13½ Prince Albert Street,
Brighton
Tel: (0273) 29247

COCKTAIL/ DRINKING

London
Beverley,
30 Church Street, Marylebone, NW8
Tel: 01-262 1576

EPHEMERA

CIGARETTE CARDS

London
Murray Cards (International) Ltd,
51 Watford Way, Hendon Central, NW4
Tel: 01-202 5688

Avon
Winstone Stamp Company,
S.82 Great Western Antiques Centre, Bartlett Street, Bath
Tel: (0225) 310388

Middlesex

Albert's Cigarette Card Specialists,
113 London Road, Twickenham
Tel: 01-891 3067

Somerset

The London Cigarette Card Co Ltd,
Sutton Road, Somerton
Tel: (0458) 73452

Suffolk

W. L. Hoad,
9 St Peter's Road, Kirkley, Lowestoft
Tel: (0502) 587758

COMICS

London

Forbidden Planet,
71 New Oxford Street, W1
Tel: 01-379 6042

Gosh Comics,
39 Great Russell Street, WC1
Tel: 01-636 1011

Heroes,
21 Canonbury Lane, Islington, N1 Tel: 01-359 8329

Somerset

Yesterday's Paper,
40 South View, Holcombe Rogus, Wellington
Tel: (0823) 672774

GREETINGS CARDS

London

Images (Peter Stockham),
16 Cecil Court, Charing Cross Road, WC2
Tel: 01-836 8661

Pleasures of Past Times,
11 Cecil Court, Charing Cross Road, WC2
Tel: 01-836 1142

MATCHBOXES

Kent

Kollectomania,
4 Catherine Street, Rochester
Tel: (0634) 45099

POSTCARDS

London

Memories,
18 Bell Lane, Hendon, NW4
Tel: 01-203 1772/01-202 9080

Cheshire

Avalon,
1 City Walls, Northgate Street, Chester
Tel: (0244) 318406

Derbyshire

Norman King,
24 Dinting Road, Glossop
Tel: (045 74) 2946

Essex

R.F. Postcards,
17 Hilary Crescent, Rayleigh
Tel: (0268) 743222

Kent

Mike Sturge,
39 Union Street, Maidstone
Tel: (0622) 54702

West Midlands

George Sawyer,
11 Frayne Avenue, Kingswinford
Tel: (0384) 273847

Norfolk

Bluebird Arts,
1 Mount Street, Cromer
Tel: (0263) 512384/78487

Northamptonshire

Shelron,
9 Brackley Road, Towcester
Tel: (0327) 50242

Nottinghamshire

Reflections of a Bygone Age,
15 Debdale Lane, Keyworth
Tel: (06077) 4079

T. Vennett Smith,
11 Nottingham Road, Gotham
Tel: (0602) 830541

East Sussex

John & Mary Bartholomew,
The Mint Arcade, 71 The Mint, Rye
Tel: (0797) 225952

West Sussex

Bygones, Collectors Shop,
123 South Street, Lancing
Tel: (0903) 750051/763470

Wiltshire

David Wells,
Salisbury Antique & Collectors Market, 37 Catherine Street, Salisbury
Tel: (0425) 476899

BEER MATS

West Midlands

Roger Summers,
92 Nursery Road, Edgbaston, Birmingham

PLAYING CARDS

London

Intercol (Yasha Beresiner),
1A Camden Walk, Islington Green, N1
Tel: 01-354 2599

SCRIPOPHILY

Essex

G.K.R. Bonds Ltd.,
PO Box 1, Kelvedon
Tel: (0376) 71711

FANS

Kent

The Variety Box,
16 Chapel Place, Tunbridge Wells
Tel: (0892) 31868/21589

Shropshire

F. C. Manser & Son Ltd,
53-54 Wyle Cop, Shrewsbury
Tel: (0743) 51120

FISHING

Dorset

Yesterday's Tackle & Books,
42 Clingan Road, Southbourne
Tel: (0202) 476586

Shropshire

Vintage Fishing Tackle Shop and Angling Art Gallery,
103 Longden Coleham, Shrewsbury
Tel: (0743) 69373

Scotland

Jamie Maxtone Graham,
Lyne Haugh, Lyne Station, Peebles
Tel: (072 14) 304

Jess Miller,
PO Box 1, Birnam, Dunkeld, Perthshire
Tel: (03502) 522

Wales

Brindley John Ayers,
45 St. Anne's Road, Hakin, Milford Haven, Pembrokeshire
Tel: (06462) 78359

GOLFING

London

Sarah Baddiel,
The Book Gallery, B.12 Grays Mews, 1-7 Davies Mews, W1
Tel: 01-408 1239/01-452 7243

King & Country,
Unit 46, Alfie's Antique Market, 13-25 Church Street, NW8
Tel: 01-724 3439

GLASS – EARLY 18thC/19thC

London

Christine Bridge,
78 Castelnau, SW13
Tel: 01-741 5501

Pryce & Brise,
79 Moore Park Road, Fulham, SW6
Tel: 01-736 1864

Mark J. West – Cobb Antiques,
39B High Street, Wimbledon Village, SW19
Tel: 01-946 2811/01-540 7982

Avon

Somervale Antiques,
6 Radstock Road, Midsomer Norton, Bath
Tel: (0761) 412686

Kent

Variety Box,
16 Chapel Place, Tunbridge Wells
Tel: (0892) 31868/21589

Warwickshire

Sharon Ball,
Stratford-on-Avon Antique Centre, Ely Street, Stratford-on-Avon
Tel: (0789) 204180

GLASS – 20thC

London

Frank Andrews – Monart and Vasart,
10 Vincent Road, London, N22
Tel: 01-889 3445 (Business)
Tel: 01-881 0658 (Home)

Beverley – Cloud Glass,
30 Church Street, NW8
Tel: 01-262 1576

The Scottish Connection,
Alfie's Antique Market,
13-25 Church Street, NW8
Tel: 01-723 6066

Stephen Watson – Powell,
Alfie's Antique Market,
13-25 Church Street, NW8
Tel: 01-723 0678

HAIRDRESSING/ HAT PINS

London

Ursula,
P16, 15 & 14 Antiquarius,
135 Kings Road, SW3
Tel: 01-352 2203

Kent

The Lace Basket,
1A East Cross, Tenterden
Tel: (05806) 3923

Variety Box,
16 Chapel Place, Tunbridge Wells
Tel: (0892) 31868/21589

INKWELLS

London

Jasmin Cameron,
Green & Stone, 259 Kings Road, SW3
Tel: 01-352 0837/6521

Patrician,
1st Floor, Georgian Village, Camden Passage, N1
Tel: 01-359 4560/01-435 3159

Berkshire

Mostly Boxes,
92 & 52B High Street, Eton, Windsor
Tel: (0753) 858470

Kent
Ann Lingard,
Ropewalk Antiques, Rye
Tel: (0797) 223486

JEWELLERY

VICTORIAN/ EDWARDIAN

Gloucestershire
Lynn Greenwold,
Digbeth Street,
Stow-on-the-Wold
Tel: (0451) 30398

Kent
Old Saddlers Antiques,
Church Road, Goudhurst,
Cranbrook
Tel: (0580) 211458

Norfolk
Peter Howkins,
39, 40 and 135 King Street,
Great Yarmouth
Tel: (0493) 844639

ART DECO

London
Pierre De Fresne 'Beaux Bijoux',
Q 9/10 Antiquarius, 135 Kings Road, SW3
Tel: 01-352 8882

Ziggurat,
J22 Grays Mews, 1-7 Davies Mews, W1
Tel: 01-630 7943

JUKE BOXES

Hertfordshire
Connexions (UK) plc
Unit 3, South Mimms Distribution Centre, Huggins Lane, Welham Green
Tel: (07072) 72091

Surrey
Nostalgia Amusements,
73 Angus Close, Chessington
Tel: 01-397 6867

KITCHENALIA

London
David,
141 Grays Antique Market,
Davies Street, W1
Tel: 01-493 0208

Relic Antiques,
248 Camden High Street,
London, NW1
Tel: 01-485 8072

Hampshire
Millers of Chelsea Ltd,
Netherbrook House,
Christchurch Road, Ringwood
Tel: (0425) 472062

Lancashire
The Old Bakery,
36 Inglewhite Road, Longridge,
Nr. Preston
Tel: (0772) 785411

Kent
Penny Lampard,
28 High Street, Headcorn
Tel: (0622) 890682

Up Country,
Old Corn Stores, 68 St John's Road, Tunbridge Wells
Tel: (0892) 23341

West Midlands
The Dog House,
309 Bloxwich Road, Walsall
Tel: (0922) 30829

Surrey
Wych House Antiques,
Wych Hill, Woking
Tel: (04862) 64636

East Sussex
Ann Lingard,
Rope Walk Antiques, Rye
Tel: (0797) 223486

LE BLOND PRINTS

Warwickshire
Janice Paull,
Beehive Antiques, Warwick Antique Centre, 20-22 High Street, Warwick
Tel: (0926) 495704

LOCKS & KEYS

Nottinghamshire
The Keyhole,
Dragonwyck, Far Back Lane,
Farnsfield, Newark
Tel: (0623) 882590

LUGGAGE

London
Stanhope Bowery,
Grays Antique Market, Davies Street, W1
Tel: 01-629 6194

METALWARE

London
Christopher Bangs,
SW11
Tel: 01-223 5676

Jack Casimir Ltd,
The Brass Shop, 23 Pembridge Road, W11
Tel: 01-727 8643

Avon
Nick Marchant,
13 Orwell Drive, Keynsham,
Bristol
Tel: (0272) 865182

Bedfordshire
Christopher Sykes,
The Old Parsonage, Woburn
Tel: (0525) 290259

Kent
Old Saddlers Antiques,
Church Road, Goudhurst,
Cranbrook
Tel: (0580) 211458

Oxfordshire
Key Antiques,
11 Horse Fair, Chipping Norton
Tel: (0608) 3777

MILITARIA

MEDALS

Hampshire
Charles Antiques,
101 The Hundred, Romsey
Tel: (0794) 512885

Scotland
Edinburgh Coin Shop,
2 Powarth Crescent, Edinburgh
Tel: 031-229 3007/2915

East Sussex
Wallis & Wallis,
West Street Auction Galleries,
Lewes
Tel: (0273) 480208

ARMS & ARMOUR

London
Michael German,
38B Kensington Church Street,
W8
Tel: 01-937 2771

East Sussex
George Weiner,
2 Market Street, The Lanes,
Brighton
Tel: (0273) 729948

West Yorks
Andrew Spencer Bottomley,
The Coach House,
Thongsbridge, Holmfirth
Tel: (0484) 685234

ARMS & MILITARIA

London
Pieter G. K. Oosthuizen,
16 Britten Street, London, SW3
Tel: 01-352 1094/01-352 1493

Kent
Keith & Veronica Reeves,
Burgate Antiques, 10c Burgate,
Canterbury
Tel: (0227) 456500/(0634) 375098

Surrey
West Street Antiques,
63 West Street, Dorking
Tel: (0306) 883487

East Sussex
V.A.G. & Co,
Possingworth Craft Centre,
Brownings Farm, Blackboys,
Uckfield
Tel: (0323) 507488

Wallis & Wallis,
West Street Auction Galleries,
Lewes
Tel: (0273) 480208

ORIENTAL

London
Ormonde Gallery,
156 Portobello Road, W11
Tel: 01-229 9800/(042482) 226

Dorset
Lionel Geneen Ltd,
781 Christchurch Road,
Boscombe, Bournemouth
Tel: (0202) 422961

East Sussex
Chateaubriand Antique Centre,
High Street, Burwash
Tel: (0435) 882535

PAPIER MÂCHÉ

London
Sue Simpson,
The Original Chelsea Antique Market, Stand 28, 245-263 King's Road, London, SW3
Tel: 01-352 5581

Kent
Antiques & Interiors,
22 Ashford Road, Tenterden
Tel: (05806) 5422

PERFUME BOTTLES

London
Patrician Antiques,
1st Floor, Georgian Village,
Camden Passage, N1
Tel: 01-359 4560/01-435 3159

Trio (Theresa Clayton),
Grays Mews, 1-7 Davies Mews,
W1
Tel: 01-629 1184

POLICE MEMORABILIA

London
David,
141 Grays Antique Market,
Davies Street, W1
Tel: 01-493 0208

Dorset
Mervyn A. Mitton,
161 The Albany, Manor Road,
Bournemouth

RADIOS

Devon
Jonathan Hill,
2-4 Brook Street, Bampton
Tel: (0398) 31310

RADIOS

London
The Originals,
Stand 37, Alfie's Antique Market, 13-25 Church Street,
NW8
Tel: 01-724 3439

Hereford & Worcs
Radiocraft,
56 Main Street, Sedgeberrow,
Nr Evesham
Tel: (0386) 881988

RAILWAYS
Avon
Winstone Stamp Co,
Great Western Antique Market,
Bartlett Street, Bath
Tel: (0225) 310388

West Midlands
Railwayana Collectors Journal,
7 Ascot Road, Moseley,
Birmingham

Yorkshire
National Railway Museum,
Leeman Road, York
Tel: (0904) 621261

SCIENTIFIC & MEDICAL INSTRUMENTS
London
David Weston Ltd,
44 Duke Street, St James's, SW1
Tel: 01-839 1051/2/3

Bedfordshire
Christopher Sykes,
The Old Parsonage, Woburn
Tel: (0525) 290259

Surrey
David Burns,
116 Chestnut Grove, New
Malden
Tel: 01-949 7356

SEWING
London
The Thimble Society of London,
The Bees, S134 Grays Antique
Market, 58 Davies Street, W1
Tel: 01-493 0560

Kent
The Variety Box,
16 Chapel Place, Tunbridge
Wells
Tel: (0892) 31868/21589

Suffolk
Crafers Antiques,
The Hill, Wickham Market
Tel: (0728) 747347

SHIPPING
Hampshire
Cobwebs,
78 Northam Road, Southampton
Tel: (0703) 227458

SILVER
London
Donohoe,
L25/7 M10/12 Grays Mews,
1-7 Davies Mews, W1
Tel: 01-629 5633/01-455 5507

Goldsmith & Perris,
Stand 327, Alfie's Antique
Market, 13-25 Church Street,
NW8
Tel: 01-724 7051

The London Silver Vaults,
Chancery House, 53-65
Chancery Lane, WC2
Tel: 01-242 3844

Kent
The Variety Box,
16 Chapel Place, Tunbridge
Wells
Tel: (0892) 31868/21589

Oxfordshire
Thames Gallery,
Thameside, Henley-on-Thames
Tel: (0491) 572449

Shropshire
F. C. Manser & Son Ltd,
53-54 Wyle Cop, Shrewsbury
Tel: (0743) 51120

SPORT – FOOTBALL
London
Final Whistle,
50, 61-63 Alfie's Antique
Market, 13-25 Church Street,
London, NW8
Tel: 01-262 3423

TARTANWARE
London
Eureka Antiques,
Geoffrey Vanns Arcade,
105 Portobello Road, W11
(Saturdays)

Grays Antique Market,
58 Davies Street, W1
Tel: 01-629 7034

Cheshire
Eureka Antiques,
18 Northenden Road, Sale
Tel: 061-962 5629

TELEPHONES
Devon
Bampton Telephone & General
Museum of Communication and
Domestic History,
4 Brook Street, Bampton

Kent
Candlestick & Bakelite,
3 Amherst Drive, St. Mary
Cray, Orpington
Tel: (0689) 23448/01-445 1100

Scotland
Now & Then,
7 & 9 Crosscauseway,
Edinburgh
Tel: 031-668 2927

TEXTILES
SAMPLERS
London
Sophia Blanchard,
Alfie's Antique Market, Church
Street, NW8
Tel: 01-723 5731

Matthew Adams Antiques,
69 Portobello Road, W11
Tel: 01-579 5560

QUILTS, PATCHWORK, COSTUME
London
The Antique Textile Company,
100 Portland Road, Holland
Park, W11
Tel: 01-221 7730

The Gallery of Antique Costume & Textiles,
2 Church Street, Marylebone, NW8
Tel: 01-723 9981

Lincolnshire

20th Century Frocks,
Lincolnshire Art Centre, Bridge Street, Horncastle
Tel: (06582) 7794/(06588) 3638

West Yorkshire

Echoes,
650A Halifax Road, Eastwood, Todmorden
Tel: (070 681) 7505

LINEN & LACE

London

Act One Hire Ltd,
2A Scampston Mews, Cambridge Gardens, London, W10
Tel: 01-960 1456/1494

Antiquarius,
135-141 Kings Road, SW3
Tel: 01-351 5353

Audrey Field,
Alfie's Antique Market,
13-25 Church Street, NW8
Tel: 01-723 6066

Devon

Honiton Lace Shop,
44 High Street, Honiton
Tel: (0404) 42416

Kent

Antiques & Interiors,
22 Ashford Road, Tenterden
Tel: (05806) 5462

The Lace Basket,
1A East Cross, Tenterden
Tel: (05806) 3923

East Sussex

Celia Charlotte's,
7 Malling Street, Lewes
Tel: (0273) 473303

Chateaubriand Antique Centre, High Street, Burwash
Tel: (0435) 882535

TILES

London

Ilse Antiques,
30-32 The Vaults, The Georgian Village, Islington, N1

East Sussex

Ann Lingard,
Rope Walk Antiques, Rye
Tel: (0797) 223486

The Old Mint House,
Pevensey
Tel: (0323) 762337

Wales

Paul Gibbs Antiques,
25 Castle Street, Conwy
Tel: (0492) 593429

Victorian Fireplaces (Simon Priestley),
Ground Floor, Cardiff Antique Centre, 69/71 St Mary Street, Cardiff
Tel: (0222) 30970/226049

TINS & METAL SIGNS

London

Keith, Old Advertising,
Unit 14, 155A Northcote Road, Battersea, SW11
Tel: 01-228 0741/6850

Avon

Michael & Jo Saffell,
3 Walcot Buildings, London Road, Bath
Tel: (0225) 315857

Oxfordshire

R.A.T.S.,
Unit 16, Telford Road, Bicester
Tel: (0869) 242161/40842

East Sussex

RIN-TIN-TIN,
34 North Road, Brighton
Tel: (0273) 672424/
(0273) 733689 (Eves)

Wiltshire

Relic Antiques, Lea, Malmesbury
Tel: (0666) 822332

TOYS

MECHANICAL

London

Stuart Cropper,
Grays Mews, 1-7 Davies Mews, W1
Tel: 01-629 7034

Yonna Cohen,
B19 Grays Mews, 1-7 Davies Mews, London, W1
Tel: 01-629 3644

Avon

Great Western Toys, Great Western Antique Centre, Bartlett Street, Bath

TEDDY BEARS

London

Pam Hebbs,
5 The Annexe, Camden Passage, Islington, N1

DIECAST MODELS

London

Colin Baddiel,
Grays Mews, 1-7 Davies Mews, W1
Tel: 01-408 1239/01-452 7243

Mint & Boxed,
110 High Street, Edgware, Middx
Tel: 01-952 2002

Past Present Toys,
862 Green Lanes, Winchmore Hill, London N21
Tel: 01-364 1370

Buckinghamshire

Cars Only,
4 Granville Square, Willen Local Centre, Willen, Milton Keynes Tel: (0908) 690024

Cornwall

Model Garage (Redruth) Ltd,
Lanner Hill, Redruth
Tel: (0209) 215589/211311

Isle of Wight

Nostalgia Toy Museum,
High Street, Godshill
Tel: (0983) 730055

Norfolk

Trains & Olde Tyme Toys,
Aylsham Road, Norwich
Tel: (0603) 413585

Shropshire

Stretton Models,
12 Beaumont Road, Church Stretton Tel: (0694) 723737

East Sussex

Clockwork and Steam,
35 Western Street, Brighton
Tel: (0273) 203290

West Sussex

Trains,
67 London Road, Bognor Regis
Tel: (0243) 864727

Warwickshire

Time Machine,
Paul M. Kennelly, 198 Holbrook Lane, Coventry
Tel: (0203) 663557

Wiltshire

David Wells,
Salisbury Antique & Collectors Market, 37 Catherine Street, Salisbury
Tel: (0425) 476899

Yorkshire

Andrew Clarke,
42 Pollard Lane, Bradford
Tel: (0274) 636042

John & Simon Haley,
89 Northgate, Halifax
Tel: (0422) 822148

Wales

Corgi Toys Ltd,
Kingsway, Swansea Industrial Estate, Swansea
Tel: (0792) 586223

MONEY BOXES

Yorkshire

John Haley,
89 Northgate, Halifax
Tel: (0422) 822148

GAMES

London

Donay,
35 Camden Passage, N1
Tel: 01-359 1880

ROCKING HORSES

Cornwall

The Millcraft Rocking Horse Co, Lower Trannack Mill, Coverack Bridges, Helston
Tel: (0326) 573316

Wales

Stuart & Pam MacPherson,
A.P.E.S.,
Ty Isaf, Pont Y Gwyddel,
Llanfair T.H., Abergele, Clwyd
Tel: (074 579) 365

TREEN

London

Simon Castle,
38B Kensington Church Street, W8 Tel: 01-892 2840

Wynyards Antiques,
5 Ladbroke Road, W11
Tel: 01-221 7936

Buckinghamshire

A. & E. Foster,
Little Heysham, Forge Road, Naphill Tel: (024 024) 2024

TUNBRIDGEWARE

Berks

Mostly Boxes,
52B High Street, Eton
Tel: (0753) 858470

Kent

Strawsons Antiques
33, 39 & 41 The Pantiles, Tunbridge Wells
Tel: (0892) 30607

The Variety Box,
16 Chapel Place, Tunbridge Wells Tel: (0892) 31868/21589

East Sussex

Barclay Antiques,
7 Village Mews, Little Common, Bexhill-on-Sea
Tel: (0797) 222734

WALKING STICKS

London

Cekay Antiques,
Grays Antique Market,
58 Davies Street, W1
Tel: 01-629 5130

Michael German,
38B Kensington Church Street, W8 Tel: 01-937 2771

WATCHES

London

Pieces of Time, Grays Mews,
1-7 Davies Street, W1
Tel: 01-629 2422

CALENDAR OF FAIRS from June 1990

This calendar is in no way complete. If you wish your event to be included in next year's edition or if you have a change of address or telephone number, please could you inform us by December 31st 1990. Finally we would advise readers to make contact by telephone before a visit, therefore avoiding a wasted journey, which nowadays is both time consuming and expensive.

London

Sun June 3rd
Antiques Fair, The Kensington Hilton, 179-199 Holland Park Avenue, W11
Heritage Antiques Fairs.
Tel: 01-624 5173

Antiques Fair, The Portman Inter-Continental Hotel, 22 Portman Square
K.M. Fairs.
Tel: 01-794 3551/4551

Antiques Fair, The Sheraton Park Tower, 101 Knightsbridge, SW1
Monway Ltd. Tel: 01-603 0380

Antiques & Collectors Fairs, Alexandra Palace, Wood Green
Pig & Whistle Promotions.
Tel: 01-883 7061

Fri June 8th-10th
Ceramics Fair, The Cumberland Hotel, Marble Arch, W1
Wakefield Ceramics Fairs.
Tel: (0634) 723461

Fri June 8th-11th
The International Ceramics Fair & Seminar, The Park Lane Hotel, Piccadilly, W1
B. Haughton. Tel: 01-734 5491

Sat June 9th
The Kensington Broccante Antiques Fair, Kensington Town Hall Bagatelle Fairs.
Tel: 01-391 2339

Sun June 10th
Antiques Fair, The Kensington Palace Hotel, De Vere Gardens, Kensington High Street, W8
Heritage Antiques Fairs.
Tel: 01-624 5173

Antiques & Collectors Fair, Picketts-Lock Leisure Centre, Edmonton, N9
Jax Fairs. Tel: (0444) 400570

Antiques Fair, The Portman Inter-Continental Hotel, 22 Portman Square K.M. Fairs.
Tel: 01-794 3551/4551

The Dulwich College (A205)
Margaret Browne Antiques & Collectors Fairs.
Tel: 01-874 3622

Antiques Fair, The Rembrandt Hotel, Thurloe Place, SW7
Monway Ltd. Tel: 01-603 0380

Thurs June 14th-23rd
The Grosvenor House Antiques Fair, Grosvenor House Hotel, Park Lane, W1
Evan Steadman.
Tel: (0799) 26699

Sat June 16th
Wandsworth Common, Mary Magdalen Church Hall, Trinity Road Margaret Browne Antiques & Collectors Fairs.
Tel: 01-874 3622

Sun June 17th
Decorative Antiques Fair, Hampstead Old Town Hall, Haverstock Hill
Adams Antiques Fairs.
Tel: 01-254 4054

Antiques Fair, The London Marriott Hotel, Grosvenor Square
Heritage Antiques Fairs.
Tel: 01-624 5173

Antiques Fair, The Park Lane Hotel, Piccadilly, W1
Monway Ltd. Tel: 01-603 0380

Mon June 18th-19th
Antique Map & Print Fair, The Bonnington Hotel, Southampton Row, WC1
Antiquarian Map & Print Fairs.
Tel: (0242) 514287

Mon June 18th-20th
The Annual International Book Fair, The Cafe Royal, Regent Street, W1
West Country Antiques & Collectors Fairs.
Tel: (0364) 52182

Sun June 24th
Quality Antiques Fair, The Royal Horticultural Hall, Vincent Square, Victoria
Adams Antiques Fairs.
Tel: 01-254 4054

The Cafe Royal, 68 Regent Street, W1
Heritage Antiques Fairs.
Tel: 01-624 5173

Antiques Fair, The Park Lane Hotel, Piccadilly, W1
K.M. Fairs.
Tel: 01-794 3551/4551

Antiques Fair, The Rembrandt Hotel, Thurloe Place, SW7
Monway Ltd. Tel: 01-603 0380

Tues July 3rd-8th
The London International Antiques & Fine Art Fair, Connaught Rooms, Great Queen Street, WC2
Raymond Gubbay Exhibitions.
Tel: 01-441 8940

Thur Aug 16th-19th
West London Antiques Fair, Kensington Town Hall, Hornton Street, W8
Penman Antiques Fairs.
Tel: (04447) 2514

Tues Sept 4th-9th
The London Antique Dealers' Autumn Fair, The Cafe Royal, Regent Street, W1
Jane Summer. Tel: (0799) 23611

Wed Sept 5th-12th
The Decorative Antiques & Textiles Fair, The Novotel London, 1 Shortlands, W6
Harvey Management Services Ltd. Tel: 01-624 5173

Tues Sept 11th-22nd
Chelsea Antiques Fair, Chelsea Old Town Hall, King's Road, SW3
Penman Antiques Fairs.
Tel: (04447) 2514

Fri Sept 21st-22nd
London Arms Fair, The Ramada Inn, Lillie Road, SW6
Arms Fairs Ltd.
Tel: 01-405 7933

Wed Sept 26th-30th
The 20th Century British Art Fair, The Cumberland Hotel, Marble Arch, W1
Heather McConnell.
Tel: 01-493 6420

Mon Oct 1st-2nd
The 'Little Chelsea' Antiques Fair, Chelsea Old Town Hall, Kings Road, SW3
Ravenscott Fairs.
Tel: 01-727 5045

Wed Oct 3rd-8th
The Park Lane Antiques Fair, The Park Lane Hotel, Piccadilly, W1
Heather McConnell.
Tel: 01-493 6420

Tues Oct 9th-14th
The Olympia Decorative and Antiques Fair, Grand Hall, Olympia Exhibition Centre, W14
Philbeach Events.
Tel: 01-385 1200

Tues Nov 6th-11th
The 39th Kensington Antiques Fair, The Town Hall, Hornton Street, W8
Cultural Exhibitions Ltd.
Tel: (048 68) 22562

Tues Nov 20th-25th
The City of London Antiques & Art Fair, Barbican Centre, EC2
Raymond Gubbay Exhibitions.
Tel: 01-441 8940

Sat Nov 24th-25th
Putney Pictures & Prints Fair, Whitelands College, West Hill, Putney, SW15
Brian Simons. Tel: 01-946 6593

Mon Dec 3rd-4th
The 'Little Chelsea' Antiques Fair, Chelsea Old Town Hall, Kings Road, SW3
Ravenscott Fairs.
Tel: 01-727 5045

Avon

Sun June 10th
Antiques & Collectables Markets, Brunel Great Train Shed, Temple Meads Station, Bristol
Talisman Fairs.
Tel: (0225) 872522

Tues Aug 7th-8th
Bath Summer Antiques, Collectors & Book Fair, The Guildhall, Bath
West Country Antiques & Collectors Fairs.
Tel: (0364) 52182

Bedfordshire

Sun June 17th
The Weatherley Centre, Eagle Farm Road, Biggleswade (A1)
Biggleswade Antiques Fairs.
Tel: (0767) 40190

Mon Oct 15th-16th
The 29th Luton Antiques Fair, The Chiltern Hotel, Waller Avenue, Dunstable Road, Luton
R. J. Perry.
Tel: (0462) 434525/(0582) 25546

Tues Nov 13th-14th
Bedford County Antiques Fair, Woburn Abbey
Reg Cooper Antiques Fairs.
Tel: (0860) 537153

Berkshire

Mon June 4th
Loddon Hall, Twyford, Nr Reading
Granny's Attic Antique Fairs.
Tel: (0252) 317547

Sun June 10th
Antiques Fair, The Racecourse, Maidenhead Road, Windsor
Chiltern Fairs.
Tel: (09278) 2144

Sun June 24th
Antiques Fair, The Racecourse, Maidenhead Road, Windsor
Chiltern Fairs.
Tel: (09278) 2144

Buckinghamshire

Sun June 3rd
Antiques Fair, Centre for Epilepsy, Chalfont St Peter
Chiltern Fairs. Tel: (09278) 2144

Antiques Fair, Beaconsfield Old Town (Masonic Centre)
M.J. Fairs.
Tel: (0494) 726879/ (0923) 242907

Sun June 10th
Bellhouse Hotel (A40), Beaconsfield
Midas Antique & Collectors Fairs. Tel: (0494) 674170/ (0753) 886993

Sat June 16th
Antiques Fair, Little Chalfont Village Hall, Amersham
M.J. Fairs.
Tel: (0494) 726879/ (0923) 242907

Sun Aug 26th-27th
Summer Bank Holiday Fine Art & Antiques Fair, The Bell House Hotel, Beaconsfield
Midas Fairs. Tel: (0753) 886993

Cambridgeshire

Wed June 6th
Antiques & Collectors Fair, Fisher Hall, Cambridge
Charlin Fairs.
Tel: (0787) 237138

Wed June 20th
Antiques & Collectors Fair, Fisher Hall, Cambridge
Charlin Fairs.
Tel: (0787) 237138

Sat June 23rd
Antiques & Collectors Fairs, Cambridge Corn Exchange, Cambridge
T.H.C. Fairs. Tel: (0223) 232802

Sat June 23rd-24th
Antiques Fair, East of England Showground, Peterborough
Four in One Promotions.
Tel: (0533) 712589

Thurs July 5th-7th
Ceramics Fair, The Guildhall, Cambridge
Wakefield Ceramics Fairs.
Tel: (0634) 723461

Sun Aug 26th-27th
St Ivo Recreation Centre, St Ives
Herridges Antiques & Collectors Fairs Ltd.
Tel: (0234) 45725

Fri Oct 19th-21st
The Autumn Cambridgeshire Antique Dealers Fair, Chilford Hill Barns, Linton
Castle Fairs. Tel: (0937) 832029

Sat Nov 17th-18th
St Ivo Recreation Centre, St Ives
Herridges Antiques & Collectors Fairs Ltd.
Tel: (0234) 45725

Cheshire

Sat June 23rd
Northgate Arena, Victoria Road, Chester
Pamela Robertson Antique & Collectors Fairs.
Tel: (0244) 678106

Wed Sept 19th-23rd
The Tatton Park Antiques Fair, Knutsford
Robert Bailey. Tel: 01-550 5435

Sat Oct 13th-14th
The Cheshire County Antiques Fair, Arley Hall, Northwich
Reg Cooper Antiques Fairs.
Tel: (0860) 5371

Cornwall

Fri Aug 17th-18th
Truro Summer Antiques, Collectors & Book Fair, City Hall, Truro
West Country Antiques & Collectors Fairs.
Tel: (0364) 52182

Fri Oct 5th-6th
Truro Autumn Antiques, Collectors & Book Fair, City Hall, Truro
West Country Antiques & Collectors Fairs.
Tel: (0364) 52182

Cumbria

Sat June 23rd-24th
The Institute Hall, Kirkby Lonsdale
Memories Antiques Fairs.
Tel: (09693) 463

Antiques & Collectors Fair, The Village Hall, Pooley Bridge, Ullswater
Albany Fairs. Tel: 091-584 2934

Fri Nov 16th-18th
The Lake District Antiques Fair, Holker Hall, Cartmel
Robert Bailey. Tel: 01-550 5435

Derbyshire

Sat June 2nd-3rd
The Pavilion Gardens, Buxton
Unicorn Antiques & Collectors Fairs. Tel: (061 773) 7001

Sun June 24th
Antiques Fair, Derbyshire Yeoman, Ashbourne Road, Markeaton Island
Temple Fairs.
Tel: (0332) 663197

Sat July 14th-15th
Antiques Fair, The Pavilion Gardens, Buxton
Unicorn Fairs.
Tel: (061 773) 7001

Sat Aug 25th-26th
Antiques Fair, The Pavilion Gardens, Buxton
Unicorn Fairs.
Tel: (061 773) 7001

Sat Sept 8th-9th
Ceramics Fair, The Royal Crown Derby Museum, Derby
Wakefield Ceramics Fairs.
Tel: (0634) 723461

Sat Sept 22nd-24th
Antiques Fair, Bakewell Town Hall, Bakewell
Peak Fairs.
Tel: (062981) 2449

Sat Oct 29th-30th
Antiques Fair, The Pavilion Gardens, Buxton
Unicorn Fairs.
Tel: (061 773) 7001

Sun Oct 28th-29th
Antiques Fair, Bakewell Town Hall, Bakewell
Peak Fairs.
Tel: (062981) 2449

Sat Nov 10th-11th
Antiques Fair, The Pavilion Gardens, Buxton
Unicorn Fairs.
Tel: (061 773) 7001

Sun Nov 25th-26th
Antiques Fair, Bakewell Town Hall, Bakewell
Peak Fairs.
Tel: (062981) 2449

Sat Dec 29th-30th
Antiques Fair, The Pavilion Gardens, Buxton
Unicorn Fairs.
Tel: (061 773) 7001

Sat Dec 29th-Jan 1st
Antiques Fair, Bakewell Town Hall, Bakewell
Peak Fairs.
Tel: (062981) 2449

Devon

Fri June 7th-8th
Newton Abbot Summer Giant Antiques, Collectors & Book Fair, The Racecourse, Newton Abbot
West Country Antiques & Collectors Fairs.
Tel: (0364) 52182

Sat June 9th
Budleigh Salterton Antiques, Collectors & Book Fair, The Masonic Hall, Budleigh Salterton
West Country Antiques & Collectors Fairs.
Tel: (0364) 52182

Sat June 9th-10th
Antiques Fair, Westpoint Exhibition Centre, Exeter
Devon Country Antiques Fairs.
Tel: (0363) 82571

Sun June 10th
Exmouth Antiques & Collectors Fair, The Pavilion, The Sea Front, Exmouth
West Country Antiques & Collectors Fairs.
Tel: (0364) 52182

Sun June 24th
Dartmoor Antiques, Collectors & Book Fair, The Moorland Links Hotel, Yelverton
West Country Antiques & Collectors Fairs.
Tel: (0364) 52182

Exmouth Antiques & Collectors Fair, The Pavilion, The Sea Front, Exmouth
West Country Antiques & Collectors Fairs.
Tel: (0364) 52182

Sat July 21st-22nd
South Devon & Dartmoor Antiques Fair, The Moorland Hotel, Haytor
West Country Antiques & Collectors Fairs.
Tel: (0364) 52182

Sun Aug 26th-27th
Exmouth August Bank Holiday Antiques & Collectors Fair, The Pavilion, The Sea Front, Exmouth
West Country Antiques & Collectors Fairs.
Tel: (0364) 52182

Thurs Sept 13th-14th
Newton Abbot Autumn Giant Antiques, Collectors & Book Fair, The Racecourse, Newton Abbot
West Country Antiques & Collectors Fairs.
Tel: (0364) 52182

Wed Sept 19th-20th
Exmouth Annual Antiques & Collectables Fair, The Pavilion, The Sea Front, Exmouth
West Country Antiques & Collectors Fairs.
Tel: (0364) 52182

Fri Sept 28th-29th
Exeter Autumn Antiques Fair, The Exeter Court Hotel, Kenford, Exeter
West Country Antiques & Collectors Fairs.
Tel: (0364) 52182

Wed Nov 7th-8th
The South West of England Antiques Fair, The Langstone Cliff Hotel, Dawlish
West Country Antiques & Collectors Fairs.
Tel: (0364) 52182

Sat Nov 24th-25th
East Devon Autumn Antiques Fair, Salston Manor Hotel, Ottery St Mary
West Country Antiques & Collectors Fairs.
Tel: (0364) 52182

Sat Dec 1st-2nd
Newton Abbot Giant Christmas Antiques, Collectors & Book Fair, The Racecourse, Newton Abbot
West Country Antiques & Collectors Fairs.
Tel: (0364) 52182

Thurs Dec 13th-14th
Barnstaple Christmas Antiques & Collectors Fair, The Queen's Hall, Barnstaple
West Country Antiques & Collectors Fairs.
Tel: (0364) 52182

Dorset

Sat June 2nd
Antiques & Bygone Fair, Beaminster Public Hall, Beaminster
Beaminster Antiques Fairs.
Tel: (093589) 395/(0308) 862591

Sat Oct 6th-7th
Antiques Fair, Coach House Inn, Tricketts Cross, Ferndown
Ron Beech. Tel: (0273) 423355

Fri Nov 2nd-3rd
Dorset County Antiques Fair, Bryanston School, Blandford
Reg Cooper Antique Fairs.
Tel: (0860) 537153

Essex

Sat June 2nd
Antiques & Collectors Fair, Chingford Assembly Hall, The Green, Chingford
Bartholomew Fairs.
Tel: (0279) 600005

Sun June 3rd
Antiques & Collectors Fair, Harlow Moat House, Southern Way, Harlow
Bartholomew Fairs.
Tel: (0279) 600005

Tues June 5th
Antiques & Crafts Markets, The Town Hall, Saffron Walden
Lorna Quicks Four Seasons.
Tel: (0787) 281855

Sun June 10th
Antiques & Collectors Fair, The Town Hall, Highbridge Street, Waltham Abbey
Bartholomew Fairs.
Tel: (0279) 600005

Antiques & Collectors Fair, Orsett Hall (A128 Orsett)
Etonia Promotions.
Tel: (0268) 774977

Sat June 16th
Antiques & Collectors Fair, The Public Hall, St John's Road, Epping
Bartholomew Fairs.
Tel: (0279) 600005

Sun June 17th
Antiques & Collectors Fair, The Village Hall, Finchinfield, Braintree
Charlin Fairs.
Tel: (0787) 237138

Tues June 19th
Antiques & Crafts Markets, The Town Hall, Saffron Walden
Lorna Quicks Four Seasons.
Tel: (0787) 281855

Gloucestershire

Sun June 10th
Antiques & Collectors Fair, Bingham Hall, Cirencester
Keith Smith Fairs.
Tel: (0684) 575126

Thurs June 14th
Antiques & Collectors Fair, The Prestbury Suite, Cheltenham Racecourse
Melba Fairs.
Tel: (0934) 624854

Sun June 24th
Antiques Fair, The Prestbury Suite, Cheltenham Racecourse
Melba Fairs.
Tel: (0934) 624854

Sat July 21st-22nd
North Cotswolds Antiques Fair, Stanway House, Nr Winchcombe
Reg Cooper Antique Fairs.
Tel: (0860) 537153

Sat Aug 18th-19th
South Cotswolds Antiques Fair, Westonbirt School, Tetbury
Reg Cooper Antique Fairs.
Tel: (0860) 537153

Thurs Sept 13th-15th
The Cheltenham Autumn Antiques Fair, The Pittville Pump Rooms, Cheltenham
Mary Packham Antiques Fair.
Tel: (0242) 513485

Wed Oct 24th-27th
The Cotswolds Antiques Fair, Pittville Pump Rooms, Cheltenham
Robert Bailey.
Tel: 01-550 5435

Hampshire

Sun June 3rd
Winchester Guildhall
Bellamys Antiques & Collectors Fairs.
Tel: (0703) 780798

Antiques & Collectors Fair, Ringwood Recreation Centre, Parsonage Barn Lane, Ringwood
Forest Fairs. Tel: (0202) 875167

Tues June 5th
Antiques Fair, The Community Centre, Alton
Granny's Attic Antique Fairs.
Tel: (0252) 317547

Tues June 12th
Antiques Fair, The Victoria Hall, Hartley Wintney
Granny's Attic Antique Fairs.
Tel: (0252) 317547

Tues June 19th
Antiques Fair, Petersfield Town Hall, Petersfield
Granny's Attic Antique Fairs.
Tel: (0252) 317547

Sat June 23rd
Antiques & Collectors Fair, St Thomas Church Hall, High Street, Lymington
Grandma's Attic.
Tel: (0590) 677687

Sun June 24th
Antiques & Collectors Fair, Lyndhurst Park Hotel, High Street, Lyndhurst
Grandma's Attic.
Tel: (0590) 677687

Thurs June 28th
Antiques Fair, The Crookham War Memorial Hall, Church Crookham
Granny's Attic Antique Fairs.
Tel: (0252) 317547

Fri July 27th-29th
The Guildhall, Winchester
Wakefield Antiques & Fine Art Fairs.
Tel: (0634) 723461

Fri Aug 24th-27th
The Hampshire Antique Dealers' Fair, Royal College of Maritime Studies, Warsash, Southampton
Castle Fairs.
Tel: (0937) 832029

Wed Sept 5th-8th
Petersfield Antiques Fair, The Town Hall, Petersfield
Gamlin Exhibition Services.
Tel: (0452) 862557

Hereford & Worcs

Sun June 3rd
Antiques Fair, The Three Counties Showground, Malvern
K & S Fairs. Tel: (0278) 784912

Tues June 5th
Antiques, Bric-a-Brac & Collectors Fair, The Winter Gardens, Malvern
S & B Promotions.
Tel: (0684) 572439

Tues June 19th
Antiques, Bric-a-Brac & Collectors Fair, The Winter Gardens, Malvern
S & B Promotions.
Tel: (0684) 572439

Sat June 23rd
Flea Market, The Winter Gardens, Malvern
S & B Promotions.
Tel: (0684) 572439

Tues Oct 9th-11th
The 20th Annual Hereford Antiques Fair, Moat House Hotel, Belmont Road (A465), Hereford
Antiques in Britain Fairs.
Tel: (05474) 464

Sat Oct 20th-21st
Ceramics Fair, The Dyson Perrins Museum, Worcester
Wakefield Ceramics Fairs.
Tel: (0634) 723461

Hertfordshire

Sat June 2nd
Antiques Fair, Chorleywood Memorial Hall, Common Road
Chiltern Fairs.
Tel: (09278) 2144

Sun June 3rd
Antiques Fair, Blakemore Hotel, Little Wymondley, Hitchin, Stevenage
Biggleswade Antiques Fairs.
Tel: (0767) 40190

Sat June 9th
Antiques Fair, Chipperfield Village Hall, Kings Langley
M.J. Fairs.
Tel: (0494) 726879/(0923) 242907

Sun June 10th
Antiques & Collectors Fair, Knebworth Village Hall, nr Stevenage
G & Y Services.
Tel: (0438) 355049/(0462) 458040

Antiques Fair, Hemel Hempstead Moat House Hotel
M.J. Fairs.
Tel: (0494) 726879/(0923) 242907

Sun June 17th
Antiques & Collectors Fair, The Red Lion, Great North Road, Hatfield
Bartholomew Fairs.
Tel: (0279) 600005

Antiques Fair, Hatfield Polytechnic, College Lane, Hatfield
Chiltern Fairs.
Tel: (09278) 2144

Tues June 19th
Antiques Fair, The Public Hall, Harpenden
Chiltern Fairs.
Tel: (09278) 2144

Sat June 23rd
Antiques Fair, The Town Hall, Watford
Chiltern Fairs.
Tel: (09278) 2144

Sun June 24th
Antiques & Collectors Fair, The Broadway Hotel, The Broadway, Letchworth
Bartholomew Fairs.
Tel: (0279) 600005

The Hertfordshire Antiques & Fine Art Fair, The Public Hall, Harpenden
Robinson Gray Antique & Fine Art Fairs.
Tel: (0582) 766400

Antiques Fair, Sarratt Village Hall, Rickmansworth
M.J. Fairs.
Tel: (0494) 726879/(0923) 242907

Sat July 14th-15th
Bishop's Stortford Antiques Fair, The Rhodes Centre, Bishop's Stortford
Britannia Fairs.
Tel: (0984) 31668

Sat July 28th-29th
Antiques & Collectables' Fair, Plinston Hall, Letchworth
Herridge's Antiques & Collectors Fairs Ltd.
Tel: (0234) 45725

Sat Oct 6th-7th
Plinston Hall, Letchworth
Herridge's Antiques & Collectors Fairs Ltd.
Tel: (0234) 45725

Sat Oct 20th-21st
Bishop's Stortford Antiques Fair, The Rhodes Centre, Bishop's Stortford
Britannia Fairs.
Tel: (0984) 31668

Sat Nov 10th-11th
Plinston Hall, Letchworth
Herridge's Antiques & Collectors Fairs Ltd.
Tel: (0234) 45725

North Humberside

Sun June 24th
Antiques Fair, Willerby Manor, Hull
Abbey Antique Fairs.
Tel: (0482) 445785/(0831) 449731

Kent

Sun June 17th
Antiques & Collectors Fair, The Spa Hotel, Royal Tunbridge Wells
Cross Country Fairs.
Tel: (0860) 441672

Sun June 24th
Northdown House, Northdown Park, Cliftonville, Margate

Sun July 29th
Northdown House, Northdown Park, Cliftonville, Margate

Sun Aug 26th
Northdown House, Northdown Park, Cliftonville, Margate

Sun Sept 23rd
Chiesman Pavilion, Kent County Cricket Club Ground, Old Dover Road, Canterbury

Sun Sept 30th
Northdown House, Northdown Park, Cliftonville, Margate

Sun Oct 28th
Northdown House, Northdown Park, Cliftonville, Margate

Sun Nov 18th
Chiesman Pavilion, Kent County Cricket Club Ground, Old Dover Road, Canterbury

Sun Nov 25th
Northdown House, Northdown Park, Cliftonville, Margate

Lancashire

Sun June 10th
The Exhibition Halls, Park Hall, Charnock Richard
Unicorn Antiques & Collectors Fairs.
Tel: (061 773) 7001

Sun June 17th
The Exhibition Halls, Park Hall, Charnock Richard
Unicorn Antiques & Collectors Fairs.
Tel: (061 773) 7001

Sun June 24th
The Exhibition Halls, Park Hall, Charnock Richard
Unicorn Antiques & Collectors Fairs.
Tel: (061 773) 7001

Fri Oct 26th-28th
The Lancashire Antiques Dealers' Fair, Stonyhurst, nr Whalley
Castle Fairs.
Tel: (0937) 832029

Fri Nov 23rd-25th
The Hoghton Tower Antiques Fair, Preston
Robert Bailey.
Tel: 01-550 5435

Leicestershire

Sun June 3rd
Antiques Fair, The Hinckley Island Hotel, on A5 by M69 roundabout
Prestige Promotions.
Tel: (0533) 516045

Sun June 10th
Antiques Fair, The Granby Halls, Leicester
Four In One Promotions.
Tel: (0533) 712589

Sun June 17th
Antiques Fair, Welland Park College, Market Harborough
Four In One Promotions.
Tel: (0533) 712589

Lincolnshire

Sat Aug 11th-12th
Stamford School, Stamford
Herridge's Antiques & Collectors Fairs Ltd.
Tel: (0234) 45725

Fri Oct 5th-7th
The Harlaxton Manor Antiques Fair, Grantham
Robert Bailey.
Tel: 01-550 5435

Sat Oct 20th-21st
Stamford School, Stamford
Herridge's Antiques & Collectors Fairs Ltd.
Tel: (0234) 45725

East Midlands

Sat May 19th-20th
Antiques Fair, Donington Park Exhibition Centre
Four In One Promotions.
Tel: (0553) 712589

Middlesex

Sat June 2nd-3rd
A Little Twickenham Watercolours Fair, West London College, St Margaret's Road, Twickenham
Brian Simons.
Tel: 01-946 6593

Sun June 3rd
Park Farm Centre, Northwood
Midas Antique & Collectors Fairs.
Tel: (0494) 674170/(0753) 886993

Sun Aug 26th-27th
Hampton Pictures & Prints Fair, Hampton School, Hanworth Road, Hampton
Brian Simons. Tel: 01-946 6593

Sat Oct 6th-7th
Hampton Antiques Fair, Hampton School, Hanworth Road, Hampton
Brian Simons. Tel: 01-946 6593

Sat Oct 27th-28th
2nd Annual Twickenham Pictures & Prints Fair, St Mary's College, Waldegrave Road, Strawberry Hill, Twickenham
Brian Simon. Tel: 01-946 6593

Northamptonshire

Sun June 10th
Antiques & Collectors Fairs, The Village Hall, Yardley Hastings
King Collectables.
Tel: (0933) 311313

Sun June 17th
Antiques & Collectors Fair, The Village Hall, Cogenhoe
Magpie Antiques & Collectors Fairs. Tel: (0604) 890107

Wed Aug 15th-19th
The Castle Ashby Antiques Fair, Castle Ashby,
Robert Bailey. Tel: 01-550 5435

Sun Aug 26th-27th
Antiques & Collectors' Fair, Lamport Hall, nr Northampton (on A508)
Prestige Promotions.
Tel: (0533) 516045

Sat Sept 15th-16th
17th Autumn Antiques Fair, Lilford Hall, nr Oundle
Everyman Antiques Fairs.
Tel: (0603) 623326

Northumberland

Fri June 8th-10th
The Border Antique Dealers' Fair, Alnwick Castle
Castle Fairs. Tel: (0937) 832029

Nottinghamshire

Tues June 5th
The Summer International Fair, Newark & Nottinghamshire Showground, Newark
International Antique & Collectors Fair Co Ltd.
Tel: (0636) 702326

Fri June 22nd-24th
The Thoresby Antiques Fair, Thoresby Park Exhibition Centre, Ollerton
Whittington Exhibitions.
Tel: 01-644 9327

Fri July 6th-8th
The Welbeck Abbey Antiques Fair, Worksop
Robert Bailey. Tel: 01-550 5435

Fri Sept 21st-23rd
The Thoresby Antiques Fair, Thoresby Park Exhibition Centre, Ollerton
Whittington Exhibitions.
Tel: 01-644 9327

Oxfordshire

Sun June 24th
Antiques Fair, 'Drive in' Rugby Club, Henley-on-Thames
Magnum Antiques Fairs.
Tel: (0491) 681009

Sat Aug 11th-12th
Antiques Fair, Radley College, Radley, nr Abingdon (incorporating The Third Staffordshire Figures Fair)
Ron Beech. Tel: (0273) 423355

Thurs Oct 11th-13th
Ceramics Fair, The Town Hall, Henley-on-Thames
Wakefield Ceramics Fairs.
Tel: (0634) 723461

Shropshire

Sun June 3rd
Antiques Fair, The Beauchamp Hotel, Shrewsbury
Shropshire Antiques Fairs.
Tel: (0952) 595622

Tues July 10th-12th
Shropshire Summer Antiques Fair, Lion Hotel, Wyle Cop, Shrewsbury
Antiques In Britain Fairs.
Tel: (05474) 464

Somerset

Sat June 2nd-3rd
Somerset County Antiques Fair, Forde Abbey, Chard
Reg Cooper Antiques Fairs.
Tel: (0860) 537153

Sat Jun 30th-July 1st
Antiques Fair, Royal Bath & West Showground, Shepton Mallet
Merlin Fairs. Tel: (0278) 691616

Thurs Nov 1st-2nd
Wells Autumn Antiques Fair, The Bishop's Palace, Wells
West Country Antiques & Collectors Fairs.
Tel: (0364) 52182

Mon Nov 12th-13th
Taunton Annual Antiques, Collectors' & Book Fair, The Indoor School, The County Cricket Ground, Taunton
West Country Antiques & Collectors Fairs.
Tel: (0364) 52182

Sat Nov 17th-18th
Shepton Mallet Antiques & Collectors' Fair, Royal Bath and West Showground (A371),
Merlin Fairs. Tel: (0278) 691616

Staffordshire

Sun June 10th
Antiques Fair, The Village Hall, Monk Street, Tutbury, nr Burton-on-Trent
Temple Fairs. Tel: (0332) 663197

Fri June 15th-17th
Stafford Giant Antiques Fair, Bingley Hall, County Showground, Stafford
Bowman Antiques Fairs.
Tel: (0532) 843333

Sat June 16th
Antiques Fair, The Town Hall, Burton-on-Trent
Four In One Promotions.
Tel: (0533) 712589

Sat June 30th
Quality Antiques Fair, The Pavilion Hall, County Showground
West Midland Antiques Fairs.
Tel: (0743) 271444

Fri Aug 17th-19th
Stafford Giant Antiques Fair, Bingley Hall, County Showground, Stafford
Bowman Antiques Fairs.
Tel: (0532) 843333

Fri Oct 5th-7th
Stafford Giant Antiques Fair, Bingley Hall, County Showground, Stafford
Bowman Antiques Fairs.
Tel: (0532) 843333

Fri Dec 7th-9th
Stafford Giant Antique Fair, Bingley Hall, County Showground, Stafford
Bowman Antiques Fairs.
Tel: (0532) 843333

Suffolk

Thurs June 7th
Antiques & Crafts Markets, The Town Hall, Sudbury
Lorna Quicks Four Seasons.
Tel: (0787) 281855

Sun June 10th
Antiques & Collectors Fair, Bob Hope Recreation Centre, RAF Mildenhall
Lorna Quicks Four Seasons.
Tel: (0787) 281855

Sat June 23rd-24th
Antiques & Collectables Fair, The Old School (opp Melford Hall), Long Melford
The Best of Fairs.
Tel: (0787) 280306

Thurs June 28th
Antiques & Crafts Markets, The Town Hall, Sudbury
Lorna Quicks Four Seasons.
Tel: (0787) 281855

Wed July 25th-28th
The 24th Annual Snape Antiques Fair, The Maltings Concert Hall, Snape
Anglian Arts & Antiques.
Tel: (09867) 2368

Sat July 28th-29th
Antiques & Collectables Fair, The Old School (opp Melford Hall), Long Melford
The Best of Fairs.
Tel: (0787) 280306

Sat Aug 25th-27th
Antiques & Collectables Fair, The Old School (opp Melford Hall), Long Melford
The Best of Fairs.
Tel: (0787) 280306

Thurs Sept 6th-8th
The 24th Annual East Anglia Antiques Fair,
The Athenaeum,
Angel Hill, Bury St Edmunds
Antiques in Britain Fairs.
Tel: (05474) 464

Sat Sept 22nd-23rd
Antiques & Collectables Fair, The Old School (opp Melford Hall), Long Melford
The Best of Fairs.
Tel: (0787) 280306

Thurs Oct 25th-27th
The 19th Annual St Edmunds Antiques Fair, Bury St Edmunds
Anglian Arts & Antiques.
Tel: (09867) 2368

Sat Oct 27th-28th
Antiques & Collectables Fair, The Old School (opp Melford Hall), Long Melford
The Best of Fairs.
Tel: (0787) 280306

Sat Nov 24th-25th
Antiques & Collectables Fair, The Old School (opp Melford Hall), Long Melford
The Best of Fairs.
Tel: (0787) 280306

Sat Dec 15th-16th
Antiques & Collectables Fair, The Old School (opp Melford Hall), Long Melford
The Best of Fairs.
Tel: (0787) 280306

Surrey

Sun June 3rd
The Canons, Madeira Road, Mitcham Common
Margaret Browne Antiques & Collectors Fairs.
Tel: 01-874 3622

Thurs June 14th
Antiques Fair, The Civic Hall, Knoll Road, Camberley
Granny's Attic Antique Fairs.
Tel: (0252) 317547

Sat June 16th
Antiques & Collectors Fair, St Mary's Hall, Church Road, Leatherhead
Antique Dealers Co-Operative.
Tel: (0372) 379795

Sun June 17th
Dorking Halls, Dorking
Margaret Browne Antiques & Collectors Fairs.
Tel: 01-874 3622

Fri June 22nd
Antiques Fair, The Kiln, Badshot Lea, nr Farnham
Granny's Attic Antique Fairs.
Tel: (0252) 317547

Fri June 22nd-23rd
Antiques Fair, Village Hall, Bletchingley
Ron Beech Tel: (0273) 423355

Wed July 11th-12th
Antiques Fair, Christ's Hospital, Horsham
Ron Beech Tel: (0273) 423355

Sun Aug 26th-27th
Antiques Fair, The Dorking Halls, Dorking
Margaret Brown Antiques & Collectors Fairs.
Tel: 01-874 3622

Fri Oct 5th-9th
The 23rd Surrey Antiques Fair, Civic Hall, Guildford
Cultural Exhibitions Ltd.
Tel: (04868) 22562

Thurs Oct 25th-27th
Farnham Antiques Fair, The Church House, Farnham
Gamlin Exhibition Services.
Tel: (0452) 86557

East Sussex

Sun June 3rd
Antiques & Collectors Fair, The Winston Manor Hotel, Crowborough
Cross Country Fairs.
Tel: (0860) 441672

Thurs June 21st 24th
Provincial Antiques & Period Furnishings Show, The Corn Exchange, Royal Pavilion Grounds Brighton
Caroline Penman & Barbara Bell. Tel: (04447) 2514

Sat June 30th
Antiques & Collectors Fair, Filching Manor, Wannock, Polegate, Eastbourne
Bartholomew Fairs.
Tel: (0279) 600005

Thurs Sept 13th-15th
The Winter Gardens, Eastbourne
Wakefield Antiques & Fine Art Fairs.
Tel: (0634) 723461

Fri Nov 2nd-4th
Provincial Antiques & Period Furnishings Show, The Corn Exchange, Royal Pavilion Grounds, Brighton
Caroline Penman & Barbara Bell. Tel: (04447) 2514

West Sussex

Sun June 3rd
Antiques Fair, The Grange Centre, Midhurst
Magnum Antiques Fairs.
Tel: (0491) 681009

Fri June 15th-17th
The Summer South East Counties Antique Dealers' Fair, Goodwood House, nr Chichester
Castle Fairs.
Tel: (0937) 832029

Tues Aug 21st-Sept 2nd
The Petworth Antiques Fair, Seaford College, Petworth
Robert Bailey.
Tel: 01-550 5435

Fri Aug 24th-25th
Antiques Fair, King Edward Hall, Lindfield
Ron Beech
Tel: (0273) 423355

Sat Sept 29th-30th
Ceramics Fair, The Felbridge Hotel, East Grinstead
Wakefield Ceramics Fairs.
Tel: (0634) 723461

Sat Oct 20th-21st
Antiques Fair, Village Hall, Wiveslfield Green, nr Haywards Heath
Ron Beech.
Tel: (0273) 423355

Fri Nov 23rd-25th
The Christmas South-East Counties Antique Dealers' Fair, Goodwood House, nr Chichester
Castle Fairs.
Tel: (0937) 832029

Sat Dec 29th-Jan 3rd 1991
The Petworth Antiques Fair, Seaford College, Petworth
Robert Bailey.
Tel: 01-550 5435

Warwickshire

Sun June 3rd
Antiques Fair, K Marriott Leisure Centre, Rugby
Four In One Promotions.
Tel: (0533) 712589

Sun June 17th
Antiques Fair, Castle Donington Community College, Mount Pleasant, Castle Donington
Temple Fairs.
Tel: (0332) 663197

Tues Oct 23rd-27th
The Kenilworth Antique Dealers' Fair, Chesford Grange, Kenilworth
Jane Summer.
Tel: (0799) 23611

Fri Nov 30th-Dec 2nd
Antiques & Fine Art Fair, Ragley Hall, Alcester
Wakefield Antiques & Fine Art Fairs.
Tel: (0634) 723461

West Midlands

Sun June 17th
Antiques Fair, The Belfry, National Golf Centre, nr Sutton Coldfield, Junction A446 & A091
Prestige Promotions.
Tel: (0533) 516045

Thurs Aug 2nd-5th
NEC August Fair, National Exhibition Centre, Birmingham
Tel: 021-780 4141

Fri Aug 24th-25th
West Midlands Antiques Fair, Sutton Coldfield Town Hall
Reg Cooper Antiques Fairs.
Tel: (0860) 537153

Thurs Sept 20th-22nd
Warwickshire County Antiques Fair, Warwickshire County Cricket Ground, Edgbaston, Birmingham
Bob Harris & Sons.
Tel: 021-743 2259

Fri Nov 9th-11th
Warwickshire County Antiques Fair, Warwickshire County Cricket Ground, Edgbaston, Birmingham
Bob Harris & Sons.
Tel: 021-743 2259

Wiltshire

Fri Nov 23rd-25th
Ceramics Fair, The Michael Herbert Hall, Wilton
Wakefield Ceramics Fairs.
Tel: (0634) 723461

North Yorkshire

Fri June 1st
Antiques Fair, The Parish Rooms, Leyburn
Memories Antiques Fairs.
Tel: (09693) 463

Sun June 3rd
Antiques Fair, Old Swan Hotel, Harrogate
Abbey Antique Fairs.
Tel: (0482) 445785/(0831) 449731

Mon June 4th
Antiques Fairs, The Town Hall, Thirsk
Memories Antiques Fairs.
Tel: (09693) 463

Tues June 5th
Antiques Fair, The Conservative Club, Hawes
Memories Antiques Fairs.
Tel: (09693) 463

Fri June 8th
Antiques Fair, The Parish Rooms, Leyburn
Memories Antiques Fairs.
Tel: (09693) 463

Sat June 9th-10th
Antiques Fair, Hawes Market Hall, Hawes
Memories Antiques Fairs.
Tel: (09693) 463

Tues June 12th
Antiques Fair, The Conservative Club, Hawes
Memories Antiques Fairs.
Tel: (09693) 463

Fri June 15th
Antiques Fair, The Parish Rooms, Leyburn
Memories Antiques Fairs.
Tel: (09693) 463

Mon June 18th
Antiques Fair, The Town Hall, Thirsk
Memories Antiques Fairs.
Tel: (09693) 463

Tues June 19th
Antiques Fair, The Conservative Club, Hawes
Memories Antiques Fairs.
Tel: (09693) 463

Fri June 22nd
Antiques Fair, The Parish Rooms, Leyburn
Memories Antiques Fairs.
Tel: (09693) 463

Tues June 26th
Antiques Fair, The Conservative Club, Hawes
Memories Antiques Fairs.
Tel: (09693) 463

Fri June 29th
Antiques Fair, The Parish Rooms, Leyburn
Memories Antiques Fairs.
Tel: (09693) 463

Fri July 20th-22nd
The Harrogate Antiques Fair, Granby Hotel, Harrogate
Robert Bailey.
Tel: 01-550 5435

Sat Sept 1st-2nd
Antiques Fair, The Great Yorkshire Showground, Harrogate
Northern Antiques Fairs.
Tel: (0642) 550268

Fri Sept 14th-16th
The Ridings Antiques Dealers' Fair, Hazelwood Castle, nr Tadcaster
Castle Fairs.
Tel: (0937) 832029

Thurs Sept 27th-Oct 3rd
The 40th Northern Antiques Fair, Royal Baths Assembly Rooms, Harrogate
Northern Antique Dealers' Fairs Ltd.
Tel: (0423) 770385

Fri Sept 28th-30th
The Autumn Dales antique Dealers' Fair, Settrington House, nr Malton
Castle Fairs.
Tel: (0937) 832029

The Carlton Towers Antiques Fair, nr Goole
Robert Bailey.
Tel: 01-550 5435

Thurs Oct 18th-20th
The 23rd Annual York Antiques Fair, Assembly Rooms, Blake Street, York
Antiques In Britain Fairs.
Tel: (05474) 464

Fri Nov 2nd-3rd
Antiques Fair, The Great Yorkshire Showground, Harrogate
Northern Antiques Fairs.
Tel: (0642) 550268

Fri Nov 9th-11th
The County Antique Dealers' Fair, Rudding Park House, nr Harrogate
Castle Fairs.
Tel: (0937) 832029

Ceramics Fair, The Crown Hotel, Crown Place, Harrogate
Wakefield Ceramics Fairs.
Tel: (0634) 723461

Fri Dec 30th
The Harrogate Antiques Fair, Old Swan Hotel, Harrogate
Robert Bailey.
Tel: 01-550 5435

Wed Dec 5th-9th
The Castle Howard Antiques Fairs, Castle Howard
Robert Bailey.
Tel: 01-550 5435

South Yorkshire

Sun June 10th
Antiques Fair, Keresforth Hall, Barnsley
Abbey Antique Fairs.
Tel: (0482) 445785/(0831) 449731

West Yorkshire

Sat June 2nd-3rd
Antiques Fair, The Robert Craven Memorial Hall, Bramhope
Memories Antiques Fairs.
Tel: (09693) 463

Sat June 16th
Antiques Fair, The Town Hall, Wetherby
Memories Antiques Fairs.
Tel: (09693) 463

Sun June 17th
Antiques Fair, Bankfield Hotel, Bingley
Abbey Antique Fairs.
Tel: (0482) 445785/(0831) 449731

Fri Aug 24th-27th
The Ilkley Antiques Fair, King's Hall & Winter Gardens, Ilkley
Robert Bailey.
Tel: 01-550 5435

Scotland

Sat June 2nd
Antiques & Collectors Fair, Albert Halls, Stirling
Scot Fairs. Tel: (0764) 3592

Sun June 3rd
Antiques & Collectors Fair, Mitchell Theatre, Granville Street, Glasgow
Scot Fairs. Tel: (0764) 3592

Antiques & Collectors Fair, Skean Dhu Hotel, Dyce, Aberdeen
Scot Fairs. Tel: (0764) 3592

Sat June 9th
Antiques & Collectors Fair, Dan Park Hall, Ayr
Scot Fairs. Tel: (0764) 3592

Fri June 15th
Antiques & Collectors Fair, The Town Hall, Moffat
Albany Fairs.
Tel: (091 584) 2934

Sat June 16th
Antiques & Collectors Fair, The Town Hall, Moffat
Albany Fairs.
Tel: (091 584) 2934

Sun June 17th
Antiques & Collectors Fair, Marryat Hall, City Square, Dundee
Scot Fairs. Tel: (0764) 3592

Sun June 24th
Antiques & Collectors Fair, Mitchell Theatre, Granville Street, Glasgow
Scot Fairs. Tel: (0764) 3592

Tues July 24th-26th
The 19th Annual Edinburgh Antiques Fair, Roxburghe Hotel, Charlotte Square, Edinburgh
Antiques in Britain Fairs.
Tel: (05474) 464

Fri Oct 12th-14th
The Antique Dealers' Fair of Scotland, Hopetoun House, South Queensferry
Castle Fairs.
Tel: (0937) 832029

Fri Nov 16th-18th
The 14th Annual Edinburgh Winter Antiques Fair, Roxburghe Hotel, Charlotte Square, Edinburgh
Antiques In Britain Fairs.
Tel: (05474) 464

Wales

Sun June 3rd
Antiques & Collectors Fair, Two Rivers Hotel, Chepstow
Isca Fairs. Tel: (0633) 264384

Antiques Fair, The Leisure Centre, Chepstow
Puzzle House Fairs.
Tel: (0594) 60653

Sun June 10th
Antiques & Collectors Fair, St Mellons Hotel & Country Club, St Mellons, Cardiff
David Robinson Fairs.
Tel: (0222) 620520

Sun June 17th
Antiques & Collectors Fair, Glyn Clydach Hotel, Longford Road, Neath Abbey, Neath
David Robinson Fairs.
Tel: (0222) 620520

Antiques & Collectors FAir, Cwrt Bleddyn, Llangybi, nr Usk
Isca Fairs. Tel: (0633) 263384

Sun June 24th
Antiques & Collectors Fair, Pontillanfraith Leisure Centre, Pontillanfraith, Blackwood
Isca Fairs. Tel: (0633) 264384

Thurs Sept 20th-22nd
Antiques Fair, Castle of Brecon Hotel, Powys
Ron Beech. Tel: (0273) 423355

Northern Ireland

Thurs Oct 4th-6th
The Northern Ireland Antique Dealers' Fair, Cultra Manor House, Holywood, nr Bangor, Co Down
Castle Fairs. Tel: (0937) 832029

A set of 9 Steiff skittles in the form of brown felt monkeys, the kingpin in red felt tailcoat and red felt crown edged with gold thread, 3 bells and one tail end missing, 8in (20.5cm).
£2,000-2,500 *Bon*

DIRECTORY OF MARKETS & CENTRES

This directory is in no way complete. If you wish to be included in next year's directory or if you have a change of address or telephone number, please could you inform us by December 31st 1990. Entries will be repeated in subsequent editions unless we are requested otherwise.

London

Alfies Antique Market,
13-25 Church Street, NW8
Tel: 01-723 6066
Tues-Sat 10-6pm

Angel Arcade,
116-118 Islington High Street,
Camden Passage, N1
Open Wed & Sat

Antiquarius Antique Market,
135/141 Kings Road, Chelsea, SW3
Tel: 01-351 5353
Open Mon-Sat 10-6pm

Bermondsey Antiques Market,
corner of Long Lane and
Bermondsey Street, London, SE1
Friday 5am-2pm

Bermondsey Antique Warehouse,
173 Bermondsey Street, SE1
Tel: 01-407 2040/4250
Open 9.30-5.30pm, Thurs 9.30-8pm,
Fri 7-5.30pm. Closed Sat and Sun

Bond Street Antiques Centre,
124 New Bond Street, W1
Tel: 01-351 5353
Open Mon-Fri 10-5.45pm,
Sat 10-4pm

Camden Antiques Market,
Corner of Camden High Street,
and Buck Street, Camden Town,
NW1 Thurs 7-4pm

Camden Passage Antique Centre,
357 Upper St Pierrepont Arcade,
Islington, N1
Tel: 01-359 0190
Stalls open Wed 8-3pm (Thurs
Books 9-4pm), Sat 9-5pm

Chapel Street Market,
Jubilee Shopping Hall,
65-67 Chapel Market, Islington,
N1
Tel: 01-278 9942
Open Wed, Fri, Sat & Sun

Chelsea Antiques Market,
245-253 Kings Road, SW3
Tel: 01-352 5689/9695/1424
Open 10-6pm

Chenil Galleries,
181-183 Kings Road, SW3
Tel: 01-351 5353
Mon-Sat 10-6pm

Corner Portobello Antiques
Supermarket,
282, 284, 288, 290 Westbourne
Grove, W11
Tel: 01-727 2027
Open Fri 12-4pm, Sat 7-6pm

Covent Garden Antiques Market,
Jubilee Market, Covent Garden
Piazza, WC2
Tel: 01-240 7405
Mon only 6-4pm

Cutler Street Antiques Market,
Goulston Street, near Aldgate
End, E1
Sun 7-2pm

Crystal Palace Collectors Market,
Jasper Road, Westow Hill, Crystal
Palace, SE19
Tel: 01-761 3737
Open Wed, Thurs 9-4pm, Fri,
Sat 9-5pm, Sun 10-3pm

Dixons Antique Centre,
471 Upper Richmond Road West,
East Sheen, SW14
Tel: 01-878 6788
Open 10-5.30pm, Sun 1.30-5.30pm.
Closed Wed

Franklin's Camberwell Antiques
Market,
161 Camberwell Road, SE5
Tel: 01-703 8089
Open 10-6pm, Sun 1-6pm.
Closed Mon

Georgian Village Antiques
Market,
100 Wood Street, Walthamstow,
E17
Tel: 01-520 2443/989 4914
Open 10-5pm. Closed Thurs

Georgian Village,
Islington Green, N1
Tel: 01-226 1571
Open Wed 10-4pm, Sat 7-5pm

Good Fairy Open Market,
100 Portobello Road, W11
Tel: 01-351 5950
Open Sat 6-5pm

Grays Antique Market,
58 Davies Street, W1
Tel: 01-629 7034
Open 10-6pm. Closed Sat

Grays Mews,
1-7 Davies Street, W1
Tel: 01-629 7034
Open 10-6pm. Closed Sat

Grays Portobello,
138 Portobello Road, W11
Tel: 01-221 3069
Open Sat 7-4pm

Greenwich Antiques Market,
Stockwell Street by "The Letting
Office", Greenwich, SE10
Open Sat & Sun 9-4pm

Greenwich Antiques Market,
Greenwich Market, College
Approach (near Cutty Sark), SE10
Tel: 01-240 7405
Open Sat & Sun 10-4pm

Hampstead Antique Emporium,
12 Heath Street, Hampstead, NW3
Tel: 01-794 3297
Open 10-6pm.
Closed Mon

Jubilee Market,
Covent Garden, WC2
Tel: 01-836 2139 Open Mon

L'aiglon Antique Centre,
220 Westbourne Grove, W11
Tel: 01-221 1121 Open 10-6pm

The London Silver Vaults,
Chancery House,
53-65 Chancery Lane, WC2
Tel: 01-242 3844
Open 9-5.30pm. Closed Sat pm

The Mall Antiques Arcade,
Camden Passage, Islington, N1
Tues, Thurs, Fri 10-5pm,
Wed 7.30-5pm, Sat 9-6pm

Northcote Road Antiques Market,
155A Northcote Road, Battersea,
SW11 Tel: 01-228 6850
Open Mon-Sat 10-6pm,
Sun 12-5pm

Peckham Indoor Market,
Rye Lane Bargain Centre,
48 Rye Lane, Peckham, SE15
Tel: 01-639 2463 Open Tues-Sat

Pierrepont Arcade,
Camden Passage, N1
Tel: 01-359 0190 Open Wed & Sat

Portobello Road Market,
London, W11 Open Sat 5.30-5pm

Red Lion Market,
165/169 Portobello Road, W11
Open Sat 5.30-5pm
Tel: 01-221 7638/229 4010

Roger's Antique Gallery,
65 Portobello Road, W11
Tel: 01-351 5353 Open Sat 7-5pm

Rochefort Antique Gallery,
32/34 The Green, Winchmore Hill,
London, N21
Tel: 01-886 4779/01-363 0910
Open 10-1pm, 2.30-6pm

Roman Road Market,
Jubilee Shopping Hall,
568 Roman Road, Bow, E3
Open Tues, Thur & Sat

Streatham Traders & Shippers
Market,
United Reform Church Hall,
Streatham High Street, SW16
Tel: 01-764 3602
Open Tues 8-3pm

Wimbledon Market, Car Park,
Wimbledon Greyhound Stadium,
Plough Lane, SW19
Tel: (0774) 258115 Open Sun

Willesden Market, Car Park,
White Hart Public House,
Willesden, NW10
Tel: 01-240 7405/6
Open Wed & Sat

World Famous Portobello Market,
177 Portobello Road and
1-3 Elgin Crescent, W11
Tel: 01-221 7638/229 4010
Open Sat 5-6pm

York Arcade,
80 Islington High Street, N1
Tel: 01-837 8768
Open Wed & Sat 8-5pm, Tues,
Thurs, Fri 11-3pm

Greater London

Antiques Arcade,
22 Richmond Hill, Richmond,
Surrey
Tel: 01-940 2035
Open Tues, Thurs, Fri 10.30-5.30,
Sun 2-5.30pm

Beckenham Antique Market,
Old Council Hall, Bromley Road,
Beckenham, Kent
Tel: 01-684 5891
Open Wed 9.30-2pm

Avon

Great Western Antique Centre,
Bartlett Street, Bath
Tel: (0225) 24243/28731/20686/
310388
Open 9.30-5pm Mon-Sat

Bristol Antique Market,
St Nicholas Markets,
The Exchange, Corn Street
Tel: (0272) 260021
Open Thurs & Fri 9-4pm

Clifton Antiques Market,
26/28 The Mall, Clifton, Bristol
Tel: (0272) 741627
Open 10-6pm. Closed Mon

Bedfordshire

Antiques Finder,
59 North Street, Leighton Buzzard
Tel: (0525) 382954
Open 10-5pm. Closed Thurs

The Woburn Abbey Antiques
Centre,
Woburn
Tel: (0525) 290350
Open every day 11-5pm Nov to
Easter. 10-6pm Easter to Oct

Reading Emporium,
1A Merchant Place (off Friar
Street), Reading
Tel: (0734) 590290
Open 9-5pm

Twyford Antiques Centre,
1 High Street, Twyford
Tel: (0734) 342161
Open 9.30-12.30pm & 1.30-5.30pm
Open Sun. Closed Wed

Buckinghamshire

Old Amersham Antique Centre,
20-22 Whieldon Street,
Old Amersham
Tel: (0494) 431282
Open 10-6pm

Regency Antiques,
Great Missenden Arcade, 76 High Street, Great Missenden
Tel: (024 06) 2330
Open 10-5pm. Closed Thurs

Marlow Antique Centre,
5 Spittal Street, Marlow
Tel: (06284) 76837
Open 9.30-5.30pm, Sun 10.30-5pm

Olney Antiques Centre,
Rose Court, Olney
Tel: (0234) 712172
Open 10-5.30pm, Sun 12-5.30pm

Bell Street Antiques Centre,
20/22 Bell Street, Princes Risborough
Tel: (084 44) 3034
Open 9.30-5.30pm, Sun 11-5pm

Tingewick Antiques Centre,
Main Street, Tingewick
Tel: (028 04) 7922
Open 10.30-5 inc. Sun

Cambridgeshire

Collectors Market,
Dales Brewery, Gwydir Street
(off Mill Road), Cambridge
Open 9.30-5pm

Silhouette Antique Centre,
Chequers Street, Fenstanton
Tel: (0480) 66746/63269
Open 10-5pm Fri-Sun

Willingham Antiques & Collectors Market,
25-29 Green Street, Willingham
Tel: (0945) 60283
Open 10-5pm. Closed Thurs

Cheshire

Chester Antique Hypermarket,
41 Lower Bridge Street, Chester
Tel: (0244) 314991 Open 10-5pm

Stancie Cutler Antique & Collectors Fairs,
Nantwich Civic Hall, Nantwich
Tel: (0270) 666802
Open 1st Thurs each month 12-9pm, Bank Hols & New Years Day. 2nd Sat of each month Collectors Market 9-4pm, 10-6pm

Nantwich Antique Centre,
The Old Police Station, Welsh Row, Nantwich Tel: (0270) 624035
Open 10-5.30pm. Closed Wed

Cornwall

Waterfront Antique Complex,
1st Floor, 4 Quay Street, Falmouth
Tel: (0326) 311491
Open 10-5pm

New Generation Antique Market,
61/62 Chapel Street, Penzance
Tel: (0736) 63267 Open 10-5pm

Truro Antique Centre,
108 Kenwyn Street, Truro
Tel: (0872) 78400
Open 9.30-5pm

Cumbria

Carlisle Antique & Craft Centre,
Cecil Hall, Cecil Street, Carlisle
Tel: (0228) 21970
Open 9-5.30pm

Cockermouth Antiques Market,
Courthouse, Main Street,
Cockermouth
Tel: (0900) 824346
Open 10-5pm

Devon

Dartmoor Antiques Centre,
Off West Street, Ashburton
Tel: (0364) 52182
Open Wed 9-4pm

The Antique Centre on the Quay,
The Quay, Exeter
Tel: (0392) 214180
Open 10-5pm

The Antique Centre,
Abingdon House,
136 High Street,
Honiton
Tel: (0404) 2108
Open 10-5pm

Newton Abbot Antiques Centre,
55 East Street, Newton Abbot
Tel: (0626) 54074
Open Tues 9-3pm

Barbican Antiques Market,
82-84 Vauxhall Street,
Barbican, Plymouth
Tel: (0752) 266927
Open 9.30-5pm

Dorset

Painted Lady Antique Centre,
5 West Allington, Bridport
Tel: (0308) 25885
Open 9.30-5pm

The Antique Centre,
837-839 Christchurch Road,
Boscombe East, Bournemouth
Tel: (0202) 421052
Six days a week 9.30-5.30

Sherborne Antique Arcade,
Mattar Arcade, 17 Newlands,
Sherborne
Tel: (0935) 813464
Open 9-5pm

Barnes House Antiques Centre,
West Row, Wimborne Minster
Tel: (0202) 886275
Open 10-5pm

Durham

The Imperial Antiques Arcade,
Grange Road, Darlington
Tel: (0325) 481685
Open 10-4pm. Closed Wed

Essex

Battlesbridge Antiques Centre,
Battlesbridge
Tel: (0268) 734005/763500/763344

Berkshire

Hungerford Arcade,
High Street, Hungerford
Tel: (0488) 83701
Open 9.30-5.30pm, Sun 10-6pm

Sheredays Antiques Centre,
Billericay
Tel: (0277) 624356
Open 10-4-30pm.
Closed Thurs

East Hill Antiques Centre,
29 East Hill, Colchester
Tel: (0206) 868623
Open 9.30-5pm, Thurs 9.30-1pm

Trinity Antiques Centre,
7 Trinity Street, Colchester
Tel: (0206) 577775
Open 9.30-5pm

Gloucestershire

Cirencester Antique Market,
Market Place, Cirencester
Tel: 01-240 0428
Antique Forum Ltd
Open Fri

Gloucester Antiques Centre,
Severn Road, Gloucester
Tel: (0452) 29716
Open Mon-Fri 9.30-5pm,
Sat 9.30-4.30pm, Sun 1-5pm

Hampshire

Folly Antiques Centre,
College Street, Petersfield
Tel: (0730) 64816
Open 9.30-5pm, Thurs 9.30-1pm

The House of Antiques,
4 College Street, Petersfield
Tel: (0730) 62172
Open 9.30-5pm.
Closed Thurs pm

St George's Antiques Centre,
10A St George Street, Winchester
Tel: (0962) 56317
Open 10-4.30pm

Hereford & Worcester

Leominster Antiques Market,
14 Broad Street, Leominster
Tel: (0568) 2189
Open 10-5pm, Sat 10-4pm

The Great Malvern Antiques Arcade,
Salisbury House, 6 Abbey Road,
Malvern
Tel: (06845) 5490
Open 9.30-5pm

Hertfordshire

St Albans Antique Market,
Town Hall, Chequer Street,
St Albans
Tel: (0727) 50427
Open Mon 9.30-4pm

By George! Antiques Centre,
23 George Street, St Albans
Tel: (0727) 53032
Open 10-5pm

The Herts & Essex Antique Centre,
The Maltings, Station Road,
Sawbridgeworth
Tel: (0279) 722044

Humberside

New Pocklington Antiques Centre,
26 George Street, Pocklington
near York
Tel: (0759) 303032
Open Mon-Sat 10-5pm

Kent

Canterbury Antique Centre,
Ivy Lane, Canterbury
Tel: (0227) 60378
Open 9-5.30pm

Malthouse Arcade,
High Street, Hythe
Tel: (0303) 60103
Open Fri & Sat 10-6pm

Hythe Antique Centre,
5 High Street, Hythe
Tel: (0303) 69643
Open 10-5.30pm

Rochester Antiques & Flea Market,
Corporation Street, Rochester
Tel: 01-240 0428
(Antique Forum Ltd)
Open Sat 9-2pm

Sandgate Antiques Centre,
61-63 High Street, Sandgate
Tel: (0303) 48987
Open 10-6pm, Sun 11-6pm

The Antiques Centre,
120 London Road, Sevenoaks
Tel: (0732) 452104
Open 9-1pm, 2-5.30pm

Tudor Cottage Antiques Centre,
22-23 Shipbourne Road, Tonbridge
Tel: (0732) 351719
Open 10-5.30pm

Tunbridge Wells Antique Centre,
Union Square, The Pantiles,
Tunbridge Wells
Tel: (0892) 33708
Open 9.30-5pm

Castle Antiques Centre,
1 London Road, Westerham
Tel: (0959) 62492
Open 10-5pm

Lancashire

Last Drop Antique & Collectors Club,
Last Drop Hotel, Bromley Cross,
Bolton
Open Sun 11-4pm

Bygone Times Antique,
Eccleston (6 mins from J 27, M6)
Open 7 days-a-week 8-6pm

Eccles Antique Centre,
325/7 Liverpool Road, Patricroft
Bridge, Eccles
Tel: 061-789 4467
Open 12-6pm

Manchester Antique Hypermarket,
Levenshulme Town Hall,
965 Stockport Road, Levenshulme,
Manchester
Tel: 061-224 2410
Open 10-5pm

Royal Exchange Shopping Centre,
Antiques Gallery, St Ann's
Square, Manchester
Tel: 021-834 3731/834 1427
Open 9.30-5.30pm

North Western Antique Centre,
New Preston Mill (Horrockses
Yard), New Hall Lane, Preston
Tel: (0772) 794498
Open 8.30-5.30pm, Sat, Sun by app.

Walter Aspinall Antiques,
Pendle Antique Centre, Union
Mill, Watt Street, Sabden near
Blackburn
Tel: (0282) 76311
Open Mon-Thurs 9-8pm,
Fri-Sat 9-5pm, Sun 11-4pm

Leicestershire

The Antiques Complex,
St Nicholas Place, Leicester
Tel: (0533) 533343
Open 9.30-5.30pm

Oxford Street Antiques Centre Ltd,
16-26 Oxford Street, Leicester
Tel: (0533) 553006

Carillon Antiques,
64 Leicester Road, Loughborough
Tel: (0509) 237169
Open 10-5pm.
Closed Wed

Lincolnshire

Boston Antiques Centre,
12 West Street, Boston
Tel: (0205) 61510
Open 9-5.30pm

Hemswell Antique Centre,
Caenby Corner Estate, Hemswell
Cliff near Gainsborough
Tel: (042 773) 389, (0652) 61616
Open 10-5pm 7 days-a-week

The Lincolnshire Antiques Centre,
Bridge Street, Horncastle
Tel: (06582) 7794
Open 9-5pm

Talisman Antiques,
51 North Street, Horncastle
Tel: (065 82) 6893
Open 10.30-5pm.
Closed Mon

Eastgage Antique Centre,
Black Horse Chambers,
6 Eastgate, Lincoln
Tel: (0522) 44404
Open 9.30-5pm

Norfolk

Coltishall Antiques Centre,
High Street, Coltishall
Tel: (0603) 738306/737631
Open 10-5pm

Norfolk House Antiques Centre,
Norfolk House Yard
(off St Nicholas Street), Diss
Tel: (0379) 51433
Open 9.30-5pm

Fakenham Antique Centre,
Old Congregational Chapel,
14 Norwich Road, Fakenham
Tel: (0328) 2941
Open 10-5pm, Thurs 9-5pm

The Old Granary Antique & Collectors Centre,
King Staithe Lane,
(off Queens Street), King's Lynn
Tel: (0553) 775509
Open 10-5pm

Cloisters Antiques Fair,
St Andrew's & Blackfriars Hall,
St Andrew's Plain, Norwich
Tel: (0603) 628477
Open Wed 9.30-3.30pm

Norwich Antiques & Collectors Centre,
Quayside, Fye Bridge, Norwich
Tel: (0603) 612582
Open 10-5pm

Antique & Collectors Market,
St Michael at Plea, Bank Plain,
Norwich
Tel (0603) 619129
Open 9.30-5.00

Angel Antique Centre,
Pansthorn Farmhouse, Redgrave
Road, South Lopham, near Diss
Tel: (037 988) 317
Open 9.30-6pm inc Sun

Swaffham Antiques Centre,
Cranglegate, Market Place,
Swaffham
Tel: (0760) 21277/21052
Open 10-1pm, 2-5pm

Wymondham Antique Centre,
No 1 Town Green, Wymondham
Tel: (0953) 604817
Open 10-5pm

Northamptonshire

The Village Antique Market,
62 High Street, Weedon
Tel: (0327) 42015
Open 9.30-5.30pm,
Sun 10.30-5.30pm

Antiques & Bric-a-Brac Market,
Market Square, Town Centre,
Wellingborough
Tel: (0905) 611321
Open Tues 9-4pm

Northumberland

Colmans of Hexham,
15 St Mary's Chare, Hexham
Tel: (0434) 603812/605522

Nottinghamshire

Castle Gate Antiques Centre,
55 Castle Gate, Newark
Tel: (0636) 700076
Open 9-5.30pm

Newark Antiques Centre,
Lombard Street,
Newark-on-Trent,
Tel: (0636) 605504
Open 9.30-5pm

Newark Antique Warehouse,
Kelham Road, Newark
Tel: (0636) 74869
Open 9-5.30pm

Nottingham Antique Centre,
British Rail Goods Yard, London
Road, Nottingham
Tel: (0602) 54504/55548
Open 9-5pm.
Closed Sat

Top Hat Antiques Centre,
66-72 Derby Road, Nottingham
Tel: (0602) 419143
Open 9.30-5pm

Oxfordshire

Burford Antiques Centre
(at the roundabout), Cheltenham
Road, Burford
Tel: (099 382) 2552/3227
Open 10-5.30pm

Cotswold Gateway Antique Centre,
Cheltenham Road, Burford Roundabout, Burford
Tel: (099 382) 3678/2450/2618
Open 10-5.30pm, Sun pm-5.30pm

Chipping Norton Antique Centre,
Ivy House, Middle Row, Chipping Norton
Tel: (0608) 44212
Open 10-5pm inc Sun

Deddington Antique Centre,
Laurel House, Bull Ring, Market Square, Deddington
Tel: (0869) 38968
Open 10-5pm

Oxford Antiques Centre,
The Jam Factory, 27 Park End, Oxford
Tel: (0865) 739071
Open 10-5pm. Closed Mon

Antique & Collectors Market,
Town Hall, Thame
Tel: (0844) 28205
Open 8.30-3.30pm. Second Tues each month

The Lamb Arcade,
High Street, Wallingford
Tel: (0491) 35048/35166
Open 10-5pm, Sat 9.30-5pm, Wed 10-4pm

Wallingford Antiques Gallery,
4 Castle Street, Wallingford
Tel: (0491) 33048
Open 10-5.30pm, Sun 2-5.30pm

Span Antiques,
6 Market Place, Woodstock
Tel: (0993) 811332
Open 10-1pm, 2-5pm. Closed Wed

Shropshire

Stretton Antiques Market,
36 Sandford Avenue, Church Stretton
Tel: (0694) 723718

Ironbridge Antique Centre,
Dale End, Ironbridge
Tel: (095 245) 3784
Open 10-5pm, Sun 2-5pm

Pepper Lane Antique Centre,
Pepper Lane, Ludlow
Tel: (0584) 6494
Open 9-5.30pm

St Leonards Antiques,
Corve Street, Ludlow
Tel: (0584) 5573
Open 9-5pm

Shrewsbury Antique Centre,
15 Princess House, The Square, Shrewsbury
Tel: (0743) 247704
Open 9.30-5.30pm

Shrewsbury Antique Market,
Frankwell Quay Warehouse, Shrewsbury
Tel: (0743) 50916
Open 10-5.30pm, Sun 12-5pm

Suffolk

Waveney Antiques Centre,
Peddars Lane, Beccles
Tel: (0502) 716147
Open 10-5.30pm

St Edmund's Antique Centre,
30 St John's Street, Bury St Edmunds
Tel: (0284) 64469
Open 9.30-5.30pm

Gil Adams Antique Centre,
The Forresters Hall, High Street, Debenham
Tel: (0728) 860777
Open 9.30-5.30pm

Long Melford Antiques Centre,
The Chapel Maltings, Long Melford
Tel: (0787) 79287
Open 10-5.30pm

Old Town Hall Antiques Centre,
High Street, Needham Market
Tel: (0449) 720773
Open 10-5pm

The Barn,
Risby, Bury St Edmunds
Tel: (0284) 811126
Open 7 days-a-week

Surrey

Surrey Antiques Centre,
10 Windsor Street, Chertsey
Tel: (0932) 563313
Open 10-5pm

The Antiques Arcade,
77 Bridge Road, East Molesey
Tel: 01-979 7954
Open 10-5pm

Maltings Monthly Market,
Bridge Square, Farnham
Tel: (0252) 726234
First Sat monthly

The Antiques Centre,
22 Haydon Place corner of Martyr Road, Guildford
Tel: (0483) 67817
Open 10-5pm. Closed Mon, Wed

Wood's Wharf Antiques Bazaar,
56 High Street, Haslemere
Tel: (0428) 2125

The Old Smithy Antique Centre,
7 High Street, Merstham
Tel: (073 74) 2306
Open 10-5pm

Reigate Antiques Arcade,
57 High Street, Reigate
Tel: (0737) 222654
Open 10-5.30pm

Sutton Market,
West Street, Sutton
Tel: 01-661 1245
Open Tues & Sat

Fern Cottage Antique Centre,
28/30 High Street, Thames Ditton,
Tel: 01-398 2281 Open 10-5.30pm

Somerset

Guildhall Antique Market,
The Guildhall, Chard
Open Thurs 8-4pm

Crewkerne Antique Centre,
42 East Street, Crewkerne
Tel: (0460) 76755
Open 9.30-5.30pm

Dulverton Antique Centre,
Lower Town Hall, Dulverton
Tel: (0398) 23522

County Antiques Centre,
21/23 West Street, Ilminster
Tel: (0460) 54151
Open 10-5pm

Silver Street Antique Centre,
23 Silver Street, Taunton
Tel: (0823) 271604
Open Mon 8-3.30pm

Taunton Antique Centre,
27/29 Silver Street, Taunton
Tel: (0823) 289327
Open Mon 9-4pm

Wells Antique Centre,
6A Mill Street/High Street, Wells
Tel: (0749) 74820
Open 10-4pm

Staffordshire

Rugeley Antique Centre,
161/3 Main Road, Brereton near Rugeley
Tel: (08894) 77166
Open 10-5.30pm

The Antique Centre,
128 High Street, Kinver
Tel: (0384) 877441
Open 10-5.30pm

Antique Market,
The Stones, Newcastle-under-Lyme Tel: (088 97) 527
Open Tues 7-2pm

Barclay House Antiques,
14-16 Howard Place, Shelton, Stoke-on-Trent
Tel: (0782) 274747/657674
Open 9.30-6pm

Tutbury Mill Antiques,
6 Lower High Street, Tutbury near Burton-on-Trent
Tel: (0283) 815999
Open 7 days 9-6pm

Sussex East

Bexhill Antiques Centre,
Quakers Mill, Old Town, Bexhill
Tel: (0424) 210182/221940
Open 6 days, 10-5.30pm

Brighton Antiques Gallery,
41 Meeting House Lane, Brighton
Tel: (0273) 26693/21059
Open 10-5.30pm

Jubilee Antique Cellars & Collector's Market,
44-47 Gardner Street, Brighton
Tel: (0273) 600574 Open 9-5pm

Kollect-O-Mania,
25 Trafalgar Street, Brighton
Tel: (0273) 694229 Open 10-5pm

Prinnys Antique Gallery,
3 Meeting House Lane, Brighton
Tel: (0273) 204557 Open 10-5pm

Chateaubriand Antiques Centre,
High Street, Burwash
Tel: (0435) 882535
Open 10-5pm, Sun 12-5pm

Lewes Antique Centre,
20 Cliffe High Street, Lewes
Tel: (0273) 476148 Open 10-5pm

Newhaven Flea Market,
28 South Way, Newhaven
Tel: (0273) 517207/516065
Open every day

Polegate Antiques Centre,
97 Station Road, Polegate
Tel: (032 12) 5277
Open 9-5pm. Closed Sat

Mint Arcade,
71 The Mint, Rye
Tel: (0797) 225952
Open 10-5pm every day

Seaford's "Barn Collectors" Market & Studio Book Shop,
The Barn, Church Lane, Seaford
Tel: (0323) 890010
Open Tues, Thurs & Sat 10-4.30pm

Sussex West

Antiques & Collectors Market,
Old Orchard Building, Old House, Adversane near Billingshurst

Arundel Antiques Market,
5 River Road, Arundel
Tel: (0903) 882012
Open Sat 9-5pm

Eagle House Antiques Market,
Market Square, Midhurst
Tel: (073 081) 2718 Open daily

Midhurst Antiques Market,
Knockhundred Row, Midhurst
Tel: (073 081) 4231
Open 9.30-5.30pm

Mostyns Antique Centre,
64 Brighton Road, Lancing
Tel: (0903) 752961

Petworth Antique Market,
East Street, Petworth
Tel: (0798) 42073 Open 10-5.30pm

Tyne & Wear

Vine Lane Antique Market,
17 Vine Lane, Newcastle-upon-Tyne Tel: 091-261 2963/232 9832
Open 10-5.30pm

Warwickshire

The Antiques Centre,
High Street, Bidford-on-Avon
Tel: (0789) 773680
Open 10-5pm, Sun 2-5.30pm. Closed Mon

Dunchurch Antique Centre,
16/16A Daventry Road, Dunchurch near Rugby
Tel: (0788) 817147
Open 7 days 10-5pm

Spa Antiques Market,
4 Windsor Street, Leamington Spa
Tel: (0926) 22927
Open 9.30-5.30pm

Antiques Etc,
22 Railway Terrace, Rugby
Open 10-5pm. Closed Tues & Wed

The Antique Arcade,
Sheep Street, Stratford-upon-Avon
Tel: (0789) 297249
Open 10.30-5.30pm

Stratford Antique Centre,
Ely Street, Statford-upon-Avon
Tel: (0789) 204180
Open 10-5.30 every day

Smith Street Antiques Centre,
7 Smith Street, Warwick
Tel: (0926) 497864
Open 10-5.30pm

Vintage Antique Market,
36 Market Place, Warwick
Tel: (0926) 491527
Open 10-5.30pm

Warwick Antique Centre,
20-22 High Street, Warwick
Tel: (0926) 495704
Open 6 days-a-week

West Midlands

Birmingham Antique Centre,
141 Bromsgrove Street, Birmingham
Tel: 021-692 1414/622 2145
Open every Thurs from 9am

The City of Birmingham Antique Market,
St Martins Market, Edgbaston Street, Birmingham
Tel: 021-267 4636
Open Mon 7-2pm

Stancie Cutler Antique & Collectors Fair,
Town Hall, Sutton Coldfield
Tel: (0270) 666802
Open 2nd Wed monthly 11-8pm

Walsall Antiques Centre,
7a The (Digbeth) Arcade, Walsall
Tel: (0922) 725163/5

Wiltshire

London House Antique Centre,
High Street, Marlborough
Tel: (0672) 52331
Open Mon-Sat 9.30-5.30pm

The Marlborough Parade Antiques Centre,
The Parade, Marlborough
Tel: (0672) 55331
Open 10-5pm

Antique Market,
37 Catherine Street, Salisbury
Tel: (0722) 26033
Open 9-5.30pm

The Avon Bridge Antiques & Collectors Market,
United Reformed Church Hall, Fisherton Street, Salisbury
Open Tues 9-4pm

Mr Micawber's Attic,
73 Fisherton Street, Salisbury
Tel: (0722) 337822
Open 9.30-5pm. Closed Wed

Yorkshire North

The Ginnel,
Harrogate Antique Centre
(off Parliament Street), Harrogate
Tel: (0423) 508857
Open 9.30-5.30pm

Grove Collectors Centre,
Grove Road, Harrogate
Tel: (0423) 61680
Open 10-5pm

Montpelier Mews Antique Market,
Montpelier Street, Harrogate
Tel: (0423) 530484
Open 9.30-5.30pm

West Park Antiques Pavilion,
20 West Park, Harrogate
Tel: (0423) 61758
Open 10-5pm. Closed Mon

Micklegate Antiques Market,
73 Micklegate, York
Tel: (0904) 644438
Open Wed & Sat 10-5.30pm

York Antique Centre,
2 Lendal, York
Tel: (0904) 641582/641445

Yorkshire South

Treasure House Antiques Centre,
4-10 Swan Street, Bawtry near Doncaster
Tel: (0302) 710621
Open 10-5pm inc Sun

Yorkshire West

Halifax Antiques Centre,
Queens Road/Gibbet Street, Halifax
Tel: (0422) 366657

Scotland

Bath Street Antique Galleries,
203 Bath Street, Glasgow
Open 10-5pm, Sat 10-1pm

Corner House Antiques,
217 St Vincent Street, Glasgow
Tel: 041-248 2560
Open 10-5pm

The Victorian Village,
53 & 57 West Regent Street, Glasgow
Tel: 041-332 0808
Open 10-5pm

Wales

Pembroke Antique Centre,
The Hall, Hamilton Terrace, Pembroke
Tel: (0646) 687017
Open 10-6pm

Cardiff Antique Centre,
69-71 St Mary Street, Cardiff
Tel: (0222) 30970

Jacobs Antique Centre,
West Canal Wharf, Cardiff
Tel: (0222) 390939
Open Thurs & Sat 9.30-5pm

Offa's Dyke Antiques Centre,
4 High Street, Knighton, Powys
Tel: (0547) 528634/528940
Open Mon-Sat 10-1pm, 2-5pm, Wed 10-1pm

Swansea Antique Centre,
21 Oxford Street, Swansea
Tel: (0792) 466854

Crew Market,
Crew Airfield on A477, Port Talbot
Tel: (0639) 884834
Open Sun

Port Talbot Market,
Jubilee Shopping Hall,
64-66 Station Road, Port Talbot, Glamorgan
Tel (0639) 883184
Open Mon-Sat

Channel Islands

Union Street Antique Market,
8 Union Street, St Helier, Jersey
Tel: (0534) 73805/22475
Open 9-6pm

INDEX